COLLEGE ALGEBRA

COLLEGE
ALGEBRA

EDWIN F. BECKENBACH

University of California, Los Angeles

IRVING DROOYAN

Los Angeles Pierce College

WILLIAM WOOTON

Los Angeles Pierce College

WADSWORTH PUBLISHING COMPANY, INC.
BELMONT, CALIFORNIA

Fourth printing: December 1965

Illustrations by David A. Strassman

L.C. Cat. Card No.: 64–16511

Printed in the United States of America

PREFACE

College algebra, as a freshman college course, has come to mean different things in different schools. Courses bearing the names College Algebra, Freshman Mathematics, or something similar, may deal with a wide variety of topics and be aimed at diverse levels of mathematical sophistication. In general, college algebra is not a terminal subject in mathematics, but rather a transitional course, designed to prepare the student for more advanced mathematics in which the algebra will be employed as a tool.

The material in this book is designed for students who have completed from one to two years of high school algebra and one year of high school geometry, or equivalent courses offered at the college level, and who propose to continue their study of mathematics.

The content and spirit of the book reflect the recommendations of various curriculum study groups. Structure plays a heavy role in the development, and is used to advantage in introducing matrices, complex numbers, and vectors. Beginning with the set of real numbers in Chapter 1, the student is shown that this set comprises a complete field. In Chapter 2, the integral domain of polynomials is explored, and this chapter, together with Chapter 3, provides a concentrated review of routine operations with polynomials and irrational expressions. Chapter 9, on matrices, introduces the notions of ring and vector space, and all these structures appear again in Chapter 10 on complex numbers and vectors.

For students who have recently completed two years of algebra, Chapters 2, 3, and 4, or at least large parts of them, may be omitted. On the other hand, if students are somewhat removed in time from their study of second-year, or intermediate, algebra, all of the necessary review will be found in these chapters. The large number of explanatory examples in the book should enable students to work through the exercises on their own.

Chapters following Chapter 4 center around the function concept. In particular, polynomial functions are covered in more detail, variation is treated from the function standpoint, determinants are treated as functions of matrices, logarithms are developed from a consideration of the exponential function, sequences are treated through functions having integers as domain, and probability is discussed from a set-function standpoint. Emphasis is given to techniques for readily sketching the graphs of functions.

This book is designed for a three- to five-unit semester course or two three-unit quarter courses. Chapters 7, 8, 9, 10, 11, 12, and 13 are sufficiently independent of each other so that any of these chapters may be omitted for a short course. Furthermore, certain problems, occurring at the ends of various exercise sets throughout the book, ask for proofs omitted in the text; whether or not these problems are assigned will in general determine the level of rigor being established for the course.

Exercises are provided in each section, with the answers to most odd-numbered problems given in the appendix.

The authors wish to express their appreciation to Professors Walter Hadel and Frank Fleming of Pierce College for their helpful suggestions during the preparation of the manuscript, and to Mrs. Doris Wooton for typing the manuscript. We would also like to thank Professors Don E. Edmondson of the University of Texas, Frank Gentry of the University of New Mexico, Robert Herrera of Los Angeles City College, James Jackson of the College of San Mateo, Gerald Rogers of the University of Arizona, and Robert J. Wisner of New Mexico State University for their comments and suggestions in the manuscript stage.

Edwin F. Beckenbach
Irving Drooyan
William Wooton

CONTENTS

3

RATIONAL EXPONENTS—RADICALS   71

4

OPEN SENTENCES IN ONE VARIABLE   95

5

RELATIONS AND FUNCTIONS I   126

6

RELATIONS AND FUNCTIONS II   163

7

EXPONENTIAL AND LOGARITHMIC FUNCTIONS 199

8

SYSTEMS OF EQUATIONS 228

9

MATRICES AND DETERMINANTS 252

10

COMPLEX NUMBERS AND VECTORS 295

11

12

13

1

PROPERTIES
OF REAL
NUMBERS

Mathematics is (or has, depending on your viewpoint) a language of its own. To be sure that we shall all be talking about the same thing as we use mathematical words and phrases, it is necessary to agree on what we mean by the technical terms we employ. Just as in a dictionary, we cannot logically define any terms independently of other terms. In mathematics, however, this fact is candidly acknowledged, and we take certain fundamental notions as undefined because we have no simpler terms with which to define them.

Perhaps the most primitive concept in mathematical language is that of a set. For example, it is possible to define the counting, or natural, numbers in terms of sets. Indeed, all of mathematics can be founded on this idea. In this textbook we shall primarily be studying sets of numbers. We shall, therefore, assume that set and set membership are undefined terms, although we shall try to convey an intuitive notion of what we mean by them through synonyms and illustrations.

1.1 DEFINITIONS AND SYMBOLS

A **set** is simply a collection of some kind. It may be a collection of people, colors, numbers, or anything else. In algebra, we are interested in sets of numbers of various kinds and in their relations to sets of points or lines in a plane or in space. Any one of the collection of things in a set is called a **member** or **element** of the set, and is said to be **contained in** or **included in** (or, sometimes, just **in**) the set. For example, the counting numbers 1, 2, 3, $\cdots$

1

(where the dots indicate that the sequence continues indefinitely) are the elements of the set we call the set of **natural numbers.**

Sets are usually designated by means of capital letters, A, B, C, etc. They are identified by means of braces in which the members are either listed or described. For example, the elements might be listed as in $\{1, 2, 3\}$, or described as in {first three natural numbers}. The expression "$\{1, 2, 3\}$" is read "the set whose elements are one, two, and three"; "{first three natural numbers}" is read "the set whose elements are the first three natural numbers."

Using the undefined notion of set membership, we can be more specific about some other terms we shall be using.

DEFINITION 1.1   *Two sets A and B are **equal**, A = B, if and only if they have the same members—that is, if and only if every member of each is a member of the other.*

Thus, if A denotes $\{1, 2, 3\}$, B denotes $\{3, 2, 1\}$, C denotes $\{2, 3, 4\}$, and D denotes {natural numbers between 1 and 5}, then $A = B$ and $C = D$. The phrase "if and only if" used in this definition is simply the mathematician's way of making two statements at once. Definition 1.1 is logically equivalent to the following: "Two sets are equal if they have the same members. Two sets have the same members if they are equal."

DEFINITION 1.2   *If the elements of a set A can be paired with the elements of a set B in such fashion that each element of A is paired with one and only one element of B, and conversely, then such a pairing is called a **one-to-one correspondence** between A and B.*

For example, if $A = \{a, b, c\}$ and $B = \{1, 2, 3\}$, then the sets A and B can be put into one-to-one correspondence in six different ways, two of which are shown in Figure 1.1.

$$\{a, b, c\} \qquad \{a, c, b\}$$
$$\updownarrow \updownarrow \updownarrow \qquad\quad \updownarrow \updownarrow \updownarrow$$
$$\{1, 2, 3\} \qquad \{2, 1, 3\}$$

Figure 1.1

DEFINITION 1.3   *Two sets are **equivalent** if and only if a one-to-one correspondence exists between them.*

The symbol "$\sim$" is used to denote equivalence. Thus, $A \sim B$ is read "A is equivalent to B." Intuitively, equivalent sets are sets that contain the same number of members. Clearly, if two sets are equal, they are equivalent, but the converse is not necessarily true—equality of sets requires that the members be identical, not merely that the sets be in one-to-one correspondence.

DEFINITION 1.4 *If every member of a set A is a member of a set B, then A is a **subset** of B. If, in addition, B contains at least one member not in A, then A is a **proper subset** of B.*

The symbol "$\subseteq$" (read "is a subset of" or "is contained in") will be used to denote the subset relationship, and the symbol "$\subset$" (read "is a proper subset of" or "is properly contained in") will be used for proper subsets. Thus

$$\{1, 2, 3\} \subseteq \{1, 2, 3, 4\}$$

and

$$\{1, 2, 3\} \subseteq \{1, 2, 3\}$$

both make valid usage of $\subseteq$, but $\subset$ is valid only for the first of these pairs of sets. That is,

$$\{1, 2, 3\} \subset \{1, 2, 3, 4\}.$$

Of course, by definition, every set is a subset of itself.

For example, if $A = \{1, 2, 3\}$ and $B = \{5, 6, 7\}$, then A and B are disjoint.

If a set is equivalent to the set $\{1, 2, 3, \cdots, n\}$ for some fixed natural number n, then the set is said to be **finite**. The set that contains no elements is called the **empty set** or **null set,** and is denoted by the symbol $\emptyset$ (read "the empty set" or "the null set"); $\emptyset$ is considered to be a subset of every set, and to be a proper subset of every set except itself. A set that is not the null set and is not finite is called an **infinite set**. For example, the set of *all* natural numbers, $\{1, 2, 3, \cdots\}$, is an infinite set.

DEFINITION 1.5 *Two nonempty sets A and B are **disjoint** if and only if A and B contain no member in common.*

The symbol $\in$ (read "is a member of" or "is an element of") is used to denote membership in a set. Thus,

$$2 \in \{1, 2, 3\}.$$

Note that we write

$$\{2\} \subset \{1, 2, 3\} \quad \text{and} \quad 2 \in \{1, 2, 3\},$$

but not

$$\{2\} \in \{1, 2, 3\} \quad \text{or} \quad 2 \subset \{1, 2, 3\},$$

since $\{2\}$ is a *subset,* whereas 2 is an *element,* of $\{1, 2, 3\}$.

When discussing an individual but unspecified element of a set containing more than one member, we usually denote the element by a lower-case italic letter (for example, *a, d, s, x*), or sometimes by a letter from the Greek alphabet: α (alpha), β (beta), γ (gamma), and so on. When symbols are used in this way, they are called "variables."

DEFINITION 1.6   *A **variable** is a symbol representing an unspecified element of a given set containing more than one element.*

If the given set, called the **replacement set** of the variable, is a set of numbers, then the variable represents a number. Thus

$$x \in A$$

means that the variable x is an (unspecified) element of the set A.

A symbol used to denote the member of a set containing only one member is called a **constant.**

When discussing sets, it is often helpful to have in mind some general set from which the elements of all of the sets under consideration are drawn. For example, if we wish to talk about sets of college students, we may want to consider all college students in this country, or all students in general; or, taking a larger view, we might want to consider students as a special kind of human being—say, all those human beings who are consciously striving to increase their knowledge. Thus, we might draw sets of college students from any one of a number of different general sets. Such a general set is called the **universe of discourse** or the **universal set**, and we shall usually denote it by the capital letter U. It follows that any set in a particular discussion is a subset of U for that discussion.

The slant bar, /, drawn through certain symbols for relations, is used to indicate negation. Thus $\neq$ is read "is not equal to," $\not\subseteq$ is read "is not a subset of," and $\notin$ is read "is not an element of." For example,

$$\{1, 2\} \neq \{1, 2, 3\}, \quad \{1, 2, 3\} \not\subseteq \{1, 2\}, \text{ and } 3 \notin \{1, 2\}.$$

Another symbolism useful in discussing sets is illustrated by $\{x \mid x \in A \text{ and } x \notin B\}$ (read "the set of all x such that x is a member of A and is not a member of B"). This symbolism, called **set-builder notation**, will be used extensively in this book. What it does is to name a variable (in this case, x) and, at the same time, to state a condition on the variable (in this case, that x is contained in the set A and is not contained in the set B).

EXERCISE 1.1

Designate each of the following sets by using braces and listing the members.

Example.   {natural numbers between 8 and 12}

Solution.   {9, 10, 11}

1. {natural numbers between 3 and 10}

2. {natural numbers between 20 and 27}

3. {days in the week}

4. {months in the year}

5. {digits in your age in years}

6. {digits in your home address}

Designate each of the following sets by using set-builder notation.

Example.   {even natural numbers}

Solution. $\{x \mid x = 2n,\ n$ a natural number$\}$

7. {odd natural numbers}

8. {rational numbers}

9. {solutions of $c^z = 5$}

10. {solutions of $x^z = 5$}

11. {elements that are not in the set A}

12. {elements that are in the set B}

Let $a \in A$, but otherwise let a be unspecified. In each of the following, state whether a is a constant.

13. $A = \{6, 7, 8, 9\}$ 14. $A = \{6\}$ 15. $A = \{$natural numbers$\}$

16. $A = \{$natural numbers between 2 and 4$\}$

In Problems 17–20, replace the comma between set symbols with either $=$ or $\neq$.

17. {natural numbers less than 3}, {1, 2}

18. $\{4\}, \{7\}$ 19. $\emptyset, \{0\}$ 20. $\{5, 7, 9\}, \{7, 9, 5\}$

In Problems 21–24, replace the comma between set symbols with either $\in$ or $\notin$.

21. $3, \{2, 3, 4\}$ 22. $5, \{x \mid x$ is an even natural number$\}$

23. $\{2\}, \{2, 3, 4\}$ 24. $\emptyset, \{2, 3, 4\}$

In Problems 25–28, replace the comma between set symbols with either $\subset$ or $\not\subset$.

25. $5, \{4, 5, 6\}$ 26. $\{5\}, \{4, 5, 6\}$

27. $\emptyset, \{4, 5, 6\}$ 28. $\{3, 4\}, \{4, 5, 6\}$

29. Let $U = \{5, 6, 7\}$. List the subsets of U that contain
     a. three members   b. two members
     c. one member   d. no members

30. Let $U = \{1, 2, 3, 4\}$.   List the subsets of U that contain
    a. four members   b. three members   c. two members
    d. one member   e. no members

31. Let $U = \{1, 2, 3, 4, 5, 6, 7, 8, 9\}$, $A = \{1, 2, 3, 4\}$, $B = \{4, 5, 6, 7\}$,   and
    $C = \{6, 7\}$.   Replace the comma in each of the following with either $\subset$ or $\not\subset$.
    a. A, U b. C, A c. A, B d. C, B

32. Let $U = \{$natural numbers$\}$, $A = \{$even natural numbers$\}$, $B = \{$odd natural
    numbers$\}$, $C = \{x \mid x$ is between 1 and 10$\}$, and $D = \{x \mid x$ is less than 9$\}$.
    Which of the following are true?
    a. $A \sim D$ b. $C = D$ c. $C \subset D$
    d. $A \sim B$ e. $A = B$ f. $D \subset C$
    g. $A \sim U$ h. $A \subset U$ i. A and B are disjoint
    j. $C \sim D$ k. $C \subset A$ l. C and B are disjoint

33. Let $A \subset U$, $B \subset U$, $A \subset B$, $x \in A$ and $y \in B$.
    a. Is $x \in B$?
    b. Can $y \in A$?
    c. Can there be $z \in U$ such that $z \not\in B$ and $z \not\in A$?
    d. Must there be $z \in U$ such that $z \not\in B$ and $z \not\in A$?
    e. Must there be $y \in B$ such that $y \not\in A$?

34. Let $A \subset B$, $B \subset C$, $x \in A$, $y \in B$, and $z \in C$.
    a. Can there be a z such that $z \not\in B$?
    b. Must there be a z such that $z \not\in B$?
    c. Can there be a z such that $z \not\in A$?
    d. Must there be a z such that $z \not\in A$?
    e. Can there be an x such that $x \not\in C$?
    f. Can $A = C$?

35. Consider the results of Problems 29 and 30 in this exercise.   Sets containing
    three elements evidently have 8 possible subsets, and those containing four
    elements have 16.   Determine the number of possible subsets of sets con-
    taining one and two elements, respectively, and make a conjecture about the
    number of possible subsets of a set containing n elements.

36. Explain why the following statement would constitute a valid definition for
    equality of sets.
        "If A and B are sets, then $A = B$ if and only if $A \subseteq B$ and $B \subseteq A$."

1.2   OPERATIONS ON SETS

Ideas involving universal sets, subsets thereof, and certain operations on
sets can be depicted by means of plane geometric figures called **Venn diagrams**.   Figure 1.2 is such a diagram, representing a universe having as its

elements all points of the rectangle and its interior and having a number of subsets of the universe denoted by circles and their interiors. In this figure, sets *A*, *B*, and *C* are disjoint, *D* is a subset of *C*, and *E* is neither a subset of *C* nor disjoint from *C*.

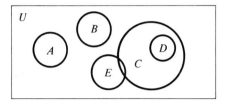

Figure 1.2

Although we are here using a rectangle and its interior for *U*, and circles and their interiors for the subsets, any closed figures will do. Also, *U* might be thought of as consisting of only certain designated points in the interior of the rectangle rather than all such points.

We can define some operations on the subsets of a given universe. A **binary operation** on the subsets of a given universe *U* is a rule that assigns to each pair *A* and *B* of subsets of *U*, taken in a definite order (*A* first and *B* second), a third subset *C* of *U*. One such operation is defined as follows.

DEFINITION 1.7   *The **union** of two sets A and B in U is the set of all elements of U that belong either to A or to B or to both.*

The symbol $\cup$ is used to denote the union of sets. Thus $A \cup B$ (read "the union of *A* and *B*," or sometimes, "*A* cup *B*") is the set of all elements that are in either *A* or *B* or both.

Example.   If $A = \{1, 2, 3, 4, 5\}$ and $B = \{2, 3, 4, 5, 6\}$, what is $A \cup B$?

Solution. $A \cup B$ is the set of all numbers included in either or both of *A* and *B*. Hence,

$$A \cup B = \{1, 2, 3, 4, 5, 6\}.$$

Notice that each element in $A \cup B$ is listed only once in this example. In general, the same symbol is not used twice in a given set notation. This is because, conceptually, a symbol has only one referent, and the repetition would be redundant. Thus "2" denotes just one number, and $\{2, 2\}$ contains only one number, no matter how many times we list its name, "2." Figure 1.3 is a Venn diagram in which the shaded region depicts $A \cup B$ in the preceding example.

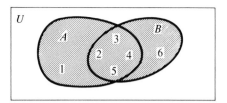

Figure 1.3

A second binary set operation of interest is defined as follows.

DEFINITION 1.8   *The **intersection** of two subsets A and B of U is the set of all elements of U that belong to both A and B.*

The symbol ∩ is used to denote intersection.   Thus $A \cap B$ (read "the intersection of A and B," or sometimes, "A cap B") denotes the set of all elements of U that are in both A and B.

Example.   If $A = \{1, 2, 3, 4, 5\}$ and $B = \{2, 3, 4, 5, 6\}$, what is $A \cap B$?

Solution. $A \cap B$ consists of those elements that are in both A and B.   Hence,

$$A \cap B = \{2, 3, 4, 5\}.$$

Figure 1.4 is a Venn diagram in which the shaded region depicts $A \cap B$ in this example.

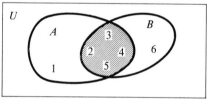

Figure 1.4

The doubly shaded region in Figure 1.5 illustrates

$$(A \cap B) \cap C = \{4, 5\},$$

with $A = \{1, 2, 3, 4, 5\}$, $B = \{2, 3, 4, 5, 6\}$, and $C = \{4, 5, 6, 7\}$.

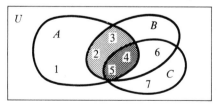

Figure 1.5

Both operations, union and intersection, are binary operations, because they are applied to two sets in relation to each other. The following operation on sets, however, applies to only one set in relation to U.

DEFINITION 1.9 *The **complement** of a set A in U is the set of all elements of U that do not belong to A.*

The symbol A' (or, sometimes, $\overline{A}$, $\sim A$, or $\tilde{A}$) denotes the complement of A in U.

Example. If $U = \{1, 2, 3, 4, 5\}$ and $A = \{2, 4\}$, what is A'?

Solution. A' contains all members of U that are not in A. Hence,

$$A' = \{1, 3, 5\}.$$

The shaded portion of the Venn diagram in Figure 1.6 represents A' in this example.

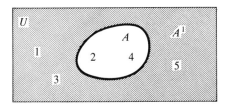

Figure 1.6

EXERCISE 1.2

Let $U = \{1, 2, 3, 4, 5, 6, 7, 8, 9, 10\}$, $A = \{2, 4, 6, 8, 10\}$, $B = \{1, 2, 3, 4, 5\}$, and $C = \{1, 3, 5, 7, 9\}$. List the members of each of the following.

1. A' 2. B' 3. C' 4. $A \cap B$

5. $A \cup B$ 6. $A \cup C$ 7. $A \cap C$ 8. $A' \cap B'$

9. $A' \cup C'$ 10. $(A \cap B)'$ 11. $A' \cup C$ 12. $C' \cap B$

For each of the Problems 13–24, copy the Venn diagram shown here on a sheet of paper. Shade the part of the diagram corresponding to each of the following.

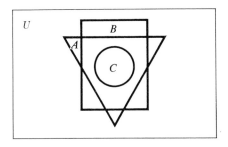

13. $A \cap B$ 14. $C \cap A$ 15. $C \cap B$ 16. $A \cap C'$

17. $B \cap C'$ 18. $B' \cup A'$ 19. $B' \cap A'$ 20. $B' \cap A$

21. $A' \cap B$ 22. $(C \cap B)'$ 23. $(C' \cap A)'$ 24. $(A' \cap B)'$

Using Venn diagrams if necessary, complete each of the following.

25. $(A')' =$ 26. $A \cap A' =$ 27. $A \cap U =$ 28. $A \cup A' =$

29. $A \cup U =$ 30. $A \cap \emptyset =$ 31. $A \cup \emptyset =$ 32. $A \cap A =$

33. $\emptyset' \cap \emptyset =$ 34. $A \cup A =$

35. Under what conditions would each of the following be true?

  a. $A \cup B = \emptyset$ b. $A \cup \emptyset = \emptyset$ c. $A \cap U = U$

  d. $A \cup B = A$ e. $A \cup \emptyset = U$ f. $A' \cap U = U$

  g. $A \cap B = A$ h. $A' \cup \emptyset = \emptyset$ i. $A \cup B = A \cap B$

36. Let us define the binary operation $A - B$ by $A - B = \{x \mid x \in A \text{ and } x \notin B\}$, where $A \subseteq U$ and $B \subseteq U$. The set $A - B$ is called the **complement of B relative to A**. Make a Venn diagram showing each of the following.

  a. $A - B$ b. $U - (A \cup B)$ c. $U - (A \cap B)$ d. $U - (A - B)$

37. Let $A - B$ be defined as in Problem 36. Use Venn diagrams to illustrate the following.

  a. $A - B = A \cap B'$ b. $U - A = A'$

  c. $(A - B)' \cap B = B$ 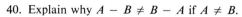   d. $(A - B) \cup (B - A) = A \cup B - A \cap B$

38. Explain why $A \cup B = B \cup A$.

39. Explain why $A \cap B = B \cap A$.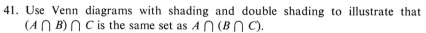

40. Explain why $A - B \neq B - A$ if $A \neq B$.

41. Use Venn diagrams with shading and double shading to illustrate that $(A \cap B) \cap C$ is the same set as $A \cap (B \cap C)$.

42. Use Venn diagrams with shading and double shading to illustrate that $(A \cup B) \cup C$ is the same set as $A \cup (B \cup C)$.

43. Use Venn diagrams with shading and double shading to examine the possibility that $A \cup (B \cap C) = (A \cup B) \cap (A \cup C)$. Does the assertion seem to be true?

44. Use Venn diagrams with shading and double shading to examine the possibility that $A \cap (B \cup C) = (A \cap B) \cup (A \cap C)$. Does the assertion seem to be true?

1.3 CLASSIFICATION OF NUMBERS

What is a number? The answer to this innocent-appearing question is fraught with considerations that are subtle and difficult. For our purpose, a number is an abstraction with which we assume everyone has an intuitive acquaintance. No one has ever seen, touched, or heard a number, yet we are able to produce an astounding amount of information about numbers, and to use them in very concrete ways. We can do this, first, because we are capable of formulating the concept of a number and, second, because we can name numbers, represent them by symbols, and through these names and symbols investigate the properties they must have if they are to conform to a few rudimentary assumptions we make about them.

Numbers have names just as people have names. The numbers whose names are one, two, three-fourths, and pi can be represented respectively by the following symbols, called **numerals**: 1, 2, 3/4, π. But the symbols (and the names) are not the numbers themselves. For example, if you were asked which is larger, 2 or 3, you would be quite justified in hesitating to answer. Does the question refer to the numbers whose names are two and three or to the symbols "2" and "3"? In one case the question has one answer, and in the other case, a different answer. Such ambiguity is anathema in mathematics.

When we write {1, 2, 3}, it is to be understood that the symbols refer to the set whose members are the *numbers* 1, 2, and 3, and not to the set whose members are the *symbols* "1," "2," and "3."

Some sets of numbers with which you should already be at least somewhat familiar are the following:

1. The set N of **natural numbers**, whose elements are the counting, or natural numbers:
$$N = \{1, 2, 3, \cdots\}.$$

2. The set J of **integers**, whose elements are the positive and negative whole numbers and zero:
$$J = \{\cdots, -2, -1, 0, 1, 2, \cdots\}.$$

3. The set Q of **rational numbers**, whose elements are all those numbers that can be represented by the symbol
$$\text{``}\frac{a}{b}\text{''} \quad \text{or} \quad \text{``}a/b\text{,''}$$
where a and b represent integers and b is not 0. Among the elements of Q are such numbers as $-3/4$, $18/27$, $3/1$, and $-6/1$. In symbols,
$$Q = \left\{\frac{a}{b} \,\middle|\, a \in J, b \in J, b \neq 0\right\}.$$

4. The set H of **irrational numbers,** whose elements are the numbers with decimal representations that are nonterminating and nonrepeating. Among the elements of this set are such numbers as $\sqrt{2}$, π, and $-\sqrt{7}$.

An irrational number cannot be represented in the form a/b, where a and b are integers. In symbols,

$$H = \{\text{irrational numbers}\}.$$

5. The set R of **real numbers**, which is the set of all rational and all irrational numbers:

$$R = \{x \mid x \in (Q \cup H)\}.$$

6. The set I of **imaginary numbers,** whose members can be represented in the form $x + yi$, where x and y are real numbers and i denotes $\sqrt{-1}$.

$$I = \{x + yi \mid x \in R, y \in R, y \neq 0, \quad i = \sqrt{-1}\}.$$

If $x = 0$, then the imaginary number $x + yi$ is written yi, with $y \in R$, $y \neq 0$. Such a number is called a *pure imaginary number.*

7. The set C of **complex numbers,** whose members can be represented in the form $x + yi$, where x and y are real numbers, and i denotes $\sqrt{-1}$:

$$C = \{x + yi \mid x \in R, y \in R, \quad i = \sqrt{-1}\}.$$

Conceptually, as will be pointed out in Chapter 10, the complex number $x + 0i$ can be distinguished from the real number x, just as the rational number $a/1$ can be distinguished from the integer a. Nevertheless, for practical purposes, it is useful and convenient to identify $x + 0i$ with x, and $a/1$ with a. What is more important from the point of view of algebraic structure, of course, is the fact that this identification is entirely consistent; thus, for example, we have

$$(3 + 0i) + (4 + 0i) = 7 + 0i,$$

just as we have

$$3 + 4 = 7.$$

With this familiar identification, the foregoing sets of numbers are related as indicated in Figure 1.7.

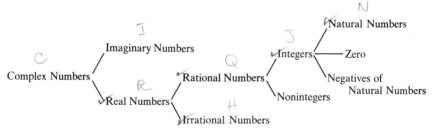

Complex Numbers — Imaginary Numbers
Real Numbers — Rational Numbers — Integers — Natural Numbers, Zero, Negatives of Natural Numbers; Nonintegers
Irrational Numbers

Figure 1.7

EXERCISE 1.3

In Problems 1–24, let N = {natural numbers}, J = {integers}, Q = {rational numbers}, H = {irrational numbers}, R = {real numbers}, I = {imaginary numbers}, and C = {complex numbers}. State whether each assertion is true or false.

1. $N \subset J$	2. $I \subset H$	3. $R \subset C$
4. $Q \subset H$	5. J and Q are disjoint	6. N and H are disjoint
7. $-5 \in N$	8. $0 \in Q$	9. $\sqrt{3} \in R$
10. $\pi \in C$	11. $-3 \in R$	12. $-7 \in H$
13. $\{-1, 1\} \subset N$	14. $\{-1, 1\} \subset J$	15. $\{-1, 1\} \subset Q$
16. $\{-1, 1\} \subset H$	17. $\{-1, 1\} \subset R$	18. $\{-1, 1\} \subset C$
19. $N \cup J = N \cap J$	20. $N \cap Q = \varnothing$	21. $H \cup R = R$
22. $J \cup Q = Q$	23. $J \cup H = R$	24. $Q \cup H = R$

List the members of each finite set, and represent infinite sets by using ellipses, "$\cdots$".

Examples.

a. {natural numbers between 5 and 9}

b. {integers greater than 3}

Solutions.

a. $\{6, 7, 8\}$ b. $\{4, 5, 6, \cdots\}$

25. {first five natural numbers}

26. {integers between -4 and 5}

27. {natural numbers less than 7}

28. {integers greater than -5}

29. {integers between -10 and -5}

30. {nonnegative integers}

Use set-builder notation, $\{x \mid \text{condition on } x\}$, to represent each set.

Example.   {natural numbers greater than 12}

Solution. $\{x \mid x \in N \text{ and } x \text{ greater than } 12\}$

31. {natural numbers}

32. {integers}

33. {real numbers}

34. {integers less than -6}

35. {real numbers between -4 and 3}

36. {nonnegative real numbers}

37. {rational numbers greater than -2}

38. {rational numbers between 8 and 12}

39. Let $A = \{4, -2, 2/5, \sqrt{-7}, 0, -3/4, \sqrt{2}, \sqrt{7}, \sqrt{-1}\}$. Designate each of the following sets by using braces and listing the members.
    a. {natural numbers contained in A}
    b. {integers contained in A}
    c. {rational numbers contained in A}
    d. {irrational numbers contained in A}

40. Let $B = \{-6, 3, \sqrt{5}, -3/4, \sqrt{-2}, 0, 5, -1, \sqrt{3}\}$. Designate each of the following sets by using braces and listing the members.
    a. {natural numbers contained in B}
    b. {integers contained in B}
    c. {irrational numbers contained in B}
    d. {real numbers contained in B}

An integer a is said to be an **integral multiple** of an integer b if and only if, for some integer k, it is true that $a = kb$. In Problems 41–44, specify the set $A \cap B$.

41. $A = $ {integral multiples of 2}
    $B = $ {integral multiples of 5}

42. $A = $ {integral multiples of 3}
    $B = $ {integral multiples of 4}

43. $A = $ {integral multiples of 6}
    $B = $ {integral multiples of 15}

44. $A = $ {integral multiples of 12}
    $B = $ {integral multiples of 9}

45. Use the results of Problems 41–44 to make a conjecture about the nature of $A \cap B$ if $A = $ {integral multiples of a} and $B = $ {integral multiples of b} where a, $b \in J$, and a and b have no common factor other than $1 \in J$.

1.4 REAL NUMBERS: THE FIELD POSTULATES

In mathematics, when we make formal assumptions about members of a set or about their properties, we call the assumptions **axioms** or **postulates**. Although we are free to formulate axioms in any way we please, it is clearly desirable that any axioms we adopt lead to useful conclusions, and that they not be contradictory. The words *property*, *law*, and *principle* are sometimes used in referring to assumptions, although these words may also be applied to certain consequences thereof.

The first assumptions to be considered here have to do with equality. An **equality**, or an "is equal to" assertion, is simply a mathematical statement that two symbols or words, or two groups of symbols or words, are names for the same thing. A number, for example, has an infinite number of numeral representations. Thus $4 - 1$ and $2 + 1$ are different symbols for the same number, and the equality

$$4 - 1 = 2 + 1$$

is a statement to this effect.

We postulate that, for any members a, b, and c of any set S, the equality ($=$) relationship satisfies the following laws:

E-1 $a = a$. *Reflexive law.*

E-2 If $a = b$, then $b = a$. *Symmetric law.*

E-3 If $a = b$ and $b = c$, then $a = c$. *Transitive law.*

E-4 If $a = b$, then a may be replaced by b *Substitution law.*
and b by a in any mathematical state-
ment without altering the truth or
falsity of the statement.

These axioms serve to clarify how we shall be using symbols, and to warn that we must not change the meaning of a symbol in the middle of a discussion or use the same symbol for two different things in the same context.

Other axioms, somewhat different conceptually, are used to characterize mathematical systems. They are assumptions made about the behavior of elements of sets under binary operations.

DEFINITION 1.10 *A **binary operation** in a set A is a rule that assigns to any pair of elements of A, taken in a definite order, another element of A.*

Thus if the chosen elements of A are a and b, with a taken first, and the operation is denoted by $*$, then the result of the operation is the element $a * b$ of A, which might or might not be equal to $b * a$. For example, A might be the set N of natural numbers, and the operation $*$ the addition of the second element to twice the first; in this case $a * b$ and $b * a$ would not always be the same.

Since the set R of real numbers is the set of greatest interest to us at the moment, let us list some of the properties we assume real numbers to possess under the binary operations of addition and multiplication, for which we shall use the familiar symbols " $+$ " and " $\times$," respectively.

We postulate the following laws for the elements a, b, and c of the set R of real numbers:

F-1 $a + b$ is a unique element of R.   *Closure for addition.*

F-2 $(a + b) + c = a + (b + c)$.   *Associative law of addition.*

F-3   There exists an element $0 \in R$ (called the **identity element for addition**) with the property $a + 0 = a$ and $0 + a = a$ for all $a \in R$.   *Identity element for addition.*

F-4   For each element $a \in R$, there exists an element $^-a \in R$ (called the **additive inverse** or **negative** of a) with the property   *Additive inverse.*
$$a + (^-a) = (^-a) + a = 0.‡$$

F-5 $a + b = b + a$.   *Commutative law of addition.*

F-6 $a \times b$ is a unique element of R.   *Closure for multiplication.*

F-7 $(a \times b) \times c = a \times (b \times c)$.   *Associative law of multiplication.*

F-8 $a \times (b + c) = a \times b + a \times c$ and $(b + c) \times a = b \times a + c \times a$.   *Distributive law.*

F-9   There exists an element $1 \in R$ (called the **identity element for multiplication**), $1 \neq 0$, with the property $a \times 1 = a$ and $1 \times a = a$ for all $a \in R$.   *Identity element for multiplication.*

F-10 $a \times b = b \times a$.   *Commutative law of multiplication.*

F-11 For each element $a \in R$, $a \neq 0$, there exists an element $a^{-1} \in R$ (called the **multiplicative inverse** or **reciprocal** of a) with the property   *Multiplicative inverse.*
$$a \times (a^{-1}) = 1 \text{ and } (a^{-1}) \times a = 1.$$

Parentheses are used in some of the relations above (and hereafter) to indicate that symbols within parentheses are to be viewed as a single entity.

Postulates F-1 and F-6 assert that the sum and product of any two real numbers are always real numbers, and that each sum and each product of real numbers is unique. When the performance of an operation on two elements of some set always results in another element of the same set, we

‡ See page 18 for an explanation of the symbol ^-a.

say that the set is **closed** with respect to that operation. Thus, we assume that the set of real numbers is closed with respect to addition and with respect to multiplication.

To give meaning to expressions $a + b + c$, $a \times b \times c$, $a + b + c + d$, and so on, let us make the following agreement.

DEFINITION 1.11   *If a, b, c, d,... are real numbers, then*

$$a + b + c = (a + b) + c, \; a + b + c + d = (a + b + c) + d, \ldots,$$

and

$$a \times b \times c = (a \times b) \times c, \; a \times b \times c \times d = (a \times b \times c) \times d, \ldots.$$

Postulates F-2 and F-7 assert, however, that three real numbers in a sum or three real factors in a product may be associated in either of two ways without altering the result. Thus, combining Definition 1.11 with Postulates F-2 and F-7, we have, for example,

$$2 + 3 + 4 = (2 + 3) + 4 = 2 + (3 + 4)$$

and

$$2 \times 3 \times 4 = (2 \times 3) \times 4 = 2 \times (3 \times 4).$$

Postulates F-3, F-4, F-9, and F-11 are "existence axioms"; they assert the existence of certain elements in the set that behave in specified ways under addition and multiplication.

Postulates F-5 and F-10 state that the order in which we add two real numbers or multiply two real factors does not affect the sum or product. Thus,

$$2 + 4 = 4 + 2$$

and

$$2 \times 4 = 4 \times 2.$$

Postulate F-8 relates the operations of addition and multiplication.

If, for a given set F and a given pair of binary operations (denoted "+" and "×" but not necessarily ordinary addition and multiplication) in F, the Postulates F-1 through F-11 (with R replaced by F throughout) are satisfied by the elements of F, then F is called a **field** under these operations. Thus, we speak of the **field R of real numbers**.

It can readily be shown that the set Q of rational numbers also forms a field under the operations of addition and multiplication. But the set H of irrational numbers is not a field under these operations. For example, this set is not closed under addition; thus, π and $1 - \pi$ are both irrational, whereas $\pi + (1 - \pi) = 1$ is rational.

In Chapter 10, we shall see that the set C of complex numbers also is a field under the operations of addition and multiplication.

In terms of the operations of addition and multiplication, let us now define two new operations on real numbers.

DEFINITION 1.12 *The **difference** of elements $a \in R$ and $b \in R$, denoted by $a - b$, is given by*

$$a - b = a + (^-b).$$

The operation of finding a difference is called *subtraction*. This definition explains why we ordinarily write $-b$ for ^-b (the negative of b).

DEFINITION 1.13 *The **quotient** of elements $a \in R$ and $b \in R$, $b \neq 0$, denoted by $\frac{a}{b}$, a/b, or $a \div b$, is given by*

$$\frac{a}{b} = a \times (b^{-1}).$$

In particular, for $a = 1$ we have

$$\frac{1}{b} = 1 \times b^{-1}, \text{ by E-4,} \quad \text{and}$$

$$1 \times b^{-1} = b^{-1}, \text{ by F-9,}$$

whence

$$\frac{1}{b} = b^{-1}, \text{ by E-3.}$$

The operation of finding a quotient is called *division*.

In all that follows, *we shall ordinarily write $-a$ for the additive inverse of a, and $\frac{1}{b}$, $1/b$, or $1 \div b$ for the multiplicative inverse of b.* We shall also follow the customary practice of writing ab or $a \cdot b$ for $a \times b$.

EXERCISE 1.4

Unless otherwise stated, each variable in the exercise denotes a real number. Each of the statements 1–6 is an application of one of the Postulates E-1 through E-4. Justify each statement by citing the appropriate postulate. (There may be more than one correct justification.)

Example. If $3 = a$, then $a = 3$.

Solution. Symmetric law of equality

1. If $a + 3 = b$ and $b = 7$, then $a + 3 = 7$.

2. If $x = 5$ and $y = x + 2$, then $y = 5 + 2$.

3. If $2 + y = 6$, then $6 = 2 + y$.

4. If $a = 2c$ and $c = 6$, then $a = 2 \cdot 6$.

5. If $3 + y = 7 + x$ and $7 + x = 2 + z$, then $3 + y = 2 + z$.

6. $x + 8 = x + 8$.

Each of the statements 7–24 is an application of one of the Postulates F-1 through F-11. Justify each statement by citing the appropriate one.

Example. $2(3 + 1) = 2 \cdot 3 + 2 \cdot 1$

Solution.   Distributive law

7. ab is a real number

8. $7 + 0 = 7$

9. $(2 \cdot 3) \cdot 4 = 2 \cdot (3 \cdot 4)$

10. $(5 + 4) + 1 = (4 + 5) + 1$

11. $3 + (-3) = 0$

12. $5 + (-2) = (-2) + 5$

13. $a\left(\dfrac{1}{a}\right) = \left(\dfrac{1}{a}\right)a \ (a \neq 0)$

14. $a(b + c) = (b + c)a$

15. $(a + b) + c = c + (a + b)$

16. $(a + b) + c = (b + a) + c$

17. $a + (b + c)d = a + bd + cd$

18. $a + (b + c)d = a + d(b + c)$

19. $a + (b + c)d = (b + c)d + a$

20. $(a + b) + [-(a + b)] = 0$

21. $\dfrac{1}{c}(a + b) = \dfrac{1}{c} \cdot a + \dfrac{1}{c} \cdot b \ (c \neq 0)$

22. $a[b + (c + d)] = ab + a(c + d)$

23. $ab + a(c + d) = ab + ac + ad$

24. $ab + ac = ba + ac$

Which of the sets in Problems 25–34 are closed under the stated operation?

25. {even natural numbers}, under addition

26. {odd natural numbers}, under addition

27. {odd natural numbers}, under multiplication

28. {even natural numbers}, under multiplication

29. $\{0, 1\}$, under multiplication

30. $\{0, 1\}$, under addition

31. {natural numbers}, under division

32. {natural numbers}, under subtraction

33. $\{3n \mid n \in \{\text{natural numbers}\}\}$, under addition

34. $\{3n \mid n \in \{\text{natural numbers}\}\}$, under division

35. Let $\circ$ be an operation such that for all real numbers a and b, $a \circ b = a + b + ab$. For example, if $a = 3$ and $b = 4$, then $a \circ b = 3 + 4 + 3 \cdot 4 = 19$.

    a. Is $\circ$ commutative?

    b. Is $\circ$ associative?

    c. For each $a \in R$ is there a number $k \in R$ such that $a \circ k = a$?

    d. For each $a \in R$ is there a number $a^* \in R$ such that $a \circ a^* = 0$?

36. Is division commutative in the field R of real numbers?

37. Is subtraction commutative in the field R of real numbers?

38. Is there an identity element for division in the field R of real numbers? That is, is there a number $p \in R$ such that $a \div p = a$ for each $a \in R$? If so, which element of R is p?

39. For which element or elements $a \in R$ does there not exist an $a^* \in R$ such that $a \div a^* = 1$? If $a \div a^* = 1$, what element of R is a^*?

40. Is there an identity element for subtraction in the set of real numbers? If so, which element of R is it?

41. For each $a \in R$, does there exist an element $a' \in R$ such that $a - a' = 0$? What is a'?

42. Argue that E-1 is a consequence of E-4 and, hence, does not need to be taken as a postulate.

43. Argue that E-2 is a consequence of E-4.

44. Argue that E-3 is a consequence of E-4.‡

1.5 THEOREMS CONCERNING FIELD PROPERTIES

The field postulates together with the postulates for equality imply other properties of the real numbers. Such implications are generally stated as **theorems**. A theorem is simply an assertion of a fact that follows logically from the postulates (or axioms) and other theorems. It consists of two parts: an "if" part, called the **hypothesis**, and a "then" part, called the **conclusion**. Proving a theorem consists of showing that the conclusion is a logical consequence of the hypothesis and the axioms in our system. Proofs are sometimes displayed in a distinctive two-column format, one column containing a chain of assertions, and the other containing a reason for each assertion.

It is interesting to note that the theorems of this section are consequences of the equality postulates and the field postulates, and nothing more. Accordingly, with appropriate changes in wording they are valid in *any* field, not just the field R of real numbers.

Consider the following result, which expresses the *addition law for equality*.

THEOREM 1.1   *If a, b, and c are real numbers, and if $a = b$, then*

$$a + c = b + c \quad and \quad c + a = c + b.$$

‡ The point made with Problems 42, 43, and 44 is that we have adopted a very powerful postulate in E-4, one that subsumes E-1, E-2, and E-3 as special cases. By wording E-4 as we have, we can eliminate a great deal of fussiness in later arguments, and, because E-1, E-2, and E-3 are fundamental properties of the equality relation, we have elected to retain them as postulates.

Proof.

Statement	Reason
1. a, b, and c are real numbers and $a = b$.	1. Hypothesis.
2. $a + c$ and $c + a$ are real numbers.	2. Closure law for addition.
3. $a + c = a + c$. 3'. $c + a = c + a$.	3, 3'. Reflexive law for equality.
4. $a + c = b + c$. 4'. $c + a = c + b$.	4, 4'. Substitution in (3) from (1) and (3') from (1), by substitution law for equality.

Thus, if the hypothesis "a, b, and c are real numbers and $a = b$" is true, then the conclusion "$a + c = b + c$ and $c + a = c + b$" follows logically.

You might wonder why both equations,

$$a + c = b + c \quad \text{and} \quad c + a = c + b,$$

were included in the conclusion of Theorem 1.1, or why one of them was not derived from the other by means of the commutative law for addition and the substitution law for equality.   Both equations were included because applications to further results are sometimes immediate from one form and sometimes from the other.   The commutative law was not employed because it is not necessary to use this law at all in the proof of the theorem; in fact, you can see from the proof that both equations in the conclusion hold for any system in which the equality laws and the closure law for addition are valid.

A theorem closely analogous to Theorem 1.1 is the following, which expresses the *multiplication law for equality.*

THEOREM 1.2   *If a, b, and c are real numbers, and if $a = b$, then*

$$ac = bc \quad \text{and} \quad ca = cb.$$

The proof of Theorem 1.2 exactly parallels that of Theorem 1.1, and is left as an exercise (Problem 23, Exercise 1.5).

The next theorem is an assertion that the additive inverse of a real number is unique—that is, that a given real number has only one additive inverse. An analogous result holds for the multiplicative inverse (Problem 24, Exercise 1.5).

THEOREM 1.3   *If a and b are real numbers, and if $a + b = 0$, then*

$$b = -a \quad \text{and} \quad a = -b.$$

Proof.

Statement	*Reason*
1. a and b are real numbers, and $a + b = 0.$	1. Hypothesis.
2. $(-a) + (a + b) = (-a) + 0.$	2. Addition law for equality, Theorem 1.1.
3. $(-a) + (a + b) = [(-a) + a] + b.$	3. Associative law of addition.
4. $[(-a) + a] + b = (-a) + 0.$	4. Substitution from (3) to (2).
5. $(-a) + a = 0.$	5. Additive inverse.
6. $0 + b = (-a) + 0.$	6. Substitution from (5) to (4).
7. $0 + b = b.$	7. Identity element for addition.
8. $b = (-a) + 0.$	8. Substitution from (7) to (6).
9. $(-a) + 0 = -a.$	9. Identity element for addition.
10. $b = -a.$	10. Substitution from (9) to (8).

This concludes the first part of the proof. Now, to show that $a = -b,$ you can just replace Step 2 by

$$(a + b) + (-b) = 0 + (-b)$$

and a similar argument applies. Notice that in this proof there are many steps involving transitivity or substitution. In actual practice, these steps are frequently omitted, and the proof for the first part of Theorem 1.3, when condensed, would appear as follows:

Statement	*Reason*
1. a and b are real numbers, and $a + b = 0.$	1. Hypothesis.
2. $(-a) + (a + b) = (-a) + 0.$	2. Addition law for equality, Theorem 1.1.
3. $[(-a) + a] + b = (-a) + 0.$	3. Associative law of addition.
4. $0 + b = (-a) + 0.$	4. Additive inverse.
5. $b = -a.$	5. Identity element for addition.

In the last step, for example, we did not state that $0 + b = b$ and $(-a) + 0 = -a$ and then argue that $b = -a$ by the substitution law, for this amount of detail now seems superfluous. The degree of rigorous detail desirable in proofs of this kind is purely relative. If a line of argument is clear and valid, most reasonable persons will not insist on the dotting of all i's and the crossing of all t's. What is important is that you be able to see and understand the argument.

For the following theorem, we give another example of a condensed proof.

THEOREM 1.4 *Cancellation law for addition. If a, b, and c are real numbers, and a + c = b + c, then a = b.*

Proof.

Statement	Reason
1. $a + c = b + c$.	1. Hypothesis.
2. $a + c + (-c) = b + c + (-c)$.	2. Addition law for equality, Theorem 1.1.
3. $a + 0 = b + 0$.	3. Additive inverse.
4. $a = b$.	4. Identity element for addition.

The following theorem is similar to Theorem 1.4. Its proof is left as an exercise (Problem 25, Exercise 1.5).

THEOREM 1.5 *Cancellation law for multiplication. If a, b, and c are real numbers, c ≠ 0, and ac = bc, then a = b.*

Two theorems about the additive identity element 0 as a factor in a product are of fundamental importance.

THEOREM 1.6 *For every $a \in R$, $a \cdot 0 = 0$.*

Proof.

Statement	Reason
1. $0 + 0 = 0$.	1. Identity element for addition.
2. $a \cdot (0 + 0) = a \cdot 0$.	2. Theorem 1.2.
3. $a \cdot 0 + a \cdot 0 = a \cdot 0$.	3. Distributive law.
4. $a \cdot 0 + a \cdot 0 = 0 + a \cdot 0$.	4. Identity element for addition.
5. $a \cdot 0 = 0$.	5. Cancellation law for addition, Theorem 1.4.

THEOREM 1.7 *If a, b ∈ R, and a · b = 0, then either a = 0, or b = 0, or both.*

Proof. If $a = 0$, then the conclusion of the theorem is true. Suppose $a \neq 0$; then, by F-11 and Theorem 1.2,

$$\frac{1}{a}(a \cdot b) = \frac{1}{a} \cdot 0.$$

By the associative law for multiplication, this can be written

$$\left(\frac{1}{a}\cdot a\right)b = \frac{1}{a}\cdot 0,$$

and since, by F-11, $\frac{1}{a}\cdot a = 1$, and, by Theorem 1.6, $\frac{1}{a}\cdot 0 = 0$, this latter statement becomes

$$1\cdot b = 0,$$

or

$$b = 0.$$

Thus, in any case the conclusion of the theorem is true if the hypothesis is true.

Note that in this proof we have used a different format for the argument, dispensing with the statement-reason form altogether. To prove parts of the next theorem, we shall use still another form, in which the argument is presented without specifically listing the reasons. You should make sure, however, that you can supply a reason for each step.

THEOREM 1.8 *If a, b* ∈ *R, then*

$$\text{I} \quad -(-a) = a,$$

$$\text{II} \quad (-a) + (-b) = -(a + b),$$

$$\text{III} \quad (-a)(b) = -(ab),$$

$$\text{IV} \quad (-a)(-b) = ab,$$

$$\text{V} \quad \frac{1}{\dfrac{1}{a}} = a \quad (a \neq 0),$$

$$\text{VI} \quad \frac{-a}{b} = \frac{a}{-b} = -\frac{a}{b} \quad (b \neq 0),$$

$$\text{VII} \quad \frac{-a}{-b} = \frac{a}{b} \quad (b \neq 0).$$

Proof of 1.8-I.

$$a + (-a) = 0$$
$$[a + (-a)] + [-(-a)] = 0 + [-(-a)]$$
$$a + [(-a) + (-(-a))] = 0 + [-(-a)]$$
$$a + 0 = 0 + [-(-a)]$$
$$a = -(-a)$$
$$-(-a) = a.$$

Proof of 1.8-II.

$$
\begin{aligned}
-(a + b) &= 0 + 0 + [-(a + b)] \\
&= [a + (-a)] + [b + (-b)] + [-(a + b)] \\
&= (a + b) + [(-a) + (-b)] + [-(a + b)] \\
&= (a + b) + [-(a + b)] + [(-a) + (-b)] \\
&= 0 + [(-a) + (-b)] \\
&= (-a) + (-b).
\end{aligned}
$$

Proof of 1.8-III.

$$
\begin{aligned}
a + (-a) &= 0 \\
[a + (-a)]b &= 0 \cdot b \\
ab + (-a)b &= 0 \cdot b \\
ab + (-a)b &= 0 \\
(-a)b &= -(ab).
\end{aligned}
$$

The proof that

$$(a)(-b) = -(ab)$$

is quite similar.

The proofs of the remaining parts of Theorem 1.8 are left as exercises (Problems 33–36, Exercise 1.5). If a and b are restricted to represent non-negative real numbers, these theorems are some of the familiar "laws of signs" for operating with real numbers.

Turning now to some properties of quotients, we have the following.

THEOREM 1.9 *If a, b, c, and d are real numbers, and b and d are not 0, then*

$$\frac{a}{b} = \frac{c}{d}$$

if and only if $ad = bc$.

Proof. We shall first prove the "if" part. Since b and d are not 0, there exist real numbers $1/b$ and $1/d$, and if

$$ad = bc,$$

then

$$\frac{1}{b} \cdot \frac{1}{d} \cdot ad = \frac{1}{b} \cdot \frac{1}{d} \cdot bc,$$

from which

$$a \cdot \frac{1}{b} \cdot \left(d \cdot \frac{1}{d}\right) = c \cdot \frac{1}{d} \cdot \left(b \cdot \frac{1}{b}\right)$$

$$\frac{a}{b} = \frac{c}{d}.$$

Now, for the "only if" part: If

$$\frac{a}{b} = \frac{c}{d},$$

then

$$bd \cdot \frac{a}{b} = bd \cdot \frac{c}{d}$$

$$bd \cdot \left(a \cdot \frac{1}{b}\right) = bd \cdot \left(c \cdot \frac{1}{d}\right)$$

$$ad \cdot \left(b \cdot \frac{1}{b}\right) = bc \cdot \left(d \cdot \frac{1}{d}\right)$$

$$ad = bc.$$

As a direct consequence of this characterization of equal quotients, we have a theorem that is sometimes referred to as the *fundamental principle of fractions:*

THEOREM 1.10 *If a, b, and c are real numbers, and if b and c are not 0, then*

$$\frac{ac}{bc} = \frac{a}{b}.$$

Proof. By Theorem 1.9,

$$\frac{ac}{bc} = \frac{a}{b}$$

if $(ac)b = a(bc)$. Since $(ac)b = a(cb) = a(bc)$, the theorem is proved.

Next, let us group a number of assertions about quotients into a single theorem.

THEOREM 1.11 *If a, b, c, and d are real numbers, then*

$$\text{I} \quad \frac{1}{a} \cdot \frac{1}{b} = \frac{1}{ab} \quad (a, b \neq 0),$$

$$\text{II} \quad \frac{a}{b} \cdot \frac{c}{d} = \frac{ac}{bd} \quad (b, d \neq 0),$$

$$\text{III} \quad \frac{a}{c} + \frac{b}{c} = \frac{a+b}{c} \quad (c \neq 0),$$

$$\text{IV} \quad \frac{a}{b} + \frac{c}{d} = \frac{ad+bc}{bd} \quad (b, d \neq 0),$$

$$\text{V} \quad \frac{a}{b} - \frac{c}{d} = \frac{ad-bc}{bd} \quad (b, d \neq 0),$$

$$\text{VI} \quad \frac{1}{\dfrac{a}{b}} = \frac{b}{a} \quad (a, b \neq 0),$$

$$\text{VII} \quad \frac{\dfrac{a}{b}}{\dfrac{c}{d}} = \frac{ad}{bc} \quad (b, c, d \neq 0).$$

We shall prove only the first of the foregoing assertions. Again, you should make sure that you can supply the reason for each statement.

Proof of 1.11-I. We have

$$ab \cdot \frac{1}{a} \frac{1}{b} = a \cdot \frac{1}{a} \cdot b \cdot \frac{1}{b} = 1 \cdot 1.$$

Hence

$$ab \cdot \frac{1}{a} \frac{1}{b} = 1.$$

If both members of this latter equation are multiplied by $1/ab$, we obtain

$$\frac{1}{ab} \cdot ab \cdot \frac{1}{a} \frac{1}{b} = \frac{1}{ab} \cdot 1,$$

$$1 \cdot \frac{1}{a} \frac{1}{b} = \frac{1}{ab} \cdot 1,$$

$$\frac{1}{a} \frac{1}{b} = \frac{1}{ab}.$$

EXERCISE 1.5

In Problems 1–20, each statement is justifiable by one part of Theorems 1.1–1.11. Cite the appropriate justification. (All variables denote real numbers.)

Example. If $p + q + 3 = 4 + 3$, then $p + q = 4$.

Solution. Theorem 1.4.

1. If $x = 3$, then $x + 9 = 3 + 9$.

2. $-2 - q = -(2 + q)$

3. $\dfrac{-2}{5} = -\dfrac{2}{5}$

4. $\dfrac{4(x + y)}{6} = \dfrac{2(x + y)}{3}$

5. $\dfrac{x}{3} + \dfrac{y + z}{3} = \dfrac{x + y + z}{3}$

6. $\dfrac{\dfrac{1}{2}}{\dfrac{3}{3}} = \dfrac{3}{2}$

7. If $4p = 0$, then $p = 0$

8. $(-5)(-6) = 30$

9. If $3x = 2y$, then $\dfrac{3}{2} = \dfrac{y}{x}$

10. $\dfrac{p}{3} \cdot \dfrac{q}{4} = \dfrac{pq}{12}$

11. $\dfrac{\frac{2}{5}}{\frac{3}{7}} = \dfrac{2 \cdot 7}{5 \cdot 3}$

12. $x - (-y) = x + y$

13. $(-3)(p) = -(3p)$

14. $\dfrac{-x}{-3} = \dfrac{x}{3}$

15. $\dfrac{x}{3} + \dfrac{y}{2} = \dfrac{2x + 3y}{3 \cdot 2}$

16. If $(x + 2y) - 3 = z - 3$, then $(x + 2y) = z$.

17. If $p + q = 7$, then $4(p + q) = 4 \cdot 7$.

18. If $(r + s) + 7 = 0$, then $r + s = -7$.

19. If $6(x - y) = 3z$, then $2(x - y) = z$.

20. $\dfrac{x + 1}{4} - \dfrac{y + 3}{3} = \dfrac{3(x + 1) - 4(y + 3)}{4 \cdot 3}$

21. _answer 1.5_

22.

Prove each of the following, using the statement-reason format. All variables and constants are understood to denote elements of the set R of real numbers.

23. If $a = b$, then $ac = bc$ and $ca = cb$.   _Multiplicative law for equality_

24. If $ab = 1$, then $b = \dfrac{1}{a}$ and $a = \dfrac{1}{b}$.

25. If $ac = bc$, and $c \neq 0$, then $a = b$.

26. $(a + b)(c + d) = ac + ad + bc + bd$

27. $(a + b) - c = a + (b - c)$

28. $(a - b) + c = a - (b - c)$

29. $(a - b) - c = a - (b + c)$

30. 0 is unique; that is, there is only one identity element for addition. *Hint:* Assume that $a + 0 = a$ and $a + 0' = a$ for all $a \in R$ and prove that $0 = 0'$.

31. 1 is unique; that is, there is only one identity element for multiplication. *Hint:* Assume that $a \cdot 1 = a$ and $a \cdot 1' = a$ for all $a \in R$ and prove that $1 = 1'$.

32. $\dfrac{1}{a}$ $(a \neq 0)$ is unique.

33. $(-a)(-b) = ab$.

34. $\dfrac{1}{\dfrac{1}{a}} = a \quad (a \neq 0)$

35. $\dfrac{-a}{b} = \dfrac{a}{-b} = -\dfrac{a}{b} \quad (b \neq 0)$

36. $\dfrac{-a}{-b} = \dfrac{a}{b} \quad (b \neq 0)$

37. $\dfrac{a}{b} \cdot \dfrac{c}{d} = \dfrac{ac}{bd} \quad (b, d \neq 0)$

38. $\dfrac{a}{c} + \dfrac{b}{c} = \dfrac{a+b}{c} \quad (c \neq 0)$

39. $\dfrac{a}{b} + \dfrac{c}{d} = \dfrac{ad + bc}{bd} \quad (b, d \neq 0)$

40. $\dfrac{a}{b} - \dfrac{c}{d} = \dfrac{ad - bc}{bd} \quad (b, d \neq 0)$

41. $\dfrac{1}{\dfrac{a}{b}} = \dfrac{b}{a} \quad (a, b \neq 0)$

42. $\dfrac{\dfrac{a}{b}}{\dfrac{c}{d}} = \dfrac{a}{b} \dfrac{d}{c} \quad (b, c, d \neq 0)$

43. If $\dfrac{a}{b} = q \quad (b \neq 0)$, then $a = bq$.

44. If $a = bq \quad (b \neq 0)$, then $\dfrac{a}{b} = q$.

45. $\dfrac{a}{a} = 1 \quad (a \neq 0)$

46. $-1 \cdot a = -a$

47. If $x + a = b$, then $x = b - a$.

48. If $ax = b \quad (a \neq 0)$, then $x = \dfrac{b}{a}.$

49. If $x - a = b$, then $x = a + b$.

50. If $a = b$, and $c \neq 0$, then $\dfrac{a}{c} = \dfrac{b}{c}.$

51. If $\dfrac{a}{c} = \dfrac{b}{c} \quad (c \neq 0)$, then $a = b$.

52. $\dfrac{\dfrac{a}{b}}{c} = \dfrac{a}{bc} \quad (b, c \neq 0)$

53. $\dfrac{a}{\dfrac{b}{c}} = \dfrac{ac}{b} \quad (b, c \neq 0)$

$a(b+c) = ab + ac$ Comm
$a(c+b) = ab + ac$
$(c+b)a = ba + ca$

54. Derive the second equation,

$$(b + c)a = ba + ca,$$

in Field Postulate F-8 from the other postulates and the first equation,

$$a(b + c) = ab + ac.$$

55. Give two reasons for including both equations in Field Postulates F-3, F-8, and F-9 even though either equation can be derived from the other from the commutative law and the substitution law for equality. NO REASON

1.6   REAL NUMBERS: ORDER AND COMPLETENESS

Let us now make the assumption of the existence of a one-to-one correspondence between the real numbers and the points on a geometric line (for each real number there corresponds one and only one point on the line, and vice versa), as illustrated in Figure 1.8.

Sets of numbers can be visualized by means of this correspondence.   For example, to represent {1, 3, 5} on a line, we simply scale the line in convenient units, with positive direction (from 0 toward 1) denoted by an arrowhead, and indicate the required points with solid dots.   This geometric representation of a set of real numbers is called a **line graph** or a **number line**. The real number corresponding to a point on a number line is called the **coordinate** of the point, and the point is called the **graph** of the number.

Figure 1.8

A horizontal number line directed to the right can be used to illustrate the separation of the real numbers into three disjoint subsets: {negative real numbers}, {0}, {positive real numbers}.   The point associated with 0 is called the **origin**.   The set of numbers whose elements are associated with the points on the right-hand side of the origin belong to the set R_+ of **positive real numbers,** and the set whose elements are associated with the points on the other side belong to the set R_- of **negative real numbers**.   Notice that the word "negative" has now been used in two ways.   In one case, we refer to the *negative of a number*, as in Postulate F-4, whereas in the other we refer to a *negative number*, which is the negative (or opposite) of a positive number. The ideas are quite distinct.   Of course, $-(3)$, the negative of 3, is the negative number -3, and, accordingly, *we use the latter symbol for both notions.*

It is possible to categorize the set of positive real numbers without recourse to geometric considerations, though of course we shall continue to find it convenient to refer to the number line also.   With this in mind, let us state two more postulates that apply to real numbers.

O-1 If a is a real number, then exactly   *Trichotomy law.*
one of the following is true: a is
positive, a is zero, or $-a$ is positive.

O-2 If a and b are positive real numbers,   *Closure law for positive*
then $a + b$ is positive and ab is positive.   *numbers.*

The first of these postulates states that every real number belongs either to the set R_+, the set {0}, or the set R_-, but to only one of them.   The second asserts that the set R_+ of positive real numbers is closed with respect to the binary operations of addition and multiplication.

Since the set R of real numbers satisfies Postulates O-1 and O-2 as well as Postulates F-1 through F-11, we say that R is an **ordered field**.   Similarly, the set Q of rational numbers is an ordered field.   But as we shall see in Chapter 10, the set C of complex numbers is not an ordered field even though it is a field.

By Postulate O-2, if a and b are positive real numbers, then ab is a positive real number. This fact, together with Parts III and IV of Theorem 1.8, is sufficient to establish that the product of a positive real number and a negative real number is a negative real number, while the product of two negative real numbers is a positive real number. More formally, we have the following.

THEOREM 1.12 *The product of a positive real number and a negative real number is a negative real number.*

THEOREM 1.13 *The product of two negative real numbers is a positive real number.*

Theorem 1.13 and Postulate O-2, together, imply the following.

THEOREM 1.14 *If $a \in R$, $a \neq 0$, then $a \cdot a$ is a positive real number.*

The addition of a positive real number d to a real number a can be visualized on a number line as the process of locating the point corresponding to a on the line, and then moving along the line d units to the right to arrive at the point corresponding to $a + d$ (Figure 1.9). With this idea in mind, we can

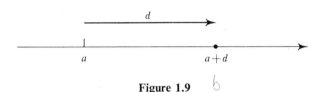

Figure 1.9

define what is meant by "less than."

DEFINITION 1.14 *If a and b are real numbers, then a is less than b if and only if there exists a positive number d such that $a + d = b$.*

Since d is positive, this definition implies that of any two real numbers, a and b, if the graph of a lies to the left of the graph of b, then a is less than b. The inequality symbol "$<$" is used to denote the phrase "is less than," and $a < b$ is read "a is less than b." The inequality symbol "$>$" means "is greater than." The statements $a < b$ and $b > a$ are taken as equivalent.

Again, since d is positive and $d = b - a$, the inequality $a < b$ is equivalent to the relation $b - a \in R_+$. In particular, for $a = 0$, the inequality $b > 0$ means the same as $b \in R_+$.

Now let us consider some important basic relationships resulting from our definition of "less than" and "greater than." First we restate Postulates O-1 and O-2 for real numbers a and b.

O-1′ If $a \in R$, then exactly one of the following is true: $a > 0$, $a = 0$, or $-a > 0$.

O-2′ If $a > 0$ and $b > 0$, then $a + b > 0$ and $ab > 0$.

Similarly, Theorems 1.12 and 1.13 can be stated thus:

Theorem 1.12′ *If $\overset{+}{a} > 0$ and $\overset{-}{b} < 0$, then $ab < 0$.*

Theorem 1.13′ *If $\overset{-}{a} < 0$ and $\overset{-}{b} < 0$, then $ab > 0$.*

We introduce the symbols $\leq$ and $\geq$ (read "is less than or equal to" and "is greater than or equal to," respectively) in giving a more precise formulation to Theorem 1.14.

Theorem 1.14′ *If $a \in R$, then $a \cdot a \geq 0$, with the sign of equality holding if and only if $a = 0$.*

Thus we have

$$(2)(2) = 4 > 0, \quad (-3)(-3) = 9 > 0, \quad \text{but} \quad (0)(0) = 0.$$

The simple relation $a \cdot a \geq 0$ is probably the most useful and famous of all inequalities.

THEOREM 1.15 *Let $a, b, c \in R$.*

    I *If $a < b$ and $b < c$, then $a < c$.*

    II *If $a < b$, then $a + c < b + c$.*

    III *If $a < b$ and $c > 0$, then $ac < bc$.*

    IV *If $a < b$ and $c < 0$, then $ac > bc$.*

Proof of 1.15-I.

Statement	*Reason*
1. $a < b$ and $b < c$.	1. Hypothesis.
2. $a + d_1 = b$ and $b + d_2 = c$, where d_1 and d_2 are positive real numbers.	2. Definition of $<$.
3. $b = c - d_2$.	3. Theorem 1.1.
4. $a + d_1 = c - d_2$.	4. E-3 applied to Steps (2) and (3).
5. $a + d_1 + d_2 = c$.	5. Theorem 1.1.
6. $d_1 + d_2 = d_3$, where d_3 is a positive real number.	6. O-2.
7. $a + d_3 = c$.	7. E-4 applied to Steps (5) and (6).
8. $a < c$.	8. Definition of $<$.

As you can see, this result is comparable to the transitive law of equality. That is, we can say that "less than" is a transitive relationship. The proofs of the remaining parts of this theorem are left as exercises. It is worth observing that Part II corresponds to the addition law of equality (Theorem 1.1), and Parts III and IV are akin to the multiplication law of equality (Theorem 1.2), except that two different statements are necessary: one for $c > 0$ and one for $c < 0$.

The graphs of the numbers a and $-a$ on a number line lie the same distance from the origin, but on opposite sides of it. If we wish to refer to the *distance* of the graph of a number from the origin, and not to the side of the origin on which it is located, the term "absolute value" is used. Thus, the absolute value of a and the absolute value of $-a$ are the same. The symbol $|a|$ is used to denote the absolute value of a. We formalize the definition as follows:

DEFINITION 1.15 *If a is a real number, then the **absolute value** of a is*

$$|a| = \begin{cases} a, & \text{if } a \geq 0, \\ -a, & \text{if } a < 0. \end{cases}$$

Thus, the absolute value of a real number is always nonnegative. For example, $|-3| = 3$, $|7| = 7$, and $|0| = 0$.

The set of real numbers has one further property that is of fundamental importance, and one that is needed to establish the existence of irrational real numbers. Before stating the property, let us introduce some terminology.

DEFINITION 1.16 *If S is a nonempty subset of the set R of real numbers, and if b is a real number such that for every $x \in S$ we have $b \geq x$, then b is an **upper bound** of S. If $b \leq x$ for every $x \in S$, then b is a **lower bound** of S.*

For example, if $S = \{1, 3, 4\}$, then 6 and 4 are upper bounds of S, and -7 is a lower bound of S.

If a subset S of the set R of real numbers has an upper bound, it is said to be **bounded above**; otherwise it is **unbounded above**. Similarly, if it has a lower bound it is said to be **bounded below,** and otherwise it is **unbounded below.** For example, the set $N = \{1, 2, 3, \cdots\}$ of natural numbers is bounded below but unbounded above.

DEFINITION 1.17 *If b is an upper bound for a nonempty set S of real numbers, and if no real number $b' < b$ is an upper bound for S, then b is the **least upper bound** for S. If b is a lower bound for S, and no real number $b' > b$ is a lower bound for S, then b is the **greatest lower bound** for S.*

If a set has a least upper bound or a greatest lower bound, these bounds may or may not be in the set. For example, consider the set of real numbers

$S = \{x \mid 0 < x \text{ and } x \leq 1\}$. Ordinarily, we write the two inequalities together thus: $S = \{x \mid 0 < x \leq 1\}$. Since for every $x \in S$, we have $0 < x$ and $1 \geq x$, 0 is a lower and 1 an upper bound for S. Moreover, it is intuitively evident that there exists no real number b such that for every $x \in S$ we have $0 < b \leq x$ or $x \leq b < 1$. Thus, 0 is the greatest lower bound and 1 the least upper bound for S. In this example, the least upper bound is a member of S, while the greatest lower bound is not a member of S.

With these definitions, we are prepared to state the following, which is called the **postulate of completeness**.

O-3   Every nonempty subset of the real   *Postulate of completeness.*
      numbers that is bounded above
      has a least upper bound.

This postulate assures us, for example, that there is a real number, called $\sqrt{2}$, which is the least upper bound of $\{x \mid x \in R \text{ and } x^2 \leq 2\}$.

Thus the set R of real numbers is a **complete ordered field** under the binary operations of addition and multiplication. The set Q of rational numbers is an ordered field under these operations, but not a complete ordered field.

We have now come to the end of our list of postulates for the real number system R. It can be shown that *any* complete ordered field R' can be put in one-to-one correspondence with R in such a way that the results of its two operations are consistent with the results of the operations of addition and multiplication, respectively, in R. For example, if we have

$$
\begin{array}{cccccc}
R & 1 & 2 & 3 & + & \times \\
& \updownarrow & \updownarrow & \updownarrow & \updownarrow & \updownarrow \quad \text{etc.,} \\
R' & 1 & 2 & 3 & + & \times
\end{array}
$$

then $1 + 2 = 3, 1 \times 2 = 2$, etc. We call such a relation-preserving one-to-one correspondence an **isomorphism**. Thus any complete ordered field R' is isomorphic with R.

EXERCISE 1.6

In Problems 1–8, each statement is justifiable by one part of Theorem 1.15. Cite the appropriate justification.

Example.   If $2 < 3x$, then $-4 > -6x$.

Solution.   Part IV. Each member of $2 < 3x$ is multiplied by -2 to yield $-4 > -6x$.

1. If $x < 3$, and $y < x$, then $y < 3$.   2. If $x + 1 < 0$, then $x < -1$.

3. If $y < 8$, then $3y < 24$.   4. If $y < 4$, then $y + 2 < 6$.

5. If $x < 7$, then $x - 2 < 5$.   6. If $x < 9$, then $-2x > -18$.

7. If $-6x < 12$, then $x > -2$.   8. If $x - 3 < 5$, then $x < 8$.

In Problems 9–18, express each statement by means of symbols.

Examples

a. 5 is not greater than 7

b. x is between 5 and 8

Solutions.

a. $5 \not> 7$ or $5 \leq 7$

b. $5 < x < 8$

9. 7 is greater than 3 $7 > 3$

10. 2 is less than 5 $2 < 5$

11. -4 is less than -3 $-4 < -3$

12. -4 is greater than -7 $-4 > -7$

13. x is between 1 and -1, inclusive $-1 \leq x \leq 1$

14. x is negative x is $-$

15. x is positive x is $+$

16. x is nonpositive x is $-$

17. x is nonnegative x is $+$

18. $|2x|$ is less than or equal to 8 $|2x| \leq 8$

Replace the comma in Problems 19–24 with an appropriate order symbol.

19. $-2, 5$ $-2 < 5$ 20. $3, 4$ $3 < 4$ 21. $-7, -1$ $-7 < -1$

22. $|-3|, |-5|$ $|-3| < |-5|$ 23. $|-3|, |3|$ $|-3| < |3|$ 24. $|-x|, 0$ $(x \in R)$ $|-x| < 0$

In Problems 25–30, write an equivalent relation without using the negation symbol, $/$.

25. $2 \not> 5$ $2 < 5$ 26. $-1 \not< -2$ $-1 > -2$ 27. $7 \not> 8$ $7 < 8$

28. $|x| \not< 3$ $|x| \geq 3$ 29. $|x| \not> 3$ $|x| < 3$ 30. $x \not> |y|$ $x \leq |y|$

Prove each of the following, using the statement-reason format.   All variables are understood to denote elements of the set of real numbers.

31. If $a > 0$ and $b < 0$, then $ab < 0$.

32. If $a < b$, then $a + c < b + c$.

33. If $a < b$, and $c > 0$, then $ac < bc$.   *contrapositives*

34. If $a < b$, and $c < 0$, then $ac > bc$.

35. If $a < c$ and $b < d$, then $a + b < c + d$.   *Sub. change + add*

36. If $a < 0$ and $b < 0$, then $a + b < 0$.   *Don't always start*

37. If $\dfrac{a}{b} < \dfrac{c}{d}$ and $bd > 0$, then $ad < bc$.   *with if – start from*

38. If $ad < bc$ and $bd > 0$, then $\dfrac{a}{b} < \dfrac{c}{d}$.   *then*

39. If $a + c < b + c$, then $a < b$.   *Use indirect proof*

40. If $ac < bc$, and $c > 0$, then $a < b$.

41. If $ac < bc$, and $c < 0$, then $a > b$.

42. $a + \dfrac{1}{a} \geq 2, a > 0$.   *Hint:* Apply Theorem 1.14.

43. If $a > 1$, then $a^2 > a$.

44. If $0 < a < 1$, then $0 < a^2 < a$.

45. If $a < b$, then $a < \dfrac{a + b}{2} < b$; that is, $a < \dfrac{a + b}{2}$ and $\dfrac{a + b}{2} < b$.

46. What is the greatest lower bound of $\{x \mid x \in R$ and $x > 0\}$?

47. What is the least upper bound of $\{x \mid x \in R$ and $|x| < 1\}$?

48. What is the least upper bound of $\{x \mid x \in R$ and $x^2 < 7\}$?

49. What is the greatest lower bound of $\{x \mid x \in R_+$ and $x^2 > 9\}$?

POLYNOMIALS

2.1 DEFINITIONS; SUMS OF POLYNOMIALS

Any grouping of constants and variables generated by applying a finite number of the elementary operations—addition, subtraction, multiplication, division, or the extraction of roots—is called an **algebraic expression.** For example,

$$\frac{3x^2 + \sqrt{2x - 1}}{3} \quad \text{and} \quad xy + 3x^2z - \sqrt[5]{z}$$

are algebraic expressions.

You should recall that an expression of the form x^n is called a power of x, where x is the **base** of the power and n is the **exponent** of the power.

DEFINITION 2.1 *If* $n \in N$ *(i.e.,* $n \in \{natural\ numbers\}$*) and* $x \in R$ *(i.e.,* $x \in real\ numbers$*), then the nth **power** of x is*

$$x^n = \underbrace{x \cdot x \cdot x \cdots x.}_{n\ factors}$$

$$x^n = x_1 \cdot x_2 \cdot x \cdots x_n \quad \text{where} \quad x_i = x$$

In any algebraic expression of the form $A + B + C + \cdots$, where A, B, $C, \cdots$ are algebraic expressions that do not themselves appear as sums or differences, A, B, $C, \cdots$ are called **terms** of the expression. If an algebraic expression contains no variable in a denominator and contains only non-negative integral powers of a variable, then the expression is a **polynomial**. For example,

$$5x, \frac{3x^2}{2} - \frac{7x}{2}, 0, 2x^2 - 3x + 4, \text{ and } \frac{y}{4} - \frac{\sqrt{7}}{4}, \quad x, y \in R,$$

are polynomials, whereas

$$\frac{3}{x}, 3 + \sqrt{x}, \text{ and } 3^{z-1} + 7, \quad x \in R,$$

are algebraic expressions, but not polynomials, in the variable x.

Polynomials consisting of one, two, or three terms are also called **monomials, binomials,** and **trinomials,** respectively. Thus $3x^2y$ is a monomial, $x + 4x^2$ is a binomial, and $x + y + z$ is a trinomial.

The **degree** of a monomial is given by the exponent of the variable in the monomial. Thus, 5 is of degree zero, $2x$ is of the first degree, and $3x^4$ is of fourth degree; but no degree is assigned to the special monomial 0. If a monomial contains more than one variable, its degree is given by the sum of the exponents on the variables; $3x^2y^3z$ is of sixth degree in x, y, and z. It can also be described as being of second degree in x, third degree in y, fifth degree in x and y, and so on. The **degree of a polynomial** is the same as the degree of its term of largest degree. Since no degree is assigned to the monomial 0, no degree is assigned to the zero polynomial 0, either.

Because $a - b$ is defined to be $a + (-b)$, we shall view the signs in any polynomial as signs denoting positive or negative coefficients, and the operation involved to be addition. Thus

$$3x - 5x + 4x = (3x) + (-5x) + (4x).$$

Again, an expression such as

$$a - (bx + cx^2),$$

in which a set of parentheses is preceded by a negative sign, can be written

$$a + [-(bx + cx^2)],$$

or

$$a + [-bx - cx^2],$$

or, finally,

$$a + (-bx) + (-cx^2).$$

Also, as regards multiplication and division, since

$$\frac{a}{b} = a\left(\frac{1}{b}\right),$$

we can view division by a constant as multiplication by its reciprocal (multiplicative inverse), and, for example, write

$$\frac{3x^2}{4} + \frac{x}{2} \text{ as } \frac{1}{4}(3x^2) + \frac{1}{2}x.$$

Accordingly, since a polynomial can be considered to involve only the operations of addition and multiplication, and since the set R of real numbers

$x^0 = 1$

is closed with respect to these operations, it follows that, for any specific real value of x, a polynomial with real coefficients represents a real number. Therefore, the postulates for the real numbers are applicable to the terms in such polynomials and to the polynomials themselves.

In Chapter 1 we used grouping devices, such as parentheses, to indicate that various sums or products were to be viewed as a single number. Similarly, for example, the expression

$$(3x + 2x) + 4x$$

represents the sum of $3x + 2x$ and $4x$, whereas the expression

$$3x + (2x + 4x)$$

represents the sum of $3x$ and $2x + 4x$. The associative law asserts that, for each fixed value of x, these expressions are equal. By Definition 1.11 and Postulate F-2, the expression

$$3x + 2x + 4x$$

is equal to either of the foregoing grouped expressions.

By applying the commutative, associative, and distributive laws in various ways, we can frequently rewrite polynomials and sums of polynomials in what might be termed "simpler" forms. For example, we can write

$$(2x^2 + 3x + 5) + 2x + (6x^2 + 7)$$

in the form

$$2x^2 + 6x^2 + 3x + 2x + 5 + 7,$$

from which, by the distributive law, we have

$$(2 + 6)x^2 + (3 + 2)x + 5 + 7,$$

or

$$8x^2 + 5x + 12,$$

in which we have reduced the number of terms from six to three.

We shall often be concerned with polynomials in one variable. A polynomial of degree n, $n \geq 0$, in x can be represented—when its terms are rearranged, if need be, in the manner described above—by an expression of the form

$$a_0x^n + a_1x^{n-1} + a_2x^{n-2} + \cdots + a_{n-1}x + a_n, \quad a_0 \neq 0,$$

where it is understood that the a's are the (constant) coefficients of the powers of x in the polynomial.

The term a_0x^n is called the **leading term**, and the coefficient a_0 is called the **leading coefficient** in the polynomial. It is often convenient to have the leading term of the form x^n. In this case, that is, when $a_0 = 1$, the polynomial is said to be **monic**.

If the coefficients in a polynomial $P(x)$ are real numbers, then the polynomial is called a **polynomial over the real number field**, or simply a **polynomial over R**. If the variables are restricted to represent only real numbers, then the polynomial is said to be a **polynomial in the real variable x**. If *both* the coefficients and the variable are restricted to real values, we say that $P(x)$ is a **real polynomial**.

Polynomials are frequently represented by symbols such as

$$P(x), \ D(y), \ Q(z),$$

where the symbol in the parentheses designates the variable. Thus, we might write

$$P(x) = 2x^3 - 3x + 2,$$
$$D(y) = y^6 - 2y^2 + 3y - 2,$$
$$Q(z) = 8z^4 + 3z^3 - 2z^2 + z - 1.$$

The notation $P(x)$ can be used to denote values of the polynomial for specific values of x. Thus, $P(2)$ means the value of the polynomial $P(x)$ when x is replaced by 2. For example, if

$$P(x) = x^2 - 2x + 1,$$

then

$$P(2) = 2^2 - 2(2) + 1 = 1,$$
$$P(3) = 3^2 - 2(3) + 1 = 4,$$

and

$$P(-4) = (-4)^2 - 2(-4) + 1 = 25.$$

DEFINITION 2.2 *Two real polynomials are said to be **equal** if and only if they are of the same degree and their respective coefficients of terms of the same degree are equal.*

Thus

$$(2 + 3)x + 4 \quad \text{and} \quad 5x + 4$$

are equal polynomials, but

$$P(x) = 5x + 4 \quad \text{and} \quad Q(x) = 4x + 5$$

are not.

In accordance with Definition 2.2, two equal polynomials are equal for *all* values of the variables. For this reason, we often express the fact that two polynomials $P(x)$ and $Q(x)$ are equal by writing

$$P(x) \equiv Q(x),$$

= reflexive
symmetric
transitive

and sometimes, to avoid the possibility of a misunderstanding, we say that such polynomials are **identically equal**.   An equation such as

$$P(x) = 0$$

ordinarily is true for some values of x but not true for others.

The set of all real polynomials $P(x)$ is denoted by the symbol $R[x]$.   Then, because

$$P(x) = 2x - 3$$

is a polynomial over the field R of real numbers, we have

$$P(x) \in R[x].$$

Since for each real number x a real polynomial $P(x)$ names a real number, Postulates E-1 through E-4 (see page 15) for equality of elements of sets hold in particular for elements $P(x)$ in the set $R[x]$.   Thus, we have the following counterparts for the equality properties for real numbers.

If $P(x)$, $Q(x)$, and $S(x) \in R[x]$:

1. $P(x) \equiv P(x)$.   *Reflexive law.*

2. If $P(x) \equiv Q(x)$, then $Q(x) \equiv P(x)$.   *Symmetric law.*

3. If $P(x) \equiv Q(x)$ and $Q(x) \equiv S(x)$, then $P(x) \equiv S(x)$.   *Transitive law.*

4. If $P(x) \equiv Q(x)$, then $P(x)$ may be replaced by $Q(x)$ *Substitution law.*
   in any mathematical statement without altering the
   truth or falsity of the statement.

Now let us look at a few typical illustrations of addition in the set $R[x]$ of real polynomials $P(x)$:

$$(x^2 - 2x + 1) + (x - 2) = x^2 - x - 1 \tag{1}$$

$$\left.\begin{aligned}(x^2 - 1) + [(3x - 2) + (5x + 2)] &= (x^2 - 1) + (8x) \\ &= x^2 + 8x - 1 \\ [(x^2 - 1) + (3x - 2)] + (5x + 2) &= (x^2 + 3x - 3) + (5x + 2) \\ &= x^2 + 8x - 1\end{aligned}\right\} \tag{2}$$

$$\begin{aligned}(x^7 + 2x^5 - x^3 + x) + 0 &= 0 + (x^7 + 2x^5 - x^3 + x) \\ &= x^7 + 2x^5 - x^3 + x\end{aligned} \tag{3}$$

$$\begin{aligned}(x^4 - x^3 + 3x + 1) + (-x^4 + x^3 - 3x - 1) \\ = (-x^4 + x^3 - 3x - 1) + (x^4 - x^3 + 3x + 1) = 0\end{aligned} \tag{4}$$

$$(x + 3) + (x^2 - x + 2) = (x^2 - x + 2) + (x + 3) = x^2 + 5 \tag{5}$$

The examples (1)–(5) illustrate the following properties of the set $R[x]$, which you should compare with Postulates F-1 through F-5 for the real numbers.

binary operation – performed on two elements of set

If $P(x)$, $R(x)$, and $S(x) \in R[x]$:

1. $P(x) + Q(x) \in R[x]$.   *Closure for addition.*

2. $P(x) + [Q(x) + S(x)] =$ *Associative law of addition.*
   $[P(x) + Q(x)] + S(x)$.

3. $P(x) + 0 = 0 + P(x) = P(x)$.   *Identity element for addition.*

4. For each $P(x)$, there is an element   *Additive inverse.*
   $-P(x) \in R[x]$ such that
   $P(x) + [-P(x)] = [-P(x)] + P(x) = 0$.

5. $P(x) + Q(x) = Q(x) + P(x)$.   *Commutative law of addition.*

EXERCISE 2.1

In Problems 1–6, give the degree of each polynomial. If the expression is not a polynomial, so state.

Example. $x^3y^2 + y^4 + x$

Solution. Fifth degree in x and y; fourth degree in y; third degree in x.

1. $y^3 + 6y + 4$ *3*   2. $x^2 - x$ *3*   3. $x^3y - xy^2 + x^2$ *x- 3*

4. $4 - \dfrac{2}{x^2}$ *not*   5. $\dfrac{x^2 + 3}{x^3}$ *not*   6. $x^4 - x^3y^2 - y^3$

Find the values of the polynomial for the specified values of the variable.

Example. If $P(x) = 2x^2 - x + 3$, find $P(3)$, $P(-3)$, $P(0)$, $P(a)$.

Solution.

$$P(3) = 2(3)^2 - (3) + 3 = 18$$
$$P(-3) = 2(-3)^2 - (-3) + 3 = 24$$
$$P(0) = 2(0)^2 - (0) + 3 = 3$$
$$P(a) = 2a^2 - a + 3$$

7. If $P(x) = x^3 - 3x^2 + x + 1$, find $P(2)$, $P(-2)$, $P(0)$.

8. If $P(x) = 2x^3 + x^2 - 3x + 4$, find $P(3)$, $P(-3)$, $P(0)$.

9. If $P(x) = x^{12}$, find $P(1)$, $P(-1)$, $P(0)$.

10. If $P(x) = x^{13}$, find $P(1)$, $P(-1)$, $P(0)$.

Example. If $P(x) = x - 4$ and $Q(x) = x + 2$, find $P[Q(2)]$ and $P[Q(x)]$.

Solution.

$$Q(2) = 2 + 2 = 4, \text{ so } P[Q(2)] = P(4) = 4 - 4 = 0$$
$$P[Q(x)] = (x + 2) - 4 = x - 2$$

11. If $P(x) = x + 2$ and $Q(x) = x - 3$, find $P[Q(2)]$, $Q[P(2)]$, $P(x) - Q(x)$.

12. If $P(x) = 2x + 1$ and $Q(x) = \frac{1}{2}(x - 1)$, find $P[Q(x)]$, $Q[P(x)]$, $[P(2)]^2$.

13. If $P(x) = x^2 + 3$ and $Q(x) = 6$, find $P[Q(2)]$, $Q[P(2)]$, $P[Q(0)]$.

14. If $P(x) = 2x^2 - 3x$, and $Q(x) = x^2 + 1$, find $P[Q(0)]$, $Q[P(0)]$, $P[Q(1)] - Q[P(-2)]$.

In Problems 15–18, express as a polynomial a. $P(x) + Q(x)$ and b. $P(x) - Q(x)$.

15. $P(x) = 3x - 2$, $Q(x) = 3 - x$

16. $P(x) = x^2 + 3x - 2$, $Q(x) = 2x^2 + x - 2$

17. $P(x) = x^2 - 2x + 3$, $Q(x) = 2x^2 - 2x - 1$

18. $P(x) = 2x^3 - 3x^2 + x - 1$, $Q(x) = x^3 + 3x - 2$

In Problems 19–24, if $P(x) = 2x^2 - 3x + 2$, $Q(x) = 3 - 2x + x^2$, and $S(x) = -2x^2 + 3x - 5$, write the given expression as a polynomial.

19. $P(x) + Q(x)$ 20. $P(x) + [Q(x) - S(x)]$

21. $P(x) - [Q(x) + S(x)]$ 22. $P(x) - [Q(x) - S(x)]$

23. $[Q(x) - P(x)] - S(x)$ 24. $S(x) - [-P(x) - Q(x)]$

25. If $P(x)$ is of degree n and $Q(x)$ is of degree $n - 2$, what is the degree of $P(x) + Q(x)$? Of $P(x) - Q(x)$?

26. If $P(x)$ and $Q(x)$ are polynomials, with $P(0) = 4$ and $Q(0) = 3$, what is the value of $P(x) + Q(x)$ for $x = 0$? Of $P(x) - Q(x)$ for $x = 0$?

27. If $P(x) = 3x^2 - 2x + 1$, find A and B in $Q(x) = (A - 2)x^2 + (3 + B)x + 1$ so that $P(x) = Q(x)$.

28. If $P(x) = x^3 - 2x^2 - 1$, find A, B, and C in $Q(x) = (A + 4)x^3 - 2x^2 + (B + 3)x - 2 - C$ so that $P(x) = Q(x)$.

2.2 PRODUCTS OF POLYNOMIALS

By definition, for $x \in R$ and $n \in N$, we have

$$x^n = \underbrace{x \cdot x \cdot x \cdots x}_{n \text{ factors}}.$$

Now, consider the product $x^m \cdot x^n$, where m and n are natural numbers.

Since

$$x^m = x \cdot x \cdot x \cdots x \quad (m \text{ factors})$$

and

$$x^n = x \cdot x \cdot x \cdots x \quad (n \text{ factors}),$$

it follows that

$$x^m \cdot x^n = \underbrace{(x \cdot x \cdot x \cdots x)}_{m \text{ factors}} \underbrace{(x \cdot x \cdot x \cdots x)}_{n \text{ factors}}$$

$$= \underbrace{x \cdot x \cdot x \cdots x.}_{(m + n) \text{ factors}}$$

We state the result formally:

THEOREM 2.1 *First law of exponents. If $x \in R$ and m, $n \in N$, then*

$$x^m x^n = x^{m+n}.$$

This theorem justifies writing the product of two natural-number powers of the same base as a power (of the same base) with an exponent equal to the sum of the two exponents. For example,

$$x^2 x^3 = x^5,$$
$$y^3 y^4 y^2 = y^9.$$

In rewriting the product of two monomials, say

$$(3x^2 y)(2xy^2),$$

we use the commutative and associative laws and Theorem 2.1 to write

$$6x^3 y^3.$$

The **generalized distributive law,**

$$a(b_1 + b_2 + \cdots + b_n) = ab_1 + ab_2 + \cdots + ab_n,$$

can be applied to write as a polynomial the product of a monomial and a polynomial containing more than one term. For example,

$$3x(x + y + z) = 3x^2 + 3xy + 3xz.$$

In its complete form, the generalized distributive law requires mathematical induction for its proof, but its validity as applied in our example here—or in any similar example—can readily be verified; thus we have

$$3x(x + y + z) = 3x[(x + y) + z] = 3x(x + y) + 3xz$$
$$= 3x^2 + 3xy + 3xz.$$

The distributive law can be applied successively to the products of polynomials containing more than one term.   For example,

$$(3x + 2y)(x - y) = 3x(x - y) + 2y(x - y)$$
$$= 3x^2 - 3xy + 2xy - 2y^2$$
$$= 3x^2 - xy - 2y^2.$$

The following binomial products are types so frequently encountered that you should learn to recognize them on sight:

$$(x + a)(x + b) = x^2 + (a + b)x + ab,$$
$$(x + a)^2 = x^2 + 2ax + a^2,$$
$$(x + a)(x - a) = x^2 - a^2.$$

Regarding procedures for multiplying polynomials, consider the following examples, which we number following the pattern of Postulates F-6 through F-10 for the real numbers:

$$(x + 1)(x^2 - 2) = x^3 + x^2 - 2x - 2 \tag{6}$$

$$\left.\begin{array}{l} (x + 1)[(x - 2)(x)] = (x + 1)(x^2 - 2x) = x^3 - x^2 - 2x \\ [(x + 1)(x - 2)](x) = (x^2 - x - 2)(x) = x^3 - x^2 - 2x \end{array}\right\} \tag{7}$$

$$\left.\begin{array}{l} (x)[(x + 1) + (x^2 - 1)] = (x)(x^2 + x) = x^3 + x^2 \\ (x)(x + 1) + (x)(x^2 - 1) = (x^2 + x) + (x^3 - x) = x^3 + x^2 \end{array}\right\} \tag{8}$$

$$(x^3 + 4x^2 - 2)(1) = (1)(x^3 + 4x^2 - 2) = x^3 + 4x^2 - 2 \tag{9}$$

$$(x + 1)(x - 1) = (x - 1)(x + 1) = x^2 - 1 \tag{10}$$

These examples illustrate the following properties of the set $R[x]$ of real polynomials, in addition to those already listed in Section 2.1.

If $P(x)$, $Q(x)$, and $S(x) \in R[x]$:

6. $P(x) \cdot Q(x) \in R[x].$ *Closure for multiplication.*

7. $P(x)[Q(x) \cdot S(x)] = [P(x) \cdot Q(x)] \cdot S(x).$ *Associative law of multiplication.*

8. $P(x)[Q(x) + S(x)] =$ *Distributive law.*
   $P(x) \cdot Q(x) + P(x) \cdot S(x),$
   and $[Q(x) + S(x)]P(x) =$
   $Q(x) \cdot P(x) + S(x) \cdot P(x).$

9. $P(x) \cdot 1 = 1 \cdot P(x) = P(x).$ *Multiplicative identity.*

10. $P(x) \cdot Q(x) = Q(x) \cdot P(x).$ *Commutative law of multiplication.*

As for Postulate F-11, note that although $1/[P(x)]$ can be evaluated for each x for which $P(x) \neq 0$, the quotient $1/[P(x)]$ ordinarily is not a polynomial in x. For example, $(1 + x^2) \in R[x]$ and $1 + x^2 \neq 0$ for any $x \in R$, but

$$\frac{1}{1 + x^2} \notin R[x].$$

Thus F-11 does not extend to the set of real polynomials. Nevertheless, the cancellation law for multiplication (Theorem 1.5), which is a consequence of F-11 along with the other field postulates, does hold for polynomials.

THEOREM 2.2 *Cancellation for multiplication. If* $P(x)$, $Q(x)$, *and* $S(x) \in R[x]$, *with* $P(x)$ *not the zero polynomial, and*

$$[P(x)][Q(x)] = [P(x)][S(x)], \tag{1}$$

then

$$Q(x) = S(x). \tag{2}$$

Proof. We can write (1) equivalently as

$$[P(x)][Q(x) - S(x)] = 0. \tag{3}$$

Now, in mathematics, a statement is either true or false; it cannot be both. Suppose (2) were not true. Then by Definition 2.2 the difference $Q(x) - S(x)$ would not be the zero polynomial, and we could write

$$Q(x) - S(x) = a_0 x^n + \cdots + a_n, \quad a_0 \neq 0.$$

But by hypothesis, $P(x)$ also is not the zero polynomial, so we can write it as

$$P(x) = b_0 x^m + \cdots + b_m, \quad b_0 \neq 0.$$

Then we would have

$$[P(x)][Q(x) - S(x)] = a_0 b_0 x^{m+n} + \cdots + a_0 b_0 \neq 0,$$

a contradiction of (3). Hence (2) cannot be false, and therefore must be true.

Proofs such as the foregoing are called **indirect proofs.**

Since Theorem 2.2 and Postulates 1–10 listed in Sections 2.1 and 2.2, as well as the equality Postulates 1–4 listed in Section 2.1, hold for all real polynomials, we say that the set $R[x]$ of real polynomials is an **integral domain.** The choice of name reflects the fact that the set J of integers, $J = \{\cdots, -2, -1, 0, 1, 2, \cdots\}$, has analogous properties.

Corresponding to any property of the real numbers that follows from the field postulates, with the cancellation law in place of the (stronger) multiplicative-inverse postulate, there is an analogous property in the integral domain $R[x]$, or in the integral domain J, or in any other integral domain.

That is, every field is an integral domain.   The difference between an integral domain and a field is simply that not every nonzero element in an integral domain has a multiplicative inverse, while every nonzero element in a field does.

EXERCISE 2.2

Write each product in polynomial form in which constants and powers of each variable in each term are combined.

Examples.

a. $(-2x^2)(3xy)(y^2)$ b. $a^n \cdot a^{n+1}$

Solutions.

a. $-6x^3y^3$ b. $a^{n+(n+1)}$
          a^{2n+1}

1. $(-3x^2)(-2xy)(-y^3) - 6x^3y^4$ 2. $(a^3)(-2ab^2)(-b^3)$ $2a^4b^5$

3. $a^{n+1} \cdot a^{n-1}$ a^{2n} 4. $y^{2n-1} \cdot y^{n+2}$ y^{3n+1}

Examples.

a. $2(x^2 - x - 1)$ b. $(x - 3)(x + 5)$

Solutions.

a. $2x^2 - 2x - 2$ b. $x^2 + 5x - 3x - 15$
          $x^2 + 2x - 15$

5. $abc(a - b + 2c)$ $a^2bc - ab^2c + 2abc^2$ 6. $-ab(2a - b + 3c)$

7. $(x + 2)(x + 5)$ $x^2 + 7x + 10$ 8. $(x - 3)(x + 2)$

9. $(x - 2y)^2$ 10. $(2x - y)^2$

11. $(5x + 1)(2x + 3)$ 12. $(2x + 3)(x - 5)$

13. $(3a + 2b)(3a - 2b)$ 14. $(5x - y)(5x + y)$

15. $(x + 4)(x^2 + 2x - 1)$ 16. $(x - 2)(x^2 - x + 3)$

17. $2(x + 1)(x + 3)$ 18. $3(x - 1)(x + 2)$

19. $-(2a - b)(c - 3d)$ 20. $-(3a - b)(c + 3d)$

21. $a(a - b)(a^2 + ab + b^2)$ 22. $b(a + b)(a^2 - ab + b^2)$

23. $2\{a - [a - 2(a + 1) + 1] + 1\}$ 24. $-\{4 - [3 - 2(a - 1) + a] + a\}$

25. $2x\{x + 3[2(2x - 1) - (x - 1)] + 5\}$

26. $-x\{4 - 2[(x + 1) - 3(x + 2)] - x\}$

27. If $P(x) = x^2 - 3x + 7$, find $P(x - 1)$, $P(2 - x)$.

28. If $P(x) = x^2 + 2x + 1$, find $P(x + h)$, $P(x - h)$.

29. If $P(x) = x^2 - 3x$, find $[P(-x)]^2$, $[P(a^2)]^2 - P(a^2)$, $[P(2x) - P(x)]^2$.

30. If $P(x) = 3 - x^2$, find $[P(3)]^2$, $[P(3)]^2 - P(3^2)$, $P(x + b) - P(x)$.

31. Find the difference $(a + b)^2 - (a^2 + b^2)$. What are the conditions on a and b for $a^2 + b^2$ to be greater than $(a + b)^2$? For $a^2 + b^2$ to be less than $(a + b)^2$?

32. If $P(x)$ and $Q(x)$ are polynomials of degree m and n, respectively, what is the degree of $P(x) \cdot Q(x)$?

33. If $P(x) = K$ ($K \neq 0$), where K is constant for every value of x, then $P(x)$ is called a **constant polynomial** and is assigned degree 0. If $P(x) = 0$, then $P(x)$ is called the zero polynomial and is not assigned a degree. Explain why assigning degree 0 to the zero polynomial would render your answer in Problem 32 erroneous.

34. Which of the following sets are fields? Which are integral domains?

    a. The set N of natural numbers.

    b. The set J of integers.

    c. The set Q of rational numbers.

    d. The set H of irrational numbers.

    e. The set R of real numbers.

    f. The set $R[x]$ of polynomials.

    g. The set $J[x]$ of polynomials in the real variable x over the integral domain of the set J of integers.

2.3 FACTORING POLYNOMIALS

What do we mean when we say that we have *factored* an integer or a polynomial? It is true, for example, that

$$2 = 4\left(\frac{1}{2}\right),$$

but we would not ordinarily say that 4 and 1/2 are factors of 2. On the other hand, since

$$10 = (2)(5),$$

we do say that 2 and 5 are factors of 10 in the domain J of integers.

Now consider the polynomial

$$2x^2 - 10.$$

As we shall presently see, in the domain $J[x]$ of polynomials in x having integer coefficients, its complete factorization is given by

$$2x^2 - 10 = 2(x^2 - 5);$$

but in the domain $R[x]$ of polynomials in x having real numbers as co-efficients, its complete factorization is

$$2x^2 - 10 = 2(x - \sqrt{5})(x + \sqrt{5}).$$

Thus the result depends in part on the integral domain in which we consider that the factorization is being performed.

For the moment, let us consider monic polynomials—that is, polynomials with leading coefficient 1.

all prop of reals ⎰ *has all props of integers*

DEFINITION 2.3 *A monic polynomial $P(x)$ in the integral domain $F[x]$ of polynomials in x over the field F is reducible if and only if there exist non-constant monic polynomials $S(x)$ and $T(x)$ in $F[x]$ such that*

$$P(x) = [S(x)][T(x)].$$

only cons mon poly = 1

If $P(x)$ is not reducible, then we say that $P(x)$ is irreducible.

For example, the monic polynomial

$$x^2 - \frac{4}{9}$$

can be written equivalently as

$$\left(x - \frac{2}{3}\right)\left(x + \frac{2}{3}\right);$$

thus it is reducible in the domain $Q[x]$ of polynomials in x over the field Q of rational numbers, and also in the domain $R[x]$ of polynomials in x over the field R of real numbers. On the other hand, the polynomial

$$x^2 - 5$$

is not reducible in $Q[x]$; but since

$$x^2 - 5 = (x - \sqrt{5})(x + \sqrt{5}),$$

it is reducible in $R[x]$.

As a guide to what follows, we state the following theorem, the proof of which will not be given.

THEOREM 2.3 *If $F[x]$ is the domain of polynomials in x over the field F, and if $P(x) \in F[x]$, then $P(x)$ can be expressed as a product of a constant and monic polynomials irreducible in $F[x]$ in one and only one way, except for the order of the factors:*

$$P(x) = c[M_1(x)][M_2(x)] \cdots [M_k(x)].$$

The observation that the product is unique except for the order of the factors stems from the fact that multiplication is commutative. The choice of order of factors being arbitrary, the arrangement that seems most "natural" should be used, although this is admittedly not always easy to determine. For instance, the forms $a(x - 2)(x + 2)$ and $a(x + 2)(x - 2)$ are equivalent, but it is difficult to affirm one as more "natural" than the other. Ordinarily, however, we write monomial factors first, and order the terms within a factor according to descending degree of the variable.

In factoring polynomials in the domain $J[x]$ of polynomials having integer coefficients, the requirements are similar but not quite the same. Instead of monic polynomials, we consider polynomials having integer coefficients with no common integer factor other than 1 or -1, and say that such a polynomial is **prime** if it is not the product of two polynomials of this sort.

For example, in the polynomial

$$2x^2 + x - 3,$$

the coefficients 2, 1, and -3 have no common integer factor other than 1 or -1, but the polynomial is not prime; instead, it is the product of two prime polynomials, namely,

$$2x^2 + x - 3 = (2x + 3)(x - 1).$$

We say that a polynomial other than 0 or 1 in $J[x]$ is **completely factored** if it is written equivalently as a product of prime polynomials. Thus

$$6x^4 - 96 = (2)(3)(x - 2)(x + 2)(x^2 + 4).$$

One very common type of factoring is that involving quadratic (second-degree) binomials or trinomials in the domain $J[x]$ of polynomials with integer coefficients. From Section 2.2, we recall that

$$(x + a)(x + b) = x^2 + (a + b)x + ab, \qquad (1)$$

$$(x + a)^2 = x^2 + 2ax + a^2, \qquad (2)$$

$$(x + a)(x - a) = x^2 - a^2. \qquad (3)$$

These three forms, each of which involves irreducible polynomial factors, are those most commonly encountered in the chapters that follow. In this section, we are interested in viewing these relationships from right to left—that is, from polynomial to factored form. Lacking specific information, we assume that the coefficients are integers without common factors other than 1 and -1.

There are a few other polynomials that occur frequently enough to justify a study of their factorization. In particular, the forms

$$(a + b)(x + y) = ax + ay + bx + by, \qquad (4)$$

$$(x + a)(x^2 - ax + a^2) = x^3 + a^3, \qquad (5)$$

$$(x - a)(x^2 + ax + a^2) = x^3 - a^3 \qquad (6)$$

are often encountered in one or another part of mathematics.   We are again interested in viewing these relationships from right to left.   Expressions such as the right-hand member of form (4) are factorable by grouping.   For example, to factor

$$3x^2y + 2y + 3xy^2 + 2x,$$

we write it in the form

$$3x^2y + 2x + 3xy^2 + 2y$$

and factor the common monomial x from the first group of two terms and y from the second group of two terms, obtaining

$$x(3xy + 2) + y(3xy + 2).$$

If now we factor the common binomial $(3xy + 2)$ from each term, we have

$$(3xy + 2)(x + y),$$

both of which are prime.

The application of forms (5) and (6) is direct.   Thus

$$
\begin{aligned}
(8a^3 + b^3) &= [(2a)^3 + b^3] \\
&= (2a + b)[(2a)^2 - 2ab + b^2] \\
&= (2a + b)[4a^2 - 2ab + b^2].
\end{aligned}
$$

EXERCISE 2.3

Factor completely in the domain $J[x]$ of polynomials with integer coefficients. (Assume that all variables in exponents represent natural numbers.)

Examples.

  a. $18x^2y - 24xy^2 + 6xy$ b. $x^{2n} + x^n$ c. $4a^3 - 5a^2 + a$

Solutions.

  a. $(2)(3)xy(3x - 4y + 1)$ b. $x^n(x^n + 1)$ c. $a(4a^2 - 5a + 1)$
                                                  $a(4a - 1)(a - 1)$

1. $9x^5y - 3x^4y + 6x^3y$ 2. $x^2y^2z^2 + 2xyz - xz$

3. $x^{3n} + x^n$ $x^n(x^{2n} + 1)$ 4. $x^{4n} - x^{2n}$

5. $x^{n+2} - x^{n+1} + 2x^n$ $x^n(x^{+2} - x^{+1} + 2)$ 6. $x^{n-2} - 3x^{n-1} + x^n$

7. $x^2 - 8x + 12$ $(x - 2)(x - 6)$ 8. $6 - a - a^2$

9. $x^2 - 25$ $(x + 5)(x - 5)$ 10. $4x^2 + 12x + 9$

11. $3x^2 + 12x + 12$ $3(x^2 + 4x + 4)$ 12. $x^4y^2 - x^2y^2$
                          $3[(x + 2)(x + 2)]$

Examples.

  a. $by - ay + bx - ax$ b. $8x^3 - y^3$

Solutions.

  a. $y(b - a) + x(b - a)$ b. $(2x)^3 - y^3$
     $(b - a)(y + x)$ $(2x - y)(4x^2 + 2xy + y^2)$

13. $y^4 + 3y^2 + 2$ 14. $x^4 - 5x^2 + 4$

15. $2a^4 - a^2 - 1$ 16. $3z^4 - 11z^2 - 4$

17. $x^4 - (y - 2x)^4$ 18. $ax^2 + x + ax + 1$

19. $x^2 + ax + xy + ay$ 20. $3x + y - 6x^2 - 2xy$

21. $a^3 + 2ab^2 - 4b^3 - 2a^2b$ 22. $6x^3 - 4x^2 + 3x - 2$

23. $y^3 - 27x^3$ 24. $8 + x^3y^3$

25. $x^3 + (x - y)^3$ 26. $(x + y)^3 - z^3$

Examples.

  a. $a^{2n} - 9$ b. $x^{4n} - 3x^{2n} - 4$

Solutions.

  a. $(a^n - 3)(a^n + 3)$ b. $(x^{2n} - 4)(x^{2n} + 1)$
                                                            $(x^n - 2)(x^n + 2)(x^{2n} + 1)$

27. $a^{2n} - 4 \left(a^n + 2 \right) \left(a^2 - 2 \right)$ 28. $x^{2n} - y^{2n}$

29. $x^{4n} - y^{4n} \left(x^{2n} + y^{2n} \right) \left(x^{2n} - y^{2n} \right)$ 30. $x^{4n} - 2x^{2n} + 1$

31. $3x^{4n} - 10x^{2n} + 3$ 32. $6y^{2n} + 30y^n - 900$

33. $2y^{2n} - 12y^n - 1440$ 34. $2x^{2n} - 23x^ny^n - 39y^{2n}$

In Problems 35–40, factor the given polynomial completely:

a. In the domain $J[x]$ of polynomials having integer coefficients.

b. In the domain $Q[x]$ of polynomials having rational coefficients.

Example. $3x^2 + x - 2$

Solution.

  a. $(3x - 2)(x + 1)$ b. $3(x - \frac{2}{3})(x + 1)$

35. $2x^2 + x - 6$ 36. $4x^2 - x - 3$ 37. $4x^2 - 4x - 3$

38. $6x^2 + 7x + 2$ 39. $12x^2 + 2x - 2$ 40. $12x^2 + 24x - 15$

41. Show that $ac - ad + bd - bc$ can be factored both as $(a - b)(c - d)$ and
    as $(b - a)(d - c)$.

42. Show that $a^2 - b^2 - c^2 + 2bc$ can be factored as $(a - b + c)(a + b - c)$.

43. Consider the polynomial $x^4 + x^2y^2 + 25y^4$. If $9x^2y^2$ is both added to and subtracted from this expression (thus producing an equal expression), we have

$$x^4 + x^2y^2 + 25y^4 + 9x^2y^2 - 9x^2y^2,$$

$$(x^4 + 10x^2y^2 + 25y^4) - 9x^2y^2,$$

$$(x^2 + 5y^2)^2 - 9x^2y^2,$$

$$[(x^2 + 5y^2) - 3xy][(x^2 + 5y^2) + 3xy],$$

$$(x^2 - 3xy + 5y^2)(x^2 + 3xy + 5y^2).$$

By adding and subtracting an appropriate monomial, factor $x^4 + x^2y^2 + y^4$.

44. Use the method of Problem 43 to factor $x^4 - 3x^2y^2 + y^4$.

45. Explain why, if $n \in N$, $n^3 - n$ is divisible by 6.

2.4 QUOTIENTS OF POLYNOMIALS

It is easy to show that the set of integers is not closed with respect to division; 2/3, 1/5, 8/9, and $-(3/4)$ are all examples of noninteger quotients of integers. Similarly, we can see that the set of polynomials is not closed with respect to division, because $1/x$ is a counterexample. That is, $1/x$ is the quotient of the polynomials 1 and x, but is not, itself, a polynomial. In Exercise 1.5, Problems 43 and 44, you were asked to show that if a, b, and q are real numbers, with $b \neq 0$, then

$$\frac{a}{b} = q \text{ if and only if } a = bq.$$

When we observe that the closure laws guarantee the applicability of the real-number axioms to real polynomials, these problems suffice to validate the following theorem.

THEOREM 2.4 *If A, D, and Q are real polynomials, then for values of the variables for which $D \neq 0$,*

$$\frac{A}{D} = Q \quad \text{if and only if} \quad A = DQ.$$

If a polynomial Q exists such that $A = DQ$, then A is said to be **exactly divisible** by D. If A is not exactly divisible by D, then the quotient A/D cannot be written as a polynomial.

Let us examine some ways in which we can rewrite quotients of polynomials, even if the resulting expressions are not always, themselves, polynomials. We begin with the simplest case, that in which A and D are monomials, and their quotient is a polynomial.   Consider

$$\frac{x^m}{x^n} \quad (x \neq 0,\ n \in N,\ \text{and}\ m > n).$$

We have

$$\frac{x^m}{x^n} = x^m \cdot \frac{1}{x^n}$$

$$= (x^{m-n} \cdot x^n) \cdot \frac{1}{x^n}$$

$$= x^{m-n} \cdot \left(x^n \cdot \frac{1}{x^n}\right)$$

$$= x^{m-n} \cdot 1,$$

$$\frac{x^m}{x^n} = x^{m-n}.$$

This last equality is useful enough to be given a name, and to be enrolled in our list of theorems.

THEOREM 2.5   *Second law of exponents.   If $x \in R$, $x \neq 0$, m, $n \in N$, and $m > n$, then*

$$\frac{x^m}{x^n} = x^{m-n}.$$

The theorem enables us, for example, to write

$$\frac{12a^5 b^3}{4a^2 b^2}$$

as

$$\frac{12}{4} \cdot a^{5-2} b^{3-2},$$

and then as

$$3a^3 b \quad (a,\ b \neq 0).$$

Note that a and b are not permitted to take the value 0, because if this were permitted, $3a^3 b$ would represent a real number, 0, although $(12a^5 b^3)/(4a^2 b^2)$ would not be defined.

Theorem 1.11-III (together with the closure laws) permits us to rewrite quotients of polynomials of the form $(A + B)/C$, $C \neq 0$, in the form $A/C + B/C$, and then to do such further rewriting as seems indicated.   For example,

$$\frac{2x^3 + 4x^2 + 8x}{2x} = \frac{2x^3}{2x} + \frac{4x^2}{2x} + \frac{8x}{2x},$$

and, by applying Theorem 2.5, the right-hand member can then be denoted by the expression

$$x^2 + 2x + \frac{8x}{2x} \quad (x \neq 0).$$

Though Theorem 2.5 is not applicable to the variable factors in expressions such as $8x/2x$, by Theorem 1.11-II and the result in Problem 45, Exercise 1.5, we can write

$$\frac{8x}{2x} = \frac{8}{2} \cdot \frac{x}{x} = \frac{8}{2} \cdot 1 = 4,$$

for every $x \neq 0$, and the quotient

$$\frac{2x^3 + 4x^2 + 8x}{2x}$$

can be written as the polynomial

$$x^2 + 2x + 4 \quad (x \neq 0).$$

As mentioned at the start of this section, however, quotients of polynomials cannot always be represented by polynomials. For example, we have

$$\frac{2x^3 + 4x + 1}{x} = \frac{2x^3}{x} + \frac{4x}{x} + \frac{1}{x}$$

$$= 2x^2 + 4 + \frac{1}{x} \quad (x \neq 0),$$

where the resulting expression is not a polynomial.

If the divisor of a quotient contains more than one term, the familiar long-division algorithm involving successive subtractions can be used to rewrite the quotient. For example, the computation

$$
\begin{array}{r}
x - 3 \\
x^2 + 2x - 1 \overline{\big)\ x^3 - x^2 - 7x + 3} \\
\underline{x^3 + 2x^2 - x} \\
-3x^2 - 6x + 3 \\
\underline{-3x^2 - 6x + 3} \\
0
\end{array}
$$

shows that, for $x^2 + 2x - 1 \neq 0$,

$$\frac{x^3 - x^2 - 7x + 3}{x^2 + 2x - 1} = x - 3.$$

It is most convenient to arrange the dividend and the divisor in descending powers of the variable before using the division algorithm, and to leave an appropriate space for any missing terms (terms with coefficient 0) in the dividend.

When the divisor is not a factor of the dividend, the division process will produce a nonzero remainder. For example, from

$$
\begin{array}{r}
x^3 - 3x^2 + 10x - 28 \\
x + 3 \overline{)\ x^4 \qquad\quad +\ x^2 + 2x - 1} \\
\underline{x^4 + 3x^3} \\
-3x^3 + x^2 \\
\underline{-3x^3 - 9x^2} \\
10x^2 + 2x \\
\underline{10x^2 + 30x} \\
-28x - 1 \\
\underline{-28x - 84} \\
83 \ \text{(remainder)}
\end{array}
$$

we see that

$$\frac{x^4 + x^2 + 2x - 1}{x + 3} = x^3 - 3x^2 + 10x - 28 + \frac{83}{x + 3} \quad (x \neq -3).$$

Observe in the foregoing example that a space is left in the dividend for a term involving x^3, even though the dividend contains no such term.

If the divisor is of the form $x + c$, the process of dividing one polynomial by another can be simplified by a process called **synthetic division**. Consider the foregoing example. If we omit writing the variables and write only the coefficients of the terms, and use zero for the coefficient of any missing power, we have

$$
\begin{array}{r}
1 - 3 + 10 - 28 \\
1 + 3 \overline{)\ 1\ + 0 + 1 + 2 - 1} \\
\underline{[1] + 3} \\
-3 + (1) \\
\underline{[-3] - 9} \\
10 + (2) \\
\underline{[10] + 30} \\
-28 - (1) \\
\underline{[-28] - 84} \\
83 \ \text{(remainder)}.
\end{array}
$$

Now, observe that the numbers in brackets, [ ], are repetitions of the numbers written immediately above and are also repetitions of the coefficients of the associated variable in the quotient; the numbers in parentheses, ( ), are repetitions of the coefficients of the dividend. Therefore, the whole process can be written in compact form as

$$
\begin{array}{rrrrrr}
(1) & 3 \,|\, 1 & 0 & 1 & 2 & -1 \\
(2) & & 3 & -9 & 30 & -84 \\
\cline{2-6}
(3) & 1 & -3 & 10 & -28 & 83 \ \text{(remainder: 83)}
\end{array}
$$

where the repetitions are omitted and where 1, the coefficient of x in the divisor, has also been omitted.

The numbers in line (3), which are the coefficients of the variables in the quotient and the remainder, have been obtained by *subtracting* the **detached coefficients** in line (2) from the detached coefficients of terms of the same degree in line (1). We could obtain the same result by replacing 3 with -3 in the divisor and *adding* instead of subtracting at each step, and this is what is done in the *synthetic-division* process. The final form then appears:

$$
\begin{array}{llrrrr}
(1) & -3 \,|\, 1 & 0 & 1 & 2 & -1 \\
(2) & & -3 & 9 & -30 & 84 \\
(3) & 1 & -3 & 10 & -28 & 83 \;\text{(remainder: 83).}
\end{array}
$$

Comparing the results of using synthetic division with the same process using long division, we observe that the numbers in line (3) are the coefficients of the polynomial $x^3 - 3x^2 + 10x - 28$, and that there is a remainder of 83.

Example. Write $\dfrac{3x^3 - 4x - 1}{x - 2}$ in the form $Q + \dfrac{r}{D}$.

Solution. Using synthetic division, we write

$$
2 \,|\; 3 \quad 0 \quad -4 \quad -1,
$$

where 0 has been inserted in the position that would be occupied by the coefficient of a second-degree term if such a term were present in the dividend. Our divisor is the negative of -2, or 2.

$$
\begin{array}{llrrrr}
(1) & 2 \,|\, 3 & 0 & -4 & -1 \\
(2) & & 6 & 12 & 16 \\
(3) & 3 & 6 & 8 & 15 \;\text{(remainder: 15).}
\end{array}
$$

This process employs these steps:

1. 3 is "brought down" from line (1) to line (3).
2. 6, the product of 2 and 3, is written in the next position on line (2).
3. 6, the sum of 0 and 6, is written on line (3).
4. 12, the product of 2 and 6, is written in the next position on line (2).
5. 8, the sum of -4 and 12, is written on line (3).
6. 16, the product of 2 and 8, is written in the next position on line (2).
7. 15, the sum of -1 and 16, is written on line (3).

We can use the first three numbers on line (3) as coefficients to write a polynomial of degree one less than the degree of the dividend. This polynomial is the quotient lacking the remainder. The last number is the remainder. Thus, for $x - 2 \neq 0$, the quotient when $3x^3 - 4x - 1$ is divided by $x - 2$ is $3x^2 + 6x + 8$ with a remainder of 15; that is,

$$
\frac{3x^3 - 4x - 1}{x - 2} = 3x^2 + 6x + 8 + \frac{15}{x - 2} \quad (x \neq 2).
$$

The foregoing example illustrates a theorem that we shall state without proof.

THEOREM 2.6 *If $P(x)$ is a real polynomial, and c is any real number, then there exists a unique real polynomial $Q(x)$, and a real number r, such that*

$$P(x) = (x - c)Q(x) + r.$$

Although this theorem does not directly involve the quotient $\dfrac{P(x)}{x - c}$, it does assure us that, for $x \neq c$,

$$\frac{P(x)}{x - c} = Q(x) + \frac{r}{x - c}.$$

EXERCISE 2.4

Write each quotient as a polynomial. (Assume that all variables in exponents represent natural numbers.)

Examples.

a. $\dfrac{6x^2y^3}{2xy}$　　　　b. $\dfrac{x^{2n+3}}{x^{n+1}}$　　　　c. $\dfrac{2y^3 - 6y^2 + y}{y}$

Solutions.

a. $\dfrac{6}{2} \cdot x^{2-1}y^{3-1}$

$3xy^2$ $(x, y \neq 0)$

b. $x^{2n+3-(n+1)}$

x^{n+2} $(x \neq 0)$

c. $\dfrac{2y^3}{y} - \dfrac{6y^2}{y} + \dfrac{y}{y}$

$2y^2 - 6y + 1$ $(y \neq 0)$

1. $\dfrac{8a^3y^5}{2a^2y^3}$ $4ay^2$

2. $\dfrac{38a^3b^5}{19ab^3}$ $2a^2b^2$

3. $\dfrac{x^{2n+2}}{x^{n-1}}$ x^{n+3}

4. $\dfrac{a^{2n+3}}{a^{n-4}}$ $a^n +7$

5. $\dfrac{x^{2n}y^{n+1}}{x^n y}$ $x^n y^n$

6. $\dfrac{r^{2n}s^{n+5}}{r^{n-1}s^{n+3}}$ $r^{n-1}s^2$

7. $\dfrac{8a^2 + 4a + 4}{2}$ $4a^2 +2a+2$

8. $\dfrac{12x^3 - 8x^2 + 36x}{4x}$ $3x^2 -2x+9$

9. $\dfrac{x^3 - 4x^2 - 3x}{x}$ $x^2 - 4x - 3$

10. $\dfrac{8a^2x^2 - 4ax^2 + ax}{ax}$ $8ax - 4x +1$

Write each quotient, P/D, in the form $Q + R/D$, where the degree of R is less than that of D.

Examples.

a. $\dfrac{2y^3 - 6y^2 + 2y - 4}{y}$

b. $\dfrac{y^3 + y^2 - 5y + 2}{y^2 - 2y}$

Solutions.

a. $\dfrac{2y^3}{y} - \dfrac{6y^2}{y} + \dfrac{2y}{y} - \dfrac{4}{y}$

$2y^2 - 6y + 2 - \dfrac{4}{y}$ $(y \neq 0)$

b.
$$
\begin{array}{r}
y + 3 \\
y^2 - 2y\,\overline{)\,y^3 + y^2 - 5y + 2} \\
\underline{y^3 - 2y^2} \\
3y^2 - 5y \\
\underline{3y^2 - 6y} \\
y + 2
\end{array}
$$

$y + 3 + \dfrac{y + 2}{y^2 - 2y}$ $(y \neq 0, 2)$

11. $\dfrac{15x^3y - 10x^2y + 3y}{5xy}$ $3x^2 - 2x + \dfrac{3}{5x}$

12. $\dfrac{38a^{2n} - 19a^n + 3}{19a^n}$ $2a^n - 1 + \dfrac{3}{19a^n}$

13. $\dfrac{4y^3 + 12y + 5}{2y + 1}$

14. $\dfrac{2x^4 + 13x^3 - 7}{2x - 1}$

15. $\dfrac{4y^5 - 4y^2 - 5y + 1}{2y^2 + y + 1}$

16. $\dfrac{2x^3 - 3x^2 - 15x - 1}{x^2 + 5}$

Use synthetic division to write each quotient $P(x)/D(x)$ in the form $Q(x) + r/D(x)$, where r is a constant.

Examples.

a. $\dfrac{2x^4 + x^3 - 1}{x + 2}$

b. $\dfrac{x^3 - 1}{x - 1}$

Solutions.

a.
$$
\begin{array}{r|rrrrr}
-2 & 2 & 1 & 0 & 0 & -1 \\
   &   & -4 & 6 & -12 & 24 \\
\hline
   & 2 & -3 & 6 & -12 & 23
\end{array}
$$

$2x^3 - 3x^2 + 6x - 12 + \dfrac{23}{x + 2}$

$(x \neq -2)$

b.
$$
\begin{array}{r|rrrr}
1 & 1 & 0 & 0 & -1 \\
  &   & 1 & 1 & 1 \\
\hline
  & 1 & 1 & 1 & 0
\end{array}
$$

$x^2 + x + 1$ $(x \neq 1)$

17. $\dfrac{x^4 - 3x^3 + 2x^2 - 1}{x - 2}$

18. $\dfrac{x^4 + 2x^2 - 3x + 5}{x - 3}$

19. $\dfrac{2x^3 + x - 5}{x + 1}$

20. $\dfrac{3x^3 + x^2 - 7}{x + 2}$

21. $\dfrac{2x^4 - x + 6}{x - 5}$

22. $\dfrac{3x^4 - x^2 + 1}{x - 4}$

23. $\dfrac{x^3 + 4x^2 + x - 2}{x + 2}$

24. $\dfrac{x^3 - 7x^2 - x + 3}{x + 3}$

25. $\dfrac{x^6 + x^4 - x}{x - 1}$

26. $\dfrac{x^6 + 3x^3 - 2x - 1}{x - 2}$

27. $\dfrac{x^5 - 1}{x - 1}$

28. $\dfrac{x^5 + 1}{x + 1}$

29. $\dfrac{x^6 - 1}{x - 1}$

30. $\dfrac{x^6 + 1}{x + 1}$

31. Use synthetic division to show that the first three terms in the expansion of the quotient

$$\frac{x^n - 1}{x - 1} \quad (x \neq 1, n \in N)$$

are $x^{n-1} + x^{n-2} + x^{n-3}$, and then argue that the quotient is $x^{n-1} + x^{n-2} + x^{n-3} + \cdots + x + 1$ and the remainder is 0.

32. The set $Q[x]$ of quotients of real polynomials, in which the denominator is not the zero polynomial 0, is a field under the ordinary operations of addition and multiplication. State and illustrate the eleven field postulates for the set $Q[x]$.

2.5   EQUAL FRACTIONS

A fraction is an expression denoting a quotient. If the numerator (dividend) and the denominator (divisor) are polynomials, then the fraction is said to be a **rational expression**. Trivially, any polynomial can be considered as being a rational expression, since it is the quotient of itself and 1. For each replacement of the variable(s) for which the numerator and denominator of a fraction represent real numbers and for which the denominator is not zero, a rational expression represents a real number. Of course, for any value of the variable(s) for which the denominator vanishes (is equal to zero), the fraction does not represent a real number and is said to be undefined.

Since for each replacement of the variable(s) for which its denominator is not zero, a rational expression represents a real number, some theorems for rational expressions follow directly from Theorems 1.10 and 1.11 and the laws of closure.

THEOREM 2.7 *If A, B, C, and D represent polynomials, then for values of the variables for which the denominators do not vanish,*

$$\text{I} \quad \frac{A}{B} = \frac{C}{D} \text{ if and only if } AD = BC,$$

$$\text{II} \quad -\frac{A}{B} = \frac{-A}{B} = \frac{A}{-B} = -\frac{-A}{-B},$$

$$\text{III} \quad \frac{A}{B} = \frac{-A}{-B} = -\frac{-A}{B} = -\frac{A}{-B},$$

$$\text{IV} \quad \frac{AC}{BC} = \frac{A}{B} \quad (\textit{fundamental principle of fractions}).$$

A fraction is said to be in **lowest terms** when the numerator and denominator do not contain certain prescribed types of factors in common. The arithmetic fraction a/b, where a and b are integers and $b \neq 0$, is in lowest terms provided a and b are relatively prime—that is, provided they contain no common positive integral factors other than 1. If the numerator and denominator of a fraction are polynomials with integral coefficients, then the fraction is said to be in lowest terms if the numerator and denominator cannot be expressed as products of polynomials having integral coefficients with a common factor other than ± 1.

To express a given fraction in lowest terms (called **reducing** the fraction), we can factor the numerator and denominator and apply the fundamental principle of fractions. For example,

$$\frac{y}{y^2} = \frac{1 \cdot y}{y \cdot y} = \frac{1}{y} \quad (y \neq 0).$$

Diagonal lines are sometimes used to abbreviate this procedure. We may write

$$\frac{y}{y^2} = \frac{\overset{1}{\cancel{y}}}{\underset{y}{\cancel{y^2}}} = \frac{1}{y} \quad (y \neq 0),$$

and

$$\frac{yx^2}{y^2x} = \frac{\overset{x}{\cancel{yx^2}}}{\underset{y}{\cancel{y^2x}}} = \frac{x}{y} \quad (x, y \neq 0),$$

using the diagonal lines instead of writing

$$\frac{1 \cdot y}{y \cdot y} \quad \text{or} \quad \frac{x \cdot xy}{y \cdot xy}.$$

Reducing a fraction to lowest terms should be accomplished mentally whenever possible.

To reduce fractions with polynomial numerators and denominators, you should, when possible, write them in factored form. Common factors are then evident by inspection. For example,

$$\frac{2x^2 + x - 15}{2x + 6} = \frac{(2x - 5)(x + 3)}{2(x + 3)}$$

$$= \frac{2x - 5}{2} \quad (x \neq -3).$$

The assertion that

$$\frac{2x^2 + x - 15}{2x + 6} = \frac{2x - 5}{2}$$

is true for all values of the variable except -3; for $x = -3$, the left-hand member of this equality is not defined.

We can also change fractions to equal fractions in higher terms by applying the fundamental principle in the form

$$\frac{A}{B} = \frac{AC}{BC} \quad (B, C \neq 0).$$

We might want to do this, for instance, in order to express two given fractions A/B and D/C as fractions with the same denominator BC.

In general, to change a fraction A/B to an equal fraction with BC as a denominator, the factor C can be determined by inspection, and then the numerator and the denominator of the original fraction can be multiplied by this factor.

EXERCISE 2.5

Reduce to lowest terms where possible. Specify restrictions on the variable or variables for which the reduction is not valid.

Examples.

a. $\dfrac{a - b}{b^2 - a^2}$

b. $\dfrac{a + b}{b}$

Solutions.

a. $\dfrac{-(b - a)}{(b - a)(b + a)}$

$\dfrac{-1}{b + a} \quad (b \neq a)$

b. Expression is in lowest terms.
$\quad (b \neq 0)$

1. $\dfrac{a^2bc}{ab^2c}$

2. $\dfrac{24x^4y^2z}{16x^3y^2z}$

3. $\dfrac{2x + 2y}{x + y}$

4. $\dfrac{x^2 + x}{x + 1}$

5. $\dfrac{a - b}{b - a}$

6. $\dfrac{x^2 - xy}{y - x}$

7. $\dfrac{x^2 - 1}{1 - x}$

8. $\dfrac{x^2 - 16}{4 - x}$

9. $\dfrac{2x^3 - 4x^2 - 3x}{2x}$ _prime ?_ _enough ?_

10. $\dfrac{8a^2x^2 - 4ax^2 + ax}{2ax}$

11. $\dfrac{y^2 + 5y - 14}{y - 2}$

12. $\dfrac{x^2 + 5x + 6}{x + 3}$

13. $\dfrac{4y^2 + 8y - 5}{1 - 2y}$

14. $\dfrac{2x^2 + 13x - 7}{1 - 2x}$

15. $\dfrac{x^3 - y^3}{x^2 - y^2}$

16. $\dfrac{x^4 - y^4}{x^2 + y^2}$

17. $\dfrac{y^4 - 16}{y^4 - y^2 - 12}$

18. $\dfrac{a^3 - a^2 + b^2 + b^3}{3a^2 + 6ab + 3b^2}$

19. $\dfrac{x^2 - 2xy + y^2 + x - y}{y^2 - x^2}$

20. $\dfrac{8x^2 - 8xy - x^3 - y^3 + 8y^2}{x^4 + x^2y^2 + y^4}$

Express each of the given fractions as an equal fraction with the given denominator. Specify values for the variable or variables for which equality would not hold.

21. $\dfrac{3}{4}; \dfrac{}{12}$

22. $\dfrac{1}{5}; \dfrac{}{10}$

23. $\dfrac{b}{a}; \dfrac{}{a^2 b}$

24. $\dfrac{b}{2a}; \dfrac{}{6a^3 b^2}$

25. $\dfrac{3}{y + 2}; \dfrac{}{y^2 - y - 6}$

26. $\dfrac{2}{x + 3}; \dfrac{}{x^2 + x - 6}$

27. $\dfrac{3}{a + 3}; \dfrac{}{a^3 + 27}$

28. $\dfrac{-2}{x^2 + y^2}; \dfrac{}{x^4 - y^4}$

Express each of the given pairs of fractions as a pair of fractions with the same denominator.

29. $\dfrac{3x}{ab}, \dfrac{2x}{a^2 c}$

30. $\dfrac{2x - 1}{x + 2}, \dfrac{x - 1}{x + 3}$

31. $\dfrac{3}{x^2 - a^2}, \dfrac{2}{x^2 + 2ax + a^2}$

32. $\dfrac{-1}{2a + b}, \dfrac{2}{4a^2 - b^2}$

33. $\dfrac{2}{a - b}, \dfrac{-1}{b^2 - a^2}$

34. $\dfrac{x + 1}{x^3 - y^3}, \dfrac{x}{x^2 - y^2}$

35. Is the fraction $\dfrac{x(1 - x)}{x^2 - 3x + 2}$ equal to $\dfrac{x}{2 - x}$ for all values of x? If not, for what value(s) of x does the equality fail to hold?

36. Write three equivalent forms of the fraction $1/(a - b)$ $(a \neq b)$ by changing the sign or signs of the numerator, denominator, or fraction itself.

37. What are the conditions on a and b for the fraction $-1/(a - b)$ to represent a positive number? A negative number?

38. Is the fraction $(x - 2)/(1 + x^2)$ defined for all values of $x \in R$? For what value(s) of x does the fraction equal zero?

39. Prove that $(y^2 - 3y + 2)/(1 - y) = 2 - y$ for all values of y, $y \neq 1$. That is, justify each step in your argument with a definition, a postulate, or a theorem.

40. Prove Theorem 2.7-I.

2.6 SUMS OF FRACTIONS

Since rational expressions represent real numbers for each replacement of the variable(s) for which the denominators are not zero, the following Theorem 2.8 follows directly from Theorem 1.11-III and the laws of closure.

THEOREM 2.8 *If A, B, and C are polynomials, then for values of the variables for which C ≠ 0,*

$$\frac{A}{C} + \frac{B}{C} = \frac{A+B}{C}.$$

Example. Write $\dfrac{3x^2}{5} + \dfrac{x}{5}$ as a single fraction.

Solution. $\dfrac{3x^2 + x}{5}$

This principle, of course, extends to any number of fractions.

If the fractions in a sum have unlike denominators, we can change the fractions to equal fractions having common denominators and then write the sum as a single fraction. Thus,

$$\frac{A}{B} + \frac{C}{D} = \frac{A}{B}\left(\frac{D}{D}\right) + \frac{C}{D}\left(\frac{B}{B}\right)$$
$$= \frac{AD + CB}{BD} \quad (B, D \neq 0).$$

The difference

$$\frac{A}{B} - \frac{C}{D}$$

may be viewed as the sum

$$\frac{A}{B} + \left(-\frac{C}{D}\right),$$

and written as

$$\frac{A}{B}\left(\frac{D}{D}\right) + \left[\frac{-C}{D}\left(\frac{B}{B}\right)\right] = \frac{AD - CB}{BD} \quad (B, D \neq 0).$$

In rewriting fractions in a sum so that they share a common denominator, any such denominator may be used. If the **least common multiple** of the denominators (called the **least common denominator**) is used, however, the resulting fraction will be in simpler form than if any other common denominator is employed. The least common multiple of two or more natural numbers is the smallest natural number that is exactly divisible by each of the given numbers (that is, each quotient is a natural number).

The notion of a least common multiple among several polynomial expressions is, in general, meaningless without further specification of what is desired. We can, however, define the least common multiple of a set of polynomials with integer coefficients to be the polynomial of lowest degree with integer coefficients yielding a polynomial quotient upon division by each of the given polynomials, and to be, among all such polynomials, the one having the least possible positive leading coefficient.

Very often, the least common multiple of a set of natural numbers or polynomials can be determined by inspection. When inspection fails us, however, we can find the least common multiple of a set of polynomials with integer coefficients as follows:

1. Express each polynomial in completely factored form.

2. Write as factors of a product each *different* factor occurring in any of the polynomials, including each factor the greatest number of times it occurs in any one of the given polynomials.

Example. Find the least common multiple of 12, 15, and 18.

Solution.

$$12 \qquad 15 \qquad 18$$
$$2 \cdot 2 \cdot 3 \qquad 3 \cdot 5 \qquad 3 \cdot 3 \cdot 2$$

The least common multiple is $2^2 \cdot 3^2 \cdot 5$, or 180.

Example. Find the least common multiple of x^2, $x^2 - 9$, and $x^3 - x^2 - 6x$.

Solution.

$$x^2 \qquad x^2 - 9 \qquad x^3 - x^2 - 6x$$
$$x \cdot x \qquad (x - 3)(x + 3) \qquad x(x - 3)(x + 2)$$

The least common multiple is $x^2(x + 2)(x + 3)(x - 3)$.

Now, to rewrite sums of fractions having different denominators, we can ascertain the least common denominator of the fractions, determine the factor necessary to express each of the fractions as a fraction having this common denominator, write the fractions accordingly, and then rewrite the sum as a single fraction.

Example. Write $\dfrac{3}{x} + \dfrac{2}{x^2} + \dfrac{3}{xy}$ as a single fraction.

Solution. The least common denominator of the fractions is x^2y. We have

$$\frac{3}{x} + \frac{2}{x^2} + \frac{3}{xy} = \frac{3(xy)}{x(xy)} + \frac{2(y)}{x^2(y)} + \frac{3(x)}{xy(x)}$$
$$= \frac{3xy}{x^2y} + \frac{2y}{x^2y} + \frac{3x}{x^2y}$$
$$= \frac{3xy + 2y + 3x}{x^2y} \qquad (x, y \neq 0).$$

In the following exercises and in succeeding exercises, let us agree that no variable in a denominator assumes a value for which the denominator vanishes.

EXERCISE 2.6

Write each sum or difference as a single fraction in lowest terms.

1. $\dfrac{x-1}{2y} + \dfrac{x}{2y}$

2. $\dfrac{y+1}{x} + \dfrac{y-1}{x}$

3. $\dfrac{2a-b}{a} - \dfrac{a-b}{a}$

4. $\dfrac{3a-1}{b} - \dfrac{2-a}{b}$

5. $\dfrac{a+2}{3} - \dfrac{a-3}{9}$

6. $\dfrac{a-2}{9} - \dfrac{a+1}{3}$

7. $\dfrac{2}{a+b} + \dfrac{1}{2a+2b}$

8. $\dfrac{7}{5x-10} + \dfrac{5}{3x-6}$

9. $\dfrac{2}{3-x} - \dfrac{1}{x-3}$

10. $\dfrac{7}{y-3} + \dfrac{3}{3-y}$

11. $\dfrac{a+1}{a+2} - \dfrac{a+2}{a+3}$

12. $\dfrac{5x-y}{3x+y} - \dfrac{6x-5y}{2x-y}$

13. $\dfrac{x+2y}{2x-y} - \dfrac{2x+y}{x-2y}$

14. $\dfrac{x-2y}{x+y} - \dfrac{2x-y}{x-y}$

15. $\dfrac{y}{y^2-16} - \dfrac{y+1}{y^2-5y+4} + \dfrac{1}{y+4}$

16. $\dfrac{1}{b^2-1} - \dfrac{1}{b^2+2b+1} + \dfrac{1}{b+1}$

17. $x + \dfrac{1}{x-1} - \dfrac{1}{(x-1)^2}$

18. $y - \dfrac{2y}{y^2-1} + \dfrac{3}{y+1}$

19. $x - 1 + \dfrac{3}{2x-1} - \dfrac{x}{4x^2-1}$

20. $2y - 3 - \dfrac{1}{y^2+2y+1} + \dfrac{3}{y+1}$

21. $\dfrac{y+3}{3y^2+7y+4} - \dfrac{y-7}{3y^2+13y+12}$

22. $\dfrac{a+b}{a^2+2ab-3b^2} - \dfrac{a-2b}{a^2-b^2} + \dfrac{2a+b}{a^2+4ab+3b^2}$

23. $\dfrac{xy}{(z-x)(x-y)} + \dfrac{yz}{(z-y)(x-z)} + \dfrac{xz}{(y-x)(y-z)}$

24. $\dfrac{1}{(a-b)(b-c)} + \dfrac{1}{(b-c)(c-a)} + \dfrac{1}{(c-a)(a-b)}$

25. Any set of fractions has an infinite number of common denominators. Why is it convenient to use the *least* common denominator in finding sums or differences of fractions?

26. Prove that $\dfrac{2a+3}{4} - \dfrac{a-2}{3} = \dfrac{2a+17}{12}$, That is, justify each step in the process with the appropriate definition, postulate, or theorem.

27. Prove Theorem 2.8.

2.7 PRODUCTS AND QUOTIENTS OF FRACTIONS

By Parts II and VII of Theorem 1.11 and the laws of closure, we have the following:

THEOREM 2.9 *If A, B, C, and D are real polynomials, then for values of the variables for which the denominators do not vanish,*

$$\text{I} \quad \frac{A}{B} \cdot \frac{C}{D} = \frac{AC}{BD},$$

$$\text{II} \quad \frac{A}{B} \div \frac{C}{D} = \frac{AD}{BC}.$$

The quotient $A/B \div C/D$ can also be denoted by

$$\frac{\dfrac{A}{B}}{\dfrac{C}{D}}.$$

This latter form is called a **complex fraction** (a fraction containing a fraction in either the numerator or denominator or both).

We can use Theorem 2.9 to rewrite products or quotients of fractions as a single fraction in lowest terms.

Example. Write $\dfrac{x^2 - 2x + 1}{x^2 + 2x - 3} \cdot \dfrac{x^2 + 3x}{x^2 + 2x}$ as a single fraction in lowest terms.

Solution.

$$
\begin{aligned}
\frac{x^2 - 2x + 1}{x^2 + 2x - 3} \cdot \frac{x^2 + 3x}{x^2 + 2x} &= \frac{(x - 1)(x - 1)}{(x + 3)(x - 1)} \cdot \frac{x(x + 3)}{x(x + 2)} \\
&= \frac{(x - 1)[(x - 1)(x + 3)x]}{(x + 2)[(x - 1)(x + 3)x]} \\
&= \frac{x - 1}{x + 2} \quad (x \notin \{-3, -2, 0, 1\}).
\end{aligned}
$$

Since the factors of the numerator and denominator of the product of two fractions are just the factors of the numerators and denominators, respectively, of the fractions, we can divide common factors out of the numerators and denominators before writing the product as a single fraction. Thus, in the example above, we could write

$$
\frac{x^2 - 2x + 1}{x^2 + 2x - 3} \cdot \frac{x^2 + 3x}{x^2 + 2x} = \frac{\overset{1}{\cancel{(x - 1)}}(x - 1)}{\cancel{(x + 3)}\overset{}{\cancel{(x - 1)}}} \cdot \frac{\overset{1}{\cancel{x}}\overset{1}{\cancel{(x + 3)}}}{\overset{}{\cancel{x}}(x + 2)}
$$

$$
= \frac{x - 1}{x + 2} \quad (x \notin \{-3, -2, 0, 1\}).
$$

Example. Write $\dfrac{x^3 - 8}{x^3 + 8} \div \dfrac{(x + 1)(x^2 + 2x + 4)}{(x - 1)(x^2 - 2x + 4)}$ as a single fraction in lowest terms.

Solution. We note first that the quadratic factors do not vanish for $x \in R$. Then we write

$$\frac{x^3 - 8}{x^3 + 8} \div \frac{(x + 1)(x^2 + 2x + 4)}{(x - 1)(x^2 - 2x + 4)} = \frac{x^3 - 8}{x^3 + 8} \cdot \frac{(x - 1)(x^2 - 2x + 4)}{(x + 1)(x^2 + 2x + 4)}$$

$$= \frac{(x - 2)\cancel{(x^2 + 2x + 4)}}{(x + 2)\cancel{(x^2 - 2x + 4)}} \cdot \frac{(x - 1)\cancel{(x^2 - 2x + 4)}}{(x + 1)\cancel{(x^2 + 2x + 4)}}$$

$$= \frac{(x - 2)(x - 1)}{(x + 2)(x + 1)} \quad (x \notin \{-2, -1, 1\}).$$

When the quotient of two fractions is given in the form of a complex fraction, we have a choice of procedures available to us for writing the quotient in the form of a simple (not complex) fraction.

Example. Write $\dfrac{x + \frac{3}{4}}{x - \frac{1}{2}}$ as a simple fraction in lowest terms.

Solution 1. We can apply the fundamental principle of fractions and multiply numerator and denominator by the least common denominator of the simple fractions involved. Thus, we have

$$\frac{(x + \frac{3}{4})4}{(x - \frac{1}{2})4} = \frac{4x + 3}{4x - 2} \quad (x \neq \frac{1}{2}).$$

Solution 2. Alternatively, we can rewrite the complex fraction as follows:

$$\frac{x + \dfrac{3}{4}}{x - \dfrac{1}{2}} = \frac{\dfrac{4x + 3}{4}}{\dfrac{2x - 1}{2}},$$

and the right-hand member can then be rewritten as a product,

$$\frac{4x + 3}{4} \cdot \frac{2}{2x - 1},$$

from which we have

$$\frac{4x + 3}{\cancel{4}} \cdot \frac{\cancel{2}^{\,1}}{2x - 1} = \frac{4x + 3}{4x - 2} \quad (x \neq \frac{1}{2}).$$

In the event we have more complicated expressions involving complex fractions, we can rewrite the expression by attacking small parts of it at a time.

Example. Write $\dfrac{1}{x + \dfrac{1}{x + \dfrac{1}{x}}}$ as a simple fraction in lowest terms.

Solution. We can begin by concentrating on the lower right-hand expression, $\dfrac{1}{x + \dfrac{1}{x}}$. We have

$$\frac{1}{x + \dfrac{1}{x}} = \frac{(1)x}{\left(x + \dfrac{1}{x}\right)x}$$

$$= \frac{x}{x^2 + 1}.$$

Thus,

$$\frac{1}{x + \dfrac{1}{x + \dfrac{1}{x}}} = \frac{1}{x + \dfrac{x}{x^2 + 1}}.$$

From this point, we can apply either of the methods shown in the previous example to the right-hand member above. Using the first method, we have

$$\frac{1}{x + \dfrac{1}{x + \dfrac{1}{x}}} = \frac{1(x^2 + 1)}{\left(x + \dfrac{x}{x^2 + 1}\right)(x^2 + 1)}$$

$$= \frac{x^2 + 1}{x^3 + x + x}$$

$$= \frac{x^2 + 1}{x^3 + 2x} \quad (x \neq 0).$$

EXERCISE 2.7

Write each product or quotient as a single fraction in lowest terms.

1. $\dfrac{-12a^2b}{5c} \cdot \dfrac{10b^2c}{24a^3b}$

2. $\dfrac{a^2}{xy} \cdot \dfrac{3x^3y}{4a}$

3. $\dfrac{xy}{a^2b} \div \dfrac{x^3y^2}{ab}$

4. $\dfrac{24a^3b}{-6xy^2} \div \dfrac{3a^2b}{12x}$

5. $\dfrac{x^2 - x - 20}{x^2 + 7x + 12}$

6. $\dfrac{4x^2 + 8x + 3}{2x^2 - 5x + 3} \cdot \dfrac{6x^2 - 9x}{1 - 4x^2}$

7. $\dfrac{25a^2b^2 - 16}{4ab + 1} \div \dfrac{5ab + 4}{16a^2b^2 + 16ab + 3}$

8. $\dfrac{a^2 - 25}{a^2 - 16} \div \dfrac{a^2 + 2a - 15}{a^2 + a - 12}$

9. $\dfrac{x^2 - y^2}{x^2} \cdot \dfrac{x^2 - xy + y^2}{x^2} \div \dfrac{x^3 + y^3}{x^4}$

10. $\dfrac{a^3 + 8b^3}{a^2 - 64b^2} \cdot \dfrac{a^3 + 512b^3}{a^2 - ab - 6b^2} \div \dfrac{a^4 + 4a^2b^2 + 16b^4}{a^2 + 11ab + 24b^2}$

11. $\left(1 + \dfrac{1}{x}\right) \cdot \left(1 - \dfrac{1}{x}\right)$ 12. $\left(x - \dfrac{1}{x}\right) \div \left(x + \dfrac{1}{x}\right)$

13. $\left[\dfrac{3}{x - 1} - \dfrac{2}{x + 1}\right] \cdot \dfrac{x - 1}{x}$ 14. $\left[\dfrac{x}{x^2 - 9} + \dfrac{2}{x - 3}\right] \cdot \dfrac{x - 1}{x}$

15. $\left[\dfrac{2y}{2y - 1} - \dfrac{3}{y}\right] \div \dfrac{3}{2y^2 - y}$

16. $\left[\dfrac{y}{y^2 - 1} - \dfrac{y}{y^2 - 2y + 1}\right] \div \dfrac{y}{y - 1}$

17. $\dfrac{\dfrac{2}{a} + \dfrac{3}{2a}}{5 + \dfrac{1}{a}}$ 18. $\dfrac{1 + \dfrac{1}{x}}{1 - \dfrac{1}{x}}$

19. $a - \dfrac{a}{a + \dfrac{1}{4}}$ 20. $x - \dfrac{x}{1 - \dfrac{x}{1 - x}}$

21. $1 - \dfrac{1}{1 - \dfrac{1}{y - 2}}$ 22. $2y + \dfrac{3}{3 - \dfrac{2y}{y - 1}}$

23. $\dfrac{1 + \dfrac{1}{1 - \dfrac{a}{b}}}{1 - \dfrac{3}{1 - \dfrac{a}{b}}}$ 24. $\dfrac{1 - \dfrac{1}{\dfrac{a}{b} + 2}}{1 + \dfrac{3}{\dfrac{a}{2b} + 1}}$

25. $\dfrac{a + 2 - \dfrac{12}{a + 3}}{a - 5 + \dfrac{16}{a + 3}}$ 26. $\dfrac{a + 4 - \dfrac{7}{a - 2}}{a - 1 + \dfrac{2}{a - 2}}$

27. $\left[\dfrac{a^2b^2 + 2b^4}{27a^6} \div \dfrac{a^2 - 10ab + 25b^2}{3a^5 + 6a^3b^2}\right] \cdot \dfrac{15a^3b - 3a^4}{a^4 + 4a^2b^2 + 4b^4}$

28. $\dfrac{\dfrac{9x^2 - 6x}{6x^2 - 7x + 2} \cdot \dfrac{2x^2 + 13x - 7}{2x^2 + 6x}}{\dfrac{4x^2 - 8x + 3}{2x^2 + 3x - 9}}$

29. Prove Theorem 2.9-I.

30. Prove Theorem 2.9-II.

3

RATIONAL EXPONENTS
—RADICALS

Handwritten annotations:

$x \in R; \; m, n \in N.$

Proof
Th 2.5

1. $\dfrac{x^n}{x^m} \doteq \dfrac{x^n}{x^m}$

1. hyp.
reflex.

2. $\dfrac{x^n}{x^m} = \dfrac{(x_1 \cdot x_2 \cdots x_n)}{(x_1 \cdot x_2 \cdots x_m)}$

2 Def of x^n

3. $\dfrac{x^n}{x^m} = \dfrac{x_1 \, x_2}{x_1 \, x_2} \cdot \dfrac{x_n}{x_m}$

3.1 POWERS WITH INTEGRAL EXPONENTS

In Section 2.2 the expression x^n ($x \in R$, $n \in N$) was defined to represent the product $x \cdot x \cdot x \cdots x$ containing n factors. Two theorems followed from this definition:

THEOREM 2.1 *If $x \in R$ and $m, n \in N$, then*
$$x^m \cdot x^n = x^{m+n}.$$

Handwritten: $\dfrac{x^n}{x^m} = 1$ where $m = n$

THEOREM 2.5 *If $x \in R$, $x \neq 0$, $m, n \in N$, and $m > n$, then*
$$\frac{x^m}{x^n} = x^{m-n}.$$

Handwritten: $\dfrac{x^n}{x^m} = \dfrac{1}{x^{m-n}}$ $m > n$

Now we wish to extend this definition so that powers are defined for all integer exponents and so that Theorems 2.1 and 2.5 remain valid under the extended definition. This time, let us use a for the base and see how a^n is defined for all $a \in R$ ($a \neq 0$) and $n \in J$ (that is, $n \in \{\text{integers}\}$). We have to consider two new cases, that in which $n = 0$, and that in which n is a negative integer. Let us first take $n = 0$.

Assuming that we would like whatever meaning we give to a^0 ($a \in R$, $a \neq 0$) to be such that Theorem 2.1 is true even for $m = 0$ or $n = 0$ or both, we would want, in particular,
$$a^m \cdot a^0 = a^{m+0} = a^m = a^m \cdot 1, \quad m \in N.$$

Now an application of the cancellation law for multiplication yields

$$a^0 = 1.$$

To have a consistent result, then, we are led to the following:

DEFINITION 3.1   *If $a \in R$, and $a \neq 0$, then*

$$a^0 = 1.$$

You might check that this definition gives consistent results in the equation of Theorem 2.1 also if $n \in N$ and $m = 0$; in fact, by the commutative laws, this follows from the case $n = 0$ and $m \in N$.   Again, for $m = n = 0$, we have simply

$$a^0 \cdot a^0 = 1 \cdot 1 = 1 = a^0 = a^{0+0}.$$

Similarly, you can readily check that, with a^0 defined by $a^0 = 1$, the equation in Theorem 2.5 remains valid with 0 in place of m or n or both.

With the foregoing definition available, we can turn our attention to the power a^n in case n is a negative integer, or, what amounts to the same thing, to a^{-n}, where n is a natural number.

If a^{-n}, where $a \in R$, $a \neq 0$, and $n \in N$, is to obey Theorem 2.1, we must, in particular, have

$$a^n \cdot a^{-n} = a^{n+(-n)} = a^0 = 1,$$

from which

$$a^{-n} = \frac{1}{a^n} \quad (a \neq 0).$$

Thus, to extend the validity of Theorem 2.1, we are led to the following:

DEFINITION 3.2   *If $a \in R$, $a \neq 0$, and $n \in J$, then*

$$a^{-n} = \frac{1}{a^n}.$$

Now for m and n integers ≥ 0, the equation in Theorem 2.1, with $-n$ in place of n, is

$$a^m \cdot a^{-n} = a^{m-n} \quad (a \in R, a \neq 0),$$

which is true by Definition 3.2 and Theorem 2.5 (extended to include $m = 0$ or $n = 0$ or both).   Again,

$$a^{-m} \cdot a^{-n} = \frac{1}{a^m} \cdot \frac{1}{a^n} = \frac{1}{a^{m+n}} = a^{-(m+n)} = a^{-m-n}.$$

Thus the equation in Theorem 2.1 is true for all $a \in R$, $a \neq 0$, and for all integers m, n.

Curiously enough, Definition 3.2 reduces Theorem 2.5 to a special case of Theorem 2.1. Thus, by the definition and Theorem 2.1,

$$\frac{a^m}{a^n} = a^m \cdot a^{-n} = a^{m-n},$$

which is Theorem 2.5. Nevertheless, for convenience we retain both forms and restate the two theorems together as the following extended result.

THEOREM 3.1 *If $a \in R$, $a \neq 0$, and $m, n \in J$, then*

$$\text{I} \quad a^m \cdot a^n = a^{m+n},$$

$$\text{II} \quad \frac{a^m}{a^n} = a^{m-n}.$$

There are three additional consequences of our definitions of interest to us here, and we combine them with the preceding theorem:

THEOREM 3.1 *If $a, b \in R$, $a, b \neq 0$, and $m, n \in J$, then*

$$\text{III} \quad (a^m)^n = a^{mn},$$
$$\text{IV} \quad (ab)^n = a^n b^n,$$
$$\text{V} \quad \left(\frac{a}{b}\right)^n = \frac{a^n}{b^n}.$$

The following argument should convince you of the validity of Part III. Let us consider several cases.

For $m, n \in N$,

$$(a^m)^n = (\underbrace{a \cdot a \cdot a \cdots a}_{m \text{ factors}})^n$$

$$= \underbrace{\underbrace{(a \cdot a \cdot a \cdots a)}_{m \text{ factors}}\underbrace{(a \cdot a \cdot a \cdots a)}_{m \text{ factors}} \cdots \underbrace{(a \cdot a \cdot a \cdots a)}_{m \text{ factors}}}_{n \text{ factors}}$$

$$= \underbrace{a \cdot a \cdot a \cdots a}_{mn \text{ factors}}$$

$$= a^{mn}.$$

For $m = 0$, $n \in J$,

$$(a^0)^n = (1)^n = 1 \quad \text{and} \quad a^{0 \cdot n} = a^0 = 1,$$

so that

$$(a^0)^n = a^{0 \cdot n}.$$

For $n = 0$, $m \in J$,

$$(a^m)^0 = 1 \quad \text{and} \quad a^{m \cdot 0} = a^0 = 1,$$

so that

$$(a^m)^0 = a^{m \cdot 0}.$$

It remains to show that Theorem 3.1-III is true for $(a^m)^{-n}$, $(a^{-m})^n$, and $(a^{-m})^{-n}$, where $m, n \in N$. We shall present only one of these, but the other cases are similar.

We have

$$(a^m)^{-n} = \frac{1}{(a^m)^n} = \frac{1}{a^{mn}} = a^{-mn}.$$

You will be asked in Exercise 3.1 to go through similar arguments for Parts IV and V of Theorem 3.1.

Some examples of applications of this theorem should prove enlightening.

Example. Write $(x^2)^3$ as an integral power of x.

Solution. $(x^2)^3 = x^{2 \cdot 3} = x^6$ by Theorem 3.1-III.

Example. Write $(xy)^3$ as a product of integral powers of x and y.

Solution. $(xy)^3 = x^3 y^3$ by Theorem 3.1-IV.

Example. Write $(x^2/y)^{-4}$ as a quotient of natural number powers of x and y.

Solution. $\left(\dfrac{x^2}{y}\right)^{-4} = \dfrac{(x^2)^{-4}}{(y)^{-4}}$ by Theorem 3.1-V,

$\qquad\qquad = \dfrac{x^{-8}}{y^{-4}}$ by Theorem 3.1-III,

$\qquad\qquad = \dfrac{y^4}{x^8}$ $(x, y \neq 0)$ by Definition 3.2 and Theorem 1.11-VII.

Although we shall not do anything about proving it here, Theorem 3.1-III, 3.1-IV, and 3.1-V can be shown to apply to expressions involving more than two factors. That is, not only do they apply to expressions like

$$(x^2)^3, \quad (xy)^5, \quad \text{and} \quad \left(\frac{x^2}{y}\right)^{-4},$$

but also to expressions like

$$(x^2 y^3 z^4)^5, \quad (xyz)^5, \quad \text{and} \quad \left(\frac{x^2 z^4}{5y}\right)^{-4}.$$

In order to avoid the necessity of constantly noting exceptions, we shall assume that in the exercises in this chapter the variables are restricted so that no denominator vanishes.

EXERCISE 3.1

Write each of the following as a *basic numeral*—that is, a numeral with exponent 1.

Examples.

a. $\dfrac{3^{-2}}{2^{-3}}$

b. $4^2 + 4^{-2}$

Solutions.

a. $\dfrac{2^3}{3^2}$

$\dfrac{8}{9}$

b. $16 + \dfrac{1}{16}$

$\dfrac{257}{16}$

1. 2^{-1}

2. $\dfrac{1}{3^{-1}}$

3. $\left(\dfrac{3}{5}\right)^{-1}$

4. $\left(-\dfrac{1}{3}\right)^{-2}$

5. $\dfrac{2^0}{3^{-2}}$

6. $\dfrac{5^{-1}}{3^{-2}}$

7. $(-8)^{-3}$

8. $(16)^{-3}$

9. $3^{-2} + 3^2$

10. $5^{-1} + 25^0$

11. $16^{-1} - 16^{-2}$

12. $8^{-2} - 2^0$

Write each of the following as a product or quotient in which each variable occurs, at most, once in each term, and involves positive exponents only.

Examples.

a. $x^{-3} \cdot x^5$

b. $(x^2 y^{-3})^{-1}$

c. $\left(\dfrac{x^{-1} y^2 z^0}{x^3 y^{-4} z^2}\right)^{-1}$

Solutions.

a. x^{-3+5}

x^2

b. $x^{-2} y^3$

$\dfrac{y^3}{x^2}$

c. $\dfrac{x y^{-2} z^0}{x^{-3} y^4 z^{-2}}$

$\dfrac{x^4 z^2}{y^6}$

13. $(x^2 \cdot y^3)^2$

14. $(y^3 \cdot y^4)^2$

15. $\left(\dfrac{x}{2y^3}\right)^2$

16. $\left(\dfrac{2x}{y^2}\right)^3$

17. $\dfrac{(xy^2)^3}{(x^2 y)^2}$

18. $\left(\dfrac{3x}{y^2}\right)^2 \left(\dfrac{2y^3}{x}\right)^2$

19. $x^{-3} \cdot x^4$

20. $\dfrac{x^5}{x^{-2}}$

21. $(x^{-3})^2$

22. $(x^{-2} y^3)^0$

23. $\dfrac{x^{-1}}{y^{-1}}$

24. $\dfrac{x^{-3}}{y^{-2}}$

25. $\dfrac{8^{-1} x^0 y^{-3}}{(2xy)^{-5}}$

26. $\left(\dfrac{x^{-1} y^3}{2x^0 y^{-5}}\right)^{-2}$

Represent as a single fraction involving positive exponents only.

Examples.

a. $x^{-1} + y^{-2}$

b. $(x^{-1} + x^{-2})^{-1}$

c. $\dfrac{x^{-1}}{x^{-1} + y^{-1}}$

Solutions.

a. $\dfrac{1}{x} + \dfrac{1}{y^2}$

$\dfrac{(y^2)1}{(y^2)x} + \dfrac{1\,(x)}{y^2(x)}$

$\dfrac{y^2 + x}{xy^2}$

b. $\left(\dfrac{1}{x} + \dfrac{1}{x^2}\right)^{-1}$

$\left[\dfrac{(x)1}{(x)x} + \dfrac{1}{x^2}\right]^{-1}$

$\left(\dfrac{x+1}{x^2}\right)^{-1}$

$\dfrac{x^2}{x+1}$

c. $\dfrac{\dfrac{1}{x}\ (xy)}{\left(\dfrac{1}{x} + \dfrac{1}{y}\right)(xy)}$

$\dfrac{y}{y + x}$

27. $x^{-1} - y^{-1}$

28. $x^{-2} + y^{-2}$

29. $\dfrac{x^{-1}}{y^{-1}} + \dfrac{y}{x}$

30. $\dfrac{r}{s^{-1}} + \dfrac{r^{-1}}{s}$

31. $(x + y)^{-1}$

32. $(x - y)^{-2}$

33. $xy^{-1} + x^{-1}y$

34. $x^{-1}y - xy^{-1}$

35. $\dfrac{x^{-1} + y^{-1}}{(xy)^{-1}}$

36. $\dfrac{x}{y^{-1}} + \left(\dfrac{x}{y}\right)^{-1}$

37. $(x^{-1} - y^{-1})^{-1}$

38. $\dfrac{x^{-1} + y^{-1}}{x^{-1} - y^{-1}}$

Write each expression as a monomial in which each variable occurs only once in each term.

Examples.

a. $\dfrac{x^n \cdot x^{n+1}}{x^{n-1}}$

b. $\dfrac{(y^{n-1})^2}{y^{n-2}}$

Solutions.

a. $x^{n+(n+1)-(n-1)}$

x^{n+2}

b. $y^{(2n-2)-(n-2)}$

y^n

39. $x^n \cdot x^n$

40. $\dfrac{x^{2n}x^n}{x^{n-1}}$

41. $\dfrac{(x^{n+1}x^{2n-1})^2}{x^{3n}}$

42. $\left(\dfrac{y^2 \cdot y^3}{y}\right)^{2n}$

43. $\left(\dfrac{x^{3n}x^{2n}}{x^{4n}}\right)^2$

44. $\dfrac{(y^{n+1})^n}{y^n}$

45. $\left(\dfrac{x^n}{x^{n-3}}\right)^2$

46. $\left(\dfrac{x^n}{x^{n-1}}\right)^{-1}$

47. $\dfrac{x^n y^{n+1}}{x^{2n-1}y^n}$

48. $\dfrac{b^n c^{2n-1}}{b^{n+1}c^{2n}}$

49. $\left(\dfrac{a^{2n}}{a^{n+1}}\right)^{-2}$

50. $\left(\dfrac{a^{2n}b^{n-1}}{a^{n-1}b}\right)^2$

Write each number as the product of a number between 1 and 10 and a power of 10. (This exponential form is called **scientific notation**.)

Examples.

 a. 680,000 b. 0.0000431

Solutions. Factor.

 a. $6.8 \times 100,000$ b. $4.31 \times \dfrac{1}{100,000}$

Write in exponential form.

 6.8×10^5 4.31×10^{-5}

51. 34,000 52. 253 53. 8,372,000

54. 25,300,000,000 55. 0.0014 56. 0.0000006

57. 0.0000230 58. 0.5020

59. Use an argument similar to the argument in the text to show that for $a, b \in R$, and $n \in J$,

$$(ab)^n = a^n b^n \quad \text{(Theorem 3.1-IV).}$$

60. Show that for $a, b \in R$, $b \neq 0$, and $n \in J$,

$$\left(\frac{a}{b}\right)^n = \frac{a^n}{b^n} \quad \text{(Theorem 3.1-V).}$$

3.2 POWERS WITH RATIONAL EXPONENTS

In Section 3.1, we defined powers of real numbers with 0 and negative integer exponents so that Theorem 3.1-I would be consistent with Theorem 2.1. It followed that the remaining laws of exponents hold for these exponents also. What we want to do now is to give meaning to powers of real numbers with rational numbers as exponents. As before, we shall want any such definition to be consistent with all of the laws of exponents for integers.

Let us look first at Theorem 3.1-I, and consider what it must imply if it is to apply to an expression of the form $a^{1/n}$, where $a \in R$, and n is a positive integer. We would have

$$\underbrace{a^{1/n} \cdot a^{1/n} \cdot a^{1/n} \cdots a^{1/n}}_{n \text{ factors}} = a^{\overbrace{(1/n)+(1/n)+1/n)+\cdots+(1/n)}^{n \text{ terms}}}$$
$$= a^{n/n} = a.$$

Thus, $a^{1/n}$ must be one of n equal factors of a. Accordingly, for consistency we have the following:

DEFINITION 3.3   *If $a \in R$, $n \in N$, then $a^{1/n}$ is a real number, if one exists, such that*

$$(a^{1/n})^n = a.$$

If there are two real numbers with this property, then $a^{1/n}$ denotes the positive one of them.

The number $a^{1/n}$ is called an **nth root** of a.   If n is 2 or 3, then $a^{1/n}$ is also called a **square root** or **cube root** of a, respectively.   The question of the existence of real numbers $a^{1/n}$ that behave according to our definition is not a trivial one.   While $(-27)^{1/3}$ clearly denotes the real number -3, because $(-3)^3 = -27$, there is a legitimate basis for wondering whether $3^{1/25}$ denotes a real number.   Actually it does, as follows from O-3, but we shall have to make this fact a simple matter of faith, since rigorously proving it is beyond our capabilities here.   On the other hand, there are cases in which there is no real number $a^{1/n}$ for which $(a^{1/n})^n = a$.   For example, when n is an even integer and a is negative, the statement $(a^{1/n})^n = a$ implies that an even number of positive real factors, or an even number of negative real factors, yield a negative product.   But the product of an even number of negative factors or of an even number of positive factors is always positive!   Therefore, when n is an even integer, $a^{1/n}$ is not defined in the set of real numbers if $a < 0$.   We have the following possibilities:

    a. For n an odd integer, $a^{1/n}$ is positive, negative, or zero as a is positive, negative, or zero.

    b. For n an even integer, every positive real number has two real nth roots, 0 has one nth root, and no negative number has a real nth root.

Thus, since $2^2 = 4$ and $(-2)^2 = 4$, both 2 and -2 are square roots of 4. We agree (see the above definition) that when we write $a^{1/n}$ for $a > 0$ and n even, we shall mean only the positive nth root of a.   That is, for n even,

$$(a^{1/n})^n = |a|.$$

The negative nth root will be designated by $-a^{1/n}$.

Examples.   Each of the following powers represents an integer.   In each case, write the basic numeral.

    a. $9^{1/2}$ b. $(-8)^{1/3}$ c. $-(64)^{1/3}$ d. $243^{1/5}$

Solutions.

    a. Since $3 \cdot 3 = 9$,   b. Since $(-2)(-2)(-2) = -8$,
        $9^{1/2} = 3$ $(-8)^{1/3} = -2$

    c. Since $-(4 \cdot 4 \cdot 4) = -64$,   d. Since $3 \cdot 3 \cdot 3 \cdot 3 \cdot 3 = 243$,
        $(-64)^{1/3} = -4$ $243^{1/5} = 3$

Of course, a power such as $(-64)^{1/4}$ would not correspond to any real number, integer or otherwise.

Let us see, now, about some of the other parts of Theorem 3.1. First, consider

$$(a^{1/n})^m.$$

If the theorem is to hold here for m, $n \in J$ ($n \neq 0$), then

$$(a^{1/n})^m = a^{(1/n) \cdot m} = a^{m/n}.$$

Accordingly, we are led to the following:

DEFINITION 3.4   *If $a^{1/n} \in R$, and m, $n \in J$, then*

$$a^{m/n} = (a^{1/n})^m.$$

Observe that the restriction $a^{1/n} \in R$ implies that $a \in R$, $n \neq 0$; moreover, if n is even, a must be nonnegative.

As a consequence of this definition, we can prove the following.

THEOREM 3.2   *If $a^{1/n} \in R$, and m, $n \in J$, then*

$$(a^{1/n})^m = (a^m)^{1/n}.$$

Proof.   Since, for $n \in N$, by Definition 3.4 we have

$$\underbrace{a^{m/n} \cdot a^{m/n} \cdot a^{m/n} \cdots a^{m/n}}_{n \text{ factors}} = \underbrace{(a^{1/n})^m \cdot (a^{1/n})^m \cdot (a^{1/n})^m \cdots (a^{1/n})^m}_{n \text{ factors}}$$

$$= [(a^{1/n})^m]^n$$
$$= (a^{1/n})^{mn}$$
$$= (a^{1/n})^{nm}$$
$$= [(a^{1/n})^n]^m$$
$$= a^m,$$

and it is evident that $a^{m/n}$ is an nth root of a^m. But, by definition, such a root of a^m is designated $(a^m)^{1/n}$. That is, $(a^{1/n})^m = (a^m)^{1/n}$.

Careful attention has to be paid to the restrictions in the definitions for $a^{1/n}$ and $a^{m/n}$ when m and n are integers. For example, consider the following. (The proof is omitted.)

THEOREM 3.3   *If $a^{m/n}$, $a^{mc/nc} \in R$, and m, n, $c \in J$, then*

$$a^{m/n} = a^{mc/nc}.$$

Here the stated restrictions are that both $a^{m/n}$ and $a^{mc/nc}$ are real. Implied restrictions, therefore, are first that n, $c \neq 0$, second that n is not even if a

is negative, and third that if a is negative and n is an odd integer, then c is an odd integer. The stated restrictions prevent writing such things as

$$(-2)^{1/2} = (-2)^{2/4} = [(-2)^2]^{1/4} = 4^{1/4} = [2^2]^{1/4} = 2^{2/4} = 2^{1/2}$$

and

$$(-1)^{1/3} = (-1)^{2/6} = [(-1)^2]^{1/6} = [1^2]^{1/6} = 1^{2/6} = 1^{1/3}.$$

A theorem parallel to Theorem 3.1 is the following, where m and n are rational numbers rather than integers. We state it without proof, since similar proofs have already been given for the preceding results.

THEOREM 3.4　*If a^m, a^n, b^m, $b^n \in R$, a, $b \neq 0$, and m, $n \in Q$ (i.e., $m, n \in \{rational\ numbers\}$),*

$$\text{I}\quad a^m \cdot a^n = a^{m+n},$$

$$\text{II}\quad \frac{a^m}{a^n} = a^{m-n},$$

$$\text{III}\quad (a^m)^n = a^{mn},$$

$$\text{IV}\quad (ab)^n = a^n b^n,$$

$$\text{V}\quad \left(\frac{a}{b}\right)^n = \frac{a^n}{b^n}.$$

Let us look at a few examples of applications of this theorem.

Example.　Write $\dfrac{x^{2/3}}{x^{1/3}}$ as a power of x.

Solution.

$$\frac{x^{2/3}}{x^{1/3}} = x^{2/3 - 1/3} = x^{1/3} \quad (x \neq 0). \quad \text{(By Theorem 3.4-II)}$$

Example.　Write $\left(\dfrac{a^3 b^6}{c^{12}}\right)^{2/3}$ without using parentheses.

Solution.

$$\left(\frac{a^3 b^6}{c^{12}}\right)^{2/3} = \frac{(a^3)^{2/3}(b^6)^{2/3}}{(c^{12})^{2/3}} \quad \text{(By Theorem 3.4-IV and V)}$$

$$= \frac{a^2 b^4}{c^8} \quad (c \neq 0). \quad \text{(By Theorem 3.4-III)}$$

Example.　Write $(a^6)^{1/2}$ without using parentheses.

Solution.

$$(a^6)^{1/2} = |a^3| \text{ or } a^2|a|. \quad \text{(By the definition of } a^{1/n},$$
$$n \text{ even, and Theorem 3.4-III)}$$

Observe that in the last example it was necessary to use absolute-value notation to ensure that a^3 is nonnegative for any real number a.   Otherwise, for a negative-number replacement for a, such as -1, we would have the inconsistent result

$$[(-1)^6]^{1/2} = (-1)^3,$$
$$1^{1/2} = (-1)^3,$$

and

$$1 = -1.$$

EXERCISE 3.2

Write each of the following as a basic numeral—that is, a numeral with exponent 1.

Examples.

a. $64^{1/2}$

b. $\left(\dfrac{8}{27}\right)^{-2/3}$

c. $(-27)^{4/3}$

Solutions.

a. 8

b. $\left[\left(\dfrac{8}{27}\right)^{1/3}\right]^{-2}$

$\left(\dfrac{2}{3}\right)^{-2}$

$\dfrac{9}{4}$

c. $[(-27)^{1/3}]^4$

$(-3)^4$

81

1. $(32)^{1/5}$

2. $(-27)^{1/3}$

3. $(81)^{-3/4}$

4. $(81)^{-1/2}$

5. $\left(\dfrac{1}{8}\right)^{-5/3}$

6. $\left(\dfrac{1}{8}\right)^{5/3}$

7. $\left(\dfrac{4}{9}\right)^{3/2}$

8. $\left(\dfrac{4}{9}\right)^{-3/2}$

Write each of the following as a product or quotient of powers in which each variable occurs but once, and all exponents are positive.   Assume all variable bases are positive and all variable exponents are natural numbers.

Examples.

a. $\dfrac{x^{5/6}}{x^{2/3}}$

b. $\dfrac{(x^{1/2}y^2)^2}{(x^{2/3}y)^3}$

c. $(y^{2n} \cdot y^{n/2})^4$

Solutions.

a. $x^{5/6 - 2/3}$

$x^{5/6 - 4/6}$

$x^{1/6}$

b. $\dfrac{xy^4}{x^2y^3}$

$\dfrac{y}{x}$

c. $y^{8n} \cdot y^{2n}$

y^{10n}

9. $x^{1/3} \cdot x^{5/3}$

10. $x^{4/3} \cdot x^{1/2}$

11. $a^{2/3} \cdot a^{3/4}$

12. $x^{1/2} \cdot x^{5/6}$

13. $\dfrac{x^{5/6}}{x^{1/2}}$

14. $\dfrac{x^{1/2}}{x^{1/3}}$

15. $\dfrac{x^{-2/5}}{x^{2/3}}$

16. $\left(\dfrac{a^6}{c^3}\right)^{-2/3}$

17. $\left(\dfrac{x^{1/2}}{y^2}\right)^2 \cdot \left(\dfrac{y^4}{x^2}\right)^{1/2}$ 18. $(a^2 b)\left(\dfrac{16}{ab^2}\right)^{1/4}$ 19. $\left(\dfrac{x^5 y^8}{y^{13}}\right)^{1/4}$

20. $\left(\dfrac{125 x^3 y^4}{27 x^{-6} y}\right)^{1/3}$ 21. $(x^2)^{n/2} \cdot (y^{2n})^{2/n}$ 22. $(x^{n/2})^2 \cdot (y^n)^{5/n}$

23. $\dfrac{x^{2n}}{x^{n/2}}$ 24. $\left(\dfrac{a^n}{b}\right)^{1/2} \cdot \left(\dfrac{b}{a^{2n}}\right)^{3/2}$ 25. $\dfrac{x^{3n} y^{2m-1}}{(x^n y^m)^{1/2}}$

26. $\left(\dfrac{m^{2a^2}}{n^{4a}}\right)^{1/a}$

Apply the distributive law and write each product as a sum.

27. $x^{1/3} \cdot (x^{2/3} - x^{1/3})$

28. $y^{2/3} \cdot (y^{2/3} + y^{1/3})$

29. $(x + y)^{1/2} \cdot [(x + y)^{1/2} - (x + y)]$

30. $(a - b)^{2/3} \cdot [(a - b)^{-1/3} + (a - b)]$

31. $(x^{1/2} - y^{-1/2})^2$

32. $(x^{1/2} + y^{1/2})(x^{1/2} - y^{1/2})$

33. $(x^{1/3} + y^{1/3})(x^{2/3} - x^{1/3} \cdot y^{1/3} + y^{2/3})$

34. $(a^{1/3} - b^{1/3})(a^{2/3} + a^{1/3} \cdot b^{1/3} + b^{2/3})$

Factor as indicated.

Examples.

a. $y^{-1/2} + y^{1/2} = y^{-1/2}(\ ?\ )$

b. $(x + y)^{1/2} + (x + y)^{3/2} = (x + y)^{1/2}(\ ?\ )$

Solutions.

a. $y^{-1/2}(1 + y)$ b. $(x + y)^{1/2}(1 + x + y)$

35. $x^{3/2} + x = x(\ ?\ )$ 36. $y - y^{2/3} = y^{1/3}(\ ?\ )$

37. $x^{-3/2} + x^{-1/2} = x^{-1/2}(\ ?\ )$ 38. $z^{1/2} + z^{-1/3} = z^{1/6}(\ ?\ )$

39. $(x + 1)^{1/2} - (x + 1)^{-1/2} = (x + 1)^{-1/2}(\ ?\ )$

40. $(y + 2)^{1/5} - (y + 2)^{-4/5} = (y + 2)^{-4/5}(\ ?\ )$

41. $x^{2n} + x^{n/2} = x^{n/2}(\ ?\ )$ 42. $y^{n+1} + y^{2n} = y(\ ?\ )$

43. $x - y = (x^{1/2} - y^{1/2})(\ ?\ )$ 44. $x + y = (x^{1/3} + y^{1/3})(\ ?\ )$

In the previous problems, the variables were restricted to represent positive numbers. In Problems 45–50, consider variable bases to be *any* element of the set of real numbers and simplify.

Examples.

a. $[(-3)^2]^{1/2}$ b. $[u^2(u + 5)]^{1/2}$

Solutions.

a. $[(-3)^2]^{1/2} = |-3| = 3$ b. $[u^2(u + 5)]^{1/2} = |u|(u + 5)^{1/2}$

45. $[(-5)^2]^{1/2}$ 46. $[(-3)^{12}]^{1/4}$ 47. $[4x^2]^{1/2}$

48. $[x^2(x - 1)]^{1/2}$ 49. $\dfrac{2}{[x^2(x + 1)]^{1/2}}$ 50. $\left[\dfrac{9}{x^6(x^2 + 1)}\right]^{1/2}$

3.3   RADICAL EXPRESSIONS

Powers of real numbers with rational numbers for exponents are frequently denoted by symbols involving the use of the radical sign, $\sqrt{}$.

DEFINITION 3.5   *If $a^{1/n} \in R$, and $n \in N$, then*

$$\sqrt[n]{a} = a^{1/n}.$$

DEFINITION 3.6   *If $a^{m/n} \in R$, $m \in J$, and $n \in N$, then*

$$\sqrt[n]{a^m} = a^{m/n}.$$

Naturally, the radical expressions on the left are not defined if the powers on the right are not. In the symbolism $\sqrt[n]{a}$, a is called the **radicand** and n the **index** of the radical, and the expression is called a **radical expression of order n**. If no index is shown with a radical expression, as, for example, in the case $\sqrt{a}$, then the index 2 is understood to apply. The symbol $\sqrt{a}$ denotes the nonnegative square root of a, where, of course, a cannot be negative. The symbol $\sqrt{x^2}$, where $x \in R$, therefore provides us with an alternative means of writing $|x|$. That is, $\sqrt{x^2} = |x|$.

An immediate consequence of the foregoing definitions and the theorems pertaining to exponents is the following.

THEOREM 3.5   *For real values of a and b for which all the radical expressions in the equation denote real numbers,*

      I   A. $\sqrt[n]{a^n} = a$ *(n an odd natural number)*,

            B. $\sqrt[n]{a^n} = |a|$ *(n an even natural number)*,

     II $\sqrt[n]{a^m} = (\sqrt[n]{a})^m$ *(n ∈ N, m ∈ J)*,

     III $\sqrt[n]{a} \cdot \sqrt[n]{b} = \sqrt[n]{ab}$ *(n ∈ N)*,

$$\text{IV} \quad \frac{\sqrt[n]{a}}{\sqrt[n]{b}} = \sqrt[n]{\frac{a}{b}} \quad (b \neq 0, n \in N),$$

$$\text{V} \quad \sqrt[m]{\sqrt[n]{a}} = \sqrt[mn]{a} \quad (m, n \in N),$$

$$\text{VI} \quad \sqrt[cn]{a^{cm}} = \sqrt[n]{a^m} \quad (m, c \in J, c > 0, n \in N).$$

It might be noted in III and IV that if $a < 0$, $b < 0$, and n is even, then the radicals in the left-hand member are not defined, even though the radical in the right-hand member is.

The several parts of this theorem can be used to rewrite radical expressions in various ways, and, in particular, to write them in what is called "simplest" form.   A radical expression is said to be in **simplest form** if

a. the radicand contains no polynomial factor raised to a power equal to or greater than the index of the radical,

b. the radicand contains no fractions,

c. no radical expressions are contained in denominators of fractions, and

d. the index of the radical is as small as possible.

Examples.   Write in simplest form.

a. $\sqrt[3]{24x^3y^2}$ b. $\sqrt[6]{49x^2}$ c. $\dfrac{\sqrt[3]{4a^2}}{\sqrt[3]{3}}$

Solutions.

a. $\sqrt[3]{24x^3y^2} = \sqrt[3]{8x^3}\sqrt[3]{3y^2} = 2x\sqrt[3]{3y^2}$ (By Theorem 3.5-III and the definition of $\sqrt[n]{a^n}$)

b. $\sqrt[6]{49x^2} = \sqrt[3\cdot2]{7^{1\cdot2}x^{1\cdot2}} = \sqrt[3]{7x}$ (By Theorem 3.5-VI)

c. $\dfrac{\sqrt[3]{4a^2}}{\sqrt[3]{b}} = \dfrac{\sqrt[3]{4a^2}\sqrt[3]{b^2}}{\sqrt[3]{b}\sqrt[3]{b^2}}$ (By the fundamental principle of fractions)

$= \dfrac{\sqrt[3]{4a^2b^2}}{\sqrt[3]{b^3}} = \dfrac{\sqrt[3]{4a^2b^2}}{b}$ $(b \neq 0)$ (By Theorem 3.5-III and the definition of $\sqrt[n]{a^n}$)

The process employed in simplifying the expression in part c in the foregoing example is called "rationalizing the denominator," because the result is a fraction with denominator free of radicals.   This does not exclude the possibility that the denominator is an irrational number.

Since we have defined our radical expressions so that they represent real numbers, the properties of the real numbers can be applied.   For example, the distributive law in the form

$$ac + bc = (a + b)c$$

justifies writing certain sums as products. For example,

$$2\sqrt{5} + 4\sqrt{5}$$

can be written

$$(2 + 4)\sqrt{5},$$

which is equal to the product

$$6\sqrt{5}.$$

Similarly,

$$5\sqrt{2} - 9\sqrt{2} = (5 - 9)\sqrt{2} = -4\sqrt{2}.$$

Applying the distributive law in the form

$$ca + cb = c(a + b),$$

we can write

$$5\sqrt{2} + \sqrt{75} = 5\sqrt{2} + 5\sqrt{3} = 5(\sqrt{2} + \sqrt{3}).$$

Conversely, the distributive law in the form

$$c(a + b) = ca + cb$$

permits us to write certain products as sums. For example,

$$2(\sqrt{2} - 7) = 2\sqrt{2} - 14,$$

$$(\sqrt{x} - 3)(\sqrt{x} + 3) = \sqrt{x}(\sqrt{x} + 3) - 3(\sqrt{x} + 3) = x - 9,$$

and

$$(\sqrt{x} + 2)(\sqrt{x} - 1) = \sqrt{x}(\sqrt{x} - 1) + 2(\sqrt{x} - 1)$$
$$= x - \sqrt{x} + 2\sqrt{x} - 2$$
$$= x + \sqrt{x} - 2.$$

The distributive law also provides us with a means of rationalizing denominators of fractions in which radicals occur in one or both of two terms. To accomplish this, we first recall that

$$(a - b)(a + b) = a^2 - b^2,$$

where the expression in the right-hand member contains no linear term. Each of the two factors of a product exhibiting this property is said to be the **conjugate** of the other. Now consider a fraction of the form

$$\frac{a}{b + \sqrt{c}},$$

where c is positive and $b \neq -\sqrt{c}$. If we multiply the numerator and denominator of this fraction by the conjugate of the denominator, then the denominator of the resulting fraction will contain no term involving $\sqrt{c}$, and hence will be free of radicals.   That is,

$$\frac{a(b - \sqrt{c})}{(b + \sqrt{c})(b - \sqrt{c})} = \frac{ab - a\sqrt{c}}{b^2 - c},$$

where the denominator has been rationalized.   This process is equally applicable to radical fractions of the form

$$\frac{a}{\sqrt{b} + \sqrt{c}},$$

since

$$\frac{a(\sqrt{b} - \sqrt{c})}{(\sqrt{b} + \sqrt{c})(\sqrt{b} - \sqrt{c})} = \frac{a\sqrt{b} - a\sqrt{c}}{b - c}.$$

It should be noted, though, that it is not *always* preferable, in working with fractions, to have their denominators rationalized.   Sometimes, in fact, it is desirable to rationalize the numerator.   Thus, for example,

$$\frac{\sqrt{b} + \sqrt{c}}{a} = \frac{(\sqrt{b} + \sqrt{c})(\sqrt{b} - \sqrt{c})}{a(\sqrt{b} - \sqrt{c})} = \frac{b - c}{a(\sqrt{b} - \sqrt{c})}.$$

EXERCISE 3.3

Write in radical form.   (Assume all variables and all radicands are positive except where specifically indicated to the contrary.)

Examples.

   a. $5^{1/2}$ b. $xy^{2/3}$ c. $(x - y^2)^{-1/2}$

Solutions.

   a. $\sqrt{5}$ b. $x\sqrt[3]{y^2}$ c. $\dfrac{1}{\sqrt{x - y^2}}$

1. $a^{2/3}$ 2. $x^{3/2}$ 3. $3x^{1/3}$ 4. $-6xy^{1/2}$

5. $-6(xy)^{2/3}$ 6. $x^{1/5}y^{3/5}$ 7. $(x - y)^{4/7}$ 8. $(24 - 3x)^{-3/4}$

Write an equal expression using positive fractional exponents in lowest terms.

Examples.

   a. $\sqrt{2^3}$ b. $7\sqrt[3]{a^2}$ c. $\dfrac{1}{\sqrt{a - b}}$

Solutions.

   a. $2^{3/2}$ b. $7a^{2/3}$ c. $\dfrac{1}{(a - b)^{1/2}}$

9. $\sqrt[3]{x^2}$ 　　　　　10. $\sqrt[5]{xy}$ 　　　　　11. $\sqrt[4]{2xy^2}$ 　　　　　12. $a\sqrt[5]{x^2y^3}$

13. $-3\sqrt[4]{a^3b}$ 　　　14. $7\sqrt[7]{x^5}$ 　　　　15. $\sqrt{x-y^2}$ 　　　　16. $\sqrt[4]{a+2b}$

17. $3\sqrt[3]{x^2-y}$ 　　18. $-a\sqrt[5]{x^4-y^4}$ 　19. $2\sqrt[6]{(x-y)^3}$ 　20. $3\sqrt[8]{(a+2b)^2}$

Find the root indicated.

Examples.

a. $\sqrt[5]{-32}$ 　　　　　b. $\sqrt[3]{x^6y^3}$ 　　　　　　　　c. $\sqrt{x^2-2x+1}$

Solutions.

a. -2 　　　　　　　b. x^2y 　　　　　　　　　　c. $\sqrt{(x-1)^2}$
　　　　　　　　　　　　　　　　　　　　　　　　　　$|x-1|$

21. $\sqrt{144}$ 　　　　　22. $-\sqrt{169}$ 　　　　23. $\sqrt[3]{-27}$ 　　　　24. $-\sqrt[6]{64}$

25. $\sqrt{x^4y^2}$ 　　　　26. $\sqrt[3]{8y^6}$ 　　　27. $\sqrt{\frac{4}{9}x^6y^{10}}$ 　　28. $\sqrt[3]{\frac{-8x^3}{125}}$

29. $\sqrt{x^2+8x+16}$ 　　　　　　　　30. $\sqrt{4x^4-12x^2y^2+9y^4}$

Write in simplest form.

Examples.

a. $\sqrt{300}$ 　　　　　b. $\sqrt[3]{2x^7y^3}$ 　　　　　c. $\sqrt{2xy}\sqrt{8x}$

Solutions.

a. $\sqrt{100}\sqrt{3}$ 　　　b. $\sqrt[3]{x^6y^3}\sqrt[3]{2x}$ 　　　c. $\sqrt{16x^2}\sqrt{y}$
　　$10\sqrt{3}$ 　　　　　　$x^2y\sqrt[3]{2x}$ 　　　　　　$4x\sqrt{y}$

31. $\sqrt{4x^5}$ 　　　　　32. $\sqrt{16y^3}$ 　　　　33. $\sqrt[4]{3x^5y^5}$

34. $\sqrt[3]{-8x^6}$ 　　　　35. $\sqrt[4]{9}\sqrt[4]{27}$ 　　　36. $\sqrt[3]{a^4}\sqrt[3]{a^7}$

37. $\sqrt[3]{4x^2}\sqrt[3]{2xy^2}$ 　　38. $\sqrt[6]{486x^5y^3}\sqrt[6]{288x^2y^3}$

Rationalize the denominator of each of the following.

Examples.

a. $\sqrt{\dfrac{3x}{7y}}$ 　　　　b. $\sqrt[3]{\dfrac{2}{y}}$ 　　　　c. $\dfrac{\sqrt{6a}\sqrt{5a}}{\sqrt{15}}$

Solutions.

a. $\dfrac{\sqrt{3x}}{\sqrt{7y}}\cdot\dfrac{\sqrt{7y}}{\sqrt{7y}}$

$\dfrac{\sqrt{21xy}}{7y}$

b. $\dfrac{\sqrt[3]{2}\,\sqrt[3]{y^2}}{\sqrt[3]{y}\,\sqrt[3]{y^2}}$

$\dfrac{\sqrt[3]{2y^2}}{y}$

c. $\sqrt{\dfrac{15}{15}\cdot 2a^2}$

$a\sqrt{2}$

39. $\dfrac{\sqrt{6x}}{\sqrt{2xy}}$

40. $\dfrac{\sqrt{a^5b^3}}{\sqrt{ab}}$

41. $\dfrac{\sqrt[3]{2a^2b^3}}{\sqrt[3]{a^2b^2}}$

42. $\dfrac{\sqrt[3]{42x^3}}{\sqrt[3]{\frac{1}{6}x^2}}$

43. $\dfrac{\sqrt{x}\sqrt{xy^3}}{\sqrt{y}}$

44. $\dfrac{\sqrt{ab}\sqrt{ab^4}}{\sqrt{b}}$

45. $\dfrac{\sqrt[3]{ab}\sqrt[3]{b^2}}{\sqrt[3]{a}}$

46. $\dfrac{\sqrt[3]{4ab^2}\sqrt[3]{2a}}{\sqrt[3]{16a^5b^3}}$

Rationalize the numerator of each of the following.

47. $\dfrac{\sqrt{7}}{7}$

48. $\dfrac{\sqrt{6a^3}}{\sqrt{8a}}$

49. $\dfrac{\sqrt[3]{96xy^2}}{\sqrt[3]{12x^2y}}$

50. $\dfrac{\sqrt[6]{4x^{14}}}{\sqrt[6]{32x^2}}$

Reduce the order of each radical.

Examples.

a. $\sqrt[4]{5^2}$ b. $\sqrt[12]{81}$ c. $\sqrt[4]{x^2y^2}$

Solutions.

a. $\sqrt[4/2]{5^{2/2}}$

$\sqrt{5}$

b. $\sqrt[12/4]{3^{4/4}}$

$\sqrt[3]{3}$

c. $\sqrt[4/2]{x^{2/2}y^{2/2}}$

$\sqrt{xy}$

51. $\sqrt[6]{81}$ 52. $\sqrt[10]{32}$ 53. $\sqrt[4]{16x^2}$ 54. $\sqrt[9]{8a^3}$

55. $\sqrt[6]{8x^3}$ 56. $\sqrt[6]{125z^3}$ 57. $\sqrt[6]{x^2-2x+1}$

58. $\sqrt[12]{(x-2y)^4}$

Write each of the following using fractional exponents, and then as a radical in simplest form.

Examples.

a. $\sqrt{\sqrt{6}}$ b. $\sqrt{\sqrt[3]{128}}$ c. $\sqrt{\sqrt[3]{xy^2\sqrt[4]{xy^3}}}$

Solutions.

a. $(6^{1/2})^{1/2}$

$6^{1/4}$

$\sqrt[4]{6}$

b. $[(128)^{1/3}]^{1/2}$

$(2^7)^{1/6}$

$2\sqrt[6]{2}$

c. $([xy^2(xy^3)^{1/4}]^{1/3})^{1/2}$

$x^{1/6}y^{2/6}x^{1/24}y^{3/24}$

$x^{5/24}y^{11/24}$

$\sqrt[24]{x^5y^{11}}$

59. $\sqrt{\sqrt{8}}$

60. $\sqrt{4\sqrt{16}}$

61. $\sqrt[3]{2\sqrt{8a^4b^6}}$

62. $\sqrt[5]{9\sqrt{27x^3y}}$

63. $\sqrt[3]{2\sqrt{2\sqrt{2}}}$

64. $\sqrt{\sqrt[3]{ab^2\sqrt[4]{a^3b^2}}}$

Write each sum as a product.

Examples.

a. $4\sqrt{2} + 3\sqrt{2} - \sqrt{2}$

b. $2\sqrt{3} + 4\sqrt{12}$

Solutions.

a. $(4 + 3 - 1)\sqrt{2}$
  $6\sqrt{2}$

b. $2\sqrt{3} + 4\cdot2\sqrt{3}$
  $10\sqrt{3}$

65. $\sqrt{3} + 2\sqrt{3}$

66. $3\sqrt{5} - 6\sqrt{5}$

67. $\sqrt{8} - \sqrt{50} - \sqrt{2}$

68. $\sqrt{50} + 2\sqrt{32} - \sqrt{2}$

69. $3\sqrt[3]{16} - \sqrt[3]{2}$

70. $\sqrt[3]{54} + 2\sqrt[3]{128}$

Multiply factors and write all radicals in the result in simplest form.

Examples.

a. $\sqrt{x}(\sqrt{2x} - \sqrt{x})$

b. $(\sqrt{x} - 2\sqrt{y})(2\sqrt{x} + \sqrt{y})$

$2x - 4\sqrt{xy} + \sqrt{xy} - 2y$
$2x - 3\sqrt{xy} - 2y$

Solutions.

a. $x\sqrt{2} - x$

b. $2x - 2y - 3\sqrt{xy}$

71. $\sqrt{2}(3 + \sqrt{3})$

72. $\sqrt{6}(3 + \sqrt{6})$

73. $-\sqrt{21}(\sqrt{7} + 3\sqrt{3})$

74. $\sqrt{ab}(5\sqrt{a} - 7\sqrt{b})$

75. $(3 + \sqrt{5})(2 - \sqrt{5})$

76. $(5 - \sqrt{3})(5 + \sqrt{3})$

77. $(\sqrt{x} - 2\sqrt{3})(\sqrt{x} + \sqrt{3})$

78. $(2 - \sqrt[3]{4})(2 + \sqrt[3]{4})$

79. $(\sqrt{a} + \sqrt{a - b})(\sqrt{a} - \sqrt{a - b})$

80. $\left(\sqrt[3]{\dfrac{x}{3}} - \sqrt[3]{\dfrac{3}{x}}\right)^2$

Rationalize denominators.

Examples.

a. $\dfrac{3}{\sqrt{2} - 1}$

b. $\dfrac{1}{\sqrt{x} - \sqrt{y}}$

Solutions.

a. $\dfrac{3}{(\sqrt{2} - 1)}\dfrac{(\sqrt{2} + 1)}{(\sqrt{2} + 1)}$
  $\dfrac{3\sqrt{2} + 3}{2 - 1}$
  $3\sqrt{2} + 3$

b. $\dfrac{1}{(\sqrt{x} - \sqrt{y})}\dfrac{(\sqrt{x} + \sqrt{y})}{(\sqrt{x} + \sqrt{y})}$
  $\dfrac{\sqrt{x} + \sqrt{y}}{x - y}$

81. $\dfrac{-4}{1 + \sqrt{3}}$ 82. $\dfrac{1}{2 - \sqrt{2}}$ 83. $\dfrac{x}{\sqrt{x} - 3}$

84. $\dfrac{\sqrt{x}}{\sqrt{x} - \sqrt{y}}$ 85. $\dfrac{4\sqrt{2} - \sqrt{5}}{4\sqrt{2} + \sqrt{5}}$ 86. $\dfrac{4\sqrt{a} - \sqrt{3a + 1}}{\sqrt{a} + \sqrt{3a + 1}}$

Rationalize numerators.

87. $\dfrac{1 - \sqrt{2}}{2}$ 88. $\dfrac{1 - \sqrt{x + a}}{\sqrt{x + a}}$ 89. $\dfrac{\sqrt{x} + \sqrt{y}}{\sqrt{x} - \sqrt{y}}$

90. $\dfrac{\sqrt{x + y} - \sqrt{x - y}}{\sqrt{x + y} + \sqrt{x - y}}$

91. Find the value of $y^2 - 3y + 1$, for $y = 3 - \sqrt{2}$.

92. Find the value of $3x^2 - 4x - 2$, for $x = \dfrac{2 - \sqrt{10}}{3}$.

93. Prove Part I of Theorem 3.5.

94. Prove that $\dfrac{2}{\sqrt{3} + 1} = \sqrt{3} - 1$. That is, justify each step in your argument with the appropriate definition, postulate, or theorem.

95. Show that the set of numbers of the form $x + y\sqrt{2}$, where $x, y \in Q$, constitute a field.

96. Prove that if $0 < x < 1$, then $\sqrt{x} > x$.

97. Prove that if $x > 1$, then $\sqrt{x} < x$.

98. Prove that if $a, b > 0$, then $\sqrt{ab} \le \dfrac{a + b}{2}$.

Rationalize denominators.

99. $\dfrac{1}{\sqrt[3]{a} - \sqrt[3]{b}}$ *Hint:* Multiply numerator and denominator by $\sqrt[3]{a^2} + \sqrt[3]{ab} + \sqrt[3]{b^2}$.

100. $\dfrac{1}{\sqrt[3]{a^2} - \sqrt[3]{ab} + \sqrt[3]{b^2}}$

In the previous problems, the variables were restricted to represent positive numbers. In Problems 101–106, consider variable bases to be any element of the set of real numbers and simplify.

101. $\sqrt{4x^2}$ 102. $\sqrt{9x^2y^4}$ 103. $\sqrt{9(x^3 - x^2)}$

104. $\sqrt{18(x^6 - x^7)}$ 105. $\dfrac{2}{\sqrt{u^4 + u^2}}$ 106. $\sqrt{\dfrac{9}{4u^2 + 12u^4}}$

3.4 APPROXIMATIONS FOR IRRATIONAL NUMBERS

Any rational number can be expressed either as a terminating decimal numeral or as a periodic (repeating) decimal numeral. A periodic decimal numeral is one in which a group (one or more) of successive digits repeats endlessly, without intervening digits, in the numeral. For example, $0.33\overline{3}$, $5.\overline{285714}$, and $1.13\overline{63}\overline{6}$ are repeating decimal numerals, where the bar above a digit or group of digits indicates that this group repeats without end. These particular numerals correspond to $\frac{1}{3}$, $5\frac{2}{7}$, and $1\frac{3}{22}$, respectively.

To see why every quotient of two integers a/b ($b \neq 0$) can be expressed as a terminating decimal numeral or as a repeating decimal numeral, consider the quotient 5/22. If we wished to use the division algorithm to find a decimal numeral equivalent to 5/22, we would begin by writing

$$22 \overline{\smash{\big)}\ 5.0000\cdots},$$

where we envisage an unending procession of zeros in the numeral for the dividend. Now, the first step in the division process will be to determine the initial digit in the quotient, which is 2, and then subtract the product, 2×22, from the first two digits in $5.0000\cdots$. The remainder must be one of the nonnegative integers less than 22. If the remainder is 0, the decimal numeral for the quotient terminates. As it turns out, the difference is 6:

$$
\begin{array}{r}
.2 \\
22 \overline{\smash{\big)}\ 5.0000\cdots} \\
\underline{4\,4} \\
6
\end{array}
$$

The next step, then, is to determine the next digit in the numeral for the quotient. This is also 2, so we subtract 2×22 from 60, and obtain one of the nonnegative integers less than 22 for a difference. Again, if the difference is 0, the decimal numeral for the quotient terminates. If the difference is 6, as before, then we can expect this difference to recur endlessly, since each step hereafter is a repetition of the previous one. As it turns out, the difference is 16:

$$
\begin{array}{r}
.22 \\
22 \overline{\smash{\big)}\ 5.0000\cdots} \\
\underline{4\,4} \\
60 \\
\underline{44} \\
16
\end{array}
$$

This process is then repeated until one of the differences from the set of positive integers less than 22 repeats itself or 0 occurs. This must happen within 22 steps. Actually, we have

$$
\begin{array}{r}
.227 \\
22\overline{)\ 5.0000} \\
4\,4 \\
\hline
60 \\
44 \\
\hline
160 \\
154 \\
\hline
6
\end{array}
$$

and 6 has repeated itself as a remainder. It follows, then, that the block of digits 27 will recur indefinitely, and

$$\frac{5}{22} = 0.2\overline{27}.$$

A general argument can be made to show that this must always be the case for every quotient a/b, where $a,\, b \in J$ and $b \neq 0$. In Chapter 12, conversely, we shall show a general means of finding a common fraction equivalent to any repeating decimal numeral. What we have, then, is the following assertion:

THEOREM 3.6 *Every terminating and every repeating decimal numeral names a rational number, and, conversely, every rational number can be named either by a terminating or by a repeating decimal numeral.*

Since, by this theorem, every terminating or repeating decimal numeral names a rational number, it follows that, if irrational numbers have decimal representations, these decimal numerals must be nonterminating and non-repeating. Since we wish to be able to use numerals in a practical way, we find a rational number as close as need be to any given irrational number, and use this rational number as an approximation to the irrational number.

The completeness property of the real numbers assures us, for example, that the set of real numbers $L = \{x \mid x^2 \leq 3\}$ has a least upper bound, and that the set of real numbers $U = \{x \mid x > 0 \text{ and } x^2 \geq 3\}$ has a greatest lower bound, in each case, the number $\sqrt{3}$. Therefore, we can choose from either set any rational number we please as an approximation to $\sqrt{3}$. Naturally, the one we wish to use will depend on how close an approximation we wish. For example, $1.7 \in L$ because $(1.7)^2 = 2.89$, and $1.8 \in U$ because $(1.8)^2 = 3.24$. Thus we could use either of these as an approximation for

$\sqrt{3}$ with the assurance that $1.7 < \sqrt{3} < 1.8$.   Similarly, we could get the closer approximations

$$1.73 < \sqrt{3} < 1.74$$
$$1.732 < \sqrt{3} < 1.733$$
$$1.7320 < \sqrt{3} < 1.7321$$
$$1.73205 < \sqrt{3} < 1.73206$$

and so on, as far as we please, in each case "pinching" $\sqrt{3}$ between a rational number in L and a rational number in U.

These rational numbers can be obtained in various ways, but the most practical one for finding an approximation for $\sqrt[n]{a}$, where $a \in N$, is to use a table of roots such as that found in Table IV at the end of this text, if such a table is available.   Tables of greater accuracy, as well as tables for roots of greater index, are obtainable in other publications.

If suitable tables are not available, then an intelligent guess can be made and adjusted.   For example, to approximate $\sqrt[7]{2}$, we perhaps might guess 1.1. But a computation yields $(1.1)^7 = 1.94\cdots$.   Since this is just a bit too small, we next try 1.11, etc.

Approximations for other kinds of irrational numbers, such as π or values of trigonometric or logarithmic functions, for example, are also available in tables.

Given such a table, one can find decimal numerals for approximating sums, differences, products, and quotients involving irrational numbers, and the properties of radicals can be used to simplify the calculations involved.

Example.   Find a decimal numeral approximating $\dfrac{2 - \sqrt{3}}{5 - \sqrt{3}}$.

Solution.   To make the work less laborious, we first rationalize the denominator of this expression:

$$\frac{(2 - \sqrt{3})(5 + \sqrt{3})}{(5 - \sqrt{3})(5 + \sqrt{3})} = \frac{7 - 3\sqrt{3}}{22}.$$

From the table, $\sqrt{3} \approx 1.732$, so that

$$\frac{7 - 3\sqrt{3}}{22} \approx \frac{7 - 3(1.732)}{22} = \frac{7 - 5.196}{22} = \frac{1.804}{22} = 0.082.$$

The symbol $\approx$ is read "is approximately equal to."

EXERCISE 3.4

Find a terminating or repeating decimal equivalent to the given fraction.

1. $\dfrac{2}{7}$ 2. $\dfrac{209}{700}$ 3. $\dfrac{15}{16}$

4. $\dfrac{71}{32}$ 5. $\dfrac{3}{15}$ 6. $\dfrac{5}{14}$

Find a decimal numeral approximation for each of the following. Use Table IV at the end of this book.

7. $\sqrt{3} - \sqrt{27}$

8. $\sqrt{72} - 2\sqrt{2}$

9. $\dfrac{3\sqrt{17} - 1}{3}$

10. $\dfrac{27 - 3\sqrt{17}}{5}$

11. $\dfrac{\sqrt{7} - \sqrt{3}}{3\sqrt{7} + \sqrt{3}}$

12. $\dfrac{2\sqrt{5} - \sqrt{6}}{\sqrt{5} - \sqrt{6}}$

13. $\dfrac{\sqrt{7} - 2\sqrt{3}}{1 - \sqrt{3}}$

14. $\dfrac{\sqrt{31} - \sqrt{23}}{2\sqrt{7} + 1}$

15. Find a positive rational number in $\{x \mid x^2 \le 10\}$ that approximates $\sqrt{10}$ to within 1/1000. Similarly, find a positive rational number in $\{x \mid x^2 \ge 10\}$ that approximates $\sqrt{10}$ to within 1/1000. *Hint:* Modify tabular values in Table IV as necessary.

16. Find a positive rational number in $\{x \mid x^2 < 127\}$ which approximates $\sqrt{127}$ to within 1/1000. Similarly, find such a rational number in $\{x \mid x^2 > 127\}$.

17. A numeral for an irrational number between the rational number 1.41 and the irrational number $\sqrt{2}$ can be constructed by writing 1.413, which names a rational number in the desired interval, and then assigning additional digits in such fashion as to guarantee that no group ever repeats. For example, 1.413010010001$\cdots$, where an additional zero is used each time to separate the digits 1 in the rest of the numeral. Since 1.414 < $\sqrt{2}$, our number is less than $\sqrt{2}$. Find an irrational number in $\{x \mid 1.73 < x < \sqrt{3}\}$.

18. See Problem 17. Find an irrational number in $\{x \mid 5929 \le x^2 \le 6084\}$.

19. Argue that between every two rational numbers there are infinitely many irrational numbers. *Hint:* Devise a system for naming these numbers.

20. Argue that between any two irrational numbers there are infinitely many rational numbers. *Hint:* Devise a system for naming these numbers.

4

OPEN SENTENCES
IN ONE VARIABLE

Equations and inequalities that involve variables are called **open sentences.**
Equations and inequalities involving only constants are referred to as
statements. For example, $x + 2 = 7$, $x^2 - y \geq 4$, and $|x - 3| < 2$ are
open sentences, whereas $3 + 2 = 5$, $7 < 10 - 1$, and $|3 + 2| > 0$ are
statements. Although a statement can be adjudged true or false, no such
judgment is possible in the case of an open sentence, unless it is universally
true or false. Thus, $3 - 2 = 1$ is a true statement, and $3 - 2 = 2$ and
$x \neq x$ are false, but we cannot assert that $x - 2 = 1$ is either true or
false until we know something more about x. That is, the sentence is an
open one. Open sentences can be looked upon as set selectors. Given any
set of numbers, an equation such as $x - 2 = 1$ or an inequality such as
$x - 2 > 1$ will serve to select certain numbers from the universal set U and
reject others, depending on whether or not the numbers make the resulting
statement true or false.

In this chapter, we shall be concerned with open sentences (both equations
and inequalities) in one variable.

4.1 EQUIVALENT EQUATIONS—FIRST-DEGREE EQUATIONS

If we replace the variable in an open sentence in one variable with an
element from its replacement set U, and if the resulting statement is true, the
element is called a **solution** of the sentence, and is said to **satisfy** the sentence.
Thus, if $x \in J$, i.e., if J is the universe of discourse U, then 2 is a solution of
$x + 3 = 5$, because $2 + 3 = 5$ is a true statement. On the other hand, 3 is

not a solution of the sentence because $3 + 3 = 5$ is false. The subset of U consisting of all solutions of an open sentence is said to be the **solution set** of the sentence. In the example we have been using here, $x + 3 = 5$ and $x \in J$, the solution set is $\{2\}$.

Open sentences that have identical solution sets are called **equivalent equations** or **equivalent inequalities**, depending on the sentences under discussion. For example, if $x \in J$, the equations $x + 3 = -3$ and $x = -6$ are equivalent because the solution set of each is $\{-6\}$.

Equations can be transformed to equivalent equations by performing certain operations on both members of the given equation. These transformations are governed by the following.

THEOREM 4.1 *If $P(x)$, $Q(x)$, and $R(x)$ are expressions, then for all values of x for which $P(x)$, $Q(x)$, and $R(x)$ are real, the open sentence*

$$P(x) = Q(x)$$

is equivalent to each of the following:

I $P(x) + R(x) = Q(x) + R(x)$

II $P(x) \cdot R(x) = Q(x) \cdot R(x)$

III $\dfrac{P(x)}{R(x)} = \dfrac{Q(x)}{R(x)}$ $\left. \right\}$ for $x \in \{x \mid R(x) \neq 0\}$

We shall prove only Part I here, but the proofs of Parts II and III are similar and are left as exercises.

Proof of 4.1-I. Let r denote any solution of $P(x) = Q(x)$. By definition,

$$P(r) = Q(r).$$

Moreover, the theorem assumes that $P(r)$, $Q(r)$, and $R(r)$ are real numbers. Then, applying the addition axiom of equality, we have

$$P(r) + R(r) = Q(r) + R(r).$$

But this shows that r is a solution of

$$P(x) + R(x) = Q(x) + R(x).$$

Since each step in the argument is reversible, Part I of the theorem is proved.

Any application of any part of Theorem 4.1 is called an **elementary transformation**. An elementary transformation *always* produces an equivalent equation. Care must be exercised in the application of Parts II and III, however, for we have specifically excluded multiplication or division by zero. For example, to solve the equation

$$\frac{x}{x-3} = \frac{3}{x-3} + 2, \tag{1}$$

we might first multiply each member by $(x - 3)$ to find an equation that is free of fractions.   We have

$$(x - 3)\frac{x}{x - 3} = (x - 3)\frac{3}{x - 3} + (x - 3)2,$$

or

$$x = 3 + 2x - 6, \tag{2}$$

from which

$$x = 3.$$

Thus 3 is a solution of (2).   But, upon substituting 3 for x in (1), we have

$$\frac{3}{0} = \frac{3}{0} + 2$$

and neither member is defined.   In obtaining Equation (2), each member of Equation (1) was multiplied by $(x - 3)$; but if x is 3, then $(x - 3)$ is zero, and Theorem 4.1-II is not applicable.   Equation (2) is *not* equivalent to Equation (1) for $x = 3$, and in fact Equation (1) has no solution.

   We can always ascertain whether what we think is a solution of an equation is such in reality by substituting the suggested solution in the original equation and determining whether or not the resulting statement is true.   If each of the equations in a sequence is obtained by means of an elementary transformation, the sole purpose for such checking is to detect arithmetic errors. We shall dispense with checking solution sets in the examples that follow except in cases in which we apply what may be a nonelementary transformation—that is, in which we multiply or divide by an expression that vanishes for some value or values of the variable.

   The equation

$$ax + b = 0, \tag{3}$$

where a, $b \in R$ and $a \neq 0$, is a **first-degree** or **linear equation**.   Any equation that can be reduced to this form by elementary transformations, therefore, is equivalent to a first-degree equation.   We can show that such an equation always has one and only one solution.   First, we note that $-b/a$ is a solution of (3), since

$$a\left(\frac{-b}{a}\right) + b = 0.$$

Second, suppose that there are two solutions of (3), r_1 and r_2.   Then

$$ar_1 + b = 0$$

and

$$ar_2 + b = 0,$$

from which

$$ar_1 + b = ar_2 + b.$$

Adding $-b$ to each member, we get

$$ar_1 = ar_2,$$

and dividing each member by a,

$$r_1 = r_2.$$

That is, the solutions are the same number. Therefore, since a first-degree equation in one variable has one and only one solution, this solution constitutes the solution set.

An equation containing more than one variable, or containing symbols such as a, b, and c, representing constants, can often be solved for one of the symbols in terms of the remaining symbols by applying elementary transformations until the desired symbol is obtained by itself as one member of an equation.

Equations can be used to express quantitative relations in word problems symbolically. The problem may be explicitly, concerned with numbers, or it may be concerned with numerical measures of physical quantities. In either event, we seek the set of numbers (the solution set) for which the stated relationship holds. The equation may derive from the problem itself, which may state a relationship explicitly, or from formulas or relationships that are part of our general mathematical background. In the following set of exercises you will encounter word problems that lead to such linear equations.

EXERCISE 4.1

Consider the following equations.

a. $x - 3 = 0$

b. $x + 3 = 0$

c. $2x = 3$

d. $2x = -6$

e. $\dfrac{x}{2} = 3$

f. $\dfrac{x}{3} = -2$

1. Which of the equations have solutions in the set of natural numbers?

2. Which of the equations have solutions in the set of integers?

3. Which of the equations have solutions in the set of rational numbers?

4. Which of the equations have solutions in the set of real numbers?

Solve. Consider the set of real numbers as the replacement set of the variable.

5. $-3[x - (2x + 3) - 2x] = -9$

6. $4 - (x - 3)(x + 2) = 10 - x^2$

7. $6 + 3x - x^2 = 4 - (x - 2)(x + 3)$

8. $\dfrac{y}{2} + \dfrac{y}{3} - \dfrac{y}{4} = 7$

9. $\dfrac{2x - 1}{5} = \dfrac{x + 1}{2}$

10. $\dfrac{3}{5} = \dfrac{x}{x + 2}$

11. $\dfrac{2}{x-9} = \dfrac{9}{x+12}$

12. $\dfrac{x}{x-2} = \dfrac{2}{x-2} + 7$

13. $\dfrac{5}{x-3} = \dfrac{x+2}{x-3} + 3$

14. $\dfrac{2}{y+1} + \dfrac{1}{3y+3} = \dfrac{1}{6}$

15. $\dfrac{y}{y+2} - \dfrac{3}{y-2} = \dfrac{y^2+8}{y^2-4}$

16. $\dfrac{4}{2x-3} + \dfrac{4x}{4x^2-9} = \dfrac{1}{2x+3}$

Solve. Assume that all constants are real numbers and that the replacement set of all variables is R. Leave the results in the form of an equation equivalent to the given equation. State any restrictions on the constants and variables.

17. $3y - 3b = y - b$, for y

18. $2abx + 6a = abx$, for x

19. $cx = c - x$, for x

20. $a(a - x) = b(b - x)$, for x

21. $(x - 2)(a + 3) = a$, for x

22. $\dfrac{1}{x} + \dfrac{1}{a} = 6$, for x

23. $\dfrac{1}{a} + \dfrac{1}{b} = \dfrac{1}{x}$, for x

24. $\dfrac{a-2}{b} + \dfrac{3}{2b} = \dfrac{2}{x}$, for x

25. $v = k + gt$, for k

26. $v = k + gt$, for t

27. $A = \dfrac{h}{2}(b + c)$, for c

28. $S = \dfrac{a}{1-r}$, for r

29. $l = a + (n - 1)d$, for n

30. $\dfrac{1}{r} = \dfrac{1}{r_1} + \dfrac{1}{r_2}$, for r

31. $x^2y' - 3x - 2y^3y' = 1$, for y'

32. $2xy' - 3y' + x^2 = 0$, for y'

33. $x_1x_2 - 2x_1x_3 = x_4$, for x_1

34. $3x_1x_3 + x_1x_2 = x_4$, for x_1

35. $\dfrac{y - y_1}{x - x_1} = 6$, for y

36. $\dfrac{y - y_1}{x - x_1} = 2$, for x

37. For what value of k will the equation $2x - 3 = \dfrac{4 + x}{k}$ have as its solution set $\{-1\}$?

38. Find a value of k in $3x - 1 = k$ so that the equation is equivalent to $2x + 5 = 1$.

39. Prove Theorem 4.1-II.

40. Prove Theorem 4.1-III.

41. When each side of a square is increased by five inches, the area is increased by 85 square inches. Find the length of a side of the original square.

42. How much pure alcohol should be added to 12 ounces of a 45% solution to obtain a 60% solution?

43. A sum of $2000 is invested at simple interest, part at 3% and the remainder at 4%. Find the amount invested at each rate if the yearly income from the two investments is $66.

44. An airplane travels 1260 miles in the same time that an automobile travels 420 miles. If the rate of the airplane is 120 miles per hour greater than the rate of the automobile, find the rate of each.

45. Two cars start together and travel in the same direction, one going twice as fast as the other. At the end of three hours they are 96 miles apart. How fast is each traveling?

46. Clerk A can process 50 applications in four hours, and clerk B can process 50 applications in eight hours. How long will it take both clerks working together to process 100 applications?

4.2　SECOND-DEGREE EQUATIONS

The equation

$$ax^2 + bx + c = 0 \quad (a \neq 0)$$

is a **second-degree** or **quadratic equation**. Any equation that can be reduced to this form by elementary transformations is, therefore, equivalent to a quadratic equation. We shall designate the form shown above as the **standard form** for such equations. In this chapter we shall be interested only in finding real-number solutions ($x \in R$) for quadratic equations. The following theorem will prove useful to us in this regard.

THEOREM 4.2 *If $a, b \in R$, then $ab = 0$ if and only if $a = 0$ or $b = 0$ or both.*

This theorem is a consequence of Theorems 1.6 and 1.7.

Example. Find the solution set of $x^2 + 2x - 15 = 0$.

Solution. Since $x^2 + 2x - 15 = (x + 5)(x - 3)$, the equation

$$x^2 + 2x - 15 = 0$$

is equivalent to $(x + 5)(x - 3) = 0$, and since $(x + 5)(x - 3) = 0$ is true if and only if

$$x + 5 = 0 \quad \text{or} \quad x - 3 = 0,$$

we can see by inspection that the only values of x that satisfy the original equation are -5 and 3. Hence the solution set is $\{-5, 3\}$.

In general, the solution set of a quadratic equation *over the real numbers* may contain two, one, or no real numbers as elements. The equation in the foregoing example has two real solutions. Now, consider the equation

$$x^2 - 2x + 1 = 0.$$

Since $x^2 - 2x + 1 = 0$ is equivalent to

$$(x - 1)^2 = 0,$$

and since the only value of x for which $(x - 1)^2 = 0$ is 1, this is the only member of the solution set of $x^2 - 2x + 1 = 0$. For reasons of convenience, in Chapter 11 we shall wish to consider every quadratic equation to have two roots. Accordingly, we say that the solution of any quadratic equation having only one solution is of **multiplicity two**; that is, we shall count it twice as a solution.

Before exhibiting an example of a quadratic equation over the real numbers in the real variable x having an empty solution set, let us consider the special case of a quadratic equation, $x^2 - a = 0$, where $a > 0$. Since $x^2 - a = 0$ is equivalent to $x^2 = a$, and since $x^2 = a$ asserts that, by definition, x must be a square root of a, we have as the solution set for $x^2 - a = 0$, $\{\sqrt{a}, -\sqrt{a}\}$. It is now easy to exhibit a quadratic equation having no real solutions, for example, $x^2 + 1 = 0$. Since, as we saw in Chapter 2, there exists no number $x \in R$ such that its square is negative, the solution set for the given equation is $\emptyset$. Later, when we turn our attention to the set of complex numbers, you will see that every quadratic equation over this set has a nonempty solution set.

Quadratic equations of the form

$$(x - a)^2 = b,$$

where, for now, $b \geq 0$, can be solved by observing that $x - a$ must be one of the square roots of b. That is, if $(x - a)^2 = b$, then either

$$x - a = \sqrt{b} \quad \text{or} \quad x - a = -\sqrt{b},$$

and conversely. Thus it is evident that the solution set of $(x - a)^2 = b$ ($b \geq 0$) is $\{a + \sqrt{b}, a - \sqrt{b}\}$.

Being able to find solution sets for quadratic equations of the form $(x - a)^2 = b$ enables us to find the solution set of any quadratic equation. Let us first consider the general quadratic equation in standard form

$$ax^2 + bx + c = 0, \quad a \neq 0,$$

for the special case in which $a = 1$; that is,

$$x^2 + bx + c = 0. \tag{1}$$

If we can factor the left-hand member of (1), we can solve the equation by inspection; if not, we can write the equation in the equivalent form

$$(x - p)^2 = q,$$

which we can solve as above. We begin the latter process by adding $-c$ to each member of (1), which yields

$$x^2 + bx = -c. \tag{2}$$

If we then add $(b/2)^2$ to each member of (2), we obtain

$$x^2 + bx + \left(\frac{b}{2}\right)^2 = -c + \left(\frac{b}{2}\right)^2, \tag{3}$$

in which the left-hand member is equal to $(x + b/2)^2$, and we have

$$\left(x + \frac{b}{2}\right)^2 = -c + \frac{b^2}{4}. \tag{4}$$

Since we have performed only elementary transformations, (4) is equivalent to (2), and we can solve (4) by the method of the preceding section, provided

$$-c + \frac{b^2}{4} \geq 0.$$

The technique used to obtain equations (3) and (4) is called **completing the square**. We can determine the term necessary to complete the square in (2) by dividing the coefficient b of the first-degree term by the number 2 and squaring the result. The expression obtained, $x^2 + bx + (b/2)^2$, is called a **perfect square** and may be written in the form $(x + b/2)^2$.

Because the general quadratic equation

$$ax^2 + bx + c = 0 \quad (a \neq 0)$$

can be written equivalently in the form

$$x^2 + \frac{b}{a}x + \frac{c}{a} = 0,$$

the foregoing process can be applied to obtain the **quadratic formula**

$$x = \frac{-b \pm \sqrt{b^2 - 4ac}}{2a},$$

where the **solutions** or **roots** of the general quadratic equation are expressed in terms of the coefficients. The symbol "$\pm$" is used to condense the two equations

$$x = \frac{-b + \sqrt{b^2 - 4ac}}{2a} \quad \text{and} \quad x = \frac{-b - \sqrt{b^2 - 4ac}}{2a}$$

into a single equation. We need only substitute the coefficients a, b, and c of a given quadratic equation in the formula to find the solution set for the equation.

We now have the following methods available to solve quadratic equations:

1. Factoring when convenient.
2. Extraction of roots when the member containing the variable is a perfect square. We complete the square if necessary.
3. The quadratic formula, which is simply the end product of completing the square in the general case.

An examination of the quadratic formula

$$x = \frac{-b \pm \sqrt{b^2 - 4ac}}{2a}$$

suffices to show that if $ax^2 + bx + c = 0$ is to have a nonempty solution set in the set of real numbers, then $\sqrt{b^2 - 4ac}$ must be real. This, in turn, implies that only those quadratic equations for which $b^2 - 4ac \geq 0$ will have real solutions. The number represented by $b^2 - 4ac$ is called the **discriminant** of the quadratic equation $ax^2 + bx + c = 0$. It yields the following information about the solution set of the equation:

1. If $b^2 - 4ac = 0$, there is precisely one real solution.
2. If $b^2 - 4ac < 0$, there are no real solutions.
3. If $b^2 - 4ac > 0$, there are two real solutions.

If a, b, and c are rational numbers, then the discriminant gives the following additional information:

4. If $b^2 - 4ac \geq 0$ and if it is the square of a rational number, then any solutions are rational.
5. If $b^2 - 4ac > 0$ and if it is not the square of a rational number, then any solutions are irrational.

In some cases, the mathematical model we obtain for a physical situation is a quadratic equation that has two solutions. It may be that one but not both of the solutions to the equation fits the physical situation. For example, if we were asked to find two consecutive *natural numbers* of which the product is 72, we would write the equation

$$x(x + 1) = 72$$

as our model. Solving this equation, we have

$$x^2 + x - 72 = 0,$$

$$(x + 9)(x - 8) = 0,$$

with solution set $\{8, -9\}$. Since -9 is not a natural number, we must reject it as a possible answer to our original question; the solution 8, however, leads to the consecutive natural numbers 8 and 9. As additional examples, we observe that we would not accept -6 feet as the height of a man, or $27/4$ for the number of people in a room.

A quadratic equation used as a model for a physical situation may have two, one, or no meaningful solutions—meaningful, that is, in a physical sense. Answers to word problems should always be checked against the universal set of meaningful numbers for the original problem.

EXERCISE 4.2

Solve by factoring.

Example. $x^2 + x = 30$

Solution.   Write an equivalent equation in standard form, and factor the left member.

$$x^2 + x - 30 = 0$$
$$(x + 6)(x - 5) = 0$$

Determine solutions by inspection, or set each factor equal to zero and solve each linear equation.

$$x + 6 = 0; \quad x - 5 = 0$$
$$x = -6 \qquad x = 5$$

The solution set is $\{-6, 5\}$.

1. $x^2 + 2x = 0$

2. $x^2 - x = 5x$

3. $x^2 + 5x - 14 = 0$

4. $3x^2 - 6x = -3$

5. $x(2x - 3) = -1$

6. $(x - 2)(x + 1) = 4$

7. $3 = \dfrac{10}{x^2} - \dfrac{7}{x}$

8. $\dfrac{2}{x - 3} - \dfrac{6}{x - 8} = -1$

Solve for x by the extraction of roots.

Example. $(x + 3)^2 = 7$

Solution.   Set $x + 3$ equal to each square root of 7.

$$x + 3 = \sqrt{7}, \qquad x + 3 = -\sqrt{7};$$
$$x = -3 + \sqrt{7}, \quad x = -3 - \sqrt{7}.$$

The solution set is $\{-3 + \sqrt{7}, -3 - \sqrt{7}\}$.

9. $x^2 = 4$

10. $9x^2 - 100 = 0$

11. $x^2 = 5$

12. $(x - 1)^2 = 4$

13. $(x - 6)^2 = 5$

14. $(x - a)^2 = 4$

Solve by completing the square.

Example. $2x^2 + x - 1 = 0$

Solution.   Write an equivalent equation with the constant term as the right-hand member and the coefficient of x^2 equal to 1.

$$x^2 + \frac{1}{2}x = \frac{1}{2}$$

Add the square of one-half of the coefficient of the first-degree term to each member.

$$x^2 + \frac{1}{2}x + \frac{1}{16} = \frac{1}{2} + \frac{1}{16}$$

Rewrite the left-hand member as the square of an expression.

$$\left(x + \frac{1}{4}\right)^2 = \frac{9}{16}$$

Set $x + \frac{1}{4}$ equal to each square root of $\frac{9}{16}$.

$$x + \frac{1}{4} = \frac{3}{4}; \quad x + \frac{1}{4} = -\frac{3}{4}$$

$$x = \frac{1}{2} \qquad x = -1$$

The solution set is $\{\frac{1}{2}, -1\}$.

15. $x^2 + 4x - 12 = 0$ 16. $x^2 - 2x + 1 = 0$

17. $x^2 + 9x + 20 = 0$ 18. $x^2 - 2x - 1 = 0$

19. $2x^2 = 2 - 3x$ 20. $2x^2 + 4x = -1$

Reduce each of the following equations to equivalent equations of the form $(x - h)^2 + (y - k)^2 = r^2$ by completing the squares in x and y.

Example. $x^2 + y^2 - 4x + 6y = 5$

Solution.   Write an equivalent equation in the form

$$[x^2 - 4x + (\ \ )] + [y^2 + 6y + (\ \ )] = 5 + (\ \ ) + (\ \ ).$$

Complete the squares in x and y.

$$[x^2 - 4x + 4] + [y^2 + 6y + 9] = 5 + 4 + 9$$

$$(x - 2)^2 + (y + 3)^2 = 18 \quad \text{or} \quad (x - 2)^2 + [(y - (-3)]^2 = (\sqrt{18})^2$$

21. $x^2 + y^2 - 4x - 4y - 17 = 0$ 22. $x^2 + y^2 + 6x - 6y + 18 = 0$

23. $x^2 + y^2 + 6x - 2y + 6 = 0$ 24. $x^2 + y^2 - 2x + 4y + 2 = 0$

25. $4x^2 + 4y^2 - 4x + 8y = 11$

26. $16x^2 + 16y^2 - 8x + 16y - 59 = 0$

Solve for x, using the quadratic formula.

Example. $\dfrac{x^2}{4} + \dfrac{x}{4} = 3$

Solution.   Write an equivalent equation in standard form.

$$x^2 + x = 12$$

$$x^2 + x - 12 = 0$$

Substitute 1 for a, 1 for b, and -12 for c in the quadratic formula, and simplify.

$$x = \frac{-1 \pm \sqrt{1 + 48}}{2}$$

$$x = \frac{-1 \pm 7}{2}$$

The solution set is $\{3, -4\}$.

27. $x^2 - 3x + 2 = 0$

28. $x^2 + 4x + 4 = 0$

29. $2x^2 = 7x - 6$

30. $3x^2 = 5x - 1$

31. $\dfrac{x^2}{3} = \dfrac{1}{2}x + \dfrac{3}{2}$

32. $\dfrac{x^2 - 3}{2} + \dfrac{x}{4} = 1$

33. $x^2 - 2\sqrt{5}x + 5 = 0$

34. $x^2 + 2\sqrt{2}x + 2 = 0$

35. $2x^2 - \sqrt{3}x - 3 = 0$

36. $2x^2 + \sqrt{7}x - 7 = 0$

37. $x^2 - kx - 2k^2 = 0$

38. $2x^2 - kx + 3 = 0$

39. $ax^2 - x + c = 0$

40. $x^2 + 2x + c + 3 = 0$

41. Determine k so that the roots of $kx^2 + 4x + 1 = 0$ will be equal.   *Hint:* Use the discriminant.

42. Determine k so that the roots of $x^2 - kx + 9 = 0$ will be equal.

43. Determine k so that the roots of $x^2 + 2x + k + 3 = 0$ will be real.

44. Determine k so that the roots of $x^2 + 9x + k = 2$ will be real.

45. Determine k so that the roots of $x^2 - 2x + 1 = k$ will not be real numbers.

46. Show that an alternative form for the quadratic formula is

$$x = \frac{-2c}{b \pm \sqrt{b^2 - 4ac}},$$

provided the denominator is not 0.

Since r_1 and r_2 are solutions of the quadratic equation $(x - r_1)(x - r_2) = 0$, it follows that $(x - r_1)(x - r_2) = 0$, or $x^2 - (r_1 + r_2)x + r_1 r_2 = 0$, is a quadratic equation having solutions r_1 and r_2.   Given the solutions of a quadratic equation, write the equation in standard form with integral coefficients.

47. 3 and 2

48. $-\dfrac{1}{2}$ and 3

49. $-\dfrac{2}{3}$ and $\dfrac{1}{2}$

50. $\dfrac{2}{9}$ and $-\dfrac{2}{9}$

51. $\dfrac{-b + \sqrt{b^2 - 4ac}}{2a}$ and $\dfrac{-b - \sqrt{b^2 - 4ac}}{2a}$ $(a \neq 0)$

52. Are $x^2 = 3x$ and $x = 3$ equivalent? Why or why not?

53. If r_1 and r_2 are roots of the quadratic equation $ax^2 + bx + c = 0$, show that $r_1 + r_2 = -b/a$ and $r_1 r_2 = c/a$.

Using the formulas in Problem 53, find the sums and products of the roots in Problems 54–56.

54. $x^2 - 3x + 2 = 0$ 55. $2x^2 + 3x - 6 = 0$ 56. $x^2 + 2x - 3 = 0$

57. Find two consecutive natural numbers such that the sum of their squares is 85.

58. Two airplanes with lines of flight at right angles to each other pass each other (at slightly different altitudes) at noon. One is flying at 140 miles per hour and one at 180 miles per hour. How far apart are they at 12:30 PM?

59. A box without a top is to be made from a square piece of tin by cutting a two-inch square from each corner and folding up the sides. If the box is to hold 128 cubic inches, what should be the length of the side of the original square?

60. A ball thrown vertically upward reaches a height h in feet given by the equation $h = 32t - 8t^2$, where t is the time in seconds after the throw. How long will it take the ball to reach a height of 24 feet on its way up? How long after the throw will the ball return to the ground?

61. The distance s a body falls in a vacuum is given by $s = v_0 t + \frac{1}{2}gt^2$, where s is measured in feet, t is measured in seconds, v_0 is the initial velocity in feet per second, and g is the constant of acceleration due to gravity (approximately 32 ft/sec/sec). How long will it take a body to fall 150 feet if v_0 is 20 feet per second? If the body starts from rest?

62. A man sailed a boat across a lake and back in two and a half hours. If his rate returning was two miles per hour less than his rate going, and if the distance each way was six miles, find his rate each way.

63. A man and his son working together can paint their house in four days. The man can do the job alone in six days less than the son can do it. How long would it take each of them to paint the house alone? Hint: What part of the job could each of them do in one day?

64. A theatre that is rectangular in shape seats 720 people. The number of rows needed to seat the people would be four less if each row held six more seats. How many seats would then be in each row?

65. Two tanks, each cylindrical in shape and 10 feet in length, are to be replaced by a single tank of the same length. If the two original tanks have radii that measure six feet and eight feet, respectively, what must be the length of the radius of the single tank replacing them if it is to hold the same volume of liquid?

66. If $a, b, c \in J$, and if in addition, b is an even integer, show that, for the equation

$$ax^2 + bx + c = 0,$$

the quadratic formula can be written

$$x = \frac{-b' \pm \sqrt{(b')^2 - ac}}{a},$$

where $b' = \frac{1}{2}b$.   Use this latter formula to solve $3x^2 - 24x + 47 = 0$.

4.3   EQUATIONS INVOLVING RADICALS

In order to find solution sets for equations containing radical expressions, we shall need the following result.

THEOREM 4.3   *If $U(x)$ and $V(x)$ are expressions in x, then the solution set of $U(x) = V(x)$ is a subset of the solution set of $[U(x)]^n = [V(x)]^n$, for each natural number n.*

This theorem, which simply asserts that products of equal numbers are equal numbers, permits us to raise both members of an equation to the same natural-number power with the assurance that we do not lose any solutions of the original equation in the process.   On the other hand, it does not assert that the resulting equation will be equivalent to the original equation, and indeed ordinarily it will not be.   The equation $[U(x)]^n = [V(x)]^n$ usually has additional solutions (called **extraneous solutions**) that are not solutions of $U(x) = V(x)$.   Thus, if $a = b$, then $a^4 = b^4$, but the converse does not necessarily hold.   That is, a^4 and b^4 may be equal, but $a \neq b$.   For example, $(3)^4 = (-3)^4$, but $3 \neq -3$.   The solution set of the equation $x^4 = 81$, obtained from $x = 3$ by raising each member to the fourth power, contains -3 as an extraneous solution, since -3 does not satisfy the original equation. Because the result of applying the foregoing process is not an equivalent equation, each solution obtained through its use *must* be substituted for the variable in the original equation to check its validity.   An application of this theorem is not an elementary transformation.

Example.   Find the solution set of $\sqrt[3]{x - 1} = -1$.

Solution.   If we raise each member of $\sqrt[3]{x - 1} = -1$ to the third power, we obtain

$$(\sqrt[3]{x - 1})^3 = (-1)^3,$$

$$x - 1 = -1,$$

which is equivalent to

$$x = 0.$$

Since $\sqrt[3]{0-1} = -1$, 0 is a solution of the original equation. Moreover it is the only real solution, since Theorem 4.3 guarantees that the solution set of $\sqrt[3]{x-1} = -1$ is a subset of the solution set of $x = 0$.

Example. Find the solution set of $\sqrt{x+2} + 4 = x$.

Solution. We first write the equivalent equation

$$\sqrt{x+2} = x - 4,$$

and then apply Theorem 3.3. We obtain

$$(\sqrt{x+2})^2 = (x-4)^2,$$

or

$$x + 2 = x^2 - 8x + 16.$$

This last equation is equivalent to

$$x^2 - 9x + 14 = 0,$$

or

$$(x-2)(x-7) = 0,$$

which clearly has solutions 2 and 7. Upon replacing x with 2 in the original equation, however, we obtain

$$\sqrt{2+2} + 4 = 2,$$

or

$$6 = 2,$$

which is false. Hence, 2 is not a solution of the original equation; it is an extraneous root. On the other hand, 7 does satisfy the original equation, so the solution set we seek is $\{7\}$.

It is sometimes necessary to apply Theorem 4.3 more than once in solving certain equations.

Example. Find the solution set of $\sqrt{x+4} + \sqrt{9-x} = 5$.

Solution. It is helpful if this equation is first transformed so that each member of the equivalent equation contains one of the radical expressions. Thus, by adding $-\sqrt{9-x}$ to each member, we obtain

$$\sqrt{x+4} = 5 - \sqrt{9-x}.$$

An application of Theorem 4.3 leads to

$$(\sqrt{x+4})^2 = (5 - \sqrt{9-x})^2,$$
$$x + 4 = 25 - 10\sqrt{9-x} + 9 - x,$$
$$2x - 30 = -10\sqrt{9-x},$$
$$x - 15 = -5\sqrt{9-x}.$$

Now, let us again apply Theorem 4.3 to obtain

$$(x - 15)^2 = (-5\sqrt{9 - x})^2,$$

$$x^2 - 30x + 225 = 25(9 - x),$$

$$x^2 - 5x = 0,$$

$$x(x - 5) = 0.$$

It is clear that this last equation has 0 and 5 as solutions. Since both of these satisfy the original equation, the solution set we seek is $\{0, 5\}$.

EXERCISE 4.3

Solve and check.   If there is no solution, so state.

1. $\sqrt{x} = 8$

2. $\sqrt{y + 8} = 1$

3. $\sqrt[3]{2 - y} = 3$

4. $\sqrt[5]{7 - x} = 2$

5. $2x - 3 = \sqrt{7x - 3}$

6. $\sqrt{x + 3}\,\sqrt{x - 9} = 8$

7. $\sqrt{y + 4} = \sqrt{y + 20} - 2$

8. $\sqrt{x} + \sqrt{2} = \sqrt{x + 2}$

9. $\sqrt{5 + \sqrt{x}} = \sqrt{x} - 1$

10. $\sqrt{13 + \sqrt{x}} = \sqrt{x} + 1$

11. $(5 + x)^{1/2} + x^{1/2} = 5$

12. $(y + 7)^{1/2} + (y + 4)^{1/2} = 3$

13. $(y^2 - 3y + 5)^{1/2} - (y + 2)^{1/2} = 0$

14. $(z - 3)^{1/2} + (z + 5)^{1/2} = 4$

Solve.   Leave the results in the form of an equation.

15. $r = \sqrt{\dfrac{A}{\pi}}$, for A

16. $t = \sqrt{\dfrac{2v}{g}}$, for g

17. $x\sqrt{xy} = 1$, for y

18. $P = \pi\sqrt{\dfrac{e}{g}}$, for g

19. $x = \sqrt{a^2 - y^2}$, for y

20. $y = \dfrac{1}{\sqrt{1 - x}}$, for x

4.4 SUBSTITUTION IN THE SOLUTION OF EQUATIONS

Some equations that are not polynomial equations are nevertheless polynomial in form.   For example, though $y + 2\sqrt{y} - 8 = 0$ is not a polynomial equation, if the variable p is substituted for the radical expression $\sqrt{y}$, we have $p^2 + 2p - 8 = 0$, which is a polynomial equation in p.

Example. Find the solution set of $y + 2\sqrt{y} - 8 = 0$.

Solution. Set $p = \sqrt{y}$ and substitute in the given equation. We have

$$p^2 + 2p - 8 = 0,$$
$$(p + 4)(p - 2) = 0,$$

which has -4 and 2 as solutions. Since $-4 < 0$, we must reject it as a source for solutions because $p = \sqrt{y}$, and $\sqrt{y}$ is always nonnegative. The other value, $p = 2$, leads to $\sqrt{y} = 2$ and hence $y = 4$. The solution set we seek is $\{4\}$.

The technique of substituting one variable for another— or, more generally, a variable for an expression—is not limited to cases involving radicals, but is useful in any situation in which an equation is polynomial in form.

Example. Find the solution set of $\left(x + \dfrac{1}{x}\right)^{-2} + 6\left(x + \dfrac{1}{x}\right)^{-1} + 8 = 0$.

Solution. Setting $p = \left(x + \dfrac{1}{x}\right)^{-1}$ and substituting, we obtain

$$p^2 + 6p + 8 = 0,$$

from which it follows that

$$(p + 2)(p + 4) = 0,$$

with solution set $\{-2, -4\}$. Since $p = \left(x + \dfrac{1}{x}\right)^{-1}$, we have

$$\left(x + \dfrac{1}{x}\right)^{-1} = -2 \quad \text{or} \quad \left(x + \dfrac{1}{x}\right)^{-1} = -4.$$

Solving the first of these equations for x, we get

$$\left(x + \dfrac{1}{x}\right)^{-1} = -2,$$

$$x + \dfrac{1}{x} = -\dfrac{1}{2},$$

$$2x^2 + 2 = -x,$$

or

$$2x^2 + x + 2 = 0.$$

Since the discriminant of this equation is negative, it has no real solutions. A similar treatment of

$$\left(x + \dfrac{1}{x}\right)^{-1} = -4$$

leads to

$$4x^2 + x + 4 = 0,$$

which also has no real solutions. The solution set of the original equation, therefore, is $\emptyset$.

EXERCISE 4.4

Solve for x, y, or z.

Example. $x^4 - 10x^2 + 9 = 0$.

Solution.   Set $p = x^2$ and solve for p.

$$p^2 - 10p + 9 = 0$$
$$(p - 9)(p - 1) = 0$$
$$p = 9, p = 1$$

Set each value of $p = x^2$ and solve for x.

$$x^2 = 9, x^2 = 1$$

The solution set is $\{3, -3, 1, -1\}$.

1. $x - 2\sqrt{x} - 15 = 0$ 2. $x^4 - 5x^2 + 4 = 0$

3. $2x^4 + 17x^2 - 9 = 0$ 4. $z^4 - 2z^2 - 24 = 0$

5. $(y^2 + 5y)^2 - 8y(y + 5) - 84 = 0$ 6. $y^2 - 5 - 5\sqrt{y^2 - 5} + 6 = 0$

7. $y^{2/3} - 2y^{1/3} - 8 = 0$ 8. $z^{2/3} - 2z^{1/3} = 35$

9. $y^{-2} - y^{-1} - 12 = 0$ 10. $z^{-2} + 9z^{-1} - 10 = 0$

11. $(x - 1)^{1/2} - 2(x - 1)^{1/4} - 15 = 0$ 12. $8x^{-6} + 7x^{-3} - 1 = 0$

13. $\left(x + \dfrac{4}{x}\right)^2 + \left(x + \dfrac{4}{x}\right) = 20$ 14. $\left(\dfrac{y + 2}{y - 1}\right)^2 - 5\left(\dfrac{y + 2}{y - 1}\right) = -6$

15. $(y^4 - 4y^3 + 4y^2) - 23(y^2 - 2y) + 120 = 0$

16. $(4x^4 - 12x^3 + 9x^2) - 3(2x^2 - 3x) + 2 = 0$

17. $\dfrac{9y^2}{(y + 2)^2} - \dfrac{9y}{y + 2} + 2 = 0$ 18. $\dfrac{y + 1}{2y^2} + \dfrac{36y^2}{y + 1} - 9 = 0$

4.5 SOLUTION OF INEQUALITIES

Open sentences such as

$$x + 3 \geq 10, \tag{1}$$

$$\frac{-2y - 3}{3} < 5, \tag{2}$$

are called **inequalities**. For appropriate values of the variable, one member of an inequality represents a real number that is less than ($<$), less than or equal to ($\leq$), greater than or equal to ($\geq$), or greater than ($>$) the real number represented by the other member.

Any element of the replacement set of the variable for which an inequality is valid is called a **solution**, and the set of all solutions of an inequality is called the **solution set** of the inequality. Inequalities that are true for every element in the replacement set of the variable—such as $x^2 + 1 > 0$, $x \in R$— are called **absolute** or **unconditional inequalities**. Inequalities that are not true for every element of the replacement set are called **conditional inequalities** —for example, (1) and (2) above.

As in the case with equations, we shall solve a given inequality by generating a series of equivalent inequalities (inequalities having the same solution set) until we arrive at one of which the solution set is obvious. To do this we shall need the following theorem applicable to inequalities.

THEOREM 4.4 *If $P(x)$, $Q(x)$, and $R(x)$ are expressions, then for all values of x for which $P(x)$, $Q(x)$, and $R(x)$ are real, the open sentence*

$$P(x) < Q(x)$$

is equivalent to each of the following:

   I $P(x) + R(x) < Q(x) + R(x)$,

  II $P(x) \cdot R(x) < Q(x) \cdot R(x)$

 III $\dfrac{P(x)}{R(x)} < \dfrac{Q(x)}{R(x)}$ *for* $x \in \{x \mid R(x) > 0\}$,

 IV $P(x) \cdot R(x) > Q(x) \cdot R(x)$

  V $\dfrac{P(x)}{R(x)} > \dfrac{Q(x)}{R(x)}$ *for* $x \in \{x \mid R(x) < 0\}$.

Similarly, the open sentence

$$P(x) \le Q(x)$$

is equivalent to open sentences of the form I–V, *with* $<$ *(or* $>$ *) replaced by* $\le$ *(or* $\ge$ *) under the same conditions,* $R(x) > 0$ *and* $R(x) < 0$, *on* $R(x)$ *as above.*

We shall restrict our attention to a proof of IV here.

Proof of IV.   Let r denote any solution of $P(x) < Q(x)$, for which $R(r) < 0$. Then, by definition,

$$P(r) < Q(r)$$

is true for the real numbers $P(r)$ and $Q(r)$. Since $R(r)$ is a negative real number, then Theorem 1.15-IV asserts that

$$P(r) \cdot R(r) > Q(r) \cdot R(r).$$

This shows that r is a solution of $P(x)\cdot R(x) > Q(x)\cdot R(x)$. Conversely, if r is any such solution, for which $R(r) < 0$, then Theorem 1.15-IV asserts that

$$\frac{1}{R(r)}\cdot P(r)\cdot R(r) < \frac{1}{R(r)}\cdot Q(r)\cdot R(r),$$

from which we have

$$P(r) < Q(r).$$

This asserts that r is a solution of $P(x) < Q(x)$. Thus since any solution of $P(x) < Q(x)$ is a solution of $P(x)\cdot R(x) > Q(x)\cdot R(x)$ provided $R(x) < 0$, and conversely, these sentences are equivalent. The proofs of the other parts of the theorem are left as exercises.

The theorem above can be interpreted as follows:

I. The addition or subtraction of the same expression to or from each member of an inequality produces an equivalent inequality in the same sense.

II and III. If each member of an inequality is multiplied or divided by the same positive number, the result is an equivalent inequality in the same sense.

IV and V. If each member of an inequality is multiplied or divided by the same negative number, the result is an equivalent inequality in the opposite sense.

Note that Theorem 4.4 does not permit multiplying or dividing by zero, and variables in multipliers and divisors are restricted from values for which the expression vanishes. The result of applying any part of this theorem is an elementary transformation.

Theorem 4.4 can be applied to solve inequalities in the same way that the theorems of equality are applied to solve equations. As an example, let us find the solution set of

$$\frac{x-3}{4} < \frac{2}{3}, \quad x \in R.$$

Multiplying each member by 12 gives

$$3(x - 3) < 8,$$

or

$$3x - 9 < 8.$$

Adding 9 to each member gives

$$3x < 17;$$

finally, dividing each member by 3, we obtain

$$x < \frac{17}{3},$$

and the solution set is

$$S = \left\{ x \mid x < \frac{17}{3} \right\}.$$

This set can be graphed on a line graph as shown in Figure 4.1, where the

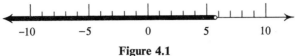

Figure 4.1

heavy line indicates points with coordinates in the solution set.
 Inequalities sometimes appear in a form such as

$$-6 < 3x \leq 15, \tag{3}$$

where an expression is bracketed between two inequality symbols. This
means $-6 < 3x$ and $3x \leq 15$. The solution set of such an inequality
is obtained in the same manner as the solution set of any other inequality.
In (3) above, each expression may be divided by 3 to obtain

$$-2 < x \leq 5.$$

The solution set,

$$S = \{x \mid -2 < x \leq 5\},$$

is illustrated on a line graph in Figure 4.2. Note here that the open circle
at the left-hand end point of the interval indicates that -2 *is not* a member
of the solution set, whereas the solid circle at the other end indicates that 5 *is*
a member of the solution set.

Figure 4.2

 Quadratic inequalities offer somewhat different problems. For example,
consider the inequality

$$x^2 + 4x < 5, \quad x \in R.$$

To determine values of x for which this condition holds, we might first
rewrite the sentence equivalently as

$$x^2 + 4x - 5 < 0,$$

and then as

$$(x + 5)(x - 1) < 0.$$

It is clear here that those values and only those values of x for which the factors $x + 5$ and $x - 1$ are opposite in sign will be in the solution set, which can be determined analytically by finding the values of x such that

$$x + 5 < 0 \quad \text{and} \quad x - 1 > 0$$

or else

$$x + 5 > 0 \quad \text{and} \quad x - 1 < 0.$$

Each of these two cases can be considered separately.

First, $x + 5 < 0$ and $x - 1 > 0$ imply $x < -5$ and $x > 1$, conditions which are not satisfied by any values of x. But $x + 5 > 0$ and $x - 1 < 0$ imply $x > -5$ and $x < 1$, which lead to the solution set

$$S = \{x \mid -5 < x < 1\}.$$

An alternative set notation for this solution set is

$$S = \{x \mid x > -5\} \cap \{x \mid x < 1\}.$$

The symbolism $\{x \mid -5 < x < 1\}$ simply describes the portions of the two sets that overlap.

One relatively easy way to visualize the solution set of a quadratic inequality is to indicate on a number line the signs associated with each factor for number replacements for the variable. Figure 4.3 shows such an arrange-

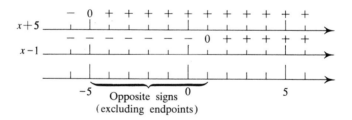

Figure 4.3

ment, or **sign graph**, for the example above. This picture is constructed by first showing on the number line the places where $x + 5$ is positive ($x > -5$) and the places where it is negative ($x < -5$), and then showing on a second line those places where $x - 1$ is positive ($x > 1$) and those where it is negative ($x < 1$). The third line can then be marked by observing those parts of the first two lines where the signs are alike and those parts where the signs are opposite. Since it is desired that the product $(x + 5)(x - 1)$ be negative, the third line shows clearly that this occurs where $-5 < x < 1$, so that the solution set of the inequality is $\{x \mid -5 < x < 1\}$. This solution set can be graphed as in Figure 4.4.

Figure 4.4

Inequalities involving fractions have to be approached with care if any fraction contains a variable in the denominator. If Theorem 4.4 is invoked to multiply each member by an expression containing the variable, we have to be careful either to distinguish between those values of the variable for which the expression denotes a positive and negative number, respectively, or else make sure that the expression by which we multiply is always positive.

Example. Find the solution set of $\dfrac{x}{x-2} \geq 5$.

Solution 1. First we note that $x = 2$ is not a solution. Next, applying Theorem 4.4-II and -IV, we multiply each member of

$$\frac{x}{x-2} \geq 5$$

by $x - 2$, observing, as we do, that two cases arise for $x \neq 2$. First, we obtain

$$x \geq 5(x - 2) \quad \text{for} \quad x - 2 > 0$$

and, second,

$$x \leq 5(x - 2) \quad \text{for} \quad x - 2 < 0.$$

Let us look at the first case, in which $x - 2 > 0$, or, equivalently, $x > 2$. We have

$$x \geq 5(x - 2),$$
$$x \geq 5x - 10,$$
$$10 \geq 4x,$$
$$\frac{5}{2} \geq x,$$

which shows that $x \leq 5/2$ will satisfy the inequality as long as $x > 2$. In terms of sets, this means that $\{x \mid x \leq 5/2\} \cap \{x \mid x > 2\}$ is in the solution set of the inequality. Another expression describing this intersection is $\{x \mid 2 < x \leq 5/2\}$. Now, examining the case $x - 2 < 0$, or equivalently, $x < 2$, we have

$$x \leq 5(x - 2),$$
$$x \leq 5x - 10,$$
$$10 \leq 4x,$$
$$\frac{5}{2} \leq x.$$

But x cannot be greater than or equal to 5/2 and at the same time less than 2, so that this case contributes nothing to the solution set. That is, $\{x \mid x \geq 5/2\} \cap \{x \mid x < 2\} = \emptyset$. This means that the entire solution set of the inequality is the above set, $\{x \mid 2 < x \leq 5/2\}$. What we have accomplished here is to determine that the solution set is given by

$$\left[\left\{x \mid x \leq \frac{5}{2}\right\} \cap \{x \mid x > 2\}\right] \cup \left[\left\{x \mid x \geq \frac{5}{2}\right\} \cap \{x \mid x < 2\}\right],$$

which we express more simply as

$$\left\{x \mid 2 < x \leq \frac{5}{2}\right\} \cup \emptyset, \quad \text{or} \quad \left\{x \mid 2 < x \leq \frac{5}{2}\right\}.$$

Solution 2. The necessity of considering separate cases for $x - 2 > 0$ and $x - 2 < 0$ can be avoided if the given equation is cleared of fractions by multiplying each member by $(x - 2)^2$, which is positive for $x \neq 2$. Doing this, we have

$$(x - 2)^2 \frac{x}{(x - 2)} \geq (x - 2)^2 \cdot 5,$$

$$x^2 - 2x \geq 5x^2 - 20x + 20,$$

$$0 \geq 4x^2 - 18x + 20,$$

$$0 \geq 2x^2 - 9x + 10,$$

$$0 \geq (2x - 5)(x - 2).$$

This latter inequality can then be solved either by sign graph or by noting that for $(2x - 5)(x - 2)$ to be nonpositive, either

$$(2x - 5) \geq 0 \quad \text{and} \quad (x - 2) < 0$$

or

$$(2x - 5) \leq 0 \quad \text{and} \quad (x - 2) > 0$$

must hold. The first of these implies that

$$x \geq \frac{5}{2} \quad \text{and} \quad x < 2,$$

which has no solution, while the second implies that

$$x \leq \frac{5}{2} \quad \text{and} \quad x > 2,$$

which leads to the solution set $\{x \mid 2 < x \leq 5/2\}$.

Solution 3. Let us approach this directly by means of a sign graph. We can rewrite the given inequality equivalently as

$$\frac{x}{x - 2} - 5 \geq 0,$$

from which we obtain

$$\frac{-4x + 10}{x - 2} \geq 0.$$

For this to be valid, $x - 2$ must not be 0, and the numerator and denominator must be of like sign.   Figure 4.5 shows that the quotient $(-4x + 10)/(x - 2)$ is

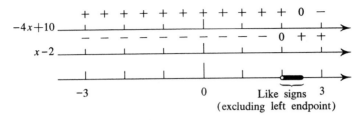

Figure 4.5

positive or zero for x between 2 and 5/2, including 5/2 but excluding 2, a value of x for which the denominator is 0.   The desired solution set is therefore $\{x \mid 2 < x \le 5/2\}$.

EXERCISE 4.5

Solve and represent the solution set on a line graph.

1. $x + 7 > 8$ 2. $x - 5 \le 7$ 3. $3x - 2 > 1 + 2x$

4. $2x + 3 \le x - 1$ 5. $\dfrac{2x - 3}{2} \le 5$ 6. $\dfrac{3x + 4}{3} > 12$

Graph each of the following sets and rewrite in simpler set notation.

Example. $\{x \mid x + 2 \ge 0\} \cap \{x \mid x - 3 < 1\}$

Solution.   Solve each inequality and graph.   Indicate the region where the graphs overlap.

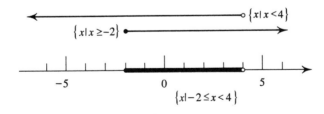

7. $\{x \mid x - 2 < 3\} \cap \{x \mid x + 4 > 2\}$

8. $\left\{ x \left| \dfrac{1 + x}{2} \le 3 \right.\right\} \cap \{x \mid x \le 6\}$

9. $\{x \mid 2x - 1 > 5\} \cap \left\{ x \left| \dfrac{x - 1}{3} \ge 4 \right.\right\}$

10. $\{x \mid 4 - x < 2\} \cap \left\{x \mid \dfrac{2x + 5}{2} < 0\right\}$

11. $\left\{x \mid \dfrac{3 - x}{4} < -2\right\} \cap \left\{x \mid \dfrac{2 + 3x}{3} \leq 1\right\}$

12. $\left\{x \mid \dfrac{2 - 3x}{3} < 0\right\} \cap \left\{x \mid \dfrac{3 - x}{4} > 0\right\}$

Solve and represent the solution set on a line graph.

13. $(x + 1)(x - 2) > 0$ 14. $(x + 2)(x + 5) < 0$

15. $x(x - 2) \leq 0$ 16. $x(x + 3) \geq 0$

17. $x^2 - 3x - 4 > 0$ 18. $x^2 - 5x - 6 \geq 0$

19. $x^2 < 5$ 20. $4x^2 + 1 < 0$

21. $x^2 > -5$ 22. $x^2 + 1 > 0$

23. $\dfrac{2}{x} \leq 4$ 24. $\dfrac{3}{x - 6} > 8$

25. $\dfrac{x}{x + 2} > 4$ 26. $\dfrac{x + 2}{x - 2} \geq 6$

27. $\dfrac{2}{x - 2} \geq \dfrac{4}{x}$ 28. $\dfrac{3}{4x + 1} > \dfrac{2}{x - 5}$

29. $x(x - 2)(x + 3) > 0$ 30. $x^3 - 4x \leq 0$

31. Show that if $a, b \in R$ and $a, b > 0$, then $(a + b)^2 > a^2 + b^2$.

32. Show that if $x, y \in R$ and $x + y = 6$, then $xy \leq 9$.

33. Show that if $a, b \in R$ and $a > b$ and $c > 0$, then $a/c > b/c$.

34. Show that if $a, b \in R$ and $a > b > 0$, then $1/a < 1/b$.

35. Show that for $x \in R$, $x^2 + 1 \geq 2x$.

36. Show that the sum of any positive number and its reciprocal is greater than or equal to 2.

37. Prove Theorem 4.4-I.

38. Prove Theorem 4.4-II.

4.6   OPEN SENTENCES INVOLVING ABSOLUTE-VALUE NOTATION

In Section 1.6, we defined the absolute value of a real number by

$$|x| = \begin{cases} x, & \text{if } x \geq 0, \\ -x, & \text{if } x < 0, \end{cases}$$

and interpreted it in terms of distance on a number line. For example, $|-5| = 5$ by definition, but 5 also denotes the distance the graph of -5 is

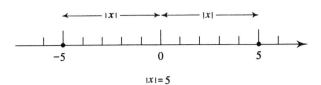

$|x| = 5$

Figure 4.6

located from the origin (Figure 4.6). More generally, then, the expression $|x - a|$ satisfies

$$|x - a| = \begin{cases} x - a, & \text{if } (x - a) \geq 0, \text{ or equivalently, if } x \geq a, \\ -(x - a), & \text{if } (x - a) < 0, \text{ or equivalently, if } x < a, \end{cases}$$

and can be interpreted on a line graph as denoting the distance the graph of x is located from the graph of a (Figure 4.7).

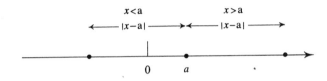

Figure 4.7

Since

$$\sqrt{x^2} = \begin{cases} x, & \text{if } x \geq 0, \\ -x, & \text{if } x < 0, \end{cases}$$

we can assert that $|x| = \sqrt{x^2}$, and, by a similar argument, that

$$|x - a| = \sqrt{(x - a)^2}.$$

Since $(x - a)^2 = (a - x)^2$, it follows that $|x - a| = |a - x|$.

All the foregoing facts can be used effectively in finding solution sets for equations involving absolute value.

Example. Find the solution set of $|x - 3| = 5$.

Solution 1. This can be solved by inspection. Since $(x - 3)$ represents the distance the graph of x is located from the graph of 3, and since by the equation this distance is 5, the two solutions of the equation are $3 + 5$, or 8, and $3 - 5$, or -2. Thus, the solution set is $\{-2, 8\}$.

Solution 2. By definition, $|x - 3| = 5$ implies that

$$(x - 3) = 5, \quad \text{when} \quad (x - 3) \geq 0,$$

and

$$-(x - 3) = 5, \quad \text{when} \quad (x - 3) < 0.$$

Solving each of these equations separately, we obtain the solution set $\{-2, 8\}$.

Solution 3.   Since $|x - 3| = \sqrt{(x - 3)^2}$, we can write the equation as

$$\sqrt{(x - 3)^2} = 5.$$

Then

$$(x - 3)^2 = 25,$$
$$x^2 - 6x + 9 = 25,$$
$$x^2 - 6x - 16 = 0,$$
$$(x - 8)(x + 2) = 0,$$

and again we are led to the solution set $\{-2, 8\}$.

The choice of approach depends on the situation, and is largely a matter of which is most convenient.

Inequalities involving absolute-value notation require some additional discussion.   For example, consider the inequality

$$|x + 1| < 3. \tag{1}$$

From the definition of absolute value, this inequality is equivalent to

$$x + 1 < 3 \text{ for } x + 1 \geq 0,$$

and to

$$-(x + 1) < 3 \text{ for } x + 1 < 0.$$

By Theorem 4.4-IV,

$$-(x + 1) < 3$$

is equivalent to

$$x + 1 > -3,$$

and (1) can be written in the compact form

$$-3 < x + 1 < 3. \tag{2}$$

Any expression of the form (1) should be written in the form (2) before elementary transformations to find the solution set are undertaken.   Adding -1 to each expression in (2), we have

$$-4 < x < 2,$$

from which the solution set is

$$S = \{x \mid -4 < x < 2\}.$$

The graph of this set is shown in Figure 4.8.   An alternative set notation for this solution set is

$$S = \{x \mid x > -4\} \cap \{x \mid x < 2\}.$$

Figure 4.8

The expression $\{x \mid -4 < x < 2\}$ simply describes the overlapping portion of the two sets $\{x \mid x > -4\}$ and $\{x \mid x < 2\}$.

A second method for solving (1) is to write it as

$$\sqrt{(x + 1)^2} < 3,$$

which, by an extension of Theorem 4.3 to inequalities involving *positive* expressions, is equivalent to

$$(x + 1)^2 < 9,$$

from which

$$x^2 + 2x + 1 < 9,$$
$$x^2 + 2x - 8 < 0,$$
$$(x + 4)(x - 2) < 0,$$

and

$$-4 < x < 2.$$

Now consider the inequality

$$|x + 1| > 3. \qquad (3)$$

By definition, (3) is equivalent to

$$x + 1 > 3 \text{ for } x + 1 \geq 0$$

and to

$$-(x + 1) > 3 \text{ for } x + 1 < 0,$$

so that the solution set is given by

$$S = \{x \mid x > 2 \text{ or } x < -4\}.$$

The graph of this set is shown in Figure 4.9. In set notation, we could also write

$$S = \{x \mid x > 2\} \cup \{x \mid x < -4\},$$

where the union gives a precise meaning to the word "or" used in the notation

$$S = \{x \mid x > 2 \text{ or } x < -4\}.$$

Figure 4.9

EXERCISE 4.6

Solve.

Example. $|x + 5| = 8$

Solution. Determine the solution set by inspection or write as two first-degree equations and solve each equation.

$$x + 5 = 8 \qquad -(x + 5) = 8$$
$$x = 3 \qquad -x - 5 = 8$$
$$x = -13$$

The solution set is $\{3, -13\}$.

1. $|x| = 6$

2. $|x| = 3$

3. $|x - 1| = 4$

4. $|x - 6| = 3$

5. $\left|x - \dfrac{2}{3}\right| = \dfrac{1}{3}$

6. $\left|x - \dfrac{3}{4}\right| = \dfrac{1}{2}$

Write each of the following equations in radical form and then solve.

Example. $|x + 5| = 8$

Solution.

$$\sqrt{(x + 5)^2} = 8$$
$$x^2 + 10x + 25 = 64$$
$$x^2 + 10x - 39 = 0$$
$$(x + 13)(x - 3) = 0$$

The solution set is $\{-13, 3\}$.

7. $|2x + 5| = 2$

8. $|3x + 7| = 1$

9. $\left|1 - \dfrac{1}{2}x\right| = \dfrac{3}{4}$

10. $\left|1 + \dfrac{3}{2}x\right| = \dfrac{1}{2}$

11. $\left|\dfrac{3x + 2}{4}\right| = 6$

12. $\left|\dfrac{2x - 1}{3}\right| = 3$

Solve and represent the solution set on a line graph.

Example. $|2x - 1| \leq 7$

Solution. Rewrite without absolute value symbol.

$$2x - 1 \leq 7 \quad \text{when} \quad 2x - 1 > 0 \quad (1)$$
$$-(2x - 1) \leq 7 \quad \text{when} \quad 2x - 1 < 0 \quad (2)$$

From (1), $x \leq 4$ when $x > 1/2$.

From (2), $x \geq -3$ when $x < 1/2$.

The solution set is $\{x \mid -3 \leq x \leq 4\}$.

13. $|x| < 2$ 14. $|x - 1| > 2$ 15. $|x + 3| \le 4$

16. $2|x + 1| \le 8$ 17. $|2x - 5| < -3$ 18. $|2x + 4| < -1$

Write each of the following inequalities in radical form and then solve.

19. $|x - 3| > 4$ 20. $|2x + 4| > 2$ 21. $|2x + 1| \ge 5$

22. $|3x - 5| \ge 4$ 23. $\left|\dfrac{2x + 1}{3}\right| < 4$ 24. $\left|\dfrac{3x - 2}{4}\right| \le 5$

Replace each of the following inequalities with a single inequality involving an absolute value.

Example. $-3 < x < 7.$

Solution. $7 + (-3) = 4.$ Therefore values of x are centered about $4/2$, or 2. Subtract 2 from each member:

$$-5 < x - 2 < 5,$$
$$|x - 2| < 5.$$

25. $1 < x < 3$ 26. $-5 \le x \le 9$ 27. $-9 \le x \le -7$

28. $5 < x < 13$ 29. $-7 \le 2x \le 12$ 30. $-5 < 3x < 10$

31. A student must have an average of at least 80%, but less than 90%, on five tests in a course to receive a B. His grades on the first four tests were 98%, 76%, 86%, and 92%. What grade on the fifth test would give him a B in the course?

32. The Fahrenheit and Centigrade temperatures are related by $C = 5/9(F - 32)$. Within what range must the temperature be in Fahrenheit degrees for the temperature in Centigrade degrees to lie between $-10°$ and $20°$, inclusive?

In Problems 33–38 consider $a, b \in R$.

33. Show that $|-a| = |a|$.   *Hint:* Consider two possible cases, a nonnegative or negative.

34. Show that $|a - b| = |b - a|$.   *Hint:* Consider two possible cases, $a - b \ge 0$ and $a - b < 0$.

35. Show that $|a^2| = |a|^2 = a^2$.

36. Show that $|ab| = |a| \cdot |b|$.   *Hint:* Consider four possible cases, a or b nonnegative or negative.

37. Show that $\left|\dfrac{a}{b}\right| = \dfrac{|a|}{|b|}$, $b \ne 0$.

38. Show that $|a - b| \le |a| + |b|$.   *Hint:* Consider four cases.

5

RELATIONS
AND FUNCTIONS I

5.1 CARTESIAN PRODUCTS

When we pair two numbers with each other, in some cases the order of pairing is immaterial, but in other cases it is important that the order be specified. For example, if we wish simply to designate the set having members 1 and 2, either $\{1, 2\}$ or $\{2, 1\}$ is acceptable; the order in which the elements are listed is of no importance. On the other hand, when we say that the score in a tennis game is 40–30, the order in which the numbers are listed is important; it means that the server has 40 points and the receiver has 30. A score of 30–40 means just the reverse.

When the order in which the numbers of a number pair are to be considered is specified, the pair is called an **ordered pair**, and the pair is denoted by a symbol such as $(3, 2)$, $(2, 3)$, $(-1, 5)$, or $(0, 3)$. Each of the two numbers in an ordered pair is called a **component** of the ordered pair, the first and second being called the **first component** and the **second component**, respectively.

Having established what is meant by an ordered pair, we are ready to define another set operation.

DEFINITION 5.1 *The **Cartesian product** of two sets A and B, denoted by $A \times B$, is the set of all ordered pairs (x, y) such that $x \in A$ and $y \in B$.*

For example, if $A = \{1, 2, 3\}$ and $B = \{5, 6\}$, then

$$A \times B = \{(1, 5), (1, 6), (2, 5), (2, 6), (3, 5), (3, 6)\}$$

and

$$B \times A = \{(5, 1), (5, 2), (5, 3), (6, 1), (6, 2), (6, 3)\}.$$

In this book we are particularly interested in the case in which $A = B$, or, more specifically, in the Cartesian product $U \times U$, where U is the universe of discourse. We shall call $U \times U$ the **Cartesian set** of U.

Example. Use set notation and list the members of the Cartesian set of $U = \{1, 2, 3\}$.

Solution. Since the Cartesian set of $\{1, 2, 3\}$ is the set of all ordered pairs that can be formed using the elements of the given set, we have

$$U \times U = \{(1, 1), (1, 2), (1, 3), (2, 1), (2, 2), (2, 3), (3, 1), (3, 2), (3, 3)\}.$$

Cartesian sets can be pictured geometrically. The graph of $A \times A$, where $A = \{1, 2, 3\}$, is shown in Figure 5.1. The set $A \times A$ appears as a rectangular lattice of points, called a **point lattice**.

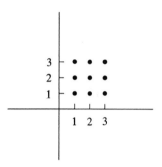

The important things to note about Cartesian sets are that the members of such sets are ordered pairs and that these ordered pairs are obtained by forming all possible ordered pairs with components drawn from a given set.

The most important Cartesian set with which we shall be concerned is that formed from the set R of real numbers. The product

Figure 5.1

$R \times R$ is the set of all possible ordered pairs of real numbers. The fact that each member of $R \times R$, that is, each ordered pair of real numbers, corresponds to a point in the geometric plane, and the coordinates of each

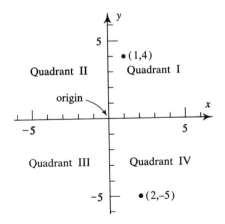

Figure 5.2

point in the geometric plane are the components of a member of $R \times R$, is the basis for all plane graphing.

The correspondence between points in the plane and ordered pairs of numbers is usually established through a **Cartesian** (or **rectangular**) **coordinate system**. You should recall that such a system consists of a pair of perpendicular number lines (called **axes**); these divide the plane into four regions (called **quadrants**), numbered as shown in Figure 5.2. Using x and y for variables, we customarily assign the variable x to a horizontal axis directed to the right and y to a vertical axis directed upward. The point of intersection of the axes is called the **origin**. The assignment of an ordered pair of real numbers (x, y) to a point in the plane can then be effected by counting x units from the origin on the x-axis and, from this point, counting y units from the x-axis along a line parallel to the y-axis. The coordinates of the origin are 0 and 0. Figure 5.2 shows the location of the origin and the two points $(2, -5)$ and $(1, 4)$. The x- and y-components of the ordered pair (x, y) are called the x- and **y-coordinates** of the point to which the ordered pair corresponds, and are sometimes called its **abscissa** and **ordinate**, respectively.

EXERCISE 5.1

Determine the Cartesian products.

Example. $A = \{1, 2, 3\}$, $B = \{5, 10\}$

Solution.

$$A \times B = \{(1, 5), (1, 10), (2, 5), (2, 10), (3, 5), (3, 10)\}$$

1. $A = \{1\}$, $B = \{-1, -2\}$ 2. $A = \{-1, -2\}$, $B = \{1\}$
3. $A = \{-1, 0, 1\}$, $B = \{0, 1\}$ 4. $A = \{5, 10\}$, $B = \{1, 2, 3, 4\}$
5. $A = \{a, b\}$, $B = \{c, d\}$ 6. $A = \{a, b, c\}$, $B = \{x\}$

Determine each Cartesian set and represent the set as a point lattice.

Example. $U = \{2, 3, 4\}$

Solution.

$$U \times U = \{(2, 2), (2, 3), (2, 4), (3, 2), (3, 3), (3, 4), (4, 2), (4, 3), (4, 4)\}$$

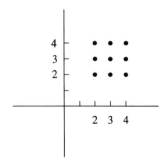

7. $U = \{1, 2\}$ 8. $U = \{0, 1\}$ 9. $U = \{-1, 0, 1\}$

10. $U = \{4, 5, 6\}$ 11. $U = \{-2, 0, 2\}$ 12. $U = \{2, 4, 6\}$

13. If $A = \{1, 2, 3, \cdots, n\}$ and $B = \{1, 2, 3, \cdots, m\}$, $n < m$, how many members has

a. $A \times B$?   b. $B \times A$?

c. $[A \times B] \cup [B \times A]$?   d. $[A \times B] \cap [B \times A]$?

14. Let $A = \{1, 2, 3, \cdots, n\}$, $B = \{1, 2, 3, \cdots, m\}$, and $n < m$.

a. How many members of $A \times B$ are of the form (a, a)?

b. Is it possible to find values for n and m such that $A \times B$ has 13 members? If so, give a pair of such values. $(13, 1)$

c. How many members (a, b) of $A \times A$ satisfy the condition that $a < b$? $a \leq b$?

15. In Chapter 13, we shall use *deleted* Cartesian sets. A **deleted Cartesian set** is a Cartesian set exclusive of its members with equal first and second components. Let $U = \{1, 2, 3, 4\}$.

a. List the deleted Cartesian set of U.

b. Represent the deleted Cartesian set of U on a lattice.

c. How many members has the deleted Cartesian set of U?

d. How many members would there be in the deleted Cartesian set of U if $U = \{1, 2, 3, \cdots, n\}$?

16. Let $A \subset U$ and $B \subseteq U$.

a. Is it possible for $[A \times B] \subseteq [U \times U]$? no

b. Is it necessary that $[A \times B] \subseteq [U \times U]$? yes

c. Is it possible for $[A \times B] \subset [U \times U]$? yes

d. Is it necessary that $[A \times B] \subset [U \times U]$? no

e. Is it possible for $[A \times B] = [U \times U]$? no

17. Let $A = \{1, 2, 3, \cdots, p\}$, $B = \{1, 2, 3, \cdots, q\}$, and $U = \{1, 2, 3, \cdots, r\}$, where $3 < p < q < r < 10$.

a. What is the least number of members possible for $A \times B$?

b. What is the greatest number of members possible for $A \times B$?

c. What is the least number of members possible for $U \times U$?

d. What is the greatest number of members possible for $A \times A$?

5.2 OPEN SENTENCES IN TWO VARIABLES

Open sentences in two variables, such as $3x + 2y = 12$, $x^2y + 3x = y^5$, and $\sqrt{xy} = y^2 - 5$, with x, $y \in R$, have, as solutions, ordered pairs of numbers. For example, if the components of $(2, 3)$ are substituted for the variables x and y, in that order, in the equation

$$3x + 2y = 12,$$

the result is

$$3(2) + 2(3) = 12,$$

which is true. On the other hand, if y is replaced with 2 and x with 3, we have

$$3(3) + 2(2) = 12,$$

which is false. The same pair of numbers can yield a true statement and a false statement, depending on the order in which the replacements are made.

DEFINITION 5.2 *For any given set A, the solution set in $A \times A$ of an equation in two variables is the set of ordered pairs in $A \times A$ that are solutions of the equation.*

We can find ordered pairs that satisfy a given equation in two variables by assigning values to one variable and determining the associated values for the other. Thus, for

$$y = x - 1, \quad x \in A = \{1, 2, 3\},$$

we can obtain all solutions in $A \times A$ by replacing x with 1, 2, and 3 in turn. This gives us $(1, 0)$, $(2, 1)$, and $(3, 2)$ as possible solutions. However, since $0 \notin A$, it follows that $(1, 0) \notin A \times A$, and therefore

$$S = \{(2, 1), (3, 2)\}$$

is the entire solution set in $A \times A$.

Open sentences in two variables can be looked upon as set selectors in the same way in which we look upon open sentences in one variable as set selectors. Given any set of ordered pairs, an equation such as $y = 2x + 1$ will serve to select certain ordered pairs from the set and reject others, depending on whether the ordered pair is or is not a solution. In general, we are interested in the entire solution set of such an equation in a given universe of ordered pairs.

Example. If $A = \{-3, -2, -1, 0, 1, 2, 3\}$, find the solution set of $y = x + 2$ for $(x, y) \in A \times A$, and show the graph of this set on the lattice $A \times A$.

Solution.   Since we insist that $(x, y) \in A \times A$, we need only replace x in $y = x + 2$ with each element of A in turn, and determine the associated value for y.   We have

$$x = -3, y = -1;$$
$$x = -2, y = 0;$$
$$x = -1, y = 1;$$
$$x = 0, y = 2;$$
$$x = 1, y = 3.$$

If we replace x with 2 or 3, we obtain a value for y that is not in A.   Hence, the entire solution set for $y = x + 2$ in $A \times A$ is

$$S = \{(-3, -1), (-2, 0), (-1, 1), (0, 2), (1, 3)\}.$$

The lattice of points (Figure 5.3) represents $A \times A$.   The circled points in the lattice represent members of the solution set S.

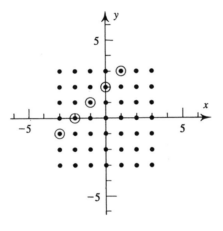

Figure 5.3

We shall be interested primarily in discussing the solution sets of equations in $R \times R$, the Cartesian set of the real numbers.   Since many open sentences in two variables will select an infinite number of ordered pairs from this set, it will not always be possible to list the members, and we shall have to use the notation

$$\{(x, y) \mid \text{condition on } x \text{ and } y\}$$

to represent the solution sets of these equations.   Of course, the graphical representation of $R \times R$ is the entire geometric plane, rather than a lattice such as occurs when the replacement sets of the variables involved are finite. We shall see graphical representations of the solution sets of equations in $R \times R$ in later sections.

EXERCISE 5.2

Find the missing component so that the ordered pair will satisfy the equation.

Example. $y - 2x = 4$

  a. $(0,\ \ )$ b. $(\ \ , 0)$ c. $(3,\ \ )$

Solutions.

  a. $y - 2x = 4$ b. $y - 2x = 4$ c. $y - 2x = 4$
      $y - 2(0) = 4$ $0 - 2x = 4$ $y - 2(3) = 4$
            $y = 4$ $x = -2$ $y = 10$
      $(0, 4)$ $(-2, 0)$ $(3, 10)$

1. $y = x + 7$
   a. $(0,\ \ )$ b. $(2,\ \ )$ c. $(-2,\ \ )$

2. $y = x - 3$
   a. $(0,\ \ )$ b. $(-1,\ \ )$ c. $(1,\ \ )$

3. $y = 2x + 1$
   a. $(2,\ \ )$ b. $(\ \ , 2)$ c. $(0,\ \ )$

4. $y = 3x - 1$

   a. $(0,\ \ )$ b. $(\ \ , 0)$ c. $\left(\dfrac{2}{3},\ \ \right)$

5. $2x + 2y = 3$

   a. $(0,\ \ )$ b. $(\ \ , 0)$ c. $\left(\dfrac{1}{2},\ \ \right)$

6. $2x + 3y = 4$
   a. $(0,\ \ )$ b. $(\ \ , 0)$ c. $(3,\ \ )$

For the given equation and given replacement set I for x, determine the solution set of the equation in $I \times I$ and represent the solution set S on the lattice in $I \times I$.

Example. $y = \dfrac{x}{3}$, $I = \{0, 3, 9\}$

Solution.

If $x = 0$, $y = \dfrac{0}{3} = 0$.

If $x = 3$, $y = \dfrac{3}{3} = 1$.

If $x = 9$, $y = \dfrac{9}{3} = 3$.

Since $1 \notin I$, $(3, 1) \notin I \times I$,
          and $S = \{(0, 0), (9, 3)\}$.

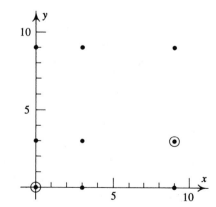

7. $y = -x, I = \{-1, 0, 1\}$ 8. $y = 2x + 1, I = \{1, 2, 3, 4\}$

9. $y = x^2, I = \{-2, -1, 0, 1, 2\}$ 10. $y = x^2 + 2x + 1, I = \{1, 2, 3\}$

11. $y = \dfrac{15}{x}, I = \{1, 3, 5\}$ 12. $y = \dfrac{12}{x - 2}, I = \{-2, -1, 0\}$

13. $x + 2y = 4, I = \{2, 4, 6\}$ 14. $x^2 - y = 0, I = \{-1, 0, 1\}$

Let $U = \{-2, -1, 0, 1, 2\}$.   List the members of each of the following sets S in $U \times U$, and circle the corresponding points in the lattice $U \times U$.

15. $S = \{(x, y) \mid 2x + y = 1\}$ 16. $S = \{(x, y) \mid 2x + y = -1\}$

17. $S = \{(x, y) \mid 2x + y = 1\} \cap \{(x, y) \mid 2x + y = -1\}$

18. $S = \{(x, y) \mid 2x + y = 1\} \cup \{(x, y) \mid 2x + y = -1\}$

19. $S = \{(x, y) \mid x = 0\} \cap \{(x, y) \mid y = 0\}$

20. $S = \{(x, y) \mid x = 0\} \cup \{(x, y) \mid y = 0\}$

21. $S = \{(x, y) \mid y = x\}'$ [i.e., the complement of $\{(x, y) \mid y = x\}$]

22. $S = \{(x, y) \mid y \neq x\}'$

Solve each of the following equations explicitly for y and represent the solution set S in the notation

$$\{(x, y) \mid \text{condition on } y \text{ in terms of } x\}.$$

Example. $x = \dfrac{3}{y + 5}$

Solution.

$$(y + 5)x = (y + 5)\frac{3}{y + 5}$$
$$xy + 5x = 3$$
$$xy = 3 - 5x$$
$$y = \frac{3 - 5x}{x}$$

The solution set S is $\left\{(x, y) \mid y = \dfrac{3 - 5x}{x}, x \in R, x \neq 0\right\}$.

23. $x + y = 7$ 24. $2x - y = 3$ 25. $2x + \dfrac{y}{3} = 5$

26. $x = \dfrac{y}{2} + 5$ 27. $x = \dfrac{2}{y}$ 28. $x = \dfrac{2}{y - 1}$

29. $yx^2 = y + 4$ 30. $yx^3 - y = 2$ 31. $2x = \dfrac{y}{y + 1}$

32. $\dfrac{x}{2} = \dfrac{y - 1}{y + 1}$ 33. $x = y + \dfrac{1}{y}$ 34. $x = y - \dfrac{4}{y}$

5.3 RELATIONS

In everyday life, the word "relationship" is quite common. It is not difficult to think of a host of examples, the "father-son" relationship, the "teacher-pupil" relationship, the "doctor-patient" relationship, and so on. An examination of the way in which the word "relationship" is used here (and in similar phrases) will show that a relationship involves two sets of things and some means of deciding whether a member of one set is or is not in the relationship with each member of the other set. In mathematics, the word "relation" is used in a very similar but more precise way.

Consider the "less-than" relationship, $y < x$. If $x, y \in R$, then $y < x$ either does or does not hold for the components of any given ordered pair (x, y). The components of $(x, y) = (1, 2)$ are not in the less-than relationship $y < x$ because 2 is not less than 1; on the other hand, $(2, 1)$ is in the relationship. To elaborate on this example, let $U = \{1, 2, 3, 4\}$. Then the set S of ordered pairs in $U \times U$, with components satisfying $y < x$, is

$$S = \{(2, 1), (3, 1), (3, 2), (4, 1), (4, 2), (4, 3)\}.$$

Figure 5.4 shows the graph of this set S on the lattice $U \times U$, where the circled points represent ordered pairs with components satisfying $y < x$.

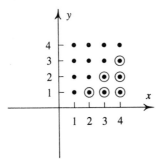

Figure 5.4

Any open sentence in two variables, x and y, expresses a relationship that might or might not hold between the elements in the replacement sets of the two variables, and this relationship precisely determines the solution set of the open sentence in two variables. For $x, y \in U$, this solution set is always a subset of $U \times U$. In short, the "relation" concept is perhaps most specifically identified with a subset of ordered pairs of some universe of discourse U. This leads us to the following.

DEFINITION 5.3 *A relation in U is a subset S of U $\times$ U.*

The relation is said to be in U because the components of the ordered pairs in the relation are elements of U. Alternatively, it is common to refer to the relationship as being in $U \times U$.

Figure 5.5-a shows a lattice depicting $A \times A$, where $A = \{-1, 0, 1\}$. Figure 5.5-b shows the graph of the relation $S = \{(-1, -1), (0, 0), (1, 1)\}$, which is a subset of $A \times A$. Another way in which this relation could be represented is $S = \{(x, y) \mid y = x\}$, where $x, y \in A$. Since $\{(x, y) \mid y = x\}$ is just the solution set of $y = x$ in $A \times A$, the question ought naturally to

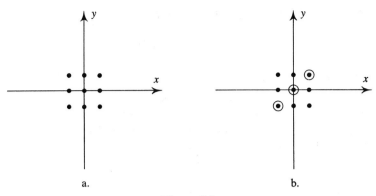

Figure 5.5

arise, "What is the difference between a relation and the solution set of an open sentence?" The answer is, "None." Every solution set of an open sentence in two variables is a relation. Moreover, any relation is a solution set of *some* open sentence in two variables, because given any relation consisting of the ordered pairs

$$(x_1, y_1), (x_2, y_2), \cdots, (x_n, y_n),$$

we can, if unable to find a more conventional open sentence, always discuss those x's and y's such that

$$(x, y) \in \{(x_1, y_1), (x_2, y_2), \cdots, (x_n, y_n)\}.$$

The set of all first components in the ordered pairs in a relation is called the **domain** of the relation, and the set of all second components is called the **range** of the relation.

Example.   What is the domain of the relation

$$\{(1, 5), (2, 10), (3, 15), (4, 20)\}?$$

The range?

Solution.   The set of all first components in this relation is $\{1, 2, 3, 4\}$, and hence this set is the domain.   The set of all second components is $\{5, 10, 15, 20\}$, and hence this set is the range.

Example.   Let $U = \{-2, -1, 0, 1, 2\}$.   What is the domain of the relation $S = \{(x, y) \mid y = x^2\}$ in U?   The range?

Solution.   The set $\{(x, y) \mid y = x^2\}$ in U is $\{(-1, 1), (0, 0), (1, 1)\}$.   (Replacement of 2 or -2 for x does not yield an element in U for y.)   By inspection, the domain of S is $\{-1, 0, 1\}$, whereas the range is $\{0, 1\}$.

Example.   Let U be the set of real numbers, and let

$$S = \left\{(x, y) \mid y = \frac{1}{x - 2}\right\}.$$

What is the domain of S?   The range?

Solution.   Since for every real number x except 2, $1/(x - 2)$ is real, it follows that the domain of S consists of all real numbers except 2.   That is, the domain of S is $\{x \mid x \in R, x \neq 2\}$.   To determine the range of S, we solve the equation $y = 1/(x - 2)$ explicitly for x to obtain $x = (1 + 2y)/y$.   Now, since for every real number y except 0, $(1 + 2y)/y$ is real, the range of S is $\{y \mid y \in R, y \neq 0\}$.

In general, we can determine the range and domain of a relation that is specified by an equation by solving the equation explicitly for each variable in turn, and then looking for excluded values.

Example.   Find the domain and the range for the relation

$$S = \{(x, y) \mid x^2 + y^2 = 25\}$$

if U is the set of real numbers.

Solution.   Solving $x^2 + y^2 = 25$ for y, we have

$$y^2 = 25 - x^2,$$

$$y = \sqrt{25 - x^2}, \quad y = -\sqrt{25 - x^2}.$$

We seek values of x for which y is real, that is, for which $25 - x^2 \geq 0$, $x^2 \leq 25$, or $|x| \leq 5$.   Thus, the domain of S is $\{x \mid |x| \leq 5\}$.   Now, solving for x, we have

$$x^2 = 25 - y^2,$$

$$x = \sqrt{25 - y^2}, \quad x = -\sqrt{25 - y^2}.$$

Next we seek values for y for which x is real, that is, for which $25 - y^2 \geq 0$, $y^2 \leq 25$, or $|y| \leq 5$, and the range of S is $\{y \mid |y| \leq 5\}$.

In simple examples such as those above, the domain and range can be determined by inspection.

EXERCISE 5.3

Form the graph (lattice) for $U \times U$.   Circle the points associated with the specified subset S.

Example.

$$U = \{-3, -2, -1, 0, 1, 2, 3\}$$

$$S = \{(-3, -3), (-1, -1), (0, 0), (1, 1), (3, 3)\}$$

Solution.

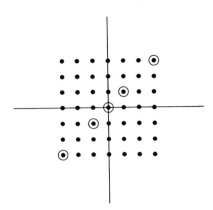

1. $U = \{1, 2, 3\}$
   $S = (1, 1), (2, 2), (3, 3)\}$

2. $U = \{1, 2, 3\}$
   $S = \{(1, 2), (2, 3)\}$

3. $U = \{-1, 0, 1\}$
   $S = \{(-1, -1), (-1, 0), (-1, 1)\}$

4. $U = \{-1, 0, 1\}$
   $S = \{(-1, 1), (0, 1), (1, 1)\}$

5. $U = \{-3, -2, -1, 0, 1, 2, 3\}$
   $S = \{(-3, 3), (0, 0), (3, -3)\}$

6. $U = \{-3, -2, -1, 0, 1, 2, 3\}$
   $S = \{(-2, 2), (-1, 2), (2, -1)\}$

Specify the domain and range of each relation S. If the relation is given in set-builder notation, list the members of the relation.

Examples.

a. $S = \{(1, 3), (2, 5), (3, 7)\}$

b. $S = \{(x, y) \mid y > x\}$, where
   $U = \{1, 2, 3\}$

Solutions.

a. The domain is $\{1, 2, 3\}$.
   The range is $\{3, 5, 7\}$.

b. $S = \{(1, 2), (1, 3), (2, 3)\}$
   The domain is $\{1, 2\}$.
   The range is $\{2, 3\}$.

7. $\{(-3, 2), (-2, 4)\}$

8. $\{(-1, 0), (0, -1)\}$

9. $\{(-1, 1), (0, 1), (1, 1)\}$

10. $\{(-1, -1), (-1, 0), (-1, 1)\}$

11. $\{(1, 2), (2, 3), (3, 4)\}$

12. $\{(0, 1), (1, 0), (0, 0)\}$

13. $\{(x, y) \mid x = 2\}$, where $U = \{1, 2, 3\}$

14. $\{(x, y) \mid y = 2\}$, where $U = \{1, 2, 3\}$

15. $\{(x, y) \mid x + y = 1\}$, where $U = \{-1, 0, 1\}$

16. $\{(x, y) \mid x - y = 1\}$, where $U = \{-1, 0, 1\}$

17. $\{(x, y) \mid y = x^2\}$, where $U = \{-2, -1, 0, 1, 2\}$

18. $\{(x, y) \mid y = x^3\}$, where $U = \{-2, -1, 0, 1, 2\}$

Specify the domain that would yield real numbers, $y \in R$, for elements in the range of the relation defined by each equation.

Examples.

a. $y = \sqrt{16 - x^2}$

b. $y = \dfrac{1}{x(x + 2)}$

Solutions. For what values of x is
$(16 - x^2) \geq 0$?

a. The domain is $\{x \mid -4 \leq x \leq 4\}$.

For what value of x is
$x(x + 2) \neq 0$?

b. The domain is
$\{x \mid x \in R, \quad x \neq 0, -2\}$.

19. $y = x + 7$

20. $y = 2x - 3$

21. $y = x^2$

22. $y = \dfrac{1}{x}$

23. $y = \dfrac{1}{x - 2}$

24. $y = \dfrac{1}{x^2 + 1}$

25. $y = \sqrt{x}$

26. $y = \sqrt{4 - x}$

27. $y = \sqrt{4 - x^2}$

28. $y = \sqrt{x^2 - 9}$

29. $y = \dfrac{4}{x(x - 1)}$

30. $y = \dfrac{x}{(x - 1)(x + 2)}$

31. Let $U = \{-2, -1, 0, 1, 2\}$. Construct a lattice for $U \times U$ and circle the graphs of the members of the relations a, b, c, d:

     a. $\{(x, y) \mid y = x\}$ b. $\{(x, y) \mid y = x^3\}$ c. $\{(x, y) \mid y = x^5\}$

     d. $\{(x, y) \mid y = x^{2n-1} \text{ and } n \in N\}$

     e. How do the relations a–d differ?

32. Let $U = \{-2, -1, 0, 1, 2\}$. Construct a lattice for $U \times U$ and circle the graphs of the members of the relations a, b, c, d:

     a. $\{(x, y) \mid y = |x|\}$ b. $\{(x, y) \mid y = x^2\}$

     c. $\{(x, y) \mid y = x^4\}$ d. $\{(x, y) \mid y = x^{2n} \text{ and } n \in N\}$

     e. How do the relations a–d differ?

33. Given $U = \{-2, -1, 0, 1, 2\}$, find an open sentence defining each of the following relations in $U \times U$.

     a. $\{(0, 1), (1, 1), (-1, 1), (2, 1), (-2, 1)\}$

     b. $\{(0, 0), (1, -1), (-1, -1)\}$

     c. $\{(0, 0), (-1, 1), (1, -1)\}$

     d. $\{(0, 0), (-1, 1), (-2, 2), (1, -1), (2, -2)\}$

34. If $U = \{1, 2, 3, \cdots, n\}$, how many different relations are there in $U \times U$?

5.4 FUNCTIONS

There is a special kind of relation that is important in mathematics. This special relation is called a **function.**

DEFINITION 5.4   *A function is a relation in which no two ordered pairs have the same first components and different second components.*

A function, therefore, associates each element in the domain with one and only one element in its range.   In a graphical sense, this implies that no two of the ordered pairs in a function will graph into points on the same vertical line.   Figure 5.6 shows three lattices upon which are the graphs of relations.   Figure 5.6-a shows the graph of a relation that is not a function, whereas 5.6-b and 5.6-c show graphs of functions.

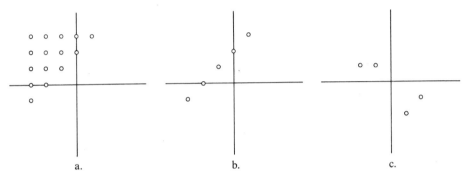

Figure 5.6

Generally, however, we want to discuss relations and functions that have the set R or a subset such as $\{x \mid -1 \le x \le 1\}$, rather than small finite sets as their domains.   As you should recall from your earlier study of algebra, graphs on $R \times R$ are generally continuous lines and curves rather than isolated points.   Figure 5.7 shows three such graphs.   Imagine a vertical line moving across each of these from left to right.   If the vertical line at any position meets the graph of the relation in more than one point, the relation is

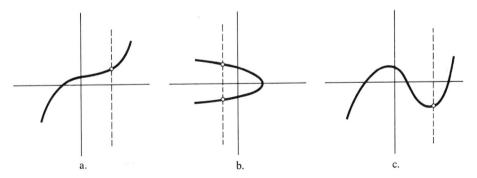

Figure 5.7

not a function. Thus, although Figures 5.7-a and 5.7-c show the graphs of relations that are functions, 5.7-b is the graph of a relation that is not a function, because the vertical line shown in the figure meets the graph in two places. What this means is that for the particular value of x involved, the relation associates two distinct values for y.

When a relation is defined by an equation, one way in which we can determine whether the relation is a function is to solve the equation explicitly for the variable representing an element in the range, and see whether more than one value of y is associated with any single value of x.

Example. Is the relation $\{(x, y) \mid y^2 = 1 + x^2\}$ in $R \times R$ a function?

Solution. Since $y^2 = 1 + x^2$ implies either $y = \sqrt{1 + x^2}$ or $y = -\sqrt{1 + x^2}$, the assignment of a real value to x will result in two different values for y, and hence the relation is not a function.

Notation such as that introduced in Chapter 2 for polynomials, namely $P(x)$, is widely used in discussing functions. In general, functions are denoted by single symbols; for example, f, g, h, and F might be so used. The symbol for a function can be used in conjunction with the variable representing an element in the domain to represent the associated element in the range. Thus $f(x)$ [read "f of x" or "the value of f at x"] is the element in the range of f associated with the element x in the domain.

Suppose

$$f = \{(x, y) \mid y = x + 3\}.$$

The alternative notation

$$f = \{[x, f(x)] \mid f(x) = x + 3\}$$

can be used, where $f(x)$ plays the same role as y. This notation is particularly useful because, by replacing x with a specific number a in the domain, we obtain $f(a)$, which then denotes the element in the range that is associated with a.

For example, if

$$f(x) = x^2 + 3,$$

then

$$f(3) = (3)^2 + 3 = 12,$$
$$f(0) = (0)^2 + 3 = 3,$$
$$f(h) = h^2 + 3,$$
$$f(h + 2) = (h + 2)^2 + 3 = h^2 + 4h + 4 + 3$$
$$= h^2 + 4h + 7.$$

As was the case when we discussed polynomials, we can continue to use $f(x), q(x), P(x)$, etc. whenever we wish to discuss expressions in the variable x.

Since in almost all cases in this book we shall be interested in functions of which the domains and ranges are sets of real numbers (such functions are called **real-valued functions** of a real variable), in any place where a function is discussed and the domain is not specified, we shall understand that the domain is *the set of all real numbers for which a real number exists in the range.*

By Definition 5.4, a function is a set of ordered pairs (x, y) such that no two have the same first components and different second components. For example,

$$\{(1, 3), (2, 5), (3, 6)\}$$

is a function f, with domain $\{1, 2, 3\}$ and range $\{3, 5, 6\}$. Also,

$$\{(1, 5), (2, 5), (3, 6)\}$$

is a function g, with domain $\{1, 2, 3\}$ and range $\{5, 6\}$. Now let us in each pair interchange the first and second components, obtaining

$$\{(3, 1), (5, 2), (6, 3)\}$$

and

$$\{(5, 1), (5, 2), (6, 3)\},$$

respectively. In the first case, we again obtain a function, called the **inverse function** of f and sometimes denoted f^{-1}, with domain $\{3, 5, 6\}$ and range $\{1, 2, 3\}$; but in the second case, in accordance with Definition 5.4, we do *not* have a function—the function g has no inverse function.

DEFINITION 5.5 *If the function f is such that no two of its ordered pairs with different first components have the same second component, then the inverse function f^{-1} is the set of ordered pairs obtained from f by interchanging the first and second components of each ordered pair in f.*

EXERCISE 5.4

State whether or not the given equation defines a function.

Examples.

a. $x^2 y = 3$ b. $x^2 + y^2 = 36$

Solutions. Solve explicitly for y.

a. $y = \dfrac{3}{x^2}$ b. $y^2 = 36 - x^2$

$$y = \pm \sqrt{36 - x^2}$$

Yes. There is only one value of y associated with each value of x ($x \neq 0$).

No. There are two values of y associated with values of x satisfying $|x| < 6$.

1. $x + y = 3$ 2. $y = -x^2$ 3. $y = \sqrt{x^2 - 5}$

4. $y = \sqrt{16 - x^2}$ 5. $x^2 + y^2 = 16$ 6. $y = \pm\sqrt{x^2}$

7. $y = \dfrac{1}{x}$ 8. $y = \sqrt[3]{x}$ 9. $y^2 = x^3$

10. $y = \dfrac{1}{x^2 - 1}$ 11. $y = ax^n$ 12. $y^2 = x^n$

If $f(x) = x + 2$, find the given element in the range.

Example. $f(3)$

Solution. Substitute 3 for x.

$$f(3) = (3) + 2 = 5$$

The element is 5.

13. $f(0)$ 14. $f(1)$ 15. $f(-3)$

16. $f\left(\dfrac{1}{2}\right)$ 17. $f(a)$ 18. $f(a + 2)$

If $g(x) = x^2 - 2x + 1$, find the given element in the range.

19. $g(-2)$ 20. $g(0)$ 21. $g(3)$

22. $g(a)$ 23. $g(a + 1)$ 24. $g(a - 1)$

If $f(x) = x + 2$ defines a function, find the element in the domain of f associated with the given element in the range.

Example. $f(x) = 5$

Solution. Replace $f(x)$ with $x + 2$.

$$x + 2 = 5$$

$$x = 3$$

The element is 3.

25. $f(x) = 3$ 26. $f(x) = -2$ 27. $f(x) = 0$

28. $f(x) = 2$ 29. $f(x) = a$ 30. $f(x) = a + 2$

If $g(x) = x^2 - 1$, find all elements in the domain of g associated with the given element in the range.

31. $g(x) = 0$ 32. $g(x) = 3$ 33. $g(x) = 8$

34. $g(x) = 5$ 35. $g(x) = a^2$ 36. $g(x) = a^2 - 1$

Find the range of the function with rule and domain as given.

Example. $f(x) = \sqrt{x + 1}$, $\{0, 1, 2\}$

Solution. Substitute 0, 1, and 2 for x.

$$f(0) = \sqrt{0 + 1} = 1, \quad f(1) = \sqrt{1 + 1} = \sqrt{2}, \quad f(2) = \sqrt{2 + 1} = \sqrt{3}$$

The range is $\{1, \sqrt{2}, \sqrt{3}\}$.

37. $f(x) = x + 2$, $\{-1, 0, 1\}$ 38. $f(x) = x^2 - 10$, $\{10, 5, 0\}$

39. $g(x) = \sqrt{x}$, $\{16, 9, 4\}$ 40. $h(x) = \sqrt{25 - x^2}$, $\{5, 4, 3, 0\}$

41. Suppose $f(x) = x + 2$ and $g(x) = x - 2$.   Find
    a. $f(0)$ b. $g(2)$ c. $f[g(2)]$ d. $f[g(x)]$

42. If $f(x) = x^2 - x + 1$, find

    a. $f(x + h) - f(x)$ b. $\dfrac{f(x + h) - f(x)}{h}$

43. What element(s) in the domain of each of the functions defined by the following equations is (are) associated with the element 9 in the range?
    a. $y = x + 9$ b. $y = 2x$ c. $y = x^2$ d. $y = 9$

44. If f is defined by the equation $f(x) = x - 3$, find an x in the domain of f for which $f(x) = f(-x)$.

45. Consider $\{[x, f(x)] \mid f(x) = x^2\}$.   Does $f(a) + f(b) = f(a + b)$?

46. Any function satisfying the condition that $f(-x) = f(x)$ is called an **even function**.   Any function satisfying the condition that $f(-x) = -f(x)$ is called an **odd function**.   Which of the following functions are even and which are odd?
    a. $\{[x, f(x)] \mid f(x) = x^2\}$ b. $\{[x, f(x)] \mid f(x) = x^3\}$
    c. $\{[x, f(x)] \mid f(x) = x^4 - x^2\}$ d. $\{[x, f(x)] \mid f(x) = x^3 - x\}$

State a rule in the form of an equation and specify a meaningful domain for a function relating, as range and domain, respectively:

Example.   The area (A) of a triangle and the base (b) if the height is six inches.

Solution.   Since $A = 1/2bh$, $A = 1/2b(6)$,

$$A = 3b, \{b \mid b > 0\}.$$

47. The circumference (C) and radius (r) of a circle.

48. The perimeter (P) of a rectangle having a length of five inches and the width (w) of the rectangle.

49. The area (A) and the height (h) of a triangle having a base eight inches in length.

50. The hypotenuse (h) and the leg (b) of a right triangle with the other leg six inches in length.

Example. The area (A) and circumference (C) of a circle.

Solution. Since

$$A = \pi r^2, \tag{1}$$

we wish to obtain an expression for r in terms of C. From

$$C = 2\pi r, \tag{2}$$

it follows that

$$r = \frac{C}{2\pi}. \tag{3}$$

Substituting the value of r in (3) for r in (1), we get

$$A = \pi \left(\frac{C}{2\pi}\right)^2$$

and

$$A = \frac{\pi \cdot C^2}{4\pi^2} = \frac{C^2}{4\pi}.$$

Thus the equation defining the function associating the area and circumference of a circle is $A = C^2/4\pi$, $\{C \mid C > 0\}$.

51. The area (A) and side (s) of an equilateral triangle. *Hint:* Use Pythagorean theorem.

52. The perimeter (P) and the area (A) of a rectangle of length 10 inches.

53. y and x if $y = u^2 - 1$ and $u = x + 1$.

54. y and x if $y = \sqrt{u - 4}$ and $u = x^2 - 1$.

55. A box is formed from a rectangular (10×22 inches) piece of tin, after a square has been cut out from each corner. Relate the volume (V) and the side (s) of the cut-out squares.

56. A rectangle is inscribed in a circle of diameter 10 inches. Relate the length (l) and width (w) of the rectangle. *Hint:* Use Pythagorean theorem.

57. Show that the set of functions defined by the equations $f_1(x) = x$, $f_2(x) = 1/x$, $f_3(x) = 1 - x$, $f_4(x) = 1/(1 - x)$, $f_5(x) = x/(x - 1)$, $f_6(x) = (x - 1)/x$ is closed with respect to the operation $f_i[f_j(x)]$, where $i, j \in \{1, 2, 3, 4, 5, 6\}$.

For each function f, state whether or not it has an inverse function f^{-1}.

58. $f(x) = x + 2$ 59. $f(x) = x^2 - 3$ 60. $f(x) = x^3$

5.5 LINEAR FUNCTIONS

A first-degree equation in two variables of the form

$$Ax + By + C = 0 \quad (B \neq 0) \tag{1}$$

defines a function having as its domain the set of real numbers x. The graph of any such function in $R \times R$ is a straight line (although we do not prove this here), and hence these functions are called **linear functions**. Since any two distinct points determine a straight line, it is evident that we need find only two solutions of such an equation to determine its graph—i.e., the graph of the solution set of the equation. In practice, the two solutions easiest to find are usually those with first and second components respectively zero—that is, the solutions $(0, y)$ and $(x, 0)$. Setting $y = 0$ in

$$Ax + By + C = 0,$$

we have

$$Ax + C = 0,$$

from which, if $A \neq 0$, we obtain

$$x = -\frac{C}{A},$$

and $(-C/A, 0)$ is one point on the graph. Similarly, for $x = 0$, we have

$$By + C = 0$$

and

$$y = -\frac{C}{B} \quad (B \neq 0),$$

whence $(0, -C/B)$ is another point on the graph. Since these two points are the points where the graph crosses the x- and y-axes, respectively, they are easy to locate. The numbers $-C/A$ and $-C/B$ are called the **x-** and **y-intercepts** of the graph, and are usually denoted by a and b. As an example, consider the function

$$f = \{(x, y) \mid 3x + 4y = 12\}. \tag{2}$$

If $y = 0$, we have $x = 4$, and the x-intercept is 4. If $x = 0$, then $y = 3$, and the y-intercept is 3. Thus the graph of (2) appears as in Figure 5.8.

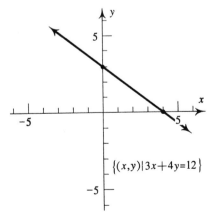

Figure 5.8

If the graph intersects both axes at or near the origin, the intercepts either do not represent two separate points, or the points are too close together to be of much use in drawing the graph. It is then necessary to plot at least one other point at a distance far enough removed from the origin to establish the line with pictorial accuracy.

There are two special cases of linear equations worth noting. First, an equation such as

$$y - 4 = 0$$

may be considered an equation in two variables,

$$0x + y = 4.$$

For each x, this equation assigns $y = 4$. That is, any ordered pair of the form $(x, 4)$ is a solution of the equation. For instance,

$$(1, 4), (2, 4), (3, 4), (4, 4), \text{etc.,}$$

are all solutions of the equation. If we graph these points and connect them with a straight line, we have Figure 5.9.

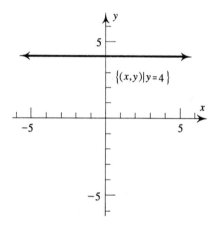

Figure 5.9

Since the equation

$$y = 4$$

assigns to each x the same value for y, the function defined by this equation is called a **constant function**.

The other special case of the linear equation is of the type

$$x = 3,$$

which may be looked upon as

$$x + 0y = 3.$$

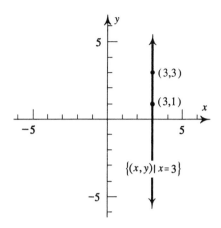

Figure 5.10

Here, only one value is permissible for x, namely 3, whereas any value may be assigned to y.   That is, any ordered pair of the form $(3, y)$ is a solution of this equation.   If we choose two solutions, say $(3, 1)$ and $(3, 3)$ and complete the graph, we have Figure 5.10.   It is clear that this equation does *not* define a function (why?), and accounts for our earlier restriction $B \neq 0$ on the general form of a first-degree equation in two variables, $Ax + By + C = 0$, in order that this should define a function.

In general, a first-degree equation in x and y is an equation equivalent to one of the form

$$Ax + By + C = 0 \quad (A \text{ and } B \text{ not both } 0).$$

If $B \neq 0$, then the equation defines a function, and its graph is a straight line which has as its y-intercept $-C/B$.   But if $B = 0$, then $A \neq 0$, and the equation does not represent a function, though its graph is still a straight line, namely, the line parallel to the y-axis at $x = -C/A$.   Thus every line in the plane can be represented by a linear equation in x and y, and conversely every linear equation in x and y represents a line in the plane.

Any single portion of finite nonzero length of a line is a **line segment**.   Clearly, any two distinct points in a plane can be looked upon as the end points of a line segment.   Two fundamental properties of a line segment are its **length** and its **inclination** with respect to the x-axis.   If we construct through P_2 a line parallel to the y-axis, and through P_1 a line parallel to the x-axis, the lines will meet at a point P_3 as shown in either 5.11-a or 5.11-b.   The x-coordinate of P_3 is evidently the same as the x-coordinate of P_2, and the y-coordinate of P_3 is the same as that of P_1; hence the coordinates of P_3 are (x_2, y_1).   By inspection, we observe that the distance from P_2 to P_3 is simply the difference in the y-coordinates of the two points, $y_2 - y_1$, and the distance between P_1 and P_3 is the difference of the x-coordinates of these points, $x_2 - x_1$.

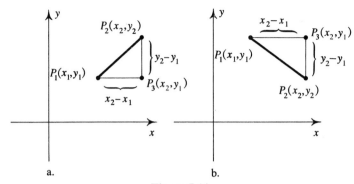

Figure 5.11

In general, since $y_2 - y_1$ is positive or negative as $y_2 > y_1$ or $y_2 < y_1$, respectively, and $x_2 - x_1$ is positive or negative as $x_2 > x_1$ or $x_2 < x_1$, respectively, it is also convenient to designate the distances represented by $x_2 - x_1$ and $y_2 - y_1$ as positive or negative. For this reason such distances are frequently called **directed distances**.

The Pythagorean theorem can be used to find the length of the line segment from P_1 to P_2. This theorem asserts that the square on the hypotenuse of any right triangle is equal to the sum of the squares on the legs. Thus, we have

$$d^2 = (x_2 - x_1)^2 + (y_2 - y_1)^2,$$

and by considering only the positive (or nonnegative) square root of the right-hand member, we thus have

$$d = \sqrt{(x_2 - x_1)^2 + (y_2 - y_1)^2}. \tag{3}$$

Since the distances $(x_2 - x_1)$ and $(y_2 - y_1)$ are squared, it makes no difference here whether they are positive or negative—the result is the same. Equation (3) is a formula for the **distance** between any two points in the plane in terms of the coordinates of the points. The distance is always taken as positive—or 0 if the points coincide. If the points P_1 and P_2 lie on the same horizontal line, we have observed that the directed distance between them is

$$d = x_2 - x_1,$$

and if they lie on the same vertical line, then

$$d = y_2 - y_1.$$

If we are concerned only with distance and not direction, then these become $d = |x_2 - x_1|$ and $d = |y_2 - y_1|$.

The second useful property of the line segment joining two points, its inclination, can be measured by comparing the *rise* of the segment with a given *run* (Figure 5.12).

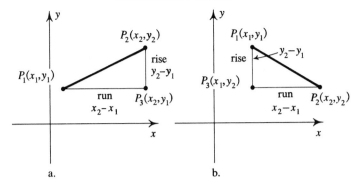

Figure 5.12

The ratio of *rise* to *run* is called the **slope** of the line segment and is designated by the letter m. Since the rise is simply $y_2 - y_1$ and the run is $x_2 - x_1$, the slope of the line segment joining P_1 and P_2 is given by

$$m = \frac{\text{rise}}{\text{run}} = \frac{y_2 - y_1}{x_2 - x_1}.$$

If P_2 is to the right of P_1, $x_2 - x_1$ will necessarily be positive, and the slope will be positive or negative as $y_2 - y_1$ is positive or negative. Thus positive slope indicates that a line is rising to the right; negative slope indicates that it is falling to the right. Since

$$\frac{y_2 - y_1}{x_2 - x_1} = \frac{-(y_1 - y_2)}{-(x_1 - x_2)} = \frac{y_1 - y_2}{x_1 - x_2},$$

the restriction that P_2 be to the right of P_1 is not necessary, and the order in which the points are considered is immaterial in determining slope.

If a line segment is parallel to the x-axis, then $y_2 - y_1 = 0$, and the line has slope 0; but if it is parallel to the y-axis, then $x_2 - x_1 = 0$, and its slope is not defined (Figure 5.13).

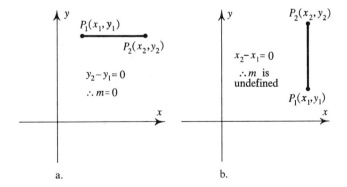

Figure 5.13

In the next section, we shall see how the slope concept is applied in discussing linear functions and their graphs.

EXERCISE 5.5

Graph.

Example. $3x + 4y = 24$

Solution.   Determine the intercepts.

If $x = 0$, then $y = 6$;
if $y = 0$, then $x = 8$.

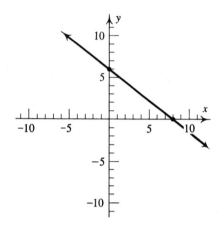

1. $y = 3x + 1$
2. $y = x - 5$
3. $y = -2x$
4. $2x + y = 3$
5. $3x - y = -2$
6. $3x = 2y$
7. $2x + 3y = 6$
8. $3x - 2y = 8$
9. $2x + 5y = 10$
10. $y = 5$
11. $x = -2$
12. $x = -3$

Example.

Graph $f(x) = x - 1$.   Represent $f(5)$ and $f(3)$ by drawing line segments from $(5, 0)$ to $[5, f(5)]$ and from $(3, 0)$ to $[3, f(3)]$.

Solution.

$f(5) = 5 - 1 = 4$
           is the ordinate at $x = 5$.
$f(3) = 3 - 1 = 2$
           is the ordinate at $x = 3$.

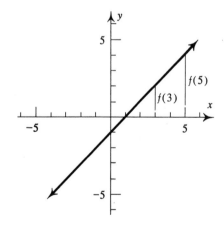

13. Plot the graph of $f(x) = 2x + 4$. Represent $f(0)$ and $f(4)$ by drawing line segments from $(0, 0)$ to $[0, f(0)]$ and from $(4, 0)$ to $[4, f(4)]$.

14. Plot the graph of $f(x) = 2x + 1$. Represent $f(3)$ and $f(-2)$ by drawing line segments from $(3, 0)$ to $[3, f(3)]$ and from $(-2, 0)$ to $[-2, f(-2)]$.

15. Suppose the function defined by $y = 2x + 1$ has as domain the set of real numbers between and including -1 and 1. Plot the graph of the function on a rectangular coordinate system. What is the range of the function?

16. Consider the two functions f and g, where $f(x) = x + 3$ with the domain of f the set $\{1, 2, 3, 4\}$ and $g(x) = x - 3$ with domain the same as the range of f. What is the range of g? Graph g on a rectangular coordinate system.

17. We observe that $x(y + 1) = xy + x$ is an identity for x and y real numbers. Describe the graph of this equation. Does it define a function? *Hint:* What ordered pairs satisfy the equation?

18. Graph $x + y = 6$ and $5x - y = 0$ on the same set of axes. Estimate the coordinates of the point of intersection. What can you say about the coordinates of this point in relation to the two linear equations?

Find the distance between each of the given pairs of points, and find the slope of the line segment joining them.

Example. $(3, -5), (2, 4)$

Solution. Consider $(3, -5)$ as P_1 and $(2, 4)$ as P_2.

$$d = \sqrt{(x_2 - x_1)^2 + (y_2 - y_1)^2} \qquad m = \frac{y_2 - y_1}{x_2 - x_1}$$

$$= \sqrt{[2 - 3]^2 + [4 - (-5)]^2} \qquad = \frac{4 - (-5)}{2 - 3}$$

$$= \sqrt{1 + 81} \qquad = \frac{9}{-1}$$

Distance, $\sqrt{82}$; slope, -9

19. $(1, 1), (4, 5)$ 20. $(-1, 1), (5, 9)$ 21. $(-3, 2), (2, 14)$

22. $(-4, -3), (1, 9)$ 23. $(2, 1), (1, 0)$ 24. $(-3, 2), (0, 0)$

25. $(5, 4), (-1, 1)$ 26. $(2, -3), (-2, -1)$ 27. $(3, 5), (-2, 5)$

28. $(2, 0), (-2, 0)$ 29. $(0, 5), (0, -5)$ 30. $(-2, -5), (-2, 3)$

Find the length of the sides of the triangle having vertices as given.

31. $(10, 1), (3, 1), (5, 9)$ 32. $(0, 6), (9, -6), (-3, 0)$

33. $(5, 6), (11, -2), (-10, -2)$ 34. $(-1, 5), (8, -7), (4, 1)$

35. Show that the triangle described in Problem 32 is a right triangle. *Hint:* Use the converse of the Pythagorean theorem; that is, if $c^2 = a^2 + b^2$, then the triangle is a right triangle.

36. The two line segments with end points at $(0, -7), (8, -5)$ and $(5, 7), (8, -5)$ are perpendicular. Find the slope of each line segment. Compare the slopes. Do the same for the perpendicular line segments with end points at $(8, 0), (6, 6)$ and $(-3, 3), (6, 6)$. Can you make a conjecture about the slopes of perpendicular line segments?

37. The graph of a linear function contains the points $(2, -3)$ and $(6, -1)$. Find an equation that defines the function.

38. Determine algebraically whether the following points lie on the same line.

    a. $(2, 7)$, $(-2, -5)$, $(0, 1)$ b. $(9, 5)$, $(-3, -1)$, $(0, 1)$

39. Show by similar triangles that the coordinates of the midpoint of the line segment joining the points $P_1(x_1, y_1)$ and $P_2(x_2, y_2)$ are given by $x = \dfrac{x_1 + x_2}{2}$ and $y = \dfrac{y_1 + y_2}{2}$.

40. Using the results of Problem 39, find the coordinates of the midpoint of the line segment joining:

    a. $(2, 4)$ and $(6, 8)$ b. $(-4, 6)$ and $(6, -10)$

5.6 FORMS FOR LINEAR EQUATIONS

In the preceding section, we used the equation

$$Ax + By + C = 0 \quad (B \neq 0) \tag{1}$$

to define a linear function. We designate (1) as **standard form** for a linear equation, and then consider three alternative forms that display useful aspects.

Point-Slope Form

Assuming that the slope of the line segment joining any two points on a line does not depend on the points, as can be shown by considering similar triangles, consider a line in the plane with given slope m and passing through a given point (x_1, y_1) (Figure 5.14). If we choose any other point on the

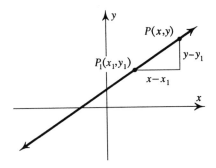

Figure 5.14

line and assign to it the coordinates (x, y), it is evident that the slope of the line is given by

$$\frac{y - y_1}{x - x_1} = m,$$

from which

$$y - y_1 = m(x - x_1). \tag{2}$$

Note that (2) is satisfied also by $(x, y) = (x_1, y_1)$. Since now x and y are the coordinates of *any* point on the line, (2) is an equation of the line passing through (x_1, y_1) with slope m. This is called the **point-slope form** for a linear equation.

Slope-Intercept Form

Now consider the equation of the line with slope m passing through a given point on the y-axis having coordinates $(0, b)$ (Figure 5.15). Substituting

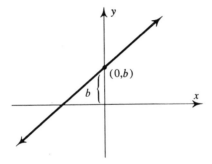

Figure 5.15

$(0, b)$ in the point-slope form of a linear equation,

$$y - y_1 = m(x - x_1),$$

we obtain

$$y - b = m(x - 0),$$

from which

$$y = mx + b. \tag{3}$$

Equation (3) is called the **slope-intercept form** for a linear equation. Any linear equation in standard form can be written in the slope-intercept form by solving for y in terms of x. For example,

$$2x + 3y - 6 = 0$$

can be written equivalently as

$$y = -\frac{2}{3}x + 2.$$

The slope of the line, $-2/3$, and the y-intercept, 2, can now be read directly from the last form of the equation.

Intercept Form

If the x- and y-intercepts of the graph of

$$y = mx + b \tag{4}$$

are a and b $(a, b \neq 0)$, respectively (Figure 5.16), then the slope m is clearly

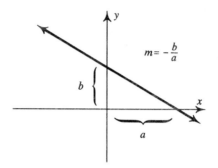

Figure 5.16

equal to $-b/a$. Replacing m in (4) with $-b/a$, we have

$$y = -\frac{b}{a}x + b,$$

$$ay = -bx + ab,$$

$$bx + ay = ab,$$

and dividing each member by ab produces

$$\frac{x}{a} + \frac{y}{b} = 1.$$

This latter form is called the **intercept form** for a linear equation. Since it was shown earlier (page 145) that for the equation $Ax + By + C = 0$, with $A, B \neq 0$, the x-intercept is $-C/A$ and the y-intercept is $-C/B$, the intercept form for $Ax + By + C = 0$ is

$$-\frac{x}{\dfrac{C}{A}} - \frac{y}{\dfrac{C}{B}} = 1,$$

provided $C \neq 0$. If $C = 0$, then both intercepts are at the origin and there is no intercept form.

Any of the three forms discussed in this section may be used to help us talk about linear functions and their graphs.

EXERCISE 5.6

Find the equation, in standard form, of the line through each of the given points and having the given slope.

Example. $(3, -5)$, $m = -2$

Solution. Substitute given values in the point-slope form of the linear equation.

$$y - y_1 = m(x - x_1)$$

$$y - (-5) = -2(x - 3)$$

$$y + 5 = -2x + 6$$

$$2x + y - 1 = 0$$

1. $(2, 1)$, $m = 4$
2. $(-2, 3)$, $m = 5$
3. $(5, 5)$, $m = -1$

4. $(-3, -2)$, $m = \frac{1}{2}$
5. $(0, 0)$, $m = 3$
6. $(-1, 0)$, $m = 1$

7. $(0, -1)$, $m = -\frac{1}{2}$
8. $(2, -1)$, $m = \frac{3}{4}$
9. $(-2, -2)$, $m = -\frac{3}{4}$

10. $(2, -3)$, $m = 0$
11. $(-4, 2)$, $m = 0$
12. $(-1, -2)$, parallel to y-axis

Write each of the equations in slope-intercept form; specify the slope of the line and the y-intercept.

Example. $2x - 3y = 5$

Solution. Solve explicitly for y.

$$-3y = 5 - 2x$$

$$3y = 2x - 5$$

$$y = \frac{2}{3}x - \frac{5}{3}$$

Compare with the general slope-intercept form $y = mx + b$.
Slope, $2/3$; y-intercept, $-5/3$

13. $x + y = 3$
14. $2x + y = -1$

15. $3x + 2y = 1$
16. $3x - y = 7$

17. $x - 3y = 2$
18. $2x - 3y = 0$

19. $8x - 3y = 0$
20. $-x = 2y - 5$

Find the equation, in standard form, of the line with the given intercepts.

Example. $x = 3; y = -1/2$

Solution.   Substitute 3 and $-1/2$ for a and b, respectively, in the slope-intercept form $x/a + y/b = 1$.

$$\frac{x}{3} + \frac{y}{-\frac{1}{2}} = 1$$

$$x - 6y - 3 = 0$$

21. $x = 2; y = 3$ 22. $x = 4; y = -1$ 23. $x = -2; y = -5$

24. $x = -1; y = 7$ 25. $x = -\frac{1}{2}; y = \frac{3}{2}$ 26. $x = \frac{2}{3}; y = -\frac{3}{4}$

27. Write the equation, in standard form, of the line with the same slope as $x - 2y = 5$ and passing through the origin.   Draw the graph of this equation.

28. Write the equation, in standard form, of the line through $(0, 5)$ with the same slope as $2y - 3x = 5$.   Draw the graph of this equation.

29. Show that, for $x_2 \neq x_1$,

pt. slope form  $\longrightarrow$

$$y - y_1 = \left(\frac{y_2 - y_1}{x_2 - x_1}\right)(x - x_1)$$

is an equation of the line joining the points (x_1, y_1) and (x_2, y_2).   This is the **two-point** form of the linear equation.

30. Using the form

$$y - y_1 = \left(\frac{y_2 - y_1}{x_2 - x_1}\right)(x - x_1),$$

find the equation of the lines through the given points.

a. $(2, 1)$ and $(-1, 3)$ b. $(3, 0)$ and $(5, 0)$
c. $(-2, 1)$ and $(3, -2)$ d. $(-1, -1)$ and $(1, 1)$

31. Consider the linear function

$$F = \{(x, y) \mid y = F(x)\}.$$

If $(2, 3)$ and $(-1, 4)$ are known to be in F, find $F(x)$ in terms of x.

5.7 SPECIAL FUNCTIONS

Functions involving the absolute value of one or both of the variables are useful in more advanced courses in mathematics, and offer interesting properties in their own right.   We recall that

$$|x| = \begin{cases} x, & \text{if } x \geq 0, \\ -x, & \text{if } x < 0. \end{cases}$$

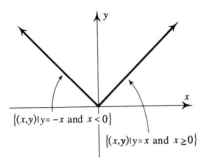

$\{(x,y) | y = -x \text{ and } x < 0\}$

$\{(x,y) | y = x \text{ and } x \geq 0\}$

Figure 5.17

Now consider the function defined by

$$y = |x|. \tag{1}$$

From the definition of $|x|$, for positive x we have

$$y = x, \tag{2}$$

and for negative x,

$$y = -x. \tag{3}$$

If we graph (2) and (3) on the same set of axes, we have the graph of $y = |x|$ (Figure 5.17). In the case of any equation involving $|x|$ or $|f(x)|$, we can always plot individual points to deduce the graph. For instance, if

$$y = |x| + 1, \tag{4}$$

we can find solutions by assigning values to x and computing values for y. Some solutions of (4) are

$$(-2, 3), (-1, 2), (0, 1), (1, 2), (2, 3),$$

which can be plotted as in Figure 5.18-a. The graph of $y = |x| + 1$,

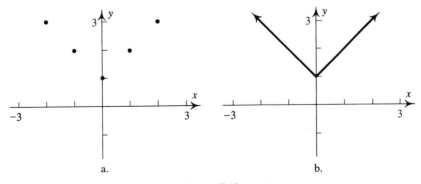

a.   b.

Figure 5.18

where $x \in R$, appears in Figure 5.18-b. As an alternate approach, the definition of $|x|$ implies that $y = |x| + 1$ is equivalent to

$$y = x + 1 \quad \text{for} \quad x \geq 0,$$
$$y = -x + 1 \quad \text{for} \quad x < 0,$$

and these can be graphed separately over the specified domains.

It is usually advisable, where possible, to avoid the plotting of large numbers of points. For instance, comparing Equations (1) and (4), that is,

$$y = |x| \tag{1}$$

and

$$y = |x| + 1, \tag{4}$$

we observe that for each x the ordinate in (4) is one unit greater than that in (1); consequently, the graph of (4) is simply the graph of (1) with each ordinate increased by 1. Whenever we can, we should use such considerations to help us graph equations.

Another interesting function (sometimes called the **bracket function**) is defined by the equation

$$f(x) = [x], \tag{5}$$

where the brackets denote "the greatest integer contained in," or "the greatest integer not greater than." Thus $[2] = 2$, $[\frac{7}{4}] = 1$, $[-2] = -2$, $[\frac{-3}{2}] = -2$, $[-\frac{5}{2}] = -3$, etc.

To graph (5), we consider unit intervals along the x-axis. If $0 \leq x < 1$, $[x]$ is 0, since the greatest integer contained in any number between 0 and 1 is 0. Similarly, if $1 \leq x < 2$, $[x]$ is 1; for $-2 \leq x < -1$, $[x]$ is -2; etc. The graph of (5), therefore, is as shown in Figure 5.19. The heavy dots on the left-hand end points of the line segments indicate that the end point is a part of the line segment. The function defined by (5) is sometimes called a "step function," for an obvious reason.

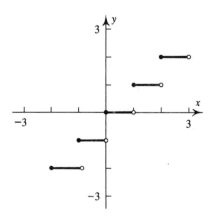

Figure 5.19

EXERCISE 5.7

Graph the function defined by the given equation over the domain $\{x \mid -5 \le x \le 5\}$.

1. $y = |x| + 2$ 2. $y = -|x| + 3$ 3. $f(x) = |x + 1|$

4. $F(x) = |x - 2|$ 5. $y = -|2x - 1|$ 6. $y = |3x + 2|$

7. $g(x) = |2x| - 3$ 8. $y = |3x| + 2$ 9. $y = |3x| - |x|$

10. $f(x) = |2x| + |x|$ 11. $y = 3|x| - x$ 12. $y = -2|x| + x$

13. $H(x) = |x^2|$ 14. $y = |x|^2$ 15. $y = |x + 1| - |x|$

16. $g(x) = |x + 1| - x$ 17. $y = [x]$ 18. $f(x) = [x] - 1$

19. $y = [x + 1]$ 20. $y = [2x]$ 21. $F(x) = [x] + x$

22. $y = \left[\frac{1}{2}x\right] + x$ 23. $y = [x] - x$ 24. $y = |[x]|$

25. The postage on a letter sent by first-class mail is c cents per ounce or fraction thereof. Write an equation relating the cost (C) of mailing a letter and the weight of the letter in ounces (x).

5.8   GRAPHS OF FIRST-DEGREE RELATIONS

An open sentence of the form

$$Ax + By + C \le 0,$$

or

$$Ax + By + C < 0,$$

A and B not both 0, is an inequality of the first degree and defines the relation

$$\{(x, y) \mid Ax + By + C \le 0\},$$

or

$$\{(x, y) \mid Ax + By + C < 0\}.$$

Such relations in $R \times R$ can be graphed on the plane, but the graph will be a region of the plane rather than a straight line. For example, consider the relation

$$S = \{(x, y) \mid 2x + y - 3 < 0\}. \tag{1}$$

When the defining relation is rewritten in the form

$$y < -2x + 3, \tag{2}$$

we see that solutions (x, y) are such that for each x, y is less than $-2x + 3$.

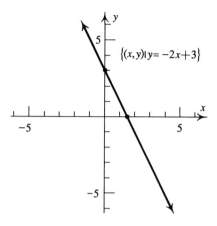

Figure 5.20

The graph of the equation

$$y = -2x + 3 \tag{3}$$

is simply a straight line, as illustrated in Figure 5.20.   To graph the relation
S, we need only observe that any point below this line has a y-coordinate
that satisfies (2), and consequently the solution set of (2), which is S, corresponds to the entire region below the line.   The region is indicated on the
graph with shading.   That the line itself is not in the graph is shown by
means of a broken line, as in Figure 5.21.   Had the inequality been

$$2x + y - 3 \leq 0,$$

the line would be a part of the graph and would be shown as a solid line.

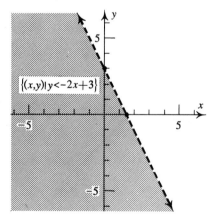

Figure 5.21

In general,

$$\{(x, y) \mid Ax + By + C < 0\}$$

or

$$\{(x, y) \mid Ax + By + C > 0\}$$

are the coordinates of all points in a half-plane on one side of the graph of

$$Ax + By + C = 0,$$

depending on the constants and inequality symbols involved.

Inequalities do not ordinarily define functions, according to our definition in Section 5.4, because it usually is not true that each element of the replacement set for the independent variable is associated with a unique element in the replacement set of the dependent variable. As an exception, though, consider the inequality $|x - y| \leq 0$, which is equivalent to the equation $x - y = 0$.

EXERCISE 5.8

Graph the relation.

Example. $\{(x, y) \mid 2x + y \geq 4\}$

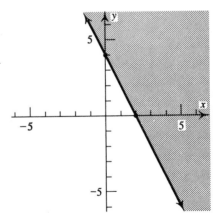

Solution. Solve the defining equation explicitly for y.

$$y \geq 4 - 2x$$

Graph the equality $y = 4 - 2x$.

Shade area above the graph of $y = 4 - 2x$.

Line is included in graph.

1. $\{(x, y) \mid y < x\}$

2. $\{(x, y) \mid y > x\}$

3. $\{(x, y) \mid y \leq x + 2\}$ 4. $\{(x, y) \mid y \geq x - 2\}$

5. $\{(x, y) \mid x + y < 5\}$ 6. $\{(x, y) \mid 2x + y < 2\}$

7. $\{(x, y) \mid x - y < 3\}$ 8. $\{(x, y) \mid x - 2y < 5\}$

9. $\{(x, y) \mid x \leq 2y - 4\}$ 10. $\{(x, y) \mid 2x \leq y + 1\}$

11. $\{(x, y) \mid 3 \geq 2x - 2y\}$ 12. $\{(x, y) \mid 0 \geq x + y\}$

Example. $\{(x, y) \mid x > 2\}$

Solution. Graph $\{(x, y) \mid x = 2\}$.

Shade area to the right
of the graph.

Line is excluded from graph.

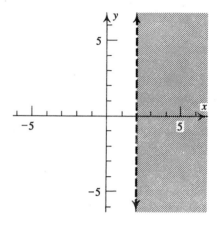

13. $\{(x, y) \mid x > 0\}$

14. $\{(x, y) \mid y < 0\}$

15. $\{(x, y) \mid x < 0\}$

16. $\{(x, y) \mid x < -2\}$

17. $\{(x, y) \mid -1 < x < 5\}$

18. $\{(x, y) \mid 0 \leq y \leq 1\}$

19. $\{(x, y) \mid |x| < 3\}$

20. $\{(x, y) \mid |y| > 1\}$

21. $\{(x, y) \mid |x| + |y| \leq 1\}$

22. $\{(x, y) \mid |x| + |y| \geq 1\}$

    Hint: Consider the graphs in each quadrant separately; $x, y \geq 0$; $x \leq 0$, $y \geq 0$; $x, y \leq 0$; and $x \geq 0$, $y \leq 0$.

23. $\{(x, y) \mid x + |x| = y\}$

24. $\{(x, y) \mid x - |x| = y\}$

6

RELATIONS
AND FUNCTIONS II

6.1 THE GRAPH OF THE QUADRATIC FUNCTION

Consider the quadratic equation in two variables,

$$y = x^2 - 4. \tag{1}$$

As with linear equations in two variables, solutions of this equation must be ordered pairs (x, y). We need replacements for both x and y in order to obtain a statement we may adjudge to be true or false. As before, such ordered pairs can be found by arbitrarily assigning values to x and computing related values for y. For instance, assigning the value -3 to x in Equation (1), we obtain

$$y = (-3)^2 - 4,$$

$$y = 5,$$

and $(-3, 5)$ is a solution. Similarly, we find that

$$(-2, 0), (-1, -3), (0, -4), (1, -3), (2, 0), \text{ and } (3, 5)$$

are also solutions of (1). Plotting the corresponding points on the plane, we have the graph in Figure 6.1. Clearly, these points do not lie on a straight line, and we might reasonably inquire whether the graph of the solution set of (1),

$$S = \{(x, y) \mid y = x^2 - 4\},$$

forms any kind of a meaningful pattern on the plane. By plotting additional

163

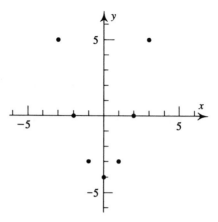

Figure 6.1

solutions of (1)—solutions with x-components between those already found—
we may be able to obtain a clearer picture. Accordingly, we find the
solutions

$$\left(\frac{-5}{2}, \frac{9}{4}\right), \left(\frac{-3}{2}, \frac{-7}{4}\right), \left(\frac{-1}{2}, \frac{-15}{4}\right), \left(\frac{1}{2}, \frac{-15}{4}\right), \left(\frac{3}{2}, \frac{-7}{4}\right), \left(\frac{5}{2}, \frac{9}{4}\right),$$

and by plotting these points in addition to those found earlier, we have the
graph in Figure 6.2. It now appears reasonable to connect these points in
sequence, say from left to right, by a smooth curve as in Figure 6.3, and to
assume that the resulting curve is a good approximation to the graph of (1).
(We should realize, of course, that regardless of how many individual
points are plotted, we have no absolute assurance that the smooth curve is a

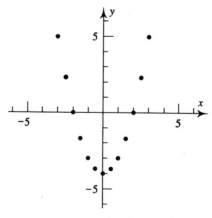

Figure 6.2

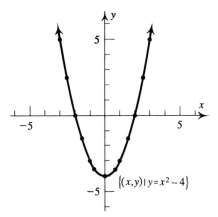

$$\{(x,y) \mid y = x^2 - 4\}$$

Figure 6.3

good approximation to the true graph; more information is needed—for example, in this case, that for $|x_2| > |x_1|$ we have correspondingly $y_2 > y_1$.) This curve is an example of a **parabola**.

More generally, the graph of the solution set of any quadratic equation of the form

$$y = ax^2 + bx + c, \tag{2}$$

where a, b, and c are real and $a \neq 0$, is a parabola.   Since for each x an equation of the form (2) will determine only one y, such an equation defines a function having as domain the entire set of real numbers and as range some subset of the reals.   For example, we observe from the graph (Figure 6.3) that the range of the function defined by (1) is the set of real numbers

$$\{y \mid y \geq -4\}.$$

To show that there is a lowest (or else a highest) point on the graph (2), we can proceed as follows, by completing the square:

$$y = ax^2 + bx + c \quad (a \neq 0)$$

$$= a\left(x^2 + \frac{b}{a}x + \frac{c}{a}\right)$$

$$= a\left(x^2 + \frac{b}{a}x + \frac{b^2}{4a^2} - \frac{b^2}{4a^2} + \frac{c}{a}\right)$$

$$= a\left(x^2 + \frac{b}{a}x + \frac{b^2}{4a^2}\right) - \frac{b^2 - 4ac}{4a}$$

$$= a\left(x + \frac{b}{2a}\right)^2 - \frac{b^2 - 4ac}{4a}. \tag{3}$$

Now if $a > 0$, then the first term on the right is 0 at $x = -b/2a$, and otherwise this term is positive; hence the lowest point on the graph is

$$\left(\frac{-b}{2a}, -\frac{b^2 - 4ac}{4a}\right). \tag{4}$$

Similarly, if $a < 0$, then the first term on the right in (3) is negative except at $x = -b/2a$, and accordingly (4) gives the highest point on the graph in this case.

In graphing a quadratic equation, it is desirable—since the entire infinite extent of the graph cannot be shown—to select first components for the ordered pairs that will ensure that the more significant parts of the parabola will be displayed.   These parts include the intercepts and the maximum or minimum (highest or lowest) point on the curve.

The graph of the function

$$S = \{[x, f(x)] \mid f(x) = ax^2 + bx + c\} \tag{5}$$

can be used to obtain the solution set of the equation

$$ax^2 + bx + c = 0. \tag{6}$$

Any value of x for which $f(x) = 0$ in (5) will be a solution of (6).   Since any point on the x-axis has y-coordinate zero [i.e., $f(x) = 0$], the x-intercepts of the graph of (2) are the real solutions of (6).   Values of x for which $f(x) = 0$ are called the **zeros of the function**.   Thus we have three different names for a single idea:

1. The *elements of the solution set* of the equation $ax^2 + bx + c = 0$. These are called the *solutions* or *roots* of the equation.
2. The *zeros of the function* defined by $f(x) = ax^2 + bx + c$.
3. The *x-intercepts* of the graph of the equation $f(x) = ax^2 + bx + c$.

Applying this concept to find the solution set for

$$2x^2 - x - 10 = 0, \tag{7}$$

we graph

$$\{[x, f(x)] \mid f(x) = 2x^2 - x - 10\}. \tag{8}$$

The graph (Figure 6.4) has x-intercepts -2 and $5/2$, so that the zeros of the function (8) are -2 and $5/2$, and the solution set of (7) is $\{-2, 5/2\}$.

The best we can ordinarily expect from a graphical solution is an approximation to the actual solution.   If the equation we are trying to solve in this way has integral solutions or relatively simple rational solutions, we may happen to hit on exact results; in general, however, we have to estimate the intercepts.

We recall from Chapter 4 that a quadratic equation may have no real solution, one real solution, or two real solutions.   If the equation has no

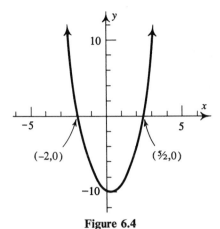

Figure 6.4

real solutions, we find that the graph of the related quadratic equation in two variables does not touch the *x*-axis; if there is one solution, the graph is tangent to the *x*-axis; if there are two real solutions, the graph crosses the *x*-axis in two distinct points (Figure 6.5).

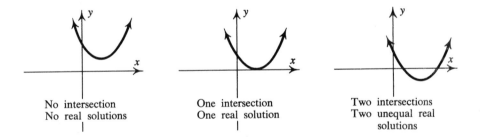

No intersection
No real solutions

One intersection
One real solution

Two intersections
Two unequal real
solutions

Figure 6.5

EXERCISE 6.1

Graph.   Select first components for the solutions so that the *x*-intercepts and the maximum or minimum point of the curve are displayed.

$f(x) = ax^2 + bx + c$

1. $\{(x, y) \mid y = x^2 - 5x + 4\}$

2. $\{[x, g(x)] \mid g(x) = x^2 - 3x + 2\}$

3. $\{[x, f(x)] \mid f(x) = -x^2 + 5x - 4\}$

4. $\{(x, y) \mid y = -x^2 + 3x - 2\}$

5. $\{(x, y) \mid y = x^2 - 6x - 7\}$

6. $\{[x, f(x)] \mid f(x) = -x^2 - 8x + 9\}$

7. $\left\{[x, g(x)] \mid g(x) = \frac{1}{2} x^2 + 2\right\}$

8. $\left\{(x, y) \mid y = -\frac{1}{2} x^2 - 2x\right\}$

9–16. For the graph of each quadratic function in 1–8 above, obtain the
x-intercepts and the maximum or minimum point by analytic methods.

Example. $\{(x, y) \mid y = x^2 - 7x + 6\}$

Solution.   Since the solution set of $x^2 - 7x + 6 = 0$ is $\{1, 6\}$, the x-intercepts
are $(1, 0)$ and $(6, 0)$.   By completing the square in the right-hand member of

$$y = x^2 - 7x + 6,$$

we obtain

$$y = \left(x^2 - 7x + \frac{49}{4}\right) - \frac{49}{4} + 6,$$

or

$$y = \left(x - \frac{7}{2}\right)^2 - \frac{25}{4}.$$

For $x = 7/2$, y has a minimum value $-25/4$.   Therefore, the minimum point is
at $(7/2, -25/4)$.

17. Graph $\{[x, f(x)] \mid f(x) = x^2 + 1\}$.   Represent $f(0)$ and $f(4)$ by drawing line
segments from $(0, 0)$ to $[0, f(0)]$ and from $(4, 0)$ to $[4, f(4)]$.

18. Graph $\{[x, g(x)] \mid g(x) = x^2 + 1\}$.   Represent $f(-3)$ and $f(2)$ by drawing
line segments from $(-3, 0)$ to $[-3, f(-3)]$ and from $(2, 0)$ to $[2, f(2)]$.

By means of a graph, estimate the members of the solution set of each of the
following equations; in each case compute the discriminant of the equation.

Example. $x^2 + 4 = 0$

Solution.   Graph $\{(x, y) \mid y = x^2 + 4\}$.

Curve does not cross the axis; therefore
there are no real zeros of the function.

The solution set in R is $\emptyset$.

Discriminant: $b^2 - 4ac = 0 - 16$
$= -16.$

19. $x^2 - 3x = 0$

20. $2x^2 - 5x = 0$

21. $x^2 - 6x + 9 = 0$

22. $4 + 3x - x^2 = 0$

23. $x^2 - 3x - 10 = 0$ 24. $x^2 - 2x + 1 = 0$

25. $16 - x^2 = 0$ 26. $x^2 - 25 = 0$

Solve Problems 27–29 by completing the square.

27. Find two numbers having sum 8 and product as large as possible.

28. Find two numbers having sum 12 and product as large as possible.

29. Find the maximum area of a rectangle with perimeter 100 inches.

30. Graph the relation $\{(x, y) \mid x = y^2\}$.
    a. What kind of a curve is the graph?
    b. Is the given relation a function? Why or why not?

31. Graph the relation $\{(x, y) \mid x = y^2 - 2y\}$.
    a. What kind of a curve is the graph?
    b. Is the given relation a function? Why or why not?

Graph each of the following relations.

32. $\{(x, y) \mid x = y^2 - 4\}$ 33. $\{(x, y) \mid x = y^2 - 2y - 3\}$

34. $\{(x, y) \mid x = y^2 - 4y + 4\}$ 35. $\{(x, y) \mid x = 2y^2 + 3y - 2\}$

6.2 CONIC SECTIONS

In addition to $y = ax^2 + bx + c$, there are three other types of second-degree equations in two variables with graphs that are of particular interest. We shall discuss each of them separately.

First, consider the relation

$$\{(x, y) \mid x^2 + y^2 = 25\}. \tag{1}$$

Solving the defining equation explicitly for y, we have

$$y = \pm \sqrt{25 - x^2}. \tag{2}$$

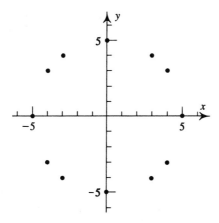

Figure 6.6

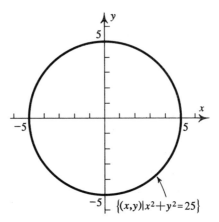

Figure 6.7

Assigning values to x, we find the following ordered pairs in the relation:

$$(-5, 0), (-4, 3), (-3, 4), (0, 5), (3, 4), (4, 3), (5, 0),$$
$$(-4, -3), (-3, -4), (0, -5), (3, -4), (4, -3).$$

Plotting these points on the plane, we have the graph shown in Figure 6.6.

Connecting these points with a smooth curve, we obtain the graph in Figure 6.7, a circle with radius 5 and center at the origin.

Since the number 25 in the right-hand member of (1) is clearly the determining factor in the length of the radius of the circle, we can generalize and observe that any relation defined by an equation of the form

$$x^2 + y^2 = r^2$$

has as its graph a circle with radius r and with center at the origin. (See Problem 39, Exercise 6.2 for a more general approach.)

Note that in the preceding example it is not necessary to assign any values to x satisfying $|x| > 5$, because y^2 is negative for these values of x. Since, except for -5 and $+5$, each permissible value for x is associated with two values for y—one positive and one negative—the relation (1) is not a function. We could represent the relationship specified by (2) by using two equations,

$$y = f(x) = \sqrt{25 - x^2} \tag{3}$$

and

$$y = g(x) = -\sqrt{25 - x^2}, \tag{3a}$$

whose graphs would appear as in Figure 6.8. Each of these equations does define a function. In both cases, the domain of the function is

$$\{x \mid |x| \leq 5\},$$

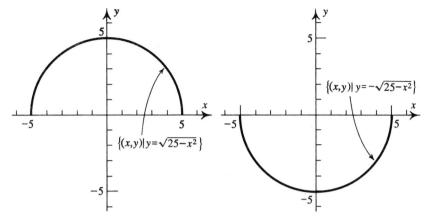

Figure 6.8

while the ranges differ.   The range of the function defined by (3) is

$$\{y \mid 0 \le y \le 5\},$$

and that of the function defined by (3a) is

$$\{y \mid -5 \le y \le 0\}.$$

The second quadratic (second-degree) relation of interest, which actually has the first as a limiting case, is that typified by

$$\{(x, y) \mid 4x^2 + 9y^2 = 36\}. \tag{4}$$

We obtain members of (4) by first solving the defining equation explicitly for y,

$$y = \pm\frac{2}{3}\sqrt{9 - x^2},$$

and assigning to x values satisfying $-3 \le x \le 3$.   (Why these values only?) We obtain, for example,

$$(-3, 0), \left(-2, \frac{2}{3}\sqrt{5}\right), \left(-1, \frac{4}{3}\sqrt{2}\right), (0, 2), \left(1, \frac{4}{3}\sqrt{2}\right), \left(2, \frac{2}{3}\sqrt{5}\right), (3, 0),$$

$$\left(-2, -\frac{2}{3}\sqrt{5}\right), \left(-1, -\frac{4}{3}\sqrt{2}\right), (0, -2), \left(1, -\frac{4}{3}\sqrt{2}\right), \left(2, -\frac{2}{3}\sqrt{5}\right).$$

Locating the corresponding points on the plane and connecting them with a smooth curve, we have the graph shown in Figure 6.9.   This curve is called an **ellipse**.

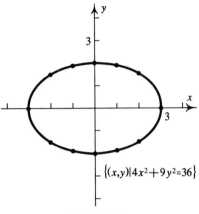

$\{(x,y)|4x^2+9y^2=36\}$

Figure 6.9

In general, the graph of the relation

$$\{(x, y) \mid Ax^2 + By^2 = C \quad (A, B, C > 0, A \neq B)\}$$

is an ellipse with center at the origin, x-intercepts $\pm \sqrt{C/A}$ and y-intercepts $\pm \sqrt{C/B}$.

The third quadratic relation with which we are presently concerned is typified by

$$\{(x, y) \mid x^2 - y^2 = 9\}.$$

Solving the defining equation for y, we obtain

$$y = \pm \sqrt{x^2 - 9},$$

which has as a part of its solution set the ordered pairs

$$(-5, 4), (-4, \sqrt{7}), (-3, 0), (3, 0), (4, \sqrt{7}), (5, 4),$$

$$(-5, -4), (-4, -\sqrt{7}), (4, -\sqrt{7}), (5, -4).$$

Plotting the corresponding points and connecting them with a smooth curve, we obtain the curve shown in Figure 6.10. This curve is called a **hyperbola**. In general, the relation

$$\{(x, y) \mid Ax^2 - By^2 = C \ (A, B, C > 0)\}$$

graphs into a hyperbola with center at the origin and x-intercepts $\pm \sqrt{C/A}$, and the relation

$$\{(x, y) \mid By^2 - Ax^2 = C \ (A, B, C > 0)\}$$

graphs into a hyperbola with center at the origin and y-intercepts at $\pm \sqrt{C/B}$.

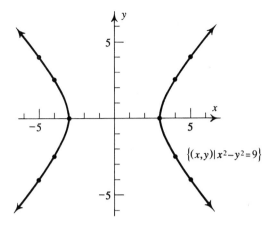

Figure 6.10

The graphs of the foregoing relations, together with the parabola of the preceding section, are called **conic sections** or **conics** because such curves result from the intersection of a plane and a cone (Figure 6.11).

We should make use of the form of the defining equation as an aid in graphing quadratic relations. With this in mind, the ideas developed in this and the preceding section may be summarized as follows:

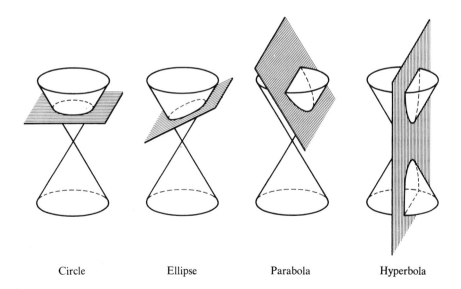

Circle   Ellipse   Parabola   Hyperbola

Figure 6.11

1. A quadratic equation of the form

$$y = ax^2 + bx + c, \quad a \neq 0, \tag{5}$$

has a graph that is a parabola, opening upward if $a > 0$ and downward if $a < 0$. Similarly, an equation of the form $x = ay^2 + by + c$, $a \neq 0$, has a graph that is a parabola, opening to the right if $a > 0$ and to the left if $a < 0$.

2. A quadratic equation of the form

$$Ax^2 + By^2 = C, \quad A^2 + B^2 \neq 0, \tag{6}$$

has a graph that is

(a) a circle if $A = B$ and A, B, and C have like signs;
(b) an ellipse if $A \neq B$ and A, B, and C have like signs;
(c) a hyperbola if A and B are opposite in sign and $C \neq 0$;
(d) two distinct lines through the origin if A and B are opposite in sign and $C = 0$ (see Problem 35, Exercise 6.2);
(e) two distinct parallel lines if one of A and $B = 0$ and the other has the same sign as C (see Problem 36, Exercise 6.2);
(f) two coincident parallel lines (one line) through the origin if one of A and $B = 0$ and also $C = 0$;
(g) a point if A and B are both > 0 or both < 0 and $C = 0$ (see Problem 37, Exercise 6.2);
(h) the null set, $\emptyset$, if A and B are both ≥ 0 and $C < 0$, or if A and B are both < 0 and $C > 0$ (see Problem 38, Exercise 6.2).

After we recognize the general form of the curve, the graph of a few points should suffice to sketch the complete graph. The intercepts, for instance, are always easy to locate. Consider the relation

$$\{(x, y) \mid x^2 + 4y^2 = 8\}. \tag{7}$$

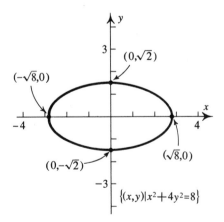

Figure 6.12

By comparing the defining equation with 2(b), we note immediately that its graph is an ellipse. If $y = 0$, then $x = \pm\sqrt{8}$, and if $x = 0$, then $y = \pm\sqrt{2}$. We can accordingly sketch the graph of (7) as in Figure 6.12.

As another example, consider the relation

$$\{(x, y) \mid x^2 - y^2 = 3\}. \tag{8}$$

By comparing the defining equation with 2(c), we see that its graph is a hyperbola. If $y = 0$, then $x = \pm\sqrt{3}$, and if $x = 0$, then y^2 would have to be negative, an impossibility in the field of real numbers (see Theorem 1.14). Thus the graph will not cross the y-axis. By assigning a few other arbitrary values to one of the variables, say x, e.g., $(4, \quad)$ and $(-4, \quad)$, we can find additional ordered pairs

$$(4, \sqrt{13}), (4, -\sqrt{13}), (-4, \sqrt{13}), (-4, -\sqrt{13})$$

which satisfy (8). The graph can then be sketched as shown in Figure 6.13.

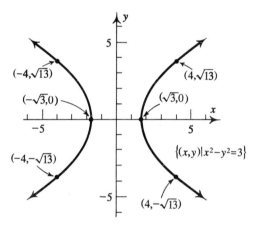

Figure 6.13

EXERCISE 6.2

(a) Rewrite each of the defining equations equivalently with y as the left-hand member.

(b) Write each equation equivalently as two separate equations, each of which defines a function.

(c) State the domain and range of each of the functions defined in (b).

Example. $\{(x, y) \mid 4x^2 + y^2 = 36\}$

Solution.

(a) $y^2 = 36 - 4x^2$

    $y = \pm 2\sqrt{9 - x^2}$

(b) $y = 2\sqrt{9 - x^2}$

    $y = -2\sqrt{9 - x^2}$

(c) The domain is $\{x \mid -3 \leq x \leq 3\}$.

    The first range is $\{y \mid 0 \leq y \leq 6\}$.   The second range is $\{y \mid -6 \leq y \leq 0\}$.

1. $\{(x, y) \mid x^2 + y^2 = 4\}$

2. $\{(x, y) \mid x^2 + y^2 = 9\}$

3. $\{(x, y) \mid 9x^2 + y^2 = 36\}$

4. $\{(x, y) \mid 4x^2 + y^2 = 4\}$

5. $\{(x, y) \mid x^2 + 4y^2 = 16\}$

6. $\{(x, y) \mid x^2 + 9y^2 = 4\}$

7. $\{(x, y) \mid 2x^2 + 3y^2 = 24\}$

8. $\{(x, y) \mid 4x^2 + 3y^2 = 12\}$

9. $\{(x, y) \mid x^2 - y^2 = 1\}$

10. $\{(x, y) \mid 4x^2 - y^2 = 1\}$

11. $\{(x, y) \mid y^2 - x^2 = 9\}$

12. $\{(x, y) \mid 4y^2 - 9x^2 = 36\}$

Sketch the graph of each of the following relations.

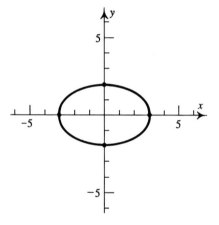

Example. $\{(x, y) \mid 4x^2 - 36 = -9y^2\}$

Solution.   Rewrite the defining equation equivalently in standard form.

$$4x^2 + 9y^2 = 36$$

By inspection, the graph is an ellipse.

Intercepts are $(0, 2)$, $(0, -2)$, $(3, 0)$, $(-3, 0)$.

Sketch the graph.

13. $\{(x, y) \mid x^2 + y^2 = 49\}$

14. $\{(x, y) \mid x^2 + y^2 = 64\}$

15. $\{(x, y) \mid x^2 + 9y = 0\}$

16. $\{(x, y) \mid 2x^2 - y = 0\}$

17. $\{(x, y) \mid 3x^2 + 25y^2 = 100\}$

18. $\{(x, y) \mid x^2 + 2y^2 = 8\}$

19. $\{(x, y) \mid x^2 = 9 + y^2\}$

20. $\{(x, y) \mid x^2 = 2y^2 + 8\}$

21. $\{(x, y) \mid 4x^2 = 4y^2\}$

22. $\{(x, y) \mid x^2 - 9y^2 = 0\}$

23. $\{(x, y) \mid 4 = x^2 - y\}$

24. $\{(x, y) \mid y = 4 - 2x^2\}$

25. $\{(x, y) \mid 4x^2 + 4y^2 = 1\}$

26. $\{(x, y) \mid 9x^2 + 9y^2 = 2\}$

27. $\{(x, y) \mid 3x^2 - 12 = -4y^2\}$

28. $\{(x, y) \mid 12 - 3y^2 = 4x^2\}$

29. $\{(x, y) \mid y - 4 = 3x - x^2\}$

30. $\{(x, y) \mid y = x^2 - 3x + 12\}$

31. $\{(x, y) \mid y = -x^2 - 5x + 4\}$

32. $\{(x, y) \mid x^2 + y = x + 2\}$

33. Sketch the family of four curves that are graphs of the function defined by $y = x^2 + k$ $(k = -2, 0, 2, 4)$ on a single set of axes. What effect does varying k have on the graph?

34. Graph $\{(x, y) \mid x^2 + y^2 = 25\}$ and $\{(x, y) \mid 4x^2 + y^2 = 36\}$ on the same set of axes. What is the significance of the coordinates of the points of intersection?

35. Graph $\{(x, y) \mid 4x^2 - y^2 = 0\}$. Generalize from the result and discuss the graph of any relation of the form $\{(x, y) \mid Ax^2 - By^2 = 0 \ (A, B > 0)\}$. .

36. Graph $\{(x, y) \mid x^2 = 4\}$. Generalize from the result and discuss the graph of any relation of the form $\{(x, y) \mid Ax^2 = C, \quad A, C > 0\}$.

37. Graph $\{(x, y) \mid 4x^2 + y^2 = 0\}$. Generalize from the result and discuss the graph of any relation of the form $\{(x, y) \mid Ax^2 + By^2 = 0, \quad A, B > 0\}$.

38. Explain why the graph of $\{(x, y) \mid x^2 + y^2 = -1\}$ is the null set. Generalize from the result and discuss the graph of any relation of the form

$$\{(x, y) \mid Ax^2 + By^2 = C, A^2 + B^2 \neq 0, \quad A, B > 0, C < 0\}.$$

39. Use the distance formula to show that the graph of $\{(x, y) \mid x^2 + y^2 = r^2\}$ is the set of all points located a distance r from the origin.

40. Show that the graph of $\{(x, y) \mid (x - h)^2 + (y - k)^2 = r^2\}$ is a circle with center at (h, k) and radius r. *Hint:* use distance formula.

41. By solving $Ax^2 - By^2 = C$ $(A, B, C > 0)$ for y, obtain the expression

$$y = \pm \sqrt{\frac{A}{B}} \, |x| \left(\sqrt{1 - \frac{C}{Ax^2}} \right)$$

and argue that the graph of $Ax^2 - By^2 = C$ approaches the graphs of $y = \pm \sqrt{A/B}|x|$ as $|x|$ increases. *Note:* these lines are called the *asymptotes* of the hyperbola. See Section 6.6.

6.3   VARIATION AS A FUNCTIONAL RELATIONSHIP

There are two types of functional relationships, widely used in the sciences, to which custom has assigned special names. First, any function defined by the equation

$$y = kx \quad (k \text{ a constant} \neq 0) \tag{1}$$

is an example of **direct variation**. The variable y is said to **vary directly** as the variable x. Another example of direct variation is

$$y = kx^2 \quad (k \text{ a constant} \neq 0), \tag{1a}$$

which indicates that y varies directly as the square of x. In general,

$$y = kx^n \quad (k \text{ a constant} \neq 0 \text{ and } n > 0) \tag{1b}$$

asserts that y varies directly as the nth power of x.

We find examples of such variation in the relationships existing between the radius of a circle and the circumference and area.   Thus

$$c = 2\pi r \tag{2}$$

asserts that the circumference of a circle varies directly as the radius, while

$$A = \pi r^2 \tag{3}$$

expresses the fact that the area of a circle varies directly as the square of the radius.   Since for each r, (2) and (3) associate only one value of c or A, both of these equations define functions; (2) is a linear function and (3) is a quadratic function.

The second important type of variation arises from the equation

$$xy = k \quad (k \text{ a constant} \neq 0), \tag{4}$$

where x and y are said to **vary inversely**.   When (4) is written in the form

$$y = \frac{k}{x}, \tag{5}$$

y is said to vary inversely as x.   Similarly, if

$$y = \frac{k}{x^2}, \tag{5a}$$

y is said to vary inversely as the square of x, etc.   As an example of inverse variation, consider the set of rectangles with area 24 square units.   Since the area of a rectangle is given by

$$lw = A,$$

we have

$$lw = 24,$$

and the length and width of the rectangle can be seen to vary inversely.

Since (5) or (5a) associates only one y with each x ($x \neq 0$), an inverse variation defines a function, with domain

$$\{x \mid x \neq 0\}.$$

The names "direct" and "inverse" as applied to variation arise from the fact that in direct variation, an assignment of increasing absolute values of x results in an association with increasing absolute values of y, whereas in inverse variation, an assignment of increasing absolute values of x results in an association with decreasing absolute values of y.

The constant involved in equations defining direct or inverse variation is called the **constant of variation**.   If we know that one variable varies directly or inversely as another, and if we have one set of associated values for the variables, we can find the constant of variation involved. For example, suppose we know that y varies directly as x^2, and that $y = 4$ when $x = 7$. We express the fact that y varies directly as x^2 by writing

$$y = kx^2, \tag{6}$$

and then substitute 7 for x and 4 for y in (6) to obtain

$$4 = k(7^2) = k(49),$$

from which

$$k = \frac{4}{49}.$$

The equation specifically expressing the direct variation is

$$y = \frac{4}{49}x^2.$$

In the event that one variable varies as the product of two or more other variables, we refer to the relationship as **joint variation**. Thus, if y varies jointly as u, v, and w, we have

$$y = kuvw. \tag{7}$$

Also, direct and inverse variation may take place concurrently. That is, y may vary directly as x and inversely as z, giving rise to the equation

$$y = k\frac{x}{z}.$$

It should be pointed out that the way in which the word "variation" is used herein is a technical one, and when the ideas of direct, inverse, or joint variation are encountered, you should always think of equations of the form (1), (5), or (7). For instance, the equations

$$y = 2x + 1,$$

$$y = \frac{1}{x} - 2,$$

and

$$y = xz + 2$$

do not describe examples of variation within our meaning of the word.

There is an alternative term used to describe the variation relationship discussed in this section. The word "proportional" is frequently used in this sense. To say that "y is directly proportional to x" or "y is inversely proportional to x" is another way of describing direct and inverse variation.

The use of the word "proportion" arises from the fact that any two solutions of an equation expressing a direct variation satisfy a fractional equation of the form

$$\frac{a}{b} = \frac{c}{d},$$

which is commonly called a proportion. For example, consider the problem in which the volume of a gas varies directly as the absolute temperature and inversely as the pressure, and can accordingly be represented by a relation of the form

$$V = \frac{kT}{P}. \tag{8}$$

For any set of values T_1, P_1, and V_1,

$$k = \frac{V_1 P_1}{T_1}, \tag{8a}$$

and for any other set of values T_2, P_2, and V_2,

$$k = \frac{V_2 P_2}{T_2}. \tag{8b}$$

Equating the right-hand members of (8a) and (8b), we get

$$\frac{V_1 P_1}{T_1} = \frac{V_2 P_2}{T_2}, \tag{8c}$$

from which any one of the six values can be determined if the other five values are known.

EXERCISE 6.3

Solve.

Example. If V varies directly as T and inversely as P, and $V = 40$ when $T = 300$ and $P = 30$, find V when $T = 324$ and $P = 24$.

Solution. Write an equation expressing the relationship between the variables.

$$V = \frac{kT}{P} \tag{1}$$

Substitute the initially known values for V, T, and P. Solve for k.

$$40 = \frac{k(300)}{30}$$

$$4 = k$$

Rewrite Equation (1) with k replaced by 4.

$$V = \frac{4T}{P}$$

Substitute the second set of values for T and P and solve for V.

$$V = \frac{4(324)}{24} = 54$$

1. If y varies directly as x^2, and $y = 9$ when $x = 3$, find y when $x = 4$.

2. If r varies directly as s and inversely as t, and $r = 12$ when $s = 8$ and $t = 2$, find r when $s = 3$ and $t = 6$.

3. The distance a particle falls in a certain medium is directly proportional to the square of the length of time it falls. If the particle falls 16 feet in two seconds, how far will it fall in 10 seconds?

4. In Problem 3, how far will the body fall *during* the seventh second?

5. The pressure exerted by a liquid at a given point varies directly as the depth of the point beneath the surface of the liquid. If a certain liquid exerts a pressure of 40 pounds per square foot at a depth of 10 feet, what would be the pressure at 40 feet?

6. The volume (V) of a gas varies directly as its temperature (T) and inversely as its pressure (P). A gas occupies 20 cubic feet at a temperature of $300°\,A$ (absolute) and a pressure of 30 pounds per square inch. What will the volume be if the temperature is raised to $360°\,A$ and the pressure decreased to 20 pounds per square inch?

7. The maximum-safe uniformly distributed load (L) for a horizontal beam varies jointly as its breadth (b) and the square of the depth (d), and inversely as the length (l). An 8-foot beam with $b = 2$ feet and $d = 4$ feet will safely support a uniformly distributed load of up to 750 pounds. How many uniformly distributed pounds will an 8-foot beam support if $b = 2$ and $d = 6$?

8. The resistance (R) of a wire varies directly as the length (l) and inversely as the square of its diameter (d). Fifty feet of wire of diameter 0.012 inches has a resistance of 10 ohms. What is the resistance of 50 feet of the same type of wire if the diameter is increased to 0.015 inches?

Represent the relationship as a proportion by eliminating the constant of variation and then solving for the required variable.

Example. If V varies directly as T and inversely as P, and $V = 40$ when $T = 300$ and $P = 30$, find V when $T = 324$ and $P = 24$.

Solution.   Write an equation expressing the relationship between the variables.

$$V = \frac{kT}{P}$$

Solve for k.

$$k = \frac{VP}{T}$$

Write a proportion relating the variables for two different sets of conditions.

$$\frac{V_1 P_1}{T_1} = \frac{V_2 P_2}{T_2}$$

Substitute the known values of the variables.

$$\frac{(40)(30)}{300} = \frac{V_2(24)}{324}$$

Solve for V_2.

$$V_2 = \frac{(324)(40)(30)}{300(24)} = 54$$

9. Problem 1 of this set.   10. Problem 2 of this set.

11. Problem 5 of this set.   12. Problem 6 of this set.

13. Problem 7 of this set.   14. Problem 8 of this set.

15. From the formula for the circumference of a circle, $c = \pi d$, show that the ratio of the circumference of two circles equals the ratio of their respective diameters.

16. From the formula for the area of a circle, $A = \pi r^2$, show that the ratio of the areas of two circles equals the ratio of the squares of their respective radii.

17. Graph on the same set of axes the linear functions defined by $y = kx$, $x \geq 0$, when $k = -3, -2, -1, 1, 2$, and 3, respectively.   Note that the constant of variation and the slope of the graph of the equation are the same.

18. Graph on the same set of axes the quadratic functions defined by $y = kx^2$, $x \geq 0$, when $k = -3, -2, -1, 1, 2$, and 3, respectively.   What effect does a change in k have on the graph of $y = kx^2$?

19. Graph on the same set of axes the equations $y = kx$, $y = kx^2$, and $y = kx^3$, when $k = 2$ and $x \geq 0$.   What effect does increasing n have on the graph of $y = kx^n$?

20. Graph on the same set of axes the functions defined by $xy = k$, for $k = -2$, $-1, 1, 2$, and $x > 0$.   What effect does a change in k have on the graph of the function?

21. Graph on the same set of axes the functions defined by $xy = k$, $x^2y = k$, and $x^3y = k$, for $k = 2$ and $x > 0$.   What effect does increasing n have on the graph of $x^n y = k$?

22. Show that if y varies directly as x and z varies directly as x, then $y + z$ varies directly as x.

23. Show that if y varies directly as x and z varies directly as x, then $\sqrt{yz}$ varies directly as x, for $x \geq 0$.

6.4 GRAPHS OF QUADRATIC INEQUALITIES

Relations of the form

$$\{(x, y) \mid y < ax^2 + bx + c\} \tag{1}$$

or

$$\{(x, y) \mid y > ax^2 + bx + c\} \tag{2}$$

can be graphed in the same manner in which we graphed relations defined by linear inequalities in two variables.   We first graph the relation defined

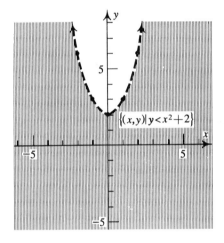

Figure 6.14

by the equation having the same members as the defining inequality and then shade an appropriate region as required.   For instance, to graph

$$\{(x, y) \mid y < x^2 + 2\}, \tag{3}$$

we first graph

$$\{(x, y) \mid y = x^2 + 2\} \tag{4}$$

and then shade the area below the curve.   Since the graph of (4) is not part of the graph of (3), a broken curve is used (Figure 6.14).

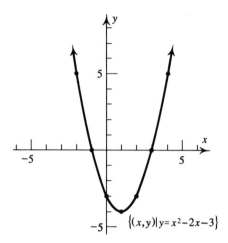

Figure 6.15

The solution set of certain inequalities in one variable can be obtained by graphical methods. For example, to find the solution set of

$$x^2 - 2x - 3 \leq 0, \tag{5}$$

we first graph the relation

$$\{(x, y) \mid y = x^2 - 2x - 3\} \tag{6}$$

as shown in Figure 6.15. Now the values of x for which the graph of $\{(x, y) \mid y = x^2 - 2x - 3\}$ lies on or below the x-axis—that is, for which

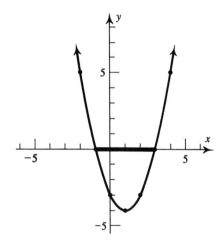

Figure 6.16

$y \le 0$ and therefore $x^2 - 2x - 3 \le 0$—constitute the solution set of (5). Thus

$$\{x \mid -1 \le x \le 3\},$$

as shown by the heavy line in Figure 6.16, is the required solution set.

EXERCISE 6.4

Graph.

Example. $\{(x, y) \mid y \ge x^2 + 2x\}$

Solution. Graph $\{(x, y) \mid y = x^2 + 2x\}$

Shade the portion of the plane above the curve.

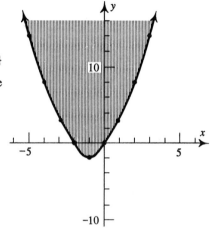

1. $\{(x, y) \mid y > x^2\}$

2. $\{(x, y) \mid y < x^2\}$

3. $\{(x, y) \mid y \ge x^2 + 3\}$

4. $\{(x, y) \mid y \le x^2 + 3\}$

5. $\{(x, y) \mid y < 3x^2 + 2x\}$

6. $\{(x, y) \mid y > 3x^2 + 2x\}$

7. $\{(x, y) \mid y \le x^2 + 3x + 2\}$ 8. $\{(x, y) \mid y \ge x^2 + 3x + 2\}$

9. $\{(x, y) \mid y \ge 2x^2 - 5x + 1\}$ 10. $\{(x, y) \mid y \le 2x^2 - 5x + 1\}$

Solve by graphical methods.

Example. $x^2 - 3x \ge 0$

Solution.
   Graph $\{(x, y) \mid y = x^2 - 3x\}$

Draw a heavy line on the x-axis to indicate those values of x for which y, or $x^2 - 3x$, is equal to or greater than zero.

The solution set is $\{x \mid x \le 0 \text{ or } x \ge 3\}$.

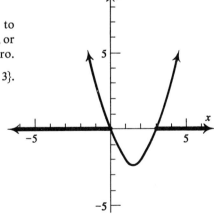

11. $x^2 - 1 \le 0$

12. $1 - x^2 > 0$

13. $x^2 - 3x + 2 \le 0$

14. $2 - x - x^2 > 0$

15. $4 + 3x - x^2 > 0$

16. $2x^2 - 5x + 2 < 0$

17. $x^2 + 3x < 10$ 18. $x^2 < 4$

19. $x^2 < x + 2$ 20. $x^2 \leq 2x - 1$

21. Graph the relation $\{(x, y) \mid x^2 + y^2 \leq 25\}$ by observing that the graph of $\{(x, y) \mid x^2 + y^2 = a^2\}$ is a circle of radius a and examining what $a \leq 5$ implies for $x^2 + y^2$.

22. Graph the relation $\{(x, y) \mid 4x^2 + 9y^2 \leq 36\}$.

23. Graph the relation $\{(x, y) \mid 16 \leq x^2 + y^2 \leq 25\}$.

24. Graph the set of points whose coordinates satisfy both

$$\{(x, y) \mid y \leq 1 - x^2\} \quad \text{and} \quad \{(x, y) \mid y \geq -1\}.$$

25. Graph the set of points whose coordinates satisfy both

$$\{(x, y) \mid y \leq 4 - x^2\} \quad \text{and} \quad \{(x, y) \mid y \geq x^2 - 4\}.$$

6.5 POLYNOMIAL FUNCTIONS

In Section 5.5, we graphed linear functions

$$\{[x, f(x)] \mid f(x) = a_0 x + a_1\},$$

and in Section 6.1, we graphed quadratic functions

$$\{[x, f(x)] \mid f(x) = a_0 x^2 + a_1 x + a_2\}.$$

We can graph any real polynomial function

$$\{[x, P(x)] \mid P(x) = a_0 x^n + a_1 x^{n-1} + \cdots + a_n\}$$

by similar methods, that is, by combining the plotting of points with a consideration of certain general properties of the defining equations. In the case of the general polynomial equation, we shall lean more heavily on the use of plotted points. There is one fact about polynomial equations, however, that can be useful: This involves *turning points*, or local maximum and minimum values of y. Thus, for example, in Figure 6.17-a there is one local maximum as well as one local minimum, or a total of two turning points, and in Figure 6.17-c one local maximum and two local minimums, for a total of the three turning points. In general, we have the following.

THEOREM 6.1 *If* $P(x) = a_0 x^n + a_1 x^{n-1} + \cdots + a_n$ *is a real polynomial equation of degree n, then the graph of*

$$\{[x, P(x)] \mid P(x) = a_0 x^n + a_1 x^{n-1} + \cdots + a_n\}$$

is a smooth curve that has at most n — 1 turning points.

The proof of this theorem involves ideas we have not discussed herein, and is omitted. As a consequence of this theorem, for example, the graphs of third- and fourth-degree polynomial functions might appear as in Figure 6.17, a, b, c, and d.

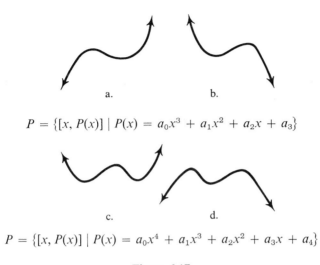

a.   b.

$$P = \{[x, P(x)] \mid P(x) = a_0 x^3 + a_1 x^2 + a_2 x + a_3\}$$

c.   d.

$$P = \{[x, P(x)] \mid P(x) = a_0 x^4 + a_1 x^3 + a_2 x^2 + a_3 x + a_4\}$$

Figure 6.17

To ascertain whether the graphs take the general form (a) and (c) rather than (b) and (d), we can examine the leading coefficient, a_0, of the right-hand member of the defining equations; if $a_0 > 0$, then we can look for forms similar to (a) and (c), whereas if $a_0 < 0$, we can expect something similar to (b) and (d). The graph ultimately goes up or down to the right according as $a_0 > 0$ or $a_0 < 0$. If $a_0 < 0$, then it ultimately goes up or down to the left according as n is odd or even.

For the actual graphing process, we can obtain ordered pairs $[x, f(x)]$ for any polynomial function by direct substitution, which we used in previous sections, or by using the following.

THEOREM 6.2 *If $P(x)$ is a real polynomial, then for every real number c there exists a unique real polynomial $Q(x)$ such that*

$$P(x) = (x - c)Q(x) + P(c).$$

Proof. From Theorem 2.6, we know that there exists a real polynomial $Q(x)$ and a real number r such that

$$P(x) = (x - c)Q(x) + r.$$

Since this is true for all $x \in R$, then it is true for $x = c$, and we have

$$P(c) = (c - c)Q(c) + r$$
$$P(c) = 0 \cdot Q(c) + r$$
$$P(c) = r,$$

and the theorem is proved.

This theorem is called the **remainder theorem** because it asserts that the remainder, when $P(x)$ is divided by $(x - r)$, is the value of P at r, that is, $P(r)$. Since synthetic division offers a quick means of obtaining this remainder, we can usually find values $P(r)$ more rapidly by synthetic division than by direct substitution.

Example. If $P(x) = x^3 - x^2 + 3$, find $P(3)$ by means of the remainder theorem.

Solution. Synthetically dividing $x^3 - x^2 + 3$ by $x - 3$, we have

$$
\begin{array}{r|rrrr}
3 & 1 & -1 & 0 & 3 \\
  &   & 3 & 6 & 18 \\
\hline
  & 1 & 2 & 6 & 21
\end{array}
$$

and, by inspection, $c = P(3) = 21$.

Example. Graph $\{[x, P(x)] \mid P(x) = 2x^3 + 13x^2 + 6x\}$.

Solution. Since P is defined by a cubic polynomial with positive leading coefficient, we shall expect a graph having a form similar to Figure 6.17-a. Now, to find points $[x, P(x)]$ lying on the graph, we shall use the process of synthetic division and find $P(x)$ by the remainder theorem. Since we know nothing about where to look for turning points, let us start with $x = 0$. By inspection $P(0) = 0$, so that the graph includes the origin. For $x = 1$, we have

$$
\begin{array}{r|rrrr}
1 & 2 & 13 & 6 & 0 \\
  &   & 2 & 15 & 21 \\
\hline
  & 2 & 15 & 21 & 21
\end{array}
$$

and $(1, 21)$ is on the graph. For $x = 2$, we get

$$
\begin{array}{r|rrrr}
2 & 2 & 13 & 6 & 0 \\
  &   & 4 & 34 & 80 \\
\hline
  & 2 & 17 & 40 & 80
\end{array}
$$

and $(2, 80)$ is on the graph. Since the signs involved at each step in the last row of the division process here are positive, it is evident that for values $x > 2$, $P(x)$ will grow increasingly large; consequently, let us turn our attention to negative values of x. For $x = -1$, we have

$$
\begin{array}{r|rrrr}
-1 & 2 & 13 & 6 & 0 \\
   &   & -2 & -11 & 5 \\
\hline
   & 2 & 11 & -5 & 5
\end{array}
$$

and $P(-1) = 5$, so that $(-1, 5)$ is on the graph. In similar fashion, we find that the following points lie on the graph of P:

$$(-2, 24), (-3, 45), (-4, 56), (-5, 45), (-6, 0), (-7, -91).$$

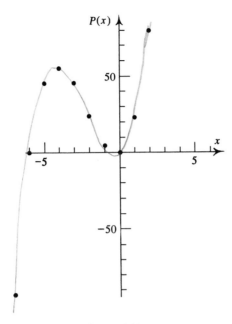

Figure 6.18

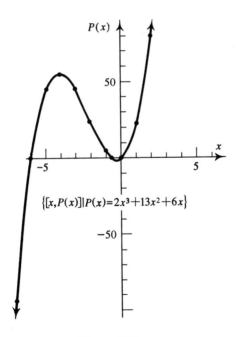

$$\{[x, P(x)] \mid P(x) = 2x^3 + 13x^2 + 6x\}$$

Figure 6.19

The graphs of the ten ordered pairs are shown in Figure 6.18. These points make the general appearance of the graph clear, and there remains only the question of whether there is a zero for the function between -1 and 0. If we let x have values $-3/4$, $-1/4$, and $-1/2$, we obtain the additional pairs $(-3/4, 63/32)$, $(-1/4, -23/32)$, $(-1/2, 0)$. Then for $-1/2 < x < 0$, we have $P(x) < 0$, and the graph can be sketched as in Figure 6.19.

EXERCISE 6.5

Use synthetic division to find values of the polynomial for the specified values of the variable.

1. $P(x) = x^3 + 2x^2 + x - 1$; find $P(1)$, $P(2)$, and $P(3)$

2. $P(x) = x^3 - 3x^2 - x + 3$; find $P(1)$, $P(2)$, and $P(3)$

3. $P(x) = 2x^4 - 3x^3 + x + 2$; find $P(-2)$, $P(2)$, and $P(4)$

4. $P(x) = 3x^4 + 3x^2 - x + 3$; find $P(-2)$, $P(2)$, and $P(4)$

5. $P(x) = 3x^5 - x^3 + 2x^2 - 1$; find $P(-3)$, $P(2)$, and $P(3)$

6. $P(x) = 2x^6 - x^4 + 3x^3 + 1$; find $P(-3)$, $P(2)$, and $P(3)$

Graph. Include approximations to all turning points and show the location of all real zeros at or between consecutive integers.

7. $\{[x, P(x)] \mid P(x) = x^3 + 3x^2 + x\}$

8. $\{[x, P(x)] \mid P(x) = x^3 - 2x^2 + 1\}$

9. $\{[x, P(x)] \mid P(x) = 2x^3 - x^2 + x + 3\}$

10. $\{[x, P(x)] \mid P(x) = 3x^3 + 2x^2 - x + 1\}$

11. $\{[x, P(x)] \mid P(x) = x^4\}$

12. $\{[x, P(x)] \mid P(x) = -x^4 + x\}$

13. $\{[x, P(x)] \mid P(x) = x^4 - x^3 + 2x^2 - 3x - 3\}$

14. $\{[x, P(x)] \mid P(x) = x^4 - 4x^3 - 4x + 12\}$

6.6 RATIONAL FUNCTIONS

A function defined by an equation of the form

$$y = \frac{P(x)}{Q(x)}, \tag{1}$$

where $P(x)$ and $Q(x)$ are polynomials in x, and $Q(x)$ is not the zero polynomial, is called a **rational function**. Such functions are of importance in the calculus and provide some interesting problems with respect to their graphs. We shall consider them only briefly here.

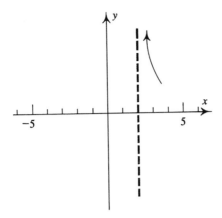

Figure 6.20

Since $[P(x)]/[Q(x)]$ is not defined for values of x for which $Q(x) = 0$, it is evident that we shall not be able to find points in $R \times R$ having such x-coordinates. We can, however, consider the graph for values of x as close as we please to a value, say x_0, for which $Q(x_0) = 0$, but still with $x \neq x_0$. This consideration is usually described by saying that x "approaches" x_0, "grows close" to x_0, etc., and correspondingly that $Q(x)$ approaches 0. Thus, the closer $Q(x)$ approaches 0, if $P(x)$ does not approach 0 at the same time, then the larger $|y|$ becomes in (1). Figure 6.20 shows the behavior of

$$\{(x, y) \mid y = 2/(x - 2)\}, \tag{2}$$

as x approaches 2 from the right. In situations such as this, the vertical lines that the curve approaches are called **vertical asymptotes.**

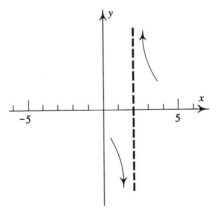

Figure 6.21

THEOREM 6.3   *The graph of the function defined by $y = [P(x)]/[Q(x)]$ has vertical asymptotes $x = a$ for any value a at which $Q(x)$ vanishes and $P(x)$ does not vanish.*

In Figure 6.20 we see the behavior of (2) as x approaches 2 from the right. We are also interested in its behavior as x approaches 2 from the left.   Figure 6.21 illustrates this.   As long as $x > 2$, we have $x - 2 > 0$ and $2/(x - 2) > 0$, but if $x < 2$, then we have $x - 2 < 0$ and $2/(x - 2) < 0$.

The graphs of some rational functions have horizontal asymptotes, which can, in general, be identified by using the following theorem.

THEOREM 6.4   *The graph of the function defined by*

$$y = \frac{a_0x^n + a_1x^{n-1} + \cdots + a_n}{b_0x^m + b_1x^{m-1} + \cdots + b_m},$$

where a_0 and b_0 are any nonzero real numbers, and n, m, are nonnegative integers has

   I   *a horizontal asymptote at $y = 0$ if $n < m$,*

   II   *a horizontal asymptote at $y = a_0/b_0$ if $n = m$,*

   III   *no horizontal asymptotes if $n > m$.*

Though we shall not give a rigorous proof of this theorem here, we can certainly make the results plausible.   If $n < m$, we can divide the numerator and denominator of the right-hand member of

$$y = \frac{a_0x^n + a_1x^{n-1} + \cdots + a_n}{b_0x^m + b_1x^{m-1} + \cdots + b_m}$$

by x^m to obtain

$$y = \frac{\dfrac{a_0}{x^{m-n}} + \dfrac{a_1}{x^{m-n+1}} + \cdots + \dfrac{a_n}{x^m}}{b_0 + \dfrac{b_1}{x} + \cdots + \dfrac{b_m}{x^m}}.$$

Now, as $|x|$ grows larger and larger, each term containing an x in the denominator grows closer and closer to 0, and we find the expression on the right approaching $0/b_0$, so that y approaches 0.   But if, as y grows close to 0, $|x|$ is increasing without bound, then y is approaching the line $y = 0$ asymptotically, and actually must approach 0 from one of the four directions shown in Figure 6.22-a.   A similar argument shows that if $n = m$, then, as $|x|$ increases without bound, y approaches the line $y = a_0/b_0$ from one of the directions shown in Figure 6.22-b.   If $n > m$, then as $|x|$ becomes larger and larger, so does $|y|$.

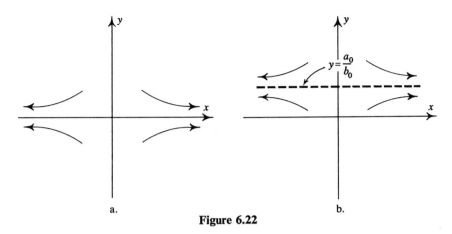

Figure 6.22

In particular, if $n = m + 1$, that is, if the numerator is of degree one greater than the denominator, we can argue that though the graph has no horizontal asymptote, it does have an oblique one. We shall illustrate a special case only, but the technique involved is quite general.

Example. Find all asymptotes for the graph of

$$\left\{(x, y) \mid y = \frac{x^2 - 4}{x - 1}\right\}.$$

Solution. We begin by observing that by Theorem 6.3, $x = 1$ is a vertical asymptote, and that by Theorem 6.4, there are no horizontal asymptotes. If, however, we rewrite $y = (x^2 - 4)/(x - 1)$ by dividing $x^2 - 4$ by $x - 1$, we obtain $y = x + 1 - 3/(x - 1)$. Now, as $|x|$ grows larger and larger, $3/(x - 1)$ grows smaller and smaller, and the graph of $y = (x^2 - 4)/(x - 1)$ grows arbitrarily close to the graph of $y = x + 1$. Hence, the graph of $y = x + 1$, which is an oblique line, is an asymptote to the curve.

Identifying asymptotes is one aid to the graphing of a rational function. Other helpful items are the following:

1. The zeros of the function, because these give us the x-intercepts.
2. The domain and range, because these tell us where we can expect to find parts of the graph and where we cannot.
3. Some specific points on the graph, because these give us guidelines in sketching.

Example. Graph $\{(x, y) \mid y = (x - 1)/(x - 2)\}$.

Solution. We can begin by observing that the numerator of the right-hand member will be equal to 0 when x is equal to 1. Therefore, when $x = 1$, we

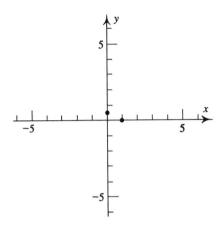

Figure 6.23

have $y = 0$, and 1 is an x-intercept.   Also, when $x = 0$, we have $y = 1/2$, so
that $1/2$ is a y-intercept.   Thus we can begin our graph as shown in Figure 6.23.
By inspection, $y = (x - 1)/(x - 2)$ is defined for all real x except $x = 2$, so that
$\{x \mid x \neq 2\}$ is the domain.   Similarly, if we solve the defining equation for x in
terms of y, we have $x = (2y - 1)/(y - 1)$, which is defined for all values of y
except 1.   Hence $\{y \mid y \neq 1\}$ is the range of the function.   From the defining
equation and Theorem 6.3, we see that there is a vertical asymptote at $x = 2$ and
a horizontal asymptote at $y = 1$.   We can then add this information to our
graph, as indicated in Figure 6.24.   Next we call our powers of observation into
play.   That the vertical asymptote, for example, is approached downward instead
of upward from the left can be confirmed by observing that if x is just less than 2,
say $2 - p$, $0 < p < 1/10$, then the denominator $x - 2$ in the expression for y is

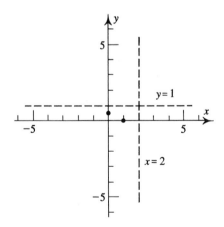

Figure 6.24

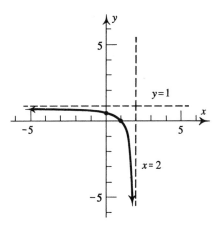

Figure 6.25

$2 - p - 2 = -p$, which is barely negative, whereas the numerator $x - 1 = 2 - p - 1 = 1 - p$ is definitely positive; hence y is negative and $|y|$ large. The graph appears in Figure 6.25.   To find the curve when $x > 2$, that is, to the right of the vertical asymptote, we simply find one or two points associated with such values of x.   For example, we might choose 3 and 4.   If $x = 3$, then $y = (3 - 1)/(3 - 2) = 2$, and $(3, 2)$ is on the curve.   If $x = 4$, then $y = (4 - 1)/(4 - 2) = 3/2$, and $(4, 3/2)$ is on the curve.   Again, the knowledge that $x = 2$ and $y = 1$ are asymptotes, together with the location of the points $(3, 2)$ and $(4, 3/2)$, leads us to the complete graph of $\{(x, y) \mid y = (x - 1)/(x - 2)\}$ (Figure 6.26).

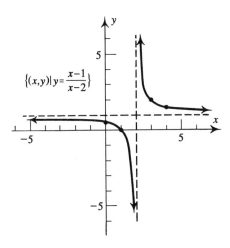

Figure 6.26

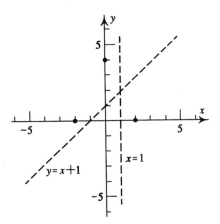

Figure 6.27

Example.   Graph $\{(x, y) \mid y = (x^2 - 4)/(x - 1)\}$.

Solution.   This is the same function we investigated in the example on page 193, where we found the vertical asymptote $x = 1$ and the oblique asymptote $y = x + 1$. By inspection, if $x = 0$, then $y = 4$, and if $y = 0$, then $x = 2$ or $x = -2$, so that there is a y-intercept at 4 as well as x-intercepts at 2 and -2.   We therefore have the situation shown in Figure 6.27.   Without any further information, we have strong reason to suspect that the graph will appear as shown in Figure 6.28. The plotting of a few check points, say $(-1, 3/2)$, $(1/2, 15/2)$, $(3/2, -7/2)$, and $(3, 5/2)$, would tend to confirm our suspicion.

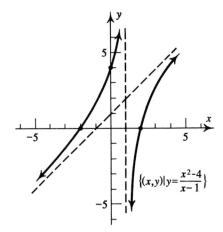

Figure 6.28

EXERCISE 6.6

Determine the vertical asymptotes of the graph of each function.

Example. $\{(x, y) \mid x^2y - 4y = 1\}$

Solution. Express y explicitly in terms of x by means of an equivalent equation.

$$y(x^2 - 4) = 1$$

$$y = \frac{1}{x^2 - 4}$$

By Theorem 6.3, there are vertical asymptotes at $x = 2, -2$.

1. $\left\{(x, y) \mid y = \frac{1}{x - 3}\right\}$

2. $\left\{(x, y) \mid y = \frac{1}{x + 4}\right\}$

3. $\left\{(x, y) \mid y = \frac{4}{(x + 2)(x - 3)}\right\}$

4. $\left\{(x, y) \mid y = \frac{8}{(x - 1)(x + 3)}\right\}$

5. $\left\{(x, y) \mid y = \frac{2x - 1}{x^2 + 5x + 4}\right\}$

6. $\left\{(x, y) \mid y = \frac{x + 3}{2x^2 - 5x - 3}\right\}$

7. $\{(x, y) \mid xy + y = 4\}$

8. $\{(x, y) \mid x^2y + xy = 3\}$

Graph.

9. $\left\{(x, y) \mid y = \frac{1}{x}\right\}$

10. $\left\{(x, y) \mid y = \frac{1}{x + 4}\right\}$

11. $\left\{(x, y) \mid y = \frac{1}{x - 3}\right\}$

12. $\left\{(x, y) \mid y = \frac{1}{x - 6}\right\}$

13. $\left\{(x, y) \mid y = \frac{4}{(x + 2)(x - 3)}\right\}$

14. $\left\{(x, y) \mid y = \frac{8}{(x - 1)(x + 3)}\right\}$

15. $\left\{(x, y) \mid y = \frac{2}{(x - 3)^2}\right\}$

16. $\left\{(x, y) \mid y = \frac{1}{(x + 4)^2}\right\}$

Determine any vertical, horizontal, or oblique asymptotes of the graphs of each of the following.

Example. $\left\{(x, y) \mid y = \frac{6x^2 + 1}{2x^2 + 5x - 3}\right\}$

Solution. The defining equation can be written equivalently as

$$y = \frac{6x^2 + 1}{(2x - 1)(x + 3)}.$$

By Theorem 6.3, there are vertical asymptotes at $x = 1/2$ and $x = -3$.

By Theorem 6.4-II, there is a horizontal asymptote at $y = 6/2$ or 3.

17. $\left\{(x, y) \mid y = \dfrac{x}{x^2 - 4}\right\}$

18. $\left\{(x, y) \mid y = \dfrac{3x + 6}{x^2 + 3x + 2}\right\}$

19. $\left\{(x, y) \mid y = \dfrac{x^2 - 9}{x - 4}\right\}$

20. $\left\{(x, y) \mid y = \dfrac{x^3 - 27}{x^2 - 1}\right\}$

21. $\left\{(x, y) \mid y = \dfrac{x^2 - 3x + 2}{x^2 - 3x - 4}\right\}$

22. $\left\{(x, y) \mid y = \dfrac{x^2}{x^2 - x - 6}\right\}$

Graph.   Use information concerning the zeros of the function, and concerning vertical, horizontal, and oblique asymptotes.

23. $\left\{(x, y) \mid y = \dfrac{x}{x - 2}\right\}$

24. $\left\{(x, y) \mid y = \dfrac{x - 1}{x + 3}\right\}$

25. $\left\{(x, y) \mid y = \dfrac{2x - 4}{x^2 - 9}\right\}$

26. $\left\{(x, y) \mid y = \dfrac{3x}{x^2 - 5x + 4}\right\}$

27. $\left\{(x, y) \mid y = \dfrac{x^2 - 4}{x^3}\right\}$

28. $\left\{(x, y) \mid y = \dfrac{x - 2}{x^2}\right\}$

29. $\left\{(x, y) \mid y = \dfrac{x^2 - 4x + 4}{x - 1}\right\}$

30. $\left\{(x, y) \mid y = \dfrac{x^2 + 4}{x - 2}\right\}$

31. $\left\{(x, y) \mid y = \dfrac{x + 1}{x(x^2 - 4)}\right\}$

32. $\left\{(x, y) \mid y = \dfrac{x^2 + x - 2}{x(x^2 - 9)}\right\}$

if $x = 0$

$y =$ undefined

$x = 2$ } asymptote – verticle

$x = -2$

EXPONENTIAL AND
LOGARITHMIC
FUNCTIONS

7.1 THE EXPONENTIAL FUNCTION

In Chapter 3, powers b^x were defined for any real number $b \neq 0$ and x an integer. The definition was extended to include x a rational number p/q. For arbitrary rational exponents, however, the base b must be restricted to positive values to ensure that $b^{p/q}$ be real.

We now inquire whether we can interpret powers with irrational exponents, such as

$$b^{\pi}, \ b^{\sqrt{2}}, \ b^{-\sqrt{3}},$$

to be real numbers. The following two theorems will be useful in helping us arrive at an answer.

THEOREM 7.1 *Let $x \in Q$, i.e., $x \in \{rational \ numbers\}$, and let $x > 0$. Then $b^x > 1$ if $b > 1$, $b^x = 1$ if $b = 1$, and $0 < b^x < 1$ if $0 < b < 1$.*

Proof. Suppose first that $x \in N$, i.e., that $x \in \{natural \ numbers\}$, say $x = n$. If $b > 1$, then $b^n > 1$ since, by Theorem 1.15-III, a product of numbers each greater than 1 is greater than any of the factors; thus $b^n > b > 1$. Similarly, if $0 < b < 1$, then, again by Theorem 1.15-III, $0 < b^n < 1$, since a product of positive numbers each less than 1 is less than any of the factors. Finally, of course, $1^n = 1$.

Next, suppose that $x = 1/n$, and set $b^x = b^{1/n} = a$. Then $a^n = b$, and it follows from the argument of the preceding paragraph that the positive numbers a and b are both > 1, both $= 1$, or both < 1.

Finally, if $x \in Q$, say $x = m/n$ with $m, n > 0$, then $b^x = (b^m)^{1/n}$. If $b > 1$, then by the arguments of the two preceding paragraphs we have $b^m > 1$ and $(b^m)^{1/n} > 1$. Similarly, if $b = 1$ then $b^{m/n} = 1$, and if $0 < b < 1$ then $0 < b^{m/n} < 1$.

THEOREM 7.2   *Let* $x, y \in Q$, *and let* $x > y > 0$. *Then* $b^x > b^y$ *if* $b > 1$, $b^x = b^y$ *if* $b = 1$, *and* $b^x < b^y$ *if* $0 < b < 1$.

Theorem 7.2 follows directly from Theorem 7.1.   For example, if $b > 1$, then by Theorem 7.1, since $x - y > 0$, we have

$$\frac{b^x}{b^y} = b^{x-y} > 1,$$

from which

$$b^x > b^y.$$

In Section 3.4, it was observed that irrational numbers can be approximated by rational numbers to as great a degree of accuracy as desired. For example, $\sqrt{2} \approx 1.4$ or $\sqrt{2} \approx 1.414$, etc.   Since b^x ($b > 0$) is defined for rational x, by Theorem 7.2 we can write the sequence of inequalities

$$2^1 < 2^2,$$

$$2^{1.4} < 2^{1.5},$$

$$2^{1.41} < 2^{1.42},$$

$$2^{1.414} < 2^{1.415}.$$

As a result of Theorem 7.2, we can be sure that b^x, $b > 1$, increases as x increases, and if $b < 1$, b^x decreases as x increases.   This process can be continued indefinitely, and it seems plausible and is actually true, though we shall not prove it, that the difference between the number on the left and that on the right can be made as small as we please.   This being the case, the completeness property 0-3 of the real numbers guarantees that there is just one number, which we denote by $2^{\sqrt{2}}$, that lies between the number on the left and the number on the right no matter how long this process of approximation is continued.   Since we can produce the same type of argument for any irrational exponent x, we shall assume that b^x ($b > 0$) is defined in this way for all real values of x and that the laws of exponents for rational exponents are valid for such powers.   This leads us to the following:

THEOREM 7.3   *If* $a, b, m, n \in R$, *and* $a, b > 0$, *then*

$$\text{I} \quad a^m \cdot a^n = a^{m+n},$$

$$\text{II} \quad \frac{a^m}{a^n} = a^{m-n} = \frac{1}{a^{n-m}},$$

$$\text{III} \quad (a^m)^n = a^{mn},$$

$$\text{IV} \quad (ab)^n = a^n b^n,$$

$$\text{V} \quad \left(\frac{a}{b}\right)^n = \frac{a^n}{b^n}.$$

Since for each real x there is one and only one number b^x, the equation

$$f(x) = b^x \quad (b > 0) \tag{1}$$

defines a function. Because $1^x = 1$ for all $x \in R$, (1) defines a constant function if $b = 1$. If $b \neq 1$, we say that (1) defines an **exponential function**.

Exponential functions can perhaps be visualized most clearly by considering their graphs. We illustrate two typical examples, in which $0 < b < 1$ and $b > 1$, respectively. Assigning values to x in the equations

$$f(x) = (\tfrac{1}{2})^x \quad \text{and} \quad f(x) = (2)^x,$$

we find some ordered pairs in each solution set and sketch the graphs of $\{[x, f(x)] \mid f(x) = (\tfrac{1}{2})^x\}$ and $\{[x, f(x)] \mid f(x) = 2^x\}$, shown in Figure 7.1.

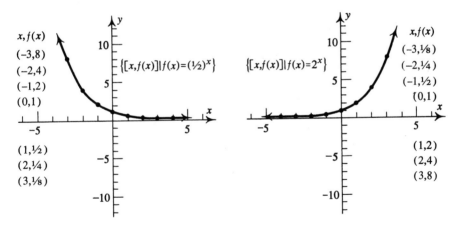

Figure 7.1

Notice that in accordance with Theorem 7.2, the graph of the function determined by $f(x) = (\tfrac{1}{2})^x$ goes *down* to the right, and the graph of the function determined by $f(x) = 2^x$ goes *up* to the right. For this reason, we say that the former function is a *decreasing* function and that the latter is an *increasing* function. In either case, the domain is the set of real numbers, and the range is the set of positive real numbers.

EXERCISE 7.1

Find the second component of each of the ordered pairs that makes the pair a solution of the equation.

1. $y = 3^x$; $(0, \quad)$, $(1, \quad)$, $(2, \quad)$

2. $y = -2^x$; $(-2, \quad)$, $(0, \quad)$, $(2, \quad)$

3. $y = -5^x$; $(-2, \quad)$, $(0, \quad)$, $(2, \quad)$

4. $y = 4^x$; $(0, \quad)$, $(1, \quad)$, $(2, \quad)$

5. $f(x) = (\tfrac{1}{2})^x$; $(-3, \quad)$, $(0, \quad)$, $(3, \quad)$

6. $f(x) = (\tfrac{1}{3})^x$; $(-3, \quad)$, $(0, \quad)$, $(3, \quad)$

7. $g(x) = 10^x$; $(-2, \quad)$, $(-1, \quad)$, $(0, \quad)$

8. $g(x) = 10^x$; $(0, \quad)$, $(1, \quad)$, $(2, \quad)$

Graph.

9. $\{(x, y) \mid y = 4^x\}$ 10. $\{(x, y) \mid y = 5^x\}$

11. $\{(x, y) \mid y = 10^x\}$ 12. $\{(x, y) \mid y = 10^{-x}\}$

13. $\{(x, y) \mid y = 2^{-x}\}$ 14. $\{(x, y) \mid y = 3^{-x}\}$

15. $\{(x, y) \mid y = (\tfrac{1}{3})^x\}$ 16. $\{(x, y) \mid y = (\tfrac{1}{4})^x\}$

17. $\{(x, y) \mid y = (\tfrac{1}{2})^{-x}\}$ 18. $\{(x, y) \mid y = (\tfrac{1}{4})^{-x}\}$

19. Graph $\{[x, f(x)] \mid f(x) = 1^x\}$. Is this an exponential function? Name the function.

20. Graph $\{(x, y) \mid y = 10^x, x > 0\}$ and $\{(x, y) \mid x = 10^y, x > 0\}$ on the same set of axes.

21. Solve for x by inspection.

 a. $10^x = \tfrac{1}{100}$ b. $(\tfrac{1}{2})^x = 16$ c. $16^x = 8$

22. Determine an integer n such that $n < x < n + 1$.

 a. $3^x = 16.2$ b. $4^x = 87.1$ c. $10^x = 0.016$

7.2 THE LOGARITHMIC FUNCTION

In the exponential function

$$\{(x, y) \mid y = b^x \quad (b > 0, b \neq 1)\}, \tag{1}$$

illustrated in Figure 7.1 for $b = 1/2$ and $b = 2$, there is only one x associated with each y. Thus, by Definition 5.5, we have the inverse function

$$\{(x, y) \mid x = b^y \quad (b > 0, b \neq 1, x > 0)\}. \tag{2}$$

Observe that the restriction $x > 0$ is made in order that y be a real number, because there is no real number y for which b^y is not positive.

The graphs of functions of this form can be illustrated by the example

$$\{(x, y) \mid x = 10^y \quad (x > 0)\}.$$

We consider x the variable denoting an element in the domain and, in the defining equation, assign arbitrary values for x, say,

$$(0.01, \ \ ), (0.1, \ \ ), (1, \ \ ), (10, \ \ ), (100, \ \ ),$$

to obtain the ordered pairs

$$(0.01, -2), (0.1, -1), (1, 0), (10, 1), (100, 2).$$

These can be plotted and connected with a smooth curve as in Figure 7.2.

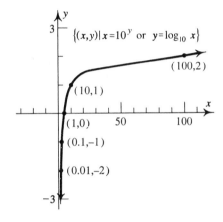

Figure 7.2

It is always useful to be able to express the variable denoting an element in the range explicitly in terms of the variable denoting an element in the domain. To do this in an equation such as that defining (2), we use the notation

$$y = \log_b x \quad (x > 0, b > 0, b \neq 1). \tag{3}$$

Functions defined by such equations are called **logarithmic functions**.

From the graph in Figure 7.2, we generalize from $\log_{10} x$ to $\log_b x$, and observe that a logarithmic function has the following properties:

1. The domain is the set of positive real numbers, and the range is the set of all real numbers.

2. If $b > 1$, then $\log_b x < 0$ for $x < 1$, $\log_b x = 0$ for $x = 1$, and $\log_b x > 0$ for $x > 1$.

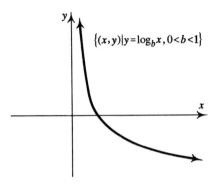

Figure 7.3

3. If $0 < b < 1$, then $\log_b x > 0$ for $x < 1$, $\log_b x = 0$ for $x = 1$, and $\log_b x < 0$ for $x > 1$.   The graph of a logarithmic function for $0 < b < 1$ is illustrated in Figure 7.3.

It should be recognized that the equations appearing in (2) and (3) are different equations determining the same function, in the same way that $x = y + 4$ and $y = x - 4$ determine the same function, and we may use whichever equation suits our purpose. Thus, exponential statements may be written in logarithmic form, and logarithmic statements may be written in exponential form.

Examples.   Write each of the following statements in logarithmic form.

a. $5^2 = 25$ b. $8^{1/3} = 2$ c. $3^{-2} = \frac{1}{9}$

Solutions.

a. $5^2 = 25$ is equivalent to $\log_5 25 = 2$.

b. $8^{1/3} = 2$ is equivalent to $\log_8 2 = \frac{1}{3}$.

c. $3^{-2} = \frac{1}{9}$ is equivalent to $\log_3 \frac{1}{9} = -2$.

Examples.   Write each of the following statements in exponential form.

a. $\log_{10} 100 = 2$ b. $\log_3 81 = 4$ c. $\log_2 \frac{1}{2} = -1$

Solutions.

a. $\log_{10} 100 = 2$ is equivalent to $10^2 = 100$.

b. $\log_3 81 = 4$ is equivalent to $3^4 = 81$.

c. $\log_2 \frac{1}{2} = -1$ is equivalent to $2^{-1} = \frac{1}{2}$.

The logarithmic function associates with each number x the exponent y such that the power b^y is equal to x.   In other words, we can think of $\log_b x$ as an exponent on b.   Thus

$$b^{\log_b x} = x.$$

Since a logarithm is an exponent, the following theorem follows directly from Theorem 7.3.

THEOREM 7.4 *If x_1 and x_2 are positive real numbers, $b > 0$, $b \neq 1$, and p, q integers, with $q \neq 0$,*

$$\text{I} \quad \log_b (x_1 x_2) = \log_b x_1 + \log_b x_2,$$

$$\text{II} \quad \log_b \frac{x_2}{x_1} = \log_b x_2 - \log_b x_1,$$

$$\text{III} \quad \log_b (x_1)^p = p \log_b x_1,$$

$$\text{IV} \quad \log_b \sqrt[q]{x_1^p} = \frac{p}{q} \log_b x_1.$$

The validity of I can be shown as follows: Since

$$x_1 = b^{\log_b x_1} \text{ and } x_2 = b^{\log_b x_2},$$

it follows that

$$x_1 x_2 = b^{\log_b x_1} \cdot b^{\log_b x_2}$$
$$= b^{\log_b x_1 + \log_b x_2},$$

and, by the definition of a logarithm,

$$\log_b (x_1 x_2) = \log_b x_1 + \log_b x_2.$$

The validity of II, III, and IV can be established in a similar manner. A more general result than Theorem 7.4-III is that for every $k \in R$,

$$\text{V} \quad \log_b (x_1)^k = k \log_b x_1,$$

but the proof is much more complicated. We shall, however, use this fact as necessary, referring to it as Theorem 7.4-V.

EXERCISE 7.2

Express in logarithmic notation.

1. $4^2 = 16$
2. $5^3 = 125$
3. $3^3 = 27$
4. $8^2 = 64$
5. $(\frac{1}{2})^2 = \frac{1}{4}$
6. $(\frac{1}{3})^2 = \frac{1}{9}$
7. $8^{-1/3} = \frac{1}{2}$
8. $64^{-1/6} = \frac{1}{2}$
9. $10^2 = 100$
10. $10^0 = 1$
11. $10^{-1} = 0.1$
12. $10^{-2} = 0.01$

Express in exponential notation.

13. $\log_2 64 = 6$
14. $\log_5 25 = 2$
15. $\log_3 9 = 2$
16. $\log_{16} 256 = 2$
17. $\log_{1/3} 9 = -2$
18. $\log_{1/2} 8 = -3$
19. $\log_{10} 1000 = 3$
20. $\log_{10} 1 = 0$
21. $\log_{10} (0.01) = -2$

Find the value of each of the following.

22. $\log_5 5$	23. $\log_7 49$	24. $\log_2 32$
25. $\log_4 64$	26. $\log_5 \sqrt{5}$	27. $\log_3 \sqrt{3}$
28. $\log_3 \frac{1}{3}$	29. $\log_5 \frac{1}{5}$	30. $\log_3 3$
31. $\log_2 2$	32. $\log_{10} 10$	33. $\log_{10} 100$
34. $\log_{10} 1$	35. $\log_{10} 0.1$	36. $\log_{10} 0.01$

Solve for x, y, or b.

Examples.

  a. $\log_2 x = 3$ $\qquad\qquad\qquad$ b. $\log_b 2 = \frac{1}{2}$

Solutions. Determine the solution by inspection or write in exponential form.

  a. $2^3 = x$ $\qquad\qquad\qquad\qquad$ b. $\quad b^{1/2} = 2$
  $\quad\; x = 8$ $\qquad\qquad\qquad\qquad\qquad (b^{1/2})^2 = (2)^2$
  $\qquad\qquad\qquad\qquad\qquad\qquad\qquad\qquad\quad b = 4$

37. $\log_3 9 = y$	38. $\log_5 125 = y$	39. $\log_b 8 = 3$
40. $\log_b 625 = 4$	41. $\log_4 x = 3$	42. $\log_{1/2} x = -5$
43. $\log_2 \frac{1}{8} = y$	44. $\log_5 5 = y$	45. $\log_b 10 = \frac{1}{2}$
46. $\log_b 0.1 = -1$	47. $\log_2 x = 2$	48. $\log_{10} x = -3$

49. Show that $\log_b 1 = 0$ for $b > 0$. $\qquad$ 50. Show that $\log_b b = 1$ for $b > 0$.

51. Show that $\log_b b^x = x$ for $b > 0$.

52. Graph $y = \log_2 x$. By examining the graph, what can you assert about $\log_2 a$ and $\log_2 b$ if $a < b$?

Express as the sum or difference of simpler logarithmic quantities.

Example. $\log_b (xy/z)^{1/2}$

Solution. By Theorem 7.4-V

$$\log_b \left(\frac{xy}{z}\right)^{1/2} = \frac{1}{2} \log_b \left(\frac{xy}{z}\right).$$

By Theorems 7.4-I and II

$$= \frac{1}{2}[\log_b x + \log_b y - \log_b z].$$

53. $\log_b (xy)$	54. $\log_b (xyz)$	55. $\log_b \left(\frac{x}{y}\right)$
56. $\log_b \left(\frac{xy}{z}\right)$	57. $\log_b x^5$	58. $\log_b x^{1/2}$

59. $\log_b \sqrt[3]{x}$ 60. $\log_b \sqrt[3]{x^2}$ 61. $\log_b \sqrt{\dfrac{x}{z}}$

62. $\log_b \sqrt{xy}$ 63. $\log_{10} \sqrt[8]{\dfrac{xy^2}{z}}$ 64. $\log_{10} \sqrt[5]{\dfrac{x^2y}{z^3}}$

65. $\log_{10} 2\pi \sqrt{\dfrac{l}{g}}$ 66. $\log_{10} \sqrt{s(s-a)(s-b)(s-c)}$

Express as a single logarithm with coefficient 1.

Example. $\frac{1}{2}(\log_b x - \log_b y)$

Solution.   By Theorems 7.4-II and V

$$\tfrac{1}{2}(\log_b x - \log_b y) = \tfrac{1}{2} \log_b \left(\frac{x}{y}\right) = \log_b \left(\frac{x}{y}\right)^{1/2}.$$

67. $\log_b x + \log_b y$ 68. $\log_b x - \log_b y$

69. $2 \log_b x + 3 \log_b y$ 70. $\frac{1}{4} \log_b x - \frac{3}{4} \log_b y$

71. $3 \log_b x + \log_b y - 2 \log_b z$ 72. $\frac{1}{3}(\log_b x + \log_b y - 2 \log_b z)$

73. $\log_{10} (x-2) + \log_{10} x - 2 \log_{10} z$

74. $\frac{1}{4}(\log_{10} x - 3 \log_{10} y - 5 \log_{10} z)$

75. Show that $\frac{1}{4} \log_{10} 8 + \frac{1}{4} \log_{10} 2 = \log_{10} 2$.

76. Show that $4 \log_{10} 3 - 2 \log_{10} 3 + 1 = \log_{10} 90$.

77. Show that $10^{2 \log_{10} x} = x^2$.

78. Show that $a^{2 \log_a 3} + b^{3 \log_b 2} = 17$.

79. Show that $\log_{10} [\log_3 (\log_5 125)] = 0$.

80. Using the definition of a logarithm ($\log_b x$ is a number such that $b^{\log_b x} = x$) and the laws of exponents (Theorem 7.3), prove Theorem 7.4-II.

7.3   LOGARITHMS TO THE BASE 10

There are two logarithmic functions of special interest in mathematics; one is defined by

$$y = \log_{10} x, \tag{1}$$

and the other by

$$y = \log_e x, \tag{2}$$

where e is an irrational number with decimal approximation 2.7182818 to eight digits. Because these functions possess similar properties, and because we are more familiar with the number 10, we shall, for the present, confine our attention to (1).

Values for $\log_{10} x$ are called **logarithms to the base 10** or **common logarithms.** From the definition of $\log_{10} x$,

$$10^{\log_{10} x} = x \quad (x > 0); \tag{3}$$

that is, $\log_{10} x$ is the exponent that must be placed on 10 so that the resulting power is x. The problem with which we are concerned in this section is that of finding, for each positive x, $\log_{10} x$. First, $\log_{10} x$ can easily be determined for all values of x that are integral powers of 10:

$$\log_{10} 10 \quad = \log_{10} 10^1 = 1,$$

$$\log_{10} 100 \quad = \log_{10} 10^2 = 2,$$

$$\log_{10} 1000 = \log_{10} 10^3 = 3,$$

etc., and similarly

$$\log_{10} 1 \quad = \log_{10} 10^0 \quad = 0,$$

$$\log_{10} 0.1 \quad = \log_{10} 10^{-1} = -1,$$

$$\log_{10} 0.01 \quad = \log_{10} 10^{-2} = -2,$$

$$\log_{10} 0.001 = \log_{10} 10^{-3} = -3.$$

A table of logarithms is used to find $\log_{10} x$ for $1 \le x \le 10$ (see page 402). Consider the excerpt from this table shown in Figure 7.4. Each number

x	0	1	2	3	4	5	6	7	8	9
3.8	.5798	.5809	.5821	.5832	.5843	.5855	.5866	.5877	.5888	.5899
3.9	.5911	.5922	.5933	.5944	.5955	.5966	.5977	.5988	.5999	.6010
4.0	.6021	.6031	.6042	.6053	.6064	.6075	.6085	.6096	.6107	.6117
4.1	.6128	.6138	.6149	.6160	.6170	.6180	.6191	.6201	.6212	.6222
4.2	.6232	.6243	.6253	.6263	.6274	.6284	.6294	.6304	.6314	.6325
4.3	.6335	.6345	.6355	.6365	.6375	.6385	.6395	.6405	.6415	.6425
4.4	.6435	.6444	.6454	.6464	.6474	.6484	.6493	.6503	.6513	.6522
4.5	.6532	.6542	.6551	.6561	.6571	.6580	.6590	.6599	.6609	.6618
4.6	.6628	.6637	.6646	.6656	.6665	.6675	.6684	.6693	.6702	.6712

Figure 7.4

in the column headed by x represents the first two significant digits of x, while each number in the row opposite x contains the third significant digit of x. The digits located at the intersection of a row and a column form the logarithm of x. For example, to find $\log_{10} 4.25$, we look at the intersection of the row opposite 4.2 under x and the column headed by 5. Thus, we see that

$$\log_{10} 4.25 = 0.6284.$$

Similarly,

$$\log_{10} 4.02 = 0.6042,$$
$$\log_{10} 4.49 = 0.6522,$$

etc. The equality sign is used here in an inexact sense. More properly, $\log_{10} 4.25 \approx 0.6284$, $\log_{10} 4.02 \approx 0.6042$, and $\log_{10} 4.49 \approx 0.6522$, because these numbers are irrational and cannot be precisely represented by a rational number. We shall follow customary usage, however, writing $=$ instead of $\approx$, and leave the intent to the context.

Now suppose we wish to find $\log_{10} x$ for values of x outside the range of the table—that is, for $0 < x < 1$ or $x > 10$. This can be done quite readily by first representing the number in scientific notation—that is, as the product of a number between 1 and 10 and a power of 10—and applying Theorem 7.4-I. For example,

$$\log_{10} 42.5 = \log_{10} (4.25 \times 10^1) = \log_{10} 4.25 + \log_{10} 10^1$$
$$= 0.6284 + 1 = 1.6284,$$

$$\log_{10} 425 = \log_{10} (4.25 \times 10^2) = \log_{10} 4.25 + \log_{10} 10^2$$
$$= 0.6284 + 2 = 2.6284,$$

$$\log_{10} 4250 = \log_{10} (4.25 \times 10^3) = \log_{10} 4.25 + \log_{10} 10^3$$
$$= 0.6284 + 3 = 3.6284.$$

Observe that the decimal portion of the logarithm is always 0.6284, and the integral portion is just the exponent on 10 when the number is written in scientific notation.

This process can be reduced to a mechanical one by considering $\log_{10} x$ to consist of two parts, an integral part (called the **characteristic**) and a nonnegative decimal fraction part (called the **mantissa**). Thus the table of values for $\log_{10} x$ for $1 < x < 10$ can be looked upon as a table of mantissas for $\log_{10} x$ for all $x > 0$.

To find $\log_{10} 43700$, we first write

$$\log_{10} 43700 = \log_{10} (4.37 \times 10^4).$$

Upon examining the table of logarithms, we find that $\log_{10} 4.37 = 0.6405$, so that

$$\log_{10} 43700 = 4.6405,$$

where we have prefixed the characteristic 4.

Now consider an example of the form $\log_{10} x$ for $0 < x < 1$. To find $\log_{10} 0.00402$, we write

$$\log_{10} 0.00402 = \log_{10} (4.02 \times 10^{-3}).$$

Examining the table, we find $\log_{10} 4.02$ is 0.6042.   Upon adding 0.6042 to the characteristic -3, we obtain

$$\log_{10} 0.00402 = -2.3958,$$

where the decimal portion of the logarithm is no longer 0.6042 as it is in the case of all numbers $x > 1$ for which the first three significant digits of x are 402.   To circumvent this situation, it is customary to write the logarithm in a form in which the fractional part is positive.   In the foregoing example, we write

$$\log_{10} 0.00402 = 0.6042 - 3$$
$$= 0.6042 + (7 - 10)$$
$$= 7.6042 - 10,$$

and the fractional part is positive.   The logarithms

$$6.6042 - 9,$$

$$12.6042 - 15,$$

etc. are equally valid representations, but $7.6042 - 10$ is customary in most cases.

It is possible to reverse the process described in this section and, being given $\log_{10} x$, to find x.   In this event, x is referred to as the **antilogarithm** (antilog$_{10}$) of $\log_{10} x$.   For example, antilog$_{10}$ 1.6395 can be obtained by locating the mantissa, 0.6395, in the body of the $\log_{10}$ tables and observing that the associated antilog$_{10}$ is 4.36.   Thus

$$\text{antilog}_{10} \ 1.6395 = 4.36 \times 10^1 = 43.6.$$

If we seek the common logarithm of a number that is not an entry in the table (for example, $\log_{10} 3712$), or if we seek x when $\log_{10} x$ is not an entry in the table, it is customary to use a procedure called **linear interpolation**.

A table of common logarithms is a set of ordered pairs.   For each number x there is an associated number $\log_{10} x$, and we have $(x, \log_{10} x)$ displayed in convenient tabular form.   Because of space limitations, only three digits for the number x and four for the number $\log_{10} x$ appear in the table.   By means of linear interpolation, however, the table can be used to find approximations to logarithms for four-digit numbers.

Let us examine geometrically the concepts involved.   A portion of the graph of

$$y = \log_{10} x$$

is shown in Figure 7.5.   The curvature is exaggerated to illustrate the principle involved.   We propose to use the straight line joining the points P_1 and P_2 as an approximation to the curve passing through the points. If a large graph of $y = \log_{10} x$ were available, the value of, say, $\log_{10} 4.257$,

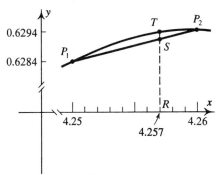

Figure 7.5

could be found by using the value of the ordinate (RT) to the curve for $x = 4.257$. Since there is no way to accomplish this with a table of values only, we shall instead use the value of the ordinate (RS) to the straight line as an approximation to the ordinate of the curve.

This can be accomplished directly from the set of numbers available in the table of logarithms. Consider Figure 7.6, where P_2P_3 and P_4P_5 are perpendicular to P_1P_3.

From geometry, we have $\Delta P_1P_4P_5 \sim \Delta P_1P_2P_3$, where the corresponding sides are proportional, and hence

$$\frac{x}{X} = \frac{y}{Y}. \tag{4}$$

If we know any three of these numbers, the fourth can be determined. For the purpose of interpolation, we assume all of our members are now four-digit numbers; that is, we consider 4.250 instead of 4.25, and 4.260 instead of 4.26. We note that the number 4.257 falls on a point just 7/10

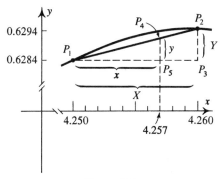

Figure 7.6

of the distance between the points corresponding to 4.250 and 4.260, respectively, and the value Y (0.0010) is just the difference between the logarithms 0.6284 and 0.6294.   It follows from (4) that

$$\frac{7}{10} = \frac{y}{0.0010},$$

from which

$$y = \frac{7}{10} (0.0010) = 0.0007.$$

We now add 0.0007 to 0.6284 and thus obtain a good approximation to the required logarithm.   That is,

$$\log_{10} 4.257 = 0.6291.$$

An example in Exercise 7.3 shows a convenient arrangement for the calculations involved in the example presented here.   The antilogarithm of a number can be found by a similar procedure.   With practice, however, it is possible to interpolate mentally in both procedures.

EXERCISE 7.3

Write the characteristic of each of the following.

Examples.

  a. $\log_{10} 248$ b. $\log_{10} 0.0057$

Solutions.   Represent the number in scientific notation.

  a. $\log_{10} (2.48 \times 10^2)$ b. $\log_{10} (5.7 \times 10^{-3})$

The exponent on the base 10 is the characteristic.

   2   -3, or $7 - 10$

1. $\log_{10} 312$ 2. $\log_{10} 0.02$ 3. $\log_{10} 0.00851$

4. $\log_{10} 8.012$ 5. $\log_{10} 0.00031$ 6. $\log_{10} 0.0004$

7. $\log_{10} (15 \times 10^3)$ 8. $\log_{10} (820 \times 10^4)$

Find each logarithm.

Examples.

  a. $\log_{10} 16.8$ b. $\log_{10} 0.043$

Solutions.   Represent the number in scientific notation.

  a. $\log_{10} (1.68 \times 10^1)$ b. $\log_{10} (4.3 \times 10^{-2})$

Determine the mantissa from the table.

   0.2253   0.6335

Add the characteristic as determined by the exponent on the base 10.

   1.2253 $8.6335 - 10$

  9. $\log_{10} 6.73$ 10. $\log_{10} 891$

11. $\log_{10} 0.813$ 12. $\log_{10} 0.00214$

13. $\log_{10} 0.08$ 14. $\log_{10} 0.000413$

15. $\log_{10} (2.48 \times 10^2)$ 16. $\log_{10} (5.39 \times 10^{-3})$

Find each antilogarithm.

Example. $\text{antilog}_{10}\ 2.7364$

Solution.   Locate the mantissa in the body of the table of mantissas and determine the associated antilog_{10} (a number between 1 and 10); write the characteristic as an exponent on the base 10.

$$5.45 \times 10^2$$

Write in standard form.

$$545$$

17. $\text{antilog}_{10} 0.6128$ 18. $\text{antilog}_{10} 0.2504$

19. $\text{antilog}_{10} 0.5647$ 20. $\text{antilog}_{10} 3.9258$

21. $\text{antilog}_{10} (8.8075 - 10)$ 22. $\text{antilog}_{10} (3.9722 - 5)$

23. $\text{antilog}_{10} 3.7388$ 24. $\text{antilog}_{10} 2.0086$

25. $\text{antilog}_{10} (6.8561 - 10)$ 26. $\text{antilog}_{10} (1.8156 - 4)$

Find each logarithm.

Example. $\log_{10} 4.257$

Solution.   Interpolate mentally or use the following procedure.

$$
\begin{array}{c c}
x & \log_{10} x \\
\end{array}
$$

$$
10\left\{ 7\left\{ \begin{array}{c|c} 4.250 & 0.6284 \\ 4.257 & ? \end{array} \right\}y \atop \begin{array}{c|c} 4.260 & 0.6294 \end{array} \right\}0.0010
$$

Set up a proportion and solve for y.

$$\frac{7}{10} = \frac{y}{0.0010}$$

$$y = 0.0007$$

Add this value of y to 0.6284.

$$\log_{10} 4.257 = 0.6284 + 0.0007$$
$$= 0.6291$$

27. $\log_{10} 4.213$ 28. $\log_{10} 8.184$ 29. $\log_{10} 1522$

30. $\log_{10} 203.4$ 31. $\log_{10} 37110$ 32. $\log_{10} 72.36$

33. $\log_{10} 0.5123$ 34. $\log_{10} 0.008351$

Find each antilogarithm.

Example. antilog$_{10}$ 0.6446

Solution. Interpolate mentally or use the following procedure.

$$\begin{array}{cc} x & \text{antilog}_{10}\ x \end{array}$$

$$0.0010 \left\{ \begin{array}{l} 0.0002 \left\{ \begin{array}{l} 0.6444 \mid 4.410 \\ 0.6446 \mid \quad ? \end{array} \right\} y \\ \\ 0.6454 \mid 4.420 \end{array} \right\} 0.010$$

Set up a proportion and solve for y.

$$\frac{0.0002}{0.0010} = \frac{y}{0.010}$$

$$y = 0.002$$

Add this value of y to 4.410.

$$\text{antilog}_{10}\ 0.6446 = 4.410 + 0.002$$
$$= 4.412$$

35. antilog$_{10}$ 0.5085   36. antilog$_{10}$ 0.8087

37. antilog$_{10}$ 1.0220   38. antilog$_{10}$ 3.0759

39. antilog$_{10}$ $(8.7055 - 10)$ 40. antilog$_{10}$ $(9.8742 - 10)$

41. antilog$_{10}$ $(2.8748 - 3)$ 42. antilog$_{10}$ $(7.7397 - 10)$

43. If we use linear interpolation to find $\log_{10} 3.751$ and $\log_{10} 3.755$, which of the resulting approximations should we expect to be more nearly correct? Why?

44. If we use linear interpolation to find $\log_{10} 1.025$ and $\log_{10} 9.025$, which of the resulting approximations should we expect to be more nearly correct? Why?

Find each of the following by means of the table of logarithms to the base 10. *Hint:* Find the antilog of the exponent.

45. $10^{0.9590}$ 46. $10^{0.8241}$ 47. $10^{3.6990}$

48. $10^{2.3874}$ 49. $10^{2.0531}$ 50. $10^{1.7396}$

51. Write the following logarithms to the base 10 in a form in which both the integral and fractional parts are negative.

   a. $9.7321 - 10$ b. $6.4187 - 10$

52. Write the following logarithms to the base 10 in a form in which the fractional part is positive.

   a. -2.7113 b. -4.6621

53. What is the characteristic of $\log_5 33$? Of $\log_2 33$? Of $\log_4 33$? Of $\log_{30} 33$?

54. What is the characteristic of $\log_2 \frac{1}{5}$? *Hint:* $\log_2 \frac{1}{4} = -2$ and $\log_2 \frac{1}{8} = -3$.

7.4 COMPUTATIONS WITH LOGARITHMS

The use of the slide rule and the advent of high-speed computing devices have almost removed the need to perform routine numerical computations with pencil and paper by logarithms.   Nevertheless, we introduce the techniques involved in making such computations because the writing of the logarithmic equations involved sheds light on the properties of the logarithmic function and on the usefulness of Theorem 7.4, which we reproduce here using the base 10.

If x_1 and x_2 are positive real numbers, k is any real number, and p, q are integers, with $q \neq 0$, then

$$\text{I}\quad \log_{10}(x_1 x_2) = \log_{10} x_1 + \log_{10} x_2,$$

$$\text{II}\quad \log_{10} \frac{x_1}{x_2} = \log_{10} x_1 - \log_{10} x_2,$$

$$\text{III}\quad \log_{10}(x_1)^p = p \log_{10} x_1,$$

$$\text{IV}\quad \log_{10} \sqrt[q]{x_1^p} = \frac{p}{q} \log_{10} x_1,$$

$$\text{V}\quad \log_{10} x_1^k = k \log_{10} x_1.$$

Before illustrating the use of these laws, let us make three observations:

L-1   If $M = N$ ($M, N > 0$), then $\log_b M = \log_b N$.

L-2   If $\log_b M = \log_b N$, then $M = N$.

L-3   If $M = N$, then $b^M = b^N$.

These assertions should seem plausible, because the values of the variables in exponential and logarithmic functions are in one-to-one correspondence.

Example.   Find the product of 3.825 and 0.00729 using logarithms.

Solution.   Let $N = (3.825)(0.00729)$.   By Property L-1,

$$\log_{10} N = \log_{10}[(3.825)(0.00729)].$$

Now, by Theorem 7.4-I,

$$\log_{10} N = \log_{10} 3.825 + \log_{10} 0.00729,$$

and from the table,

$$\log_{10} 3.825 = 0.5826,$$

$$\log_{10} 0.00729 = 7.8627 - 10,$$

so that

$$\log_{10} N = (0.5826) + (7.8627 - 10)$$
$$= 8.4453 - 10.$$

The computation is completed by referring to the table for

$$N = \text{antilog}_{10} (8.4453 - 10) = 2.788 \times 10^{-2}$$
$$= 0.02788.$$

Thus we have

$$N = (3.825)(0.00729) = 0.02788.$$

Actual computation shows the product to be 0.02788425, so that the result obtained by use of logarithms is correct to four significant digits. Some error should be expected because we are using approximations to irrational numbers when we employ a table of logarithms.

Example.   Compute $\dfrac{(8.21)^{1/2}(2.17)^{2/3}}{(3.14)^3}$.

Solution.   Setting

$$N = \frac{(8.21)^{1/2}(2.17)^{2/3}}{(3.14)^3},$$

we obtain

$$\log_{10} N = \log_{10} \frac{(8.21)^{1/2}(2.17)^{2/3}}{(3.14)^3}$$
$$= \log_{10} (8.21)^{1/2} + \log_{10} (2.17)^{2/3} - \log_{10} (3.14)^3$$
$$= \frac{1}{2} \log_{10} (8.21) + \frac{2}{3} \log_{10} (2.17) - 3 \log_{10} (3.14).$$

The table provides values for the logarithms involved here, and the remainder of the computation is routine.

EXERCISE 7.4

Compute by means of logarithms.

Example. $\dfrac{(23.4)(0.681)}{4.13}$

Solution.

$$\text{Let } P = \frac{(23.4)(0.681)}{4.13}.$$

$$\begin{aligned}
\text{Then } \log_{10} P &= \log_{10} 23.4 + \log_{10} 0.681 - \log_{10} 4.13 \\
&= (1.3692) + (9.8331 - 10) - (0.6160) \\
&= 0.5863,
\end{aligned}$$

and antilog$_{10}$ 0.5863 = 3.857.

1. $(2.32)(1.73)$

2. $(83.2)(6.12)$

3. $\dfrac{3.15}{1.37}$

4. $\dfrac{0.00214}{3.17}$

5. $(2.3)^5$

6. $(4.62)^3$

7. $\sqrt[3]{8.12}$

8. $\sqrt[5]{75}$

9. $(0.0128)^5$

10. $(0.0021)^6$

11. $\sqrt{0.0021}$

12. $\sqrt[5]{0.0471}$

13. $\dfrac{(8.12)(8.74)}{7.19}$

14. $\dfrac{(0.421)^2(84.3)}{\sqrt{21.7}}$

15. $\dfrac{(6.49)^2\sqrt[3]{8.21}}{17.9}$

16. $\dfrac{(2.61)^2(4.32)}{\sqrt{7.83}}$

17. $\dfrac{(0.3498)(27.16)}{6.814}$

18. $\dfrac{(4.813)^2(20.14)}{3.612}$

19. Find an approximate value for $2^{\sqrt{2}}$.

20. Find an approximate value for 2^{π}.

21. The period T of a simple pendulum is given by the formula $T = 2\pi\sqrt{L/g}$, where T is in seconds, L is the length of the pendulum in feet, and $g \approx 32$ ft/sec^2. Find the period of a pendulum 12 inches long.

22. The area A of a triangle in terms of the sides is given by the formula $A = \sqrt{s(s - a)(s - b)(s - c)}$, where a, b, and c are the lengths of the sides of the triangle and s equals one half of the perimeter. Find the area of a triangle in which the three sides are 2.314 inches, 4.217 inches, and 5.618 inches.

23. The pressure p and volume v of saturated steam are related by the expression $pv^{1.06} = c$, in which p is in pounds per square inch, v is in cubic feet, and c is a constant. If $v = 2.874$ cu ft when $p = 40$ lb/in.^{2}, find the volume when the pressure is doubled.

7.5   EXPONENTIAL AND LOGARITHMIC EQUATIONS

An equation in one variable in which the variable occurs in an exponent is called an **exponential equation**. Solution sets of some such equations can be found by means of logarithms.

Example.   Find the solution set of $5^x = 7$.

Solution.   Since $5^x > 0$ for all x, we can apply Property L-1 from the preceding section and write

$$\log_{10} 5^x = \log_{10} 7,$$

and from Theorem 7.4-V,

$$x \log_{10} 5 = \log_{10} 7.$$

Dividing each member by $\log_{10} 5$, we get

$$x = \frac{\log_{10} 7}{\log_{10} 5} = \frac{0.8451}{0.6990},$$

and the solution set is then

$$\{1.209\}.$$

Note that in seeking a numerical approximation to this solution, the logarithms are *divided*, not subtracted.

Example.   Find the solution set of $6^{3x-4} = 3$.

Solution.   From L-1 we have

$$\log_{10} 6^{3x-4} = \log_{10} 3,$$

and, from Theorem 7.4-V,

$$(3x - 4) \log_{10} 6 = \log_{10} 3.$$

Dividing each member by $\log_{10} 6$, we obtain

$$3x - 4 = \frac{\log_{10} 3}{\log_{10} 6}.$$

Then

$$3x = \frac{\log_{10} 3}{\log_{10} 6} + 4,$$

$$x = \frac{\log_{10} 3}{3 \log_{10} 6} + \frac{4}{3},$$

and the solution set is

$$\left\{ \frac{\log_{10} 3}{3 \log_{10} 6} + \frac{4}{3} \right\}.$$

A decimal approximation to the solution can be obtained if desired by consulting the table of logarithms and performing some routine computations.

Solution sets can also be found for some equations in which the terms involve logarithms.

Example.   Find the solution set of

$$\log_{10} x + \log_{10} (x - 3) = 1. \tag{1}$$

Solution.   From Theorem 7.4-I, any solution of (1) satisfies

$$\log_{10} x(x - 3) = 1. \tag{2}$$

Rewriting (2) in exponential form, we have

$$x(x - 3) = 10^1. \tag{3}$$

This quadratic equation can be solved as follows:

$$x^2 - 3x = 10,$$

$$x^2 - 3x - 10 = 0,$$

$$(x - 5)(x + 2) = 0,$$

$$x = 5 \quad \text{and} \quad x = -2,$$

and the solution set of (3) is $\{5, -2\}$.   Is this also the solution set of (1)?   We have
stated that any solution x of (1) must be included in the solution set of (2), but
the converse may very well not be true.   Proceeding as we did in Chapter 3
with equations involving radicals, we find a suspected solution and then check
it in the original equation.   Checking each member of $\{5, -2\}$ in Equation (1),
we note that -2 does not satisfy the equation because $\log_{10}(-2)$ is not defined.
The number 5, however, is a valid solution, and the solution set is $\{5\}$.

   Both exponential and logarithmic functions are of very great importance
in applied mathematics.   One such application of logarithms is the computation of compound interest.   The interest I on a given amount P of money
for a definite number n of periods at a specified rate r per period is called
simple interest and can be computed by the familiar formula $I = Pr^n$.   If,
however, the interest accruing to an amount of money is periodically added
to the amount, and over the next period this new total is earning interest, we
say that the principal is earning **compound interest**.   For example, if the sum
of one dollar is earning interest at a rate r per year compounded annually,
the amount present, A, is given

   after one year by $A = 1 + r$,

   after two years by $A = (1 + r) + r(1 + r) = (1 + r)^2$,

   after three years by $A = (1 + r)^2 + r(1 + r)^2 = (1 + r)^3$,

and

   after n years by $A = (1 + r)^n$.

For each dollar invested under such an arrangement, we have $(1 + r)^n$
dollars after n years, so that P dollars invested under the same arrangement,
after n years, would amount to

$$A = P(1 + r)^n. \tag{4}$$

If the interest is compounded t times yearly, then the rate per period is r/t instead of r, where r is the stated rate per year, and the number of periods is increased to tn, so that (4) becomes

$$A = P\left(1 + \frac{r}{t}\right)^{tn}. \tag{5}$$

Specifically, the amount of P dollars compounded *semiannually* for n years at a yearly rate of interest r will be

$$A = P\left(1 + \frac{r}{2}\right)^{2n}, \tag{5a}$$

and when compounded *quarterly*,

$$A = P\left(1 + \frac{r}{4}\right)^{4n}. \tag{5b}$$

Although from a practical standpoint problems similar to the following example are handled by means of tables, for illustrative purposes we shall use logarithms in this example and in the exercise set.

Example.   What rate is necessary in order that \$2500 compounded quarterly will amount to \$4800 in twelve years?

Solution.   From (5b), we have

$$4800 = 2500\left(1 + \frac{r}{4}\right)^{48},$$

or

$$\left(1 + \frac{r}{4}\right)^{48} = 1.92,$$

and

$$\left(1 + \frac{r}{4}\right) = 1.92^{1/48}.$$

Solving for r by means of logarithms, we obtain

$$\log_{10}\left(1 + \frac{r}{4}\right) = \log_{10} 1.92^{1/48}$$

$$= \frac{1}{48} \log_{10} 1.92$$

$$= \frac{1}{48}(0.2833),$$

$$\log_{10}\left(1 + \frac{r}{4}\right) = 0.0059,$$

$$\text{antilog}_{10}\, 0.0059 = 1 + \frac{r}{4} = 1.014.$$

Thus we have

$$r = 4(1.014 - 1),$$

$$r = 0.056.$$

The required rate of interest is about 5.6%.

An interesting application of logarithms occurs in the field of chemistry. The chemist defines the *pH* (hydrogen potential) of a solution by

$$pH = \log_{10} \frac{1}{[H^+]} \tag{6}$$

$$= \log_{10} [H^+]^{-1},$$

$$pH = -\log_{10} [H^+], \tag{6a}$$

where the symbol $[H^+]$ denotes a numerical value for the concentration of hydrogen ions in aqueous solution in moles per liter.

Example. Find the *pH* of a solution in which the concentration of hydrogen ions $[H^+]$ is 4.0×10^{-5}.

Solution. From (6), we have

$$pH = \log_{10} \frac{1}{4 \times 10^{-5}}$$

$$= \log_{10} (2.5 \times 10^4),$$

$$pH = 4.4.$$

Example. Find the hydrogen ion concentration $[H^+]$ of a solution with $pH = 5.6$.

Solution. From (6a), we have

$$-\log_{10} [H^+] = 5.6,$$

from which

$$\log_{10} [H^+] = -5.6.$$

To use the table of mantissas for finding the antilog$_{10}$ -5.6, we change -5.6 to $-6 + 0.4$ or $4.4 - 10$, a form in which the fractional part is positive. Thus we have

$$[H^+] = \text{antilog}_{10} (4.4 - 10)$$

$$= 2.5 \times 10^{-6}.$$

The hydrogen ion concentration in the above example can be determined by an alternative method. From (6), we obtain

$$\log_{10} \frac{1}{[H^+]} = 5.6,$$

$$\frac{1}{[H^+]} = \text{antilog}_{10} 5.6 = 3.98 \times 10^5,$$

$$[H^+] = \frac{1}{3.98 \times 10^5} = 0.25 \times 10^{-5},$$

$$[H^+] = 2.5 \times 10^{-6}.$$

EXERCISE 7.5

Solve. Leave solutions in logarithmic form using the base 10.

Example. $3^{x-2} = 16$.

Solution. By Property L-1,

$$\log_{10} 3^{x-2} = \log_{10} 16.$$

By Theorem 7.4-V,

$$(x - 2) \log_{10} 3 = \log_{10} 16,$$

from which

$$x - 2 = \frac{\log_{10} 16}{\log_{10} 3}$$

$$x = \frac{\log_{10} 16}{\log_{10} 3} + 2.$$

The solution set is $\left\{ \dfrac{\log_{10} 16}{\log_{10} 3} + 2 \right\}$.

1. $2^x = 7$ 2. $3^x = 4$ 3. $3^{x+1} = 8$

4. $2^{x-1} = 9$ 5. $7^{2x-1} = 3$ 6. $3^{x+2} = 10$

7. $4^{x^2} = 15$ 8. $8^{x^2} = 21$ 9. $3^{-x} = 10$

10. $2.13^{-x} = 8.1$ 11. $3^{1-x} = 15$ 12. $4^{2-x} = 10$

Solve. Leave the results in the form of an equation equivalent to the given equation.

13. $y = x^n$, for n 14. $y = Cx^{-n}$, for n

15. $y = e^{kt}$, for t 16. $y = Ce^{-kt}$, for t

Solve.

Example. $\log_{10} (x + 9) + \log_{10} x = 1$.

Solution. By Theorem 7.4-I, $\log_{10} (x + 9)(x) = 1$.

Write this equation in exponential form, and solve for x.

$$x^2 + 9x = 10^1$$

$$x^2 + 9x - 10 = 0$$

$$(x + 10)(x - 1) = 0$$

$$x = -10, \quad x = 1$$

Since -10 does not satisfy the original equation, the solution set is simply $\{1\}$.

17. $\log_{10} x + \log_{10} 2 = 3$

18. $\log_{10} (x - 1) - \log_{10} 4 = 2$

19. $\log_{10} x + \log_{10} (x + 21) = 2$

20. $\log_{10} (x + 3) + \log_{10} x = 1$

21. $\log_{10} (x + 2) + \log_{10} (x - 1) = 1$

22. $\log_{10} (x - 3) - \log_{10} (x + 1) = 1$

23. Solve for x: $3^{\log_3 x} = 7$.

24. Solve for x: $5^{3 \log_5 x} = 8$.

25. Show that the solution set of $3^x = 18$ is $\{\log_3 18\}$, and hence infer a means of finding $\log_a b$ in terms of $\log_{10} b$ by solving a similar equation.

26. Find a value for $\log_2 3$ using a table of logarithms to the base 10. *Hint:* Let $x = \log_2 3$ and write in exponential form, etc.

Solve for the variable n (nearest year), r (nearest $\frac{1}{2}\%$), or A (accuracy obtainable on four-place table of mantissas).

Example. $(1 + r)^{12} = 1.127$

Solution. Equate $\log_{10}$ of each member and apply Theorem 7.4-III.

$$12 \log_{10} (1 + r) = \log_{10} 1.127$$
$$= 0.0519$$

Divide each member by 12.

$$\log_{10} (1 + r) = \frac{1}{12} (0.0519)$$
$$= 0.0043$$

Determine antilog$_{10}$ 0.0043 and solve for r.

$$\text{antilog}_{10}\ 0.0043 = 1.01$$
$$1 + r = 1.01$$
$$r = 0.01 \text{ or } 1\%$$

Example. $40(1 + 0.02)^n = 51.74$

Solution. Divide each member by 40; equate $\log_{10}$ of each member, and apply Theorem 7.4, Parts II and III.

$$n \log_{10} (1.02) = \log_{10} 51.74 - \log_{10} 40$$
$$n (0.0086) = 1.7138 - 1.6021$$
$$n = \frac{0.1117}{0.0086}$$
$$n = 13 \text{ years}$$

27. $(1 + 0.03)^{10} = A$

28. $(1 + 0.04)^8 = A$

29. $(1 + r)^6 = 1.34$

30. $(1 + r)^{10} = 1.48$

$\log_{10}(100\left(1+\frac{r}{2}\right)^{10} = \log_{10} 113$

31. $(1 + 0.04)^n = 2.19$ $\log_{10}(1+\frac{r}{2})^{10}+2 =$ 32. $(1 + 0.04)^n = 1.60$
$\log_{10} 113$

33. $100\left(1 + \frac{r}{2}\right)^{10} = 113$ $_{10}(\log_{10}(1+\frac{r}{2})+2$ 34. $40\left(1 + \frac{r}{4}\right)^{12} = 50.9$

35. $150(1 + 0.01)^{4n} = 240$ $\log_{10} 113$ 36. $60(1 + 0.02)^{2n} = 116$

37. Find the compounded amount of \$5000 invested at 4% for 10 years when compounded annually. When compounded semi-annually. When compounded quarterly.

38. Two men, A and B, each invested \$10,000 at 4% for 20 years with a bank that computed interest quarterly. A withdrew his interest at the end of each three-month period but B let his investment be compounded. How much more did B earn than A from his investment over the period of 20 years?

Calculate the pH of a solution with given hydrogen ion concentration.

39. $[H^+] = 10^{-7}$ 40. $[H^+] = 4.0 \times 10^{-5}$

41. $[H^+] = 2.0 \times 10^{-8}$ 42. $[H^+] = 8.5 \times 10^{-3}$

43. $[H^+] = 6.3 \times 10^{-7}$ 44. $[H^+] = 5.7 \times 10^{-7}$

Calculate the hydrogen ion concentration $[H^+]$ of a solution with given pH.

Example. $pH = 7.4$

Solution. Substitute 7.4 for pH in the relationship $pH = \log_{10} \dfrac{1}{[H^+]}$.

$$\log_{10} \frac{1}{[H^+]} = 7.4$$

Equate antilog$_{10}$ of each member and solve for $[H^+]$.

$$\frac{1}{[H^+]} = \text{antilog}_{10}\, 7.4 = 2.5 \times 10^7$$

$$[H^+] = \frac{1}{2.5 \times 10^7} = 0.4 \times 10^{-7} = 4 \times 10^{-8}$$

45. $pH = 3.0$ 46. $pH = 4.2$ 47. $pH = 5.6$

48. $pH = 8.3$ 49. $pH = 7.2$ 50. $pH = 6.9$

7.6   LOGARITHMS TO THE BASE e

The number e ($e \approx 2.718218$) mentioned in Section 7.3 is of great mathematical interest and importance, and logarithms to the base e are frequently encountered in practical situations. It is possible to determine $\log_e x$ provided we have a table of $\log_{10} x$. Indeed, given a table of $\log_b x$, we can always find $\log_a x$ for any $a > 0$, $a \neq 1$. We can do this as follows.

Since $x > 0$ and $a \neq 1$, we have

$$x = a^{\log_a x}. \tag{1}$$

By applying Property L-1 of Section 7.4, we can equate the logarithms to the base b ($b > 0$, $b \neq 1$) of each member of (1) to obtain

$$\log_b x = \log_b a^{\log_a x}.$$

By Theorem 7.4-V, this yields

$$\log_b x = \log_a x \cdot \log_b a,$$

or

$$\log_a x = \frac{\log_b x}{\log_b a}. \tag{2}$$

Equation (2) gives us a means of finding $\log_a x$ when we have a table of logarithms to the base b. In particular, if $a = e$ and $b = 10$, we have

$$\log_e x = \frac{\log_{10} x}{\log_{10} e}. \tag{3}$$

Since $\log_{10} e \approx 0.4343$, (3) can be written

$$\log_e x = \frac{\log_{10} x}{0.4343}, \tag{4}$$

or

$$\log_e x = 2.3026 \log_{10} x, \tag{5}$$

which gives us a direct means of approximating $\log_e x$ when we have a table of logarithms to the base 10.

A table of $\log_e x$ will be found on page 405. We cannot, however, do as we did with a table of $\log_{10} x$—that is, simply list mantissas for logarithms over a certain interval and then manipulate characteristics to take care of all other intervals. Our numeration system is based on 10 and not on e. With the help of logarithms, though, we can use formula (5), above, and the table of $\log_{10} x$ on page 402 to find $\log_e x$.

Example. Find $\log_e 278$.

Solution. We shall do this in two ways.

1. Since

$$\log_e x = 2.3026 \log_{10} x,$$

we have

$$\log_e 278 \approx 2.3026 \log_{10} 278$$
$$\approx 2.3026 \,(2.4440)$$
$$\approx 5.63.$$

2. Alternatively, we observe that $278 \approx 2.8 \times 10^2$. Hence

$$\begin{aligned} \log_e 278 &\approx \log_e (2.8 \times 10^2) \approx \log_e 2.8 + 2 \log_e 10 \\ &\approx 1.0296 + 2(2.3026) \\ &\approx 1.0296 + 4.6052 \\ &\approx 5.63. \end{aligned}$$

Example.   Find $\log_e 0.278$.

Solution.   This time let us simply observe that $0.278 \approx 2.8 \times 10^{-1}$. Hence

$$\begin{aligned} \log_e 0.278 &\approx \log_e (2.8 \times 10^{-1}) = \log_e 2.8 + \log_e 10^{-1} \\ &= \log_e 2.8 - \log_e 10 \\ &\approx 1.0296 - 2.3026 \\ &\approx -1.2730. \end{aligned}$$

As one would expect, the logarithm is negative.

The process used in the preceding examples can be reversed to find anti-$\log_e x$. If, however, a table for the exponential function $\{(x, y) \mid y = e^x\}$ is available (see Table II on page 404), the antilog$_e x$ can be read directly from this, since antilog$_e x = e^x$.

Examples.

a. Find antilog$_e$ 3.2.   b. Find antilog$_e$ -3.2.

Solutions.   The values can be read directly from Table II.

a. antilog$_e$ $3.2 = e^{3.2}$ b. antilog$_e$ $-3.2 = e^{-3.2}$
   $= 24.533.$ $= 0.0408.$

EXERCISE 7.6

Find each logarithm.

Example. $\log_3 7$

Solution.   Represent the logarithm to the base 10.

$$\log_3 7 = \frac{\log_{10} 7}{\log_{10} 3}$$

$$= \frac{0.8451}{0.4771} = 1.77$$

1. $\log_2 10$ 2. $\log_2 5$ 3. $\log_5 240$ 4. $\log_3 18$

5. $\log_7 8.1$ 6. $\log_5 60$ 7. $\log_{100} 38$ 8. $\log_{100} 240$

Find each logarithm directly from Table III on page 405.

9. $\log_e 3$ 10. $\log_e 8$ 11. $\log_e 17$ 12. $\log_e 98$

13. $\log_e 327$ 14. $\log_e 107$ 15. $\log_e 450$ 16. $\log_e 605$

Find each antilogarithm directly from Table II on page 404.

17. antilog$_e$ 0.50

18. antilog$_e$ 1.5

19. antilog$_e$ 3.4

20. antilog$_e$ 4.5

21. antilog$_e$ 0.231

22. antilog$_e$ 1.43

23. antilog$_e$ −0.15

24. antilog$_e$ −0.95

25. antilog$_e$ −2.5

26. antilog$_e$ −4.2

27. antilog$_e$ −0.255

28. antilog$_e$ −3.65

Solve without using the tables of logarithms.

29. If $\log_2 8 = 3$, find $\log_8 2$.

30. If $\log_4 16 = 2$, find $\log_{16} 4$.

31. If $\log_{10} 3 = 0.4771$, find $\log_3 10$.

32. If $\log_{10} e = 0.4343$, find $\log_e 10$.

33. If $\log_{10} 5 = 0.6990$, find $\log_5 100$.

34. If $\log_{10} 3 = 0.4771$, find $\log_3 100$.

35. Show that $\log_9 7 = 1/2 \log_3 7$. By a similar argument, show that for a, $b > 0$, $a \neq 1$, $\log_{a^2} b = 1/2 \log_a b$. *Hint:* In the first case, $\log_9 7 = 1/\log_7 9$, and $9 = 3^2$.

36. Explain why $y = \log_z x \ (x > 1)$ defines a function. What is its domain? What is its range? Graph the function.

37. Show that $(\log_{10} 4 - \log_{10} 2)\log_2 10 = 1$.

38. Show that $(2 \log_2 3)(\log_9 2 + \log_9 4) = 3$.

39. The amount of a certain radioactive element remaining at any time t is given by $y = y_0 e^{-0.4t}$, where t is measured in seconds and y_0 is the amount present initially. How much of the element would remain after three seconds if 40 grams were present initially?

40. The number of bacteria present in a culture is related to time by the formula $N = N_0 e^{0.04t}$, where N_0 is the amount of bacteria present at time $t = 0$, and t is time in hours. If 10,000 bacteria are present 10 hours after the beginning of the experiment, how many were present when $t = 0$?

41. The intensity I (in lumens) of a light beam, after passing through a thickness t (in centimeters) of a medium having an absorption coefficient of 0.1, is given by $I = 1000e^{-0.1t}$. How many centimeters of the material would reduce the illumination to 800 lumens?

8

SYSTEMS
OF EQUATIONS

In Chapter 5, we observed that the solution set of an open sentence in two variables, such as

$$ax + by + c = 0$$

or

$$ax + by + c \leq 0,$$

might contain infinitely many ordered pairs of numbers. It is often necessary to consider pairs of such sentences and to inquire whether or not the solution sets of the sentences contain ordered pairs in common. More specifically, we are interested in determining the members of the intersection of their solution sets.

8.1 SYSTEMS OF LINEAR EQUATIONS IN TWO VARIABLES

We shall begin by considering the system

$$a_1 x + b_1 y + c_1 = 0 \quad (a_1, b_1 \text{ not both } 0)$$

$$a_2 x + b_2 y + c_2 = 0 \quad (a_2, b_2 \text{ not both } 0)$$

and studying $A \cap B$, where

$$A = \{(x, y) \mid a_1 x + b_1 y + c_1 = 0\}$$

and

$$B = \{(x, y) \mid a_2 x + b_2 y + c_2 = 0\}.$$

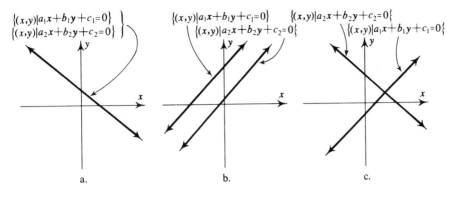

Figure 8.1

In a geometric sense, because the graphs of both A and B are straight lines, we are confronted with three possibilities, as illustrated in Figure 8.1:

a. The graphs are the same line.
b. The graphs are parallel but distinct lines.
c. The graphs intersect in one and only one point.

These possibilities lead, correspondingly, to the conclusion that one and only one of the following is true for any given system of two such linear equations in x and y:

a. The solution sets of the equations are equal, and their intersection contains all those ordered pairs found in either one of the given solution sets.
b. The intersection of the two solution sets is the null set.
c. The intersection of the two solution sets contains one and only one ordered pair.

In case (a), the left-hand members of the two linear equations in x and y are said to be **linearly dependent**, and the equations are **consistent**; in case (b), the left-hand members are **linearly independent**, and the equations are **inconsistent**; and in case (c), the left-hand members are linearly independent and the equations are consistent. If the two left-hand members are linearly dependent, then one of them can be obtained from the other through multiplication by a constant. Thus

$$2x + 4y - 8 \quad \text{and} \quad 6x + 12y - 24$$

are linearly dependent, but

$$2x + 4y - 8 \quad \text{and} \quad 6x + 12y - 23$$

are not.

More generally, two polynomials $f(x, y)$ and $g(x, y)$ are said to be linearly dependent if there exist constants a and b, not both 0, such that $af(x, y) + bg(x, y)$ is the zero polynomial. Otherwise, they are said to be linearly independent. The equations $f(x, y) = 0$ and $g(x, y) = 0$ are said to be consistent if there is at least one ordered pair (x_1, y_1) such that both $f(x_1, y_1)$ and $g(x_1, y_1)$ are equal to zero. Otherwise, the equations are inconsistent. For example, the equations

$$2x^2 + 4y = 0 \quad \text{and} \quad 3x^2 + 6y = 0$$

are consistent, but the equations

$$2x^2 + 4y = 0 \quad \text{and} \quad 3x^2 + 6y + 1 = 0$$

are inconsistent.

Similarly, three polynomials,

$$f(x, y), \quad g(x, y), \quad h(x, y),$$

are linearly dependent if and only if there exist constants a, b, c, not all zero, such that

$$af(x, y) + bg(x, y) + ch(x, y)$$

is the zero polynomial.

You will recall that equivalent open sentences are defined to be open sentences having the same solution set. Systems of open sentences may be said to be equivalent in a similar sense.

DEFINITION 8.1 *If the solution set of one system of open sentences is equal to (the same as) the solution set of another system of open sentences, then the systems are **equivalent**.*

In seeking the solution set of a system of equations, our procedure will be to generate equivalent systems until we arrive at a system of which the solution set is obvious. There are readily available to us three basic means of doing this.

THEOREM 8.1 *If any two equations in a given system are interchanged, the result is a system equivalent to the given system.*

Proof. Since, by definition, the solution set of a system is the intersection of the solution sets of the equations in the system, and since, from Problem 39, Exercise 1.2, set intersection is commutative, the theorem is valid.

THEOREM 8.2 *If any equation in a given system is replaced with an equivalent equation, the resulting system is equivalent to the given system.*

The proof of this theorem follows from the transitive property of equality, E-3, and the definition of equivalent equations and equivalent systems.

THEOREM 8.3 *If either equation in the system*

$$f(x, y) = 0$$
$$g(x, y) = 0$$

is replaced with the equation

$$af(x, y) + bg(x, y) = 0,$$

where a and b are any nonzero real numbers, then the resulting system is equivalent to the original system.

Proof. For any ordered pair (x_1, y_1) in the solution set of the system

$$f(x, y) = 0$$
$$g(x, y) = 0, \tag{1}$$

we have $f(x_1, y_1) = 0$ and $g(x_1, y_1) = 0$. Hence, for any real numbers a and b, we have

$$af(x_1, y_1) + bg(x_1, y_1) = 0.$$

Therefore, (x_1, y_1) satisfies both the system

$$f(x, y) = 0$$
$$af(x, y) + bg(x, y) = 0 \tag{2}$$

and the system

$$af(x, y) + bg(x, y) = 0$$
$$g(x, y) = 0. \tag{3}$$

Hence *every* solution of the system (1) is a solution of the system (2) and of the system (3).   Now, let (x_2, y_2) be any solution of (2); that is, let

$$f(x_2, y_2) = 0$$
$$af(x_2, y_2) + bg(x_2, y_2) = 0.$$

Since $f(x_2, y_2) = 0$, for the second equation we have

$$a(0) + bg(x_2, y_2) = 0,$$

or

$$bg(x_2, y_2) = 0,$$

and therefore, since $b \neq 0$,

$$g(x_2, y_2) = 0.$$

This means that every solution of (2) is a solution of (1). By a similar argument, every solution of (3) can be shown to be a solution of (1), and the theorem is proved.

The equation $af(x, y) + bg(x, y) = 0$, where a and b are not both 0, is said to be a **linear combination** of the equations $f(x, y) = 0$ and $g(x, y) = 0$.

Theorems 8.1, 8.2, and 8.3 are all we need to solve any linear system of the form

$$a_1 x + b_1 y + c_1 = 0 \quad (a_1, b_1 \text{ not both } 0)$$

$$a_2 x + b_2 y + c_2 = 0 \quad (a_2, b_2 \text{ not both } 0).$$

In particular, by appropriate choice of multipliers a and b, the linear combination

$$a(a_1 x + b_1 y + c_1) + b(a_2 x + b_2 y + c_2) = 0$$

will be free of one variable, and Theorem 8.3 will enable us to find the solution set very quickly.

Example.   Solve

$$2x + y - 4 = 0 \tag{4}$$
$$x - 3y + 5 = 0.$$

Solution.   If we replace $x - 3y + 5 = 0$ in this system with the linear combination

$$3(2x + y - 4) + 1(x - 3y + 5) = 0,$$

or

$$7x - 7 = 0,$$

we have, by Theorem 8.3, the equivalent system

$$7x - 7 = 0 \tag{5}$$
$$2x + y - 4 = 0.$$

Now by Theorem 8.2, the system (5) is equivalent to

$$x - 1 = 0 \tag{6}$$
$$2x + y - 4 = 0.$$

We next replace the second equation in (6) with the linear combination

$$-2(x - 1) + 1(2x + y - 4) = 0,$$

or

$$y - 2 = 0,$$

to obtain, by Theorem 8.3, the equivalent system

$$x - 1 = 0$$
$$y - 2 = 0,$$

from which we can read off the unique solution $(1, 2)$.   Hence the solution set of (4) is $\{(1, 2)\}$.

You might note that we could have proceeded somewhat differently from (5), as follows. Since any solution of the system (5) must be of the form $(1, y)$ (because any such ordered pair is a solution of $7x - 7 = 0$), and since, when x is replaced by 1 in $2x + y - 4 = 0$, we obtain $y = 2$, the only ordered pair that satisfies both equations in (5) is $(1, 2)$. Hence, again the solution set of (4) is $\{(1, 2)\}$.

In this latter way of proceeding from (5) to the solution of (4), we have used what is known as the *method of substitution*. It is based on the following simple result.

THEOREM 8.4 *The system*

$$f(x, y) = 0$$

$$y = g(x),$$

and the system

$$f[x, g(x)] = 0$$

$$y = g(x),$$

in which the expression $g(x)$ is substituted for y in the first equation of the system, are equivalent.

Proof. Since both systems contain the equation

$$y = g(x), \tag{7}$$

we have only to consider the first equation in each system. But by (7) and the substitution postulate E-4 for equality, the first equations in the two systems are equivalent, and this completes the proof.

The graphs of (4) are shown in Figure 8.2-a; the graphs of (5) are shown in Figure 8.2-b. The point of intersection in each case has coordinates $(1, 2)$.

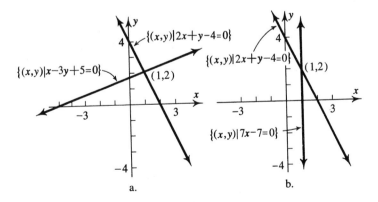

Figure 8.2

Observe that the multipliers used in the foregoing example were first 1 and 3, and later -2 and 1. These were chosen because they produced coefficients that were additive inverses, first for the terms in y and later for the terms in x. In general, the linear combination

$$b_2(a_1x + b_1y + c_1) - b_1(a_2x + b_2y + c_2) = 0$$

will always be free of y, and

$$a_2(a_1x + b_1y + c_1) - a_1(a_2x + b_2y + c_2) = 0$$

will be free of x (although there may exist multipliers smaller in absolute value than b_1 and b_2, or a_1 and a_2, that will produce equivalent results). For example, to form a useful linear combination of the equations in the system

$$2x + 6y + 7 = 0$$
$$5x + 4y + 3 = 0,$$

we might use 5 and -2, or -5 and 2, if we wish to obtain an equation that is free of x; and we might use 2 and -3, or -2 and 3, if we wish the result to obtain an equation that is free of y.

If the coefficients of the variables in one equation in a system are proportional to the corresponding coefficients in the other equation, the equations might be either consistent or inconsistent. The system

$$a_1x + b_1y + c_1 = 0$$
$$a_2x + b_2y + c_2 = 0 \quad (a_2, b_2, c_2 \neq 0)$$

is consistent if

$$\frac{a_1}{a_2} = \frac{b_1}{b_2} = \frac{c_1}{c_2},$$

and inconsistent if

$$\frac{a_1}{a_2} = \frac{b_1}{b_2} \neq \frac{c_1}{c_2}.$$

(See Exercise 8.1, Problems 26 and 27.)

Systems of simultaneous equations are quite useful in expressing relationships in practical applications. By assigning separate variables to represent separate physical quantities, the difficulty encountered in symbolically representing these relationships can usually be decreased.

EXERCISE 8.1

Solve.

Example.

$$\frac{2}{3}x - y = 2 \quad (1)$$

$$x + \frac{1}{2}y = 7 \quad (2)$$

Solution. Multiply each member of Equation (1) by 3 and each member of Equation (2) by 2.

$$2x - 3y = 6 \qquad (1')$$

$$2x + y = 14 \qquad (2')$$

Form a linear combination by adding -1 times (1') to 1 times (2') and solve for y.

$$4y = 8$$

$$y = 2 \qquad (3)$$

Equations (2) and (3) constitute an equivalent system for (1) and (2).

Substitute 2 for y in either (1), (2), (1'), or (2'), and solve for x. In this example, Equation (2) is used.

$$x + \frac{1}{2}(2) = 7$$

$$x = 6$$

The solution set is $\{(6, 2)\}$.

1. $x - y = 1$
   $x + y = 5$

2. $2x - 3y = 6$
   $x + 3y = 3$

3. $3x + y = 7$
   $2x - 5y = -1$

4. $2x - y = 7$
   $3x + 2y = 14$

5. $5x - y = -29$
   $2x + 3y = 2$

6. $6x + 4y = 12$
   $3x + 2y = 12$

7. $5x + 2y = 3$
   $x = 0$

8. $2x - y = 0$
   $x = -3$

9. $3x - 2y = 4$
   $y = -1$

10. $x + 2y = 6$
    $x = 2$

11. $\dfrac{1}{4}x - \dfrac{1}{3}y = -\dfrac{5}{12}$

    $\dfrac{1}{10}x + \dfrac{1}{5}y = \dfrac{1}{2}$

12. $\dfrac{2}{3}x - y = 4$

    $x - \dfrac{3}{4}y = 6$

13. $\dfrac{1}{7}x - \dfrac{3}{7}y = 1$

    $2x - y = -4$

14. $\dfrac{1}{3}x - \dfrac{2}{3}y = 2$

    $x - 2y = 6$

15. Find a and b so that the graph of $ax + by + 3 = 0$ passes through the points $(-1, 2)$ and $(-3, 0)$.

16. Find a and b so that the solution set of the system

$$ax + by = 4$$

$$bx - ay = -3$$

is $\{(1, 2)\}$.

17. Recall that the slope-intercept form of a straight line is given by $y = mx + b$. Find the equation of the line that passes through the points $(0, 2)$ and $(3, -8)$.

18. Find the equation of the line that passes through the points $(-6, 2)$ and $(4, 1)$.

19. Find the linear relationship between centigrade temperature C and Fahrenheit temperature F, given the fact that $F = 32°$ when $C = 0°$, and $F = 212°$ when $C = 100°$.

20. A man has \$1.80 in change consisting of three more dimes than nickels. How many dimes and nickels does he have?

21. How many pounds of an alloy containing 45% silver must be melted with an alloy containing 60% silver to obtain 40 lbs of an alloy containing 48% silver?

22. A man has three times as much money invested in 3% bonds as he has in stocks paying 5%. How much does he have invested in each if his yearly income from the investments is \$1680?

23. A man has \$1000 more invested at 5% than he has invested at 4%. If his annual income from the two investments together is \$698, how much does he have invested at each rate?

24. An airplane travels 1260 miles in the same time that an automobile travels 420 miles. If the rate of the airplane is 120 miles per hour greater than the rate of the automobile, find the rate of each.

25. Two cars start together and travel in the same direction, one going twice as fast as the other. At the end of 3 hours they are 96 miles apart. How fast is each traveling?

26. Show that the linear polynomials

$$a_1x + b_1y + c_1$$
$$a_2x + b_2y + c_2 \quad (a_2, b_2, c_2 \neq 0)$$

are dependent if and only if

$$\frac{a_1}{a_2} = \frac{b_1}{b_2} = \frac{c_1}{c_2}.$$

27. Show that the equations in the system

$$a_1x + b_1y + c_1 = 0$$
$$a_2x + b_2y + c_2 = 0 \quad (a_2, b_2, c_2 \neq 0)$$

are inconsistent if and only if

$$\frac{a_1}{a_2} = \frac{b_1}{b_2} \neq \frac{c_1}{c_2}.$$

Hint: Write the equations in slope-intercept form.

8.2 SYSTEMS OF LINEAR EQUATIONS IN THREE VARIABLES

A solution of an equation in three variables, such as

$$x + 2y - 3z + 4 = 0, \tag{1}$$

is an ordered triple of numbers (x, y, z), because all three of the variables must be replaced before we can decide whether the sentence is true. Thus, $(0, -2, 0)$ and $(-1, 0, 1)$ are solutions of (1), whereas $(1, 1, 1)$ is not. There are, of course, infinitely many members in the solution set of such an equation.

The solution set of a system of linear (first-degree) equations in three variables is the intersection of the solution sets of the separate equations in the system. We are primarily interested in systems involving three equations, such as

$$x + 2y - 3z + 4 = 0 \tag{1}$$

$$2x - y + z - 3 = 0 \tag{2}$$

$$3x + 2y + z - 10 = 0, \tag{3}$$

where the solution set is

$$\{(x, y, z) \mid x + 2y - 3z + 4 = 0\} \cap \{(x, y, z) \mid 2x - y + z - 3 = 0\}$$
$$\cap \{(x, y, z) \mid 3x + 2y + z - 10 = 0\}.$$

We can find the members of this set by methods analogous to those used in the preceding section. We shall need, however, to restate Theorem 8.3 for equations in three variables.

THEOREM 8.5 *If any equation in the system*

$$f(x, y, z) = 0$$

$$g(x, y, z) = 0$$

$$h(x, y, z) = 0$$

is replaced by a linear combination, with nonzero coefficients, of itself and any one of the other equations in the system, the result is an equivalent system.

The proof of this theorem parallels the proof of Theorem 8.3, and is omitted here. Now, to see how this theorem applies, let us examine the system (1), (2), and (3) given above. If we begin by replacing (2) with the linear combination formed by multiplying (1) by -2 and (2) by 1, that is, by

$$-2(x + 2y - 3z + 4) + 1(2x - y + z - 3) = 0,$$

or

$$-5y + 7z - 11 = 0,$$

we obtain the equivalent system

$$x + 2y - 3z + 4 = 0 \tag{1}$$

$$- 5y + 7z - 11 = 0 \tag{2'}$$

$$3x + 2y + z - 10 = 0, \tag{3}$$

where (2′) is free of x. Next, if we replace (3) by the sum of -3 times (1) and 1 times (3), we have

$$x + 2y - 3z + 4 = 0 \tag{1}$$

$$- 5y + 7z - 11 = 0 \tag{2'}$$

$$- 4y + 10z - 22 = 0, \tag{3'}$$

where both (2′) and (3′) are free of x. If now (3′) is replaced by the sum of 4 times (2′) and -5 times (3′), we have

$$x + 2y - 3z + 4 = 0 \tag{1}$$

$$- 5y + 7z - 11 = 0 \tag{2'}$$

$$- 22z + 66 = 0, \tag{3''}$$

which is equivalent to the original (1), (2), and (3). But, from (3″), we see that for any solution of (1), (2′), and (3″), $z = 3$; that is, the solution will be of the form $(x, y, 3)$. If in accordance with Theorem 8.4, 3 is substituted for z in (2′), we have $-5y + 7(3) - 11 = 0$, or $y = 2$, and any solution of the system must be of the form $(x, 2, 3)$. Substituting 2 for y and 3 for z in (1) gives $x + 2(2) - 3(3) + 4 = 0$, or $x = 1$, so that the single member of the solution set of (1), (2′), and (3″) is $(1, 2, 3)$. Therefore, the solution set of the original system is $\{(1, 2, 3)\}$.

If at any step in the procedure outlined above the resulting linear combination vanishes or yields a contradiction, the system contains linearly dependent left-hand members or else two or three inconsistent equations, and either has no members in its solution set or else an infinite number of members.

The foregoing process of solving a system of linear equations can be reduced to a series of mechanical procedures as follows.

Example. Solve.

$$x + 2y - z + 1 = 0 \tag{1}$$

$$x - 3y + z - 2 = 0 \tag{2}$$

$$2x + y + 2z - 6 = 0 \tag{3}$$

Solution. Multiply (1) by -1 and add the result to 1 times (2); multiply (1) by -2 and add the result to 1 times (3).

$$- 5y + 2z - 3 = 0 \tag{4}$$

$$- 3y + 4z - 8 = 0 \tag{5}$$

Multiply (4) by -3 and add the result to 5 times (5).

$$14z - 31 = 0 \qquad (6)$$

(1), (4), and (6) constitute a set of equations equivalent to (1), (2), and (3). Solve for z in (6).

$$z = \frac{31}{14}$$

Substitute 31/14 for z in (4).

$$-5y + 2\left(\frac{31}{14}\right) - 3 = 0$$

$$y = \frac{2}{7}$$

Substitute 2/7 for y and 31/14 for z in either (1), (2), or (3), say (1).

$$x + 2\left(\frac{2}{7}\right) - \frac{31}{14} + 1 = 0$$

$$x = \frac{9}{14}$$

The solution set is $\left\{\left(\frac{9}{14}, \frac{2}{7}, \frac{31}{14}\right)\right\}$.

By establishing a three-dimensional Cartesian coordinate system as shown in Figure 8.3, a one-to-one correspondence can be established between the points in a three-dimensional space and ordered triples of real numbers. If this is done, it can be shown that the graph of a linear equation in three variables is a plane. For example, the equation

$$x + y + z = 1$$

represents the plane through the points $(1, 0, 0)$, $(0, 1, 0)$, and $(0, 0, 1)$, as illustrated in Figure 8.3. Hence the solution set of a system of three linear

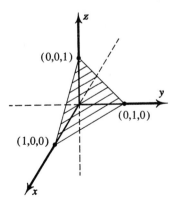

Figure 8.3

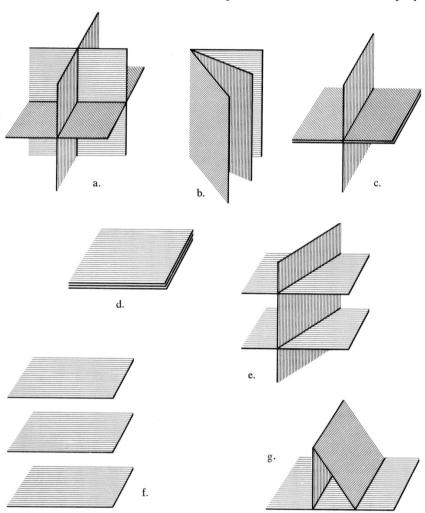

Figure 8.4

equations in three variables consists of the coordinates of the common intersection of three planes. Figure 8.4 shows some of the possibilities for such intersection. Here, in case (a), the common intersection consists of a single point, and hence the solution set of the corresponding system of three equations contains a single member. In cases (b), (c), and (d) the intersection is a line on the common plane, and the solution set of the corresponding system has infinitely many members. In cases (e), (f), and (g), the three planes have no common intersection, and the solution set of the corresponding system is the null set. Linear equations corresponding to cases (a), (b), (c), and (d) are consistent, and the others inconsistent.

The use of linear combinations to solve systems of linear equations can be extended to cover cases of n equations in n variables. Clearly, as n grows larger, the time and effort necessary to find the solution set of a system increase correspondingly. Fortunately, modern high-speed computers can handle such computations in stride for fairly large values of n. There are analytic methods other than those exhibited here which become preferable for very large systems.

EXERCISE 8.2

Solve.

1. $x + y + z = 2$
   $2x - y + z = -1$
   $x - y - z = 0$

2. $x + y + z = 1$
   $2x - y + 3z = 2$
   $2x - y - z = 2$

3. $x + y + 2z = 0$
   $2x - 2y + z = 8$
   $3x + 2y + z = 2$

4. $2x - 3y + z = 3$
   $x - y - 3z = -1$
   $-x + 2y - 3z = -4$

5. $x - 2y + z = -1$
   $2x + y - 3z = 3$
   $3x + 3y - 2z = 10$

6. $x - 2y + 4z = -3$
   $3x + y - 2z = 12$
   $2x + y - 3z = 11$

7. $4x - 2y + 3z = 4$
   $2x - y + z = 1$
   $3x - 3y + 4z = 5$

8. $x + 5y - z = 2$
   $3x - 9y + 3z = 6$
   $x - 3y + z = 4$

9. $x + z = 5$
   $y - z = -4$
   $x + y = 1$

10. $5y - 8z = -19$
    $5x - 8z = 6$
    $3x - 2y = 12$

11. $x - \dfrac{1}{2}y - \dfrac{1}{2}z = 4$

    $x - \dfrac{3}{2}y - 2z = 3$

    $\dfrac{1}{4}x + \dfrac{1}{4}y - \dfrac{1}{4}z = 0$

12. $x + 2y + \dfrac{1}{2}z = 0$

    $x + \dfrac{3}{5}y - \dfrac{2}{5}z = \dfrac{1}{5}$

    $4x - 7y - 7z = 6$

Use three variables in the solution of each of the following.

13. The sum of three numbers is 15. The second equals two times the first and the third equals the second. Find the numbers.

14. The sum of three numbers is 2. The first number is equal to the sum of the other two, and the third number is the result of subtracting the first from the second. Find the numbers.

15. A box contains $6.25 in nickels, dimes, and quarters. There are 85 coins in all, with three times as many nickels as dimes. How many coins of each kind are there?

16. The perimeter of a triangle is 155 in.   The side x is 20 in. shorter than the side y, and the side y is 5 in. longer than the side z.   Find the lengths of the sides of the triangle.

17. A man had \$446 in ten-dollar, five-dollar, and one-dollar bills.   There are 94 bills in all and 10 more five-dollar bills than ten-dollar bills.   How many bills of each kind did he have?

18. Find values for a, b, and c so that the graph of $x^2 + y^2 + ax + by + c = 0$ will contain the points $(0, 0)$, $(6, 0)$, and $(0, 8)$.

19. The equation for a circle can be written $x^2 + y^2 + ax + by + c = 0$. Find the equation of the circle with graph containing the points $(2, 3)$, $(3, 2)$, and $(-4, -5)$.

20. Find values for a, b, and c so that the graph of $y = ax^2 + bx + c$ contains the points $(-1, 2)$, $(1, 6)$, and $(2, 11)$.

21. Three solutions of the equation $ax + by + cz = 1$ are $(0, 2, 1)$, $(6, -1, 2)$, and $(0, 2, 0)$.   Find the coefficients a, b, and c.

22. Three solutions of the equation $ax + by + cz = 1$ are $(2, 1, 0)$, $(-1, 3, 2)$, and $(3, 0, 0)$.   Find the coefficients a, b, and c.

23. Show that the system

$$x + y + 2z = 2$$
$$2x - y - z = 3$$

has an infinite number of members in its solution set.   *Hint:* Express x in terms of z alone, then express y in terms of z alone.   List two ordered triples that are solutions.

24. Use an argument similar to that used in Problem 23 to show that any system of two consistent equations in three variables has an infinite number of members in its solution set.

25. Show that the system

$$x + y + z = 3 \qquad \text{(a)}$$
$$x - 2y - z = -2 \qquad \text{(b)}$$
$$x + y + 2z = 4 \qquad \text{(c)}$$
$$2x - y + 2z = 4 \qquad \text{(d)}$$

has $\emptyset$ as its solution set.   *Hint:* Does the solution set of the system (a), (b), and (c) have any member that satisfies (d)?

8.3 SYSTEMS OF NONLINEAR EQUATIONS

In Sections 8.1 and 8.2, we used Theorem 8.3 on linear combinations as a principal device for finding solution sets of systems of linear equations.   Now we shall see that substitution, in accordance with Theorem 8.4, is sometimes more convenient if nonlinear equations are present in the system. For example, consider the system

$$x^2 + y^2 = 25 \tag{1}$$

$$x + y = 7. \tag{2}$$

Equation (2) can be written equivalently in the form

$$y = 7 - x, \tag{3}$$

and by Theorem 8.4, we can replace y in (1) by $(7 - x)$ from (3). This produces

$$x^2 + (7 - x)^2 = 25, \tag{4}$$

which has as a solution set those values of x for which the ordered pair (x, y) is a common solution of (1) and (2). We can now find the solution set of (4):

$$x^2 + 49 - 14x + x^2 = 25,$$

$$x^2 - 7x + 12 = 0,$$

$$(x - 3)(x - 4) = 0,$$

which is satisfied if x is either 3 or 4. Now, by replacing x in (3) by each of these numbers in turn, we obtain

$$y = 7 - 3 = 4$$

and

$$y = 7 - 4 = 3,$$

respectively, so that the solution set of the system (1) and (2) is

$$\{(3, 4), (4, 3)\}$$

If, however, both of the equations in a system are of the second degree in both variables, the use of linear combinations of the equations often provides a simpler means of solution than does substitution.

For example, consider the system

$$3x^2 - 7y^2 + 15 = 0 \tag{5}$$

$$3x^2 - 4y^2 - 12 = 0. \tag{6}$$

By forming the linear combination of -1 times (5) and 1 times (6), we obtain

$$3y^2 - 27 = 0$$

$$y^2 = 9,$$

from which

$$y = 3 \quad \text{or} \quad y = -3,$$

and we have the y-components of the members of the solution set of the system (5) and (6).   Substituting 3 for y in either (5) or (6), say (5), we have

$$3x^2 - 7(3)^2 + 15 = 0,$$
$$x^2 = 16,$$

and

$$x = 4 \quad \text{or} \quad x = -4.$$

That is, the ordered pairs $(4, 3)$ and $(-4, -3)$ are solutions of the system. Substituting -3 for y in (5) or (6) [this time we shall use (6)] gives us

$$3x^2 - 4(-3)^2 - 12 = 0,$$
$$x^2 = 16,$$

so that

$$x = 4 \quad \text{or} \quad x = -4.$$

Thus the ordered pairs $(4, -3)$ and $(-4, 3)$ are solutions of the system, and accordingly the complete solution set is

$$\{(4, 3), (4, -3), (-4, 3), (-4, -3)\}.$$

For an example of a slightly different procedure, consider the system

$$x^2 + y^2 = 5 \tag{7}$$
$$x^2 - 2xy + y^2 = 1. \tag{8}$$

By forming the linear combination of 1 times (7) and -1 times (8), we obtain

$$2xy = 4,$$
$$xy = 2. \tag{9}$$

By Theorem 8.3, the system (7) and (8) is equivalent to the system (7) and (9). This latter system can be solved by substitution.   From (9), we have

$$y = \frac{2}{x}.$$

Replacing y in (7) by $2/x$, we find

$$x^2 + \left(\frac{2}{x}\right)^2 = 5,$$

$$x^2 + \frac{4}{x^2} = 5, \tag{10}$$

$$x^4 + 4 = 5x^2,$$
$$x^4 - 5x^2 + 4 = 0, \tag{11}$$

which is a quadratic in x^2.   The left-hand member of (11) factors to yield

$$(x^2 - 1)(x^2 - 4) = 0,$$

from which we obtain

$$x^2 - 1 = 0 \quad \text{or} \quad x^2 - 4 = 0,$$

so that

$$x = 1, \quad x = -1, \quad x = 2, \quad x = -2.$$

Since the step from (10) to (11) was a nonelementary transformation, we are careful to note that these values of x all satisfy (10). What value for x would have to be excluded if it appeared as a solution to (11)? Now substituting 1, -1, 2, and -2 in turn for x in (9), we obtain the corresponding values for y, and thus the solution set of the system (7) and (9), or equivalently the solution set of the system (7) and (8), is

$$\{(1, 2), (-1, -2), (2, 1), (-2, -1)\}.$$

There are other techniques involving substitution in conjunction with linear combinations that are useful in handling systems of higher-degree equations, but they all bear similarity to those illustrated.

In solving a set of equations, it is frequently helpful to sketch the graphs of the equations as a rough check on the algebraic solution. Any attempt to solve a set of two second-degree equations graphically on the real plane may produce only approximations to such real solutions as exist. We can expect ordinarily to find at most four and as few as no points of intersection, depending on the types of equations involved and on the coefficients and constants in the given equations.

When the degree of any equation in a set of equations is greater than two, or when the left-hand member of one of the equations of the form $f(x, y) = 0$ is not a polynomial, it may be very difficult to find common solutions analytically. In this case we can at least obtain approximations to any real solutions by graphical methods. Consider the system of equations

$$y = 2^{-x}$$
$$y = \sqrt{0.01x} \tag{12}$$

and their graphs in Figure 8.5.

Examining Figure 8.5-b, an enlargement of part of Figure 8.5-a, we observe that the curves intersect at approximately (2.6, 0.16), and from geometric considerations we conclude that this ordered pair approximates the only member in the solution set of (12).

This result shows, in particular, that the equation

$$2^{-x} - \sqrt{0.01x} = 0$$

has just one root, approximately 2.6, and suggests a method of solving similar equations.

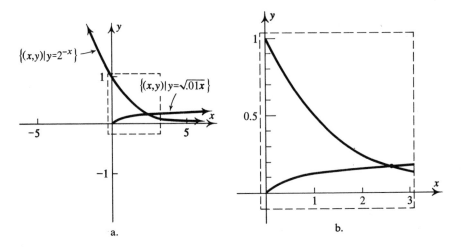

Figure 8.5

EXERCISE 8.3

Solve by the method of substitution. Check the solutions by sketching the graphs of the equations and estimating the coordinates of any points of intersection.

Example.

$$y = x^2 + 2x + 1 \qquad (1)$$

$$y - x = 3 \qquad (2)$$

Solution. Solve linear equation (2) explicitly for y.

$$y = x + 3 \qquad (2')$$

Substitute $(x + 3)$ for y in (1).

$$x + 3 = x^2 + 2x + 1 \qquad (3)$$

Solve for x.

$$x^2 + x - 2 = 0$$

$$(x + 2)(x - 1) = 0$$

$$x = -2, \ x = 1$$

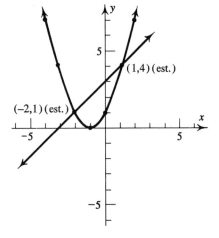

Substitute each of these values in turn in (2') to determine values for y.

$$\text{If } x = -2, \text{ then } y = 1.$$

$$\text{If } x = 1, \quad \text{then } y = 4.$$

The solution set is $\{(-2, 1), (1, 4)\}$.

1. $y = x^2 - 5$
   $y = 4x$

2. $y = x^2 - 2x + 1$
   $y + x = 3$

3. $x^2 + y^2 = 13$
   $x + y = 5$

4. $x^2 + 2y^2 = 12$
   $2x - y = 2$

5. $x + y = 1$
   $xy = -12$

6. $2x - y = 9$
   $xy = -4$

Solve analytically, using linear combinations.

7. $x^2 + y^2 = 10$
   $9x^2 + y^2 = 18$

8. $x^2 + 4y^2 = 52$
   $x^2 + y^2 = 25$

9. $x^2 - y^2 = 7$
   $2x^2 + 3y^2 = 24$

10. $x^2 + 4y^2 = 25$
    $4x^2 + y^2 = 25$

11. $4x^2 - 9y^2 + 132 = 0$
    $x^2 + 4y^2 - 67 = 0$

12. $16y^2 + 5x^2 - 26 = 0$
    $25y^2 - 4x^2 - 17 = 0$

13. $x^2 - xy + y^2 = 7$
    $x^2 + y^2 = 5$

14. $3x^2 - 2xy + 3y^2 = 34$
    $x^2 + y^2 = 17$

15. $3x^2 + 3xy - y^2 = 35$
    $x^2 - xy - 6y^2 = 0$

16. $x^2 - xy + y^2 = 21$
    $x^2 + 2xy - 8y^2 = 0$

Solve by graphing. Approximate components of solutions to nearest half unit.

17. $y = 10^x$
    $x + y = 2$

18. $y = 2^x$
    $y - x = 2$

19. $y = \log_{10} x$
    $y = x^2 - 2x + 1$

20. $y = 10^x$
    $y = x^2$

21. $y = 10^{-x}$
    $y = \log_{10} x$

22. $y = 2^{x-3}$
    $y = \log_2 x$

23. $10^{-x} - \log_{10} x = 0$

24. $2^{x-3} - \log_2 x = 0$

25. How many real solutions are possible for simultaneous systems of linearly independent equations that consist of:

    a. two linear equations in two variables?

    b. one linear equation and one quadratic equation in two variables?

    c. two quadratic equations in two variables?

    Support each of your answers with sketches.

26. The sum of the squares of two positive numbers is 13. If twice the first number is added to the second, the sum is 7. Find the numbers.

27. The sum of two numbers is 6 and their product is 35/4. Find the numbers.

28. The annual income from an investment is $32. If the amount invested were $200 more and the rate 1/2% less, the annual income would be $35. What are the amount and rate of the investment?

29. At a constant temperature, the pressure P and volume V of a gas are related by the equation $PV = K$. The product of the pressure (in pounds per square inch) and the volume (in cubic inches) of a certain gas is 30 inch-pounds. If the temperature remains constant as the pressure is increased 4 lbs per sq in., the volume is decreased by 2 cu in. Find the original pressure and volume of the gas.

30. What relationships must exist between the numbers a and b so that the solution set of the system

$$x^2 + y^2 = 25$$

$$y = ax + b$$

has two ordered pairs of real numbers? One ordered pair of real numbers? No ordered pairs of real numbers? *Hint:* Use substitution and consider the nature of the roots of the resulting quadratic equation.

31. Consider the system

$$x^2 + y^2 = 8 \tag{1}$$

$$xy = 4. \tag{2}$$

We can solve this system by substituting $4/x$ for y in (1) to obtain

$$x^2 + \frac{16}{x^2} = 8,$$

from which we obtain $x = 2$ or $x = -2$. Now if we obtain the y-components of the solution from (2), we find that for $x = 2$, $y = 2$, and for $x = -2$, $y = -2$. But if we seek y-components from (1), for $x = 2$ we have $y = \pm 2$, and for $x = -2$, $y = \pm 2$. Discuss the fact that we seem to obtain two more solutions from (1) than from (2). What is the solution set of the system?

8.4 SYSTEMS OF INEQUALITIES

In Chapters 5 and 6, we observed that the graph of the solution set of an inequality in two variables might be a region in the plane. The graph of the solution set of a system of inequalities in two variables accordingly consists of the intersection of the graphs of the inequalities in the system.

Example. Graph the solution set of the system

$$x + 2y \leq 6$$

$$2x - 3y \geq 12.$$

Solution. We begin by solving each of the inequalities for y in terms of x; this leads us to the equivalent system

$$y \leq -\frac{1}{2}x + 3$$

$$y \leq \frac{2}{3}x - 4.$$

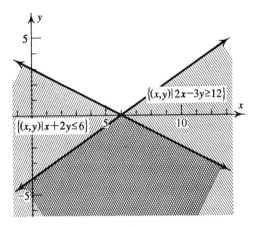

Figure 8.6

Graphing these, we obtain Figure 8.6, where the double-shaded region is the graph of the solution set of the system. We have graphed

$$\{(x, y) \mid x + 2y \le 6\} \cap \{(x, y) \mid 2x - 3y \ge 12\}.$$

Example.   Graph the solution set of

$$y \le x + 2$$
$$y \ge x^2.$$

Solution.   The graph of each inequality is shaded (Figure 8.7). The double-shaded region constitutes the graph of the solution set of the system.

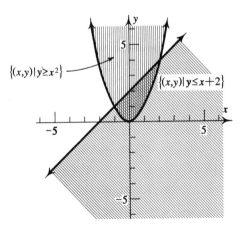

$$\{(x, y) \mid y \ge x^2\} \cap \{(x, y) \mid y \le x + 2\}$$

Figure 8.7

Example.   Graph the solution set of the system

$$y > 2$$
$$x > -2$$
$$x + y > 1.$$

Solution.   The triple-shaded region in Figure 8.8 constitutes the graph of the solution set of the system.

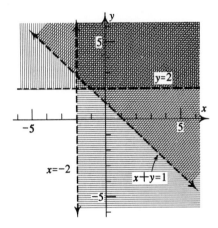

$$\{(x, y) \mid y > 2\} \cap \{(x, y) \mid x > -2\} \cap \{(x, y) \mid x + y > 1\}$$

Figure 8.8

EXERCISE 8.4

Graph the simultaneous systems. By double or triple shading, indicate the region in the plane representing the solution set of the system.

1. $y \geq x + 1$
   $y \geq 5 - x$

2. $y \geq 4$
   $x \geq 2$

3. $y - x \geq 0$
   $y + x \geq 0$

4. $2y - x \geq 1$
   $x < -3$

5. $y + 3x < 6$
   $y > 2$

6. $x > 3$
   $x + y \geq 5$

7. $x = 3$
   $x + y < 4$

8. $y = 2$
   $2y + x < 3$

9. $x - 3y < 6$
   $y + x = 1$

10. $2x + y \geq 4$
    $x - y = -2$

11. $y > x^2 + 1$
    $x + y > 4$

12. $y < x^2 + 4$
    $x - y \leq 4$

13. $x^2 + y^2 < 25$
    $y > 3$

14. $x^2 + y^2 \geq 25$
    $y > x^2$

15. $9x^2 + 4y^2 \geq 36$
    $y < x^2$

16. $y \geq 2$
    $x \geq 2$
    $y \geq x$

17. $y \geq 3$
    $x \leq 2$
    $y < x$

18. $x^2 + y^2 \leq 36$
    $x \geq 3$
    $y \geq 3$

19. $x^2 + y^2 \leq 25$
$\quad y \geq x^2 - 4$
$\quad y \leq -x^2 + 4$

20. $y \leq \log_{10} x$
$\quad y \geq x - 1$

21. $y \leq 10^x$
$\quad y \leq 2 - x^2$

22. $9 \leq x^2 + y^2 \leq 16$
$\quad -1 \leq x - y \leq 1$

23. $9 \leq x^2 + y^2 \leq 16$
$\quad x^2 + 1 \leq y \leq x^2 + 3$

24. $x^2 - 2 \leq y \leq 2 - x^2$
$\quad |x| \leq 1$

25. $\log_{10} x \leq y \leq 10^x$
$\quad 2 \leq x + y \leq 3$

26. $9 \leq x^2 + y^2 \leq 16$
$\quad |x| + 3 \leq y \leq |x| + 4$

9

MATRICES
AND DETERMINANTS

9.1 MATRIX ADDITION

A **matrix** is a rectangular array of real numbers (or other entities), which are called **entries** or **elements** of the matrix. In this book, we shall consider only real numbers as entries. A matrix is customarily displayed in a pair of brackets or parentheses (we shall use brackets). Thus

$$\begin{bmatrix} 1 & 2 & 3 \\ 4 & 5 & 6 \end{bmatrix} \text{ and } \begin{bmatrix} 2 \\ 1 \end{bmatrix}$$

are matrices. The **order** or **dimension** of a matrix is the ordered pair having as first component the number of (horizontal) **rows** and as second component the number of (vertical) **columns** in the matrix. Thus,

$$\begin{bmatrix} 1 & 2 & 3 \\ 4 & 5 & 6 \end{bmatrix}, \quad \begin{bmatrix} 1 \\ 2 \\ 3 \end{bmatrix}, \text{ and } \begin{bmatrix} a_1 & a_2 & a_3 & a_4 \\ b_1 & b_2 & b_3 & b_4 \\ c_1 & c_2 & c_3 & c_4 \\ d_1 & d_2 & d_3 & d_4 \end{bmatrix}$$

are 2×3 (read "two by three"), 3×1 (read "three by one"), and 4×4 (read "four by four") matrices, respectively. Note that the number of *rows* is given first, and then the number of *columns*. A matrix consisting of a single row is called a **row matrix** or a **row vector**, whereas a matrix consisting of a single column is called a **column matrix** or a **column vector**.

Matrices are frequently represented by capital letters. Thus, we might want to talk about the matrices A and B, where

$$A = \begin{bmatrix} a_1 & a_2 \\ b_1 & b_2 \end{bmatrix} \quad \text{and} \quad B = [b_1 \quad b_2].$$

To show that A is a 2 × 2 matrix, we can write $A_{2 \times 2}$. Similarly, $B_{1 \times 2}$ is a matrix with one row and two columns.

To represent the entries of a matrix, either single or double subscript notation is employed. Consider any 3 × 3 matrix, A. We can represent A by

$$A = \begin{bmatrix} a_1 & a_2 & a_3 \\ b_1 & b_2 & b_3 \\ c_1 & c_2 & c_3 \end{bmatrix},$$

where a different letter is used for each row, and a single subscript denotes the column in which each particular entry is located. Alternatively, we can use a different letter for each column, and let the subscript denote the row. Thus, we might write

$$A = \begin{bmatrix} a_1 & b_1 & c_1 \\ a_2 & b_2 & c_2 \\ a_3 & b_3 & c_3 \end{bmatrix}.$$

In either event, problems would clearly arise if we wanted to talk about a matrix containing a large number of rows or columns, because we would run out of letters.

A much more useful convention involves double subscripts, where a single letter, say a, is used to denote an entry in a matrix, and then *two* subscripts are appended, the first subscript telling in which *row* the entry occurs, and the second telling which *column*. Thus, we write

$$A = \begin{bmatrix} a_{11} & a_{12} & a_{13} \\ a_{21} & a_{22} & a_{23} \\ a_{31} & a_{32} & a_{33} \end{bmatrix},$$

where a_{21} is the element in the second *row* and first *column*, a_{33} is the element in the third *row* and third *column*, and, if we wish to generalize, a_{ij} is the element in the *i*th *row* and *j*th *column*.

DEFINITION 9.1 *Two matrices, A and B, are equal if and only if both matrices are of the same order and, for each i, j, $a_{ij} = b_{ij}$.*

Thus,

$$\begin{bmatrix} 2 & 1 \\ 3 & 0 \end{bmatrix} = \begin{bmatrix} \frac{4}{2} & 2-1 \\ \sqrt{9} & 0 \end{bmatrix}, \quad \text{but} \quad \begin{bmatrix} 2 & 1 \\ 3 & 0 \end{bmatrix} \neq \begin{bmatrix} 2 & 3 \\ 1 & 0 \end{bmatrix}.$$

DEFINITION 9.2 *The transpose of a matrix A, denoted by A^t, is the matrix in which the rows are the columns of A and the columns are the rows of A.*

Thus,

$$\begin{bmatrix} 2 & 1 \\ 3 & 0 \end{bmatrix}^t = \begin{bmatrix} 2 & 3 \\ 1 & 0 \end{bmatrix} \text{ and } \begin{bmatrix} 1 & 2 & 3 \\ 4 & 5 & 6 \end{bmatrix}^t = \begin{bmatrix} 1 & 4 \\ 2 & 5 \\ 3 & 6 \end{bmatrix}.$$

DEFINITION 9.3 *The sum of two matrices of the same order, $A_{m \times n}$ and $B_{m \times n}$, is the matrix $(A + B)_{m \times n}$ in which the entry in the ith row and jth column is $a_{ij} + b_{ij}$, for $i = 1, 2, 3, \cdots, m$ and $j = 1, 2, 3, \cdots, n$. The subscripts i and j are to assume each integral value in the stated sequence.*

For example,

$$\begin{bmatrix} 3 & 1 & 2 \\ 2 & 1 & 4 \end{bmatrix} + \begin{bmatrix} 1 & 0 & 2 \\ -1 & 3 & 0 \end{bmatrix} = \begin{bmatrix} 3 + 1 & 1 + 0 & 2 + 2 \\ 2 + (-1) & 1 + 3 & 4 + 0 \end{bmatrix}$$

$$= \begin{bmatrix} 4 & 1 & 4 \\ 1 & 4 & 4 \end{bmatrix}.$$

The sum of two matrices of different order is not defined.

DEFINITION 9.4 *A matrix with each entry equal to 0 is a zero matrix.*

Zero matrices are generally denoted by the symbol **0** to distinguish the zero matrix from the real number 0. For example,

$$\mathbf{0} = \begin{bmatrix} 0 & 0 & 0 & 0 \\ 0 & 0 & 0 & 0 \end{bmatrix}$$

is a 2×4 zero matrix.

DEFINITION 9.5 *The negative of the matrix $A_{m \times n}$ is denoted by $-A_{m \times n}$, and is formed by replacing each entry in the matrix $A_{m \times n}$ with its additive inverse.*

For example, if

$$A_{3 \times 2} = \begin{bmatrix} 3 & -1 \\ 2 & -2 \\ -4 & 5 \end{bmatrix},$$

then

$$-A_{3 \times 2} = \begin{bmatrix} -3 & 1 \\ -2 & 2 \\ 4 & -5 \end{bmatrix}.$$

The sum $B_{m \times n} + (-A_{m \times n})$ is called the **difference** of $B_{m \times n}$ and $A_{m \times n}$ and is denoted $B_{m \times n} - A_{m \times n}$.

At this point, we are able to establish the following facts concerning the set of all $m \times n$ matrices with real-number entries, for any given m and n.

THEOREM 9.1 *If A, B, and C are* $m \times n$ *matrices with real-number entries, then:*

I $(A + B)_{m \times n}$ *is a matrix with real number*   *Closure for addition.*
   entries.

II $(A + B) + C = A + (B + C)$.   *Associativity for addition.*

III *The matrix* $\mathbf{0}_{m \times n}$ *has the property that*   *Identity element for addition.*
   for every matrix $A_{m \times n}$,
   $A + 0 = 0 + A = A$.

IV *For every matrix* $A_{m \times n}$, *the matrix*   *Additive inverse.*
   $-A_{m \times n}$ *has the property that*
   $A + (-A) = (-A) + A = \mathbf{0}$.

Proof of 9.1-III. Since each entry of the zero matrix is 0, it follows that the entries of $A_{m \times n} + \mathbf{0}_{m \times n}$ are $a_{ij} + 0 = a_{ij}$ and the entries of $\mathbf{0}_{m \times n} + A_{m \times n}$ are $0 + a_{ij} = a_{ij}$, and the theorem is proved.

For example,

$$\begin{bmatrix} a_{11} & a_{12} \\ a_{21} & a_{22} \end{bmatrix} + \begin{bmatrix} 0 & 0 \\ 0 & 0 \end{bmatrix} = \begin{bmatrix} a_{11} & a_{12} \\ a_{21} & a_{22} \end{bmatrix}.$$

Proof of 9.1-IV. Let the entries of $A_{m \times n}$ and $-A_{m \times n}$ be a_{ij} and $-a_{ij}$, respectively. Since each entry of $A + (-A)$ is $a_{ij} - a_{ij}$, or 0, we have $A + (-A) = \mathbf{0}$. Similarly, $(-A) + A = \mathbf{0}$, and the theorem is proved.

For example, if

$$A = \begin{bmatrix} 1 & -1 & 2 \\ 3 & -1 & 1 \end{bmatrix},$$

then

$$A + (-A) = \begin{bmatrix} 1 & -1 & 2 \\ 3 & -1 & 1 \end{bmatrix} + \begin{bmatrix} -1 & 1 & -2 \\ -3 & 1 & -1 \end{bmatrix} = \begin{bmatrix} 0 & 0 & 0 \\ 0 & 0 & 0 \end{bmatrix} = \mathbf{0}.$$

The proof of Parts I and II of Theorem 9.1 are left as exercises.

A set of elements is called a **group** under a given binary operation provided that (1) the set has the properties of closure and associativity under the operation; (2) the set contains an identity element for the operation; and (3) each element has an inverse in the set with respect to the operation.

Systems that, in addition to possessing these four properties, also obey a commutative law for the group operation are called **commutative** or **Abelian groups** (after Niels Henrik Abel, 1802–1829).

THEOREM 9.2 *If A and B are m × n matrices with real-number entries, then*

$$A + B = B + A.$$

The proof of this theorem is left as an exercise.

Thus our system of $m \times n$ matrices, for m and n fixed, with real-number entries, is a commutative group for addition. Note that the group properties are concerned with *just one operation*, whereas the field properties (pages 15–16) and the properties of an integral domain (page 46) involve two operations. Also, each one of the group properties is included among the integral-domain properties, just as each one of the integral-domain properties is included among the field properties. Accordingly, each field is an integral domain, and each integral domain is a group. For example, we saw in Chapter 2 that the set J of integers and the set $J[x]$ of polynomials over J are integral domains; accordingly, both of these sets are groups with respect to addition. Also, of course, the field Q of rational numbers and the field R of real numbers are commutative groups with respect to addition.

EXERCISE 9.1

State the order and find the transpose of each matrix.

Example.

$$\begin{bmatrix} 2 & 4 \\ 1 & -3 \\ 6 & 0 \end{bmatrix}$$

Solution. 3×2 matrix

$$\begin{bmatrix} 2 & 4 \\ 1 & -3 \\ 6 & 0 \end{bmatrix}^t = \begin{bmatrix} 2 & 1 & 6 \\ 4 & -3 & 0 \end{bmatrix}$$

1. $\begin{bmatrix} 6 & -1 \\ 2 & 3 \end{bmatrix}$

2. $\begin{bmatrix} 4 & 1 \\ 0 & -2 \end{bmatrix}$

3. $\begin{bmatrix} 2 & -7 & 3 \\ 1 & 4 & 0 \end{bmatrix}$

4. $\begin{bmatrix} -3 & 1 \\ 6 & 0 \\ 0 & 2 \end{bmatrix}$

5. $\begin{bmatrix} 2 & 3 & -1 \\ 4 & 0 & 1 \\ -2 & 3 & 1 \end{bmatrix}$

6. $\begin{bmatrix} 4 & -1 & -2 \\ 3 & 0 & 0 \\ 2 & 1 & 1 \end{bmatrix}$

7. $\begin{bmatrix} 4 & -3 & -1 & 0 \\ 2 & 1 & 1 & 6 \end{bmatrix}$

8. $\begin{bmatrix} -2 & 1 & 3 & 2 \\ 4 & 0 & 0 & -2 \\ -1 & 3 & 2 & 4 \end{bmatrix}$

Write each sum as a single matrix.

Example.

$$\begin{bmatrix} 2 & 1 & 4 \\ 3 & -1 & 0 \end{bmatrix} + \begin{bmatrix} 6 & 3 & 0 \\ -2 & 1 & 0 \end{bmatrix}$$

Solution.

$$\begin{bmatrix} 2 & 1 & 4 \\ 3 & -1 & 0 \end{bmatrix} + \begin{bmatrix} 6 & 3 & 0 \\ -2 & 1 & 0 \end{bmatrix} = \begin{bmatrix} 2+6 & 1+3 & 4+0 \\ 3-2 & -1+1 & 0+0 \end{bmatrix} = \begin{bmatrix} 8 & 4 & 4 \\ 1 & 0 & 0 \end{bmatrix}$$

9. $\begin{bmatrix} 2 & 3 \\ 1 & 6 \end{bmatrix} + \begin{bmatrix} 1 & -2 \\ 2 & 3 \end{bmatrix}$

10. $\begin{bmatrix} 4 & -1 & 3 \\ 2 & 1 & 0 \end{bmatrix} + \begin{bmatrix} 3 & -1 & 0 \\ 4 & 0 & -2 \end{bmatrix}$

11. $\begin{bmatrix} 3 & 0 & -1 \\ 2 & 1 & 2 \end{bmatrix} + \begin{bmatrix} 6 & -1 & 0 \\ 0 & 2 & 4 \end{bmatrix}$

12. $[1 \quad 3 \quad 5 \quad 7] + [0 \quad -2 \quad 1 \quad 3]$

13. $\begin{bmatrix} 4 \\ 3 \\ -1 \end{bmatrix} + \begin{bmatrix} 6 \\ 0 \\ -2 \end{bmatrix}$

14. $\begin{bmatrix} 2 & 3 \\ 1 & 0 \\ -1 & 2 \end{bmatrix} + \begin{bmatrix} -2 & 0 \\ -3 & 0 \\ 4 & -1 \end{bmatrix}$

15. $\begin{bmatrix} 2 & 3 & 4 \\ -1 & 6 & 2 \\ 1 & 0 & 3 \end{bmatrix} + \begin{bmatrix} 0 & 0 & 0 \\ 0 & 0 & 0 \\ 0 & 0 & 0 \end{bmatrix}$

16. $\begin{bmatrix} 2 & -3 \\ 4 & -1 \\ -2 & 1 \end{bmatrix} + \begin{bmatrix} -2 & 3 \\ -4 & 1 \\ 2 & -1 \end{bmatrix}$

17. Prove that $0_{m \times n}$ is the only additive identity matrix of order $m \times n$.

18. Prove that $-A_{m \times n}$ is the only additive inverse of the matrix $A_{m \times n}$.

19. Prove Theorem 9.1-I.

20. Prove Theorem 9.1-II.

21. Prove Theorem 9.2.

22. Show that $\begin{bmatrix} b_{11} - a_{11} & b_{12} - a_{12} \\ b_{21} - a_{21} & b_{22} - a_{22} \end{bmatrix}$ is a solution of the matrix equation $X + A = B$, where $A = \begin{bmatrix} a_{11} & a_{12} \\ a_{21} & a_{22} \end{bmatrix}$ and $B = \begin{bmatrix} b_{11} & b_{12} \\ b_{21} & b_{22} \end{bmatrix}$.

23. Use Theorem 9.1 to argue that $X + A = B$ and $X = B - A$ are equivalent matrix equations in the system of 2×2 matrices.

Solve each of the following matrix equations.

24. $X + \begin{bmatrix} 3 & -1 \\ 2 & 1 \end{bmatrix} = \begin{bmatrix} 5 & 1 \\ -3 & 5 \end{bmatrix}$

25. $X - \begin{bmatrix} -1 & 0 \\ 0 & 0 \end{bmatrix} = \begin{bmatrix} 3 & -1 \\ 2 & 1 \end{bmatrix}^t$

26. $X + \begin{bmatrix} 3 & 2 \\ -1 & 4 \end{bmatrix} = \begin{bmatrix} 2 & 6 \\ 1 & 5 \end{bmatrix} + \begin{bmatrix} -4 & -8 \\ -2 & 0 \end{bmatrix}$

27. $\begin{bmatrix} 1 & 3 \\ -1 & 0 \end{bmatrix}^t - \begin{bmatrix} 0 & 1 \\ 1 & 0 \end{bmatrix} = \begin{bmatrix} 2 & -2 \\ -1 & 3 \end{bmatrix}^t - X$

28. Show that if $A_{3\times3} = A^t_{3\times3}$, then for each $i = 1, 2, 3$ and $j = 1, 2, 3$, $a_{ij} = a_{ji}$. Does an analogous result seem valid for $n \times n$ matrices?

29. Show that if, for each $i = 1, 2, 3$ and $j = 1, 2, 3$, $a_{ij} = a_{ji}$, then $A_{3\times3} = A^t_{3\times3}$. Does an analogous result seem valid for $n \times n$ matrices? Matrices with this property are called *symmetric* matrices.

30. Show that $[A_{2\times2} + B_{2\times2}]^t = A^t_{2\times2} + B^t_{2\times2}$. Does an analogous result seem valid for $n \times n$ matrices?

31. Show that if $A_{2\times2} = B_{2\times2}$, then $A_{2\times2} + C_{2\times2} = B_{2\times2} + C_{2\times2}$.

32. Let S be the set $\{1, 2, \cdots, 12\}$ and consider S as a group under the operation $+$ of clock addition. For example, in clock addition $8 + 6 = 2$.

   a. Give three examples illustrating the closure of S under this operation.

   b. Give an example illustrating associativity in S under this operation.

   c. What is the identity element in S under this operation?

   d. Under this operation, what element is the inverse of 3? Of 12?

   e. Give an example illustrating commutativity in S under this operation.

9.2 MATRIX MULTIPLICATION

We shall be interested in two kinds of products involving matrices: (1) the product of a matrix and a real number, and (2) the product of two matrices. Let us consider them one at a time.

DEFINITION 9.6 *The product of a real number c and an $m \times n$ matrix A with entries a_{ij} is the matrix cA with corresponding entries ca_{ij}, where $i = 1, 2, 3, \cdots, m$ and $j = 1, 2, 3, \cdots, n$.*

Thus,

$$3\begin{bmatrix} 2 & 1 \\ 0 & 5 \end{bmatrix} = \begin{bmatrix} 3 \times 2 & 3 \times 1 \\ 3 \times 0 & 3 \times 5 \end{bmatrix} = \begin{bmatrix} 6 & 3 \\ 0 & 15 \end{bmatrix}.$$

The following theorem states some simple algebraic laws for the multiplication of matrices by real numbers.

THEOREM 9.3   *If A and B are m × n matrices, and c and d are real numbers, then*

I cA is an $m \times n$ matrix,	V $1A = A$,
II $c(dA) = (cd)A$,	VI $(-1)A = -A$,
III $(c + d)A = cA + dA$,	VII $0A = \mathbf{0}$,
IV $c(A + B) = cA + cB$,	VIII $c\mathbf{0} = \mathbf{0}$.

Proof.   We shall prove only Part IV, leaving the remaining parts as exercises. Since the elements of $A + B$ are of the form $a_{ij} + b_{ij}$, it follows, by definition, that the elements of $c(A + B)$ are of the form $c(a_{ij} + b_{ij})$.   But, since a_{ij}, b_{ij}, and c denote real numbers, $c(a_{ij} + b_{ij}) = ca_{ij} + cb_{ij}$.   Now, the elements of cA are of the form ca_{ij}, and those of cB are of the form cb_{ij}, so that the elements of $cA + cB$ are of the form $ca_{ij} + cb_{ij}$ and the theorem is proved.

In pure and applied mathematics there are many instances of sets S with the following properties: (i) There is an operation (called addition, but not necessarily ordinary addition) on the elements of S with respect to which S is a commutative group.   (ii) Multiplication of elements $A, B, \cdots$ of S by real numbers is defined in such a way that Properties I–VIII of Theorem 9.3 are valid.   If conditions (i) and (ii) are satisfied, we say that S is a **vector space** over the field R of real numbers.   For example, the set $S_{2 \times 3}$ of 2×3 matrices—or more generally the set $S_{m \times n}$ of $m \times n$ matrices, with m and n fixed—is a vector space over R.   (It is also a vector space over the field Q of rational numbers.)   The set of geometric vectors in the plane and the set of geometric vectors in space are likewise vector spaces over R, and, as we shall see in Chapter 11, so is the set of all complex numbers.   The properties of these various vector spaces differ in part from one vector space to another, of course; but any result that follows strictly from the defining properties (i) and (ii) holds for *all* vector spaces.

Turning now to the product of two matrices, we have the following.

DEFINITION 9.7   *The product of the matrices $A_{m \times p}$ and $B_{p \times n}$ is the matrix $(AB)_{m \times n}$ with entries determined as follows:*

The entry c_{ij} in the ith row and jth column of $(AB)_{m \times n}$ is found by multiplying the first element in the ith row of A by the first element of the jth column of B, to this product adding the product of the second element in the ith row of A with the second element in the jth column of B, to this sum adding the product of the third element in the ith row of A with the third element in the jth column of B, and so on.

For example, the product of the matrices

$$A_{2 \times 2} = \begin{bmatrix} a_{11} & a_{12} \\ a_{21} & a_{22} \end{bmatrix} \quad \text{and} \quad B_{2 \times 2} = \begin{bmatrix} b_{11} & b_{12} \\ b_{21} & b_{22} \end{bmatrix}$$

is the matrix

$$(AB)_{2 \times 2} = \begin{bmatrix} a_{11}b_{11} + a_{12}b_{21} & a_{11}b_{12} + a_{12}b_{22} \\ a_{21}b_{11} + a_{22}b_{21} & a_{21}b_{12} + a_{22}b_{22} \end{bmatrix}.$$

The following schematic shows how to find the entry in the first row and first column of AB.

$$\begin{bmatrix} a_{11} & a_{12} \\ a_{21} & a_{22} \end{bmatrix} \begin{bmatrix} b_{11} & b_{12} \\ b_{21} & b_{22} \end{bmatrix} = \begin{bmatrix} a_{11}b_{11} + a_{12}b_{21} \end{bmatrix}.$$

Example.

If $A = \begin{bmatrix} 1 & 2 \\ -1 & 3 \end{bmatrix}$ and $B = \begin{bmatrix} 2 & 1 \\ 1 & 1 \end{bmatrix}$, find AB and BA.

Solution.

$$AB = \begin{bmatrix} 1 & 2 \\ -1 & 3 \end{bmatrix}\begin{bmatrix} 2 & 1 \\ 1 & 1 \end{bmatrix} = \begin{bmatrix} 2+2 & 1+2 \\ -2+3 & -1+3 \end{bmatrix} = \begin{bmatrix} 4 & 3 \\ 1 & 2 \end{bmatrix}$$

$$BA = \begin{bmatrix} 2 & 1 \\ 1 & 1 \end{bmatrix}\begin{bmatrix} 1 & 2 \\ -1 & 3 \end{bmatrix} = \begin{bmatrix} 2-1 & 4+3 \\ 1-1 & 2+3 \end{bmatrix} = \begin{bmatrix} 1 & 7 \\ 0 & 5 \end{bmatrix}.$$

This example shows very clearly that the multiplication of matrices, in general, is *not commutative*. Thus, when discussing products of matrices, we must specify the *order* in which the matrices are to be considered as factors.

Note that the definition of the product of two matrices, A and B, requires that the matrix A have the same number of *columns* as B has *rows*; the result, AB, then has the same number of rows as A and the same number of columns as B. The matrices A and B are said to be **conformable** for multiplication. The fact that two matrices are conformable in the order AB, however, does not mean that they necessarily are conformable in the order BA.

Example.

If $A = \begin{bmatrix} 3 & 1 & 2 \\ 1 & 0 & 1 \end{bmatrix}$ and $B = \begin{bmatrix} 1 & -1 \\ 2 & 1 \\ 3 & 1 \end{bmatrix}$, find AB.

Solution. Since A is a 2×3 matrix, and B is a 3×2 matrix, they are conformable for multiplication. We have

$$AB = \begin{bmatrix} 3 & 1 & 2 \\ 1 & 0 & 1 \end{bmatrix} \begin{bmatrix} 1 & -1 \\ 2 & 1 \\ 3 & 1 \end{bmatrix} = \begin{bmatrix} 3+2+6 & -3+1+2 \\ 1+0+3 & -1+0+1 \end{bmatrix}$$

$$= \begin{bmatrix} 11 & 0 \\ 4 & 0 \end{bmatrix}.$$

In much of the matrix work in this book, we shall focus our attention on matrices having the same number of rows as columns. For brevity, a matrix of order $n \times n$ is often called a **square matrix of order** n. Although many of the ideas we shall discuss are applicable to matrices of any order, we shall apply the notions only to square matrices.

THEOREM 9.4 *If A, B, and C are $n \times n$ square matrices, then*

$$(AB)C = A(BC).$$

THEOREM 9.5 *If A, B, and C are $n \times n$ square matrices, then*

$$C(A + B) = CA + CB$$

and

$$(A + B)C = AC + BC.$$

The proofs of these theorems involve some complicated symbolism and are omitted here, but you will be asked to show their validity for the case of 2×2 matrices in the exercises. Observe that, because matrix multiplication is not, in general, commutative, we must establish both the left-hand and the right-hand distributive property.

DEFINITION 9.8 *The **principal diagonal** of a square matrix is the ordered set of entries a_{ij}, where $i = j$, extending from the upper left-hand corner to the lower right-hand corner of the matrix. Thus, the principal diagonal contains a_{11}, a_{22}, a_{33}, etc.*

For example, the principal diagonal of

$$\begin{bmatrix} 1 & 3 & -1 \\ 5 & 2 & 3 \\ 6 & 4 & 0 \end{bmatrix}$$

consists of 1, 2, and 0, in that order.

DEFINITION 9.9   *A **diagonal matrix** is a square matrix in which all entries not in the principal diagonal are 0.*

Thus,

$$\begin{bmatrix} 4 & 0 \\ 0 & 2 \end{bmatrix} \quad \text{and} \quad \begin{bmatrix} 1 & 0 & 0 \\ 0 & 1 & 0 \\ 0 & 0 & 0 \end{bmatrix}$$

are diagonal matrices.

DEFINITION 9.10   *$I_{n \times n}$ denotes the diagonal matrix having 1's for entries on the principal diagonal (and 0's for all other entries).*

For example,

$$I_{2 \times 2} = \begin{bmatrix} 1 & 0 \\ 0 & 1 \end{bmatrix} \quad \text{and} \quad I_{4 \times 4} = \begin{bmatrix} 1 & 0 & 0 & 0 \\ 0 & 1 & 0 & 0 \\ 0 & 0 & 1 & 0 \\ 0 & 0 & 0 & 1 \end{bmatrix}.$$

The following properties are consequences of the definitions we have adopted.

THEOREM 9.6   *For each matrix $A_{n \times n}$, we have*

$$A_{n \times n} I_{n \times n} = I_{n \times n} A_{n \times n} = A_{n \times n}.$$

Further, if for the matrix $B_{n \times n}$, we have

$$A_{n \times n} B_{n \times n} = B_{n \times n} A_{n \times n}$$

for all matrices $A_{n \times n}$, then

$$B_{n \times n} = I_{n \times n}.$$

Accordingly, $I_{n \times n}$ is the identity element for multiplication in the set of $n \times n$ square matrices, and $I_{n \times n}$ is unique.   The proof of this theorem, for the illustrative case $n = 2$, is left as an exercise.

In Section 9.1, we saw that the set $S_{m \times n}$ of matrices of fixed order $m \times n$ is a group with respect to matrix addition.   Thus this set satisfies the first five of the eleven field postulates discussed in Chapter 1.   Let us see to what extent the remaining field postulates are satisfied in $S_{m \times n}$ with respect to the operation of matrix multiplication.   In the first place, since the first factor in a matrix product must have the same number of columns as the second factor has rows, we must now restrict our attention to the case $m = n$.   For this, we have the following result.

THEOREM 9.7 *If $S_{n \times n}$ is the set of $n \times n$ square matrices, for n a fixed positive integer, and A, B, $C \in S_{n \times n}$, then*

I $\quad AB \in S_{n \times n}$. *Closure for multiplication.*

II $\quad A(BC) = (AB)C$. *Associativity for multiplication.*

III $\quad A(B + C) = AB + AC$ *and* *Distributive law.*
$\quad (B + C)A = BA + CA$.

IV $\quad AI_{n \times n} = I_{n \times n}A = A$. *Identity element for multiplication.*

Proof. Property I is an immediate consequence of Definition 9.7. Properties II, III, and IV are repetitions of the properties stated in Theorems 9.4, 9.5, and 9.6, respectively.

A set S in which two operations, addition and multiplication, are defined, which is a commutative group with respect to addition, which is closed with respect to multiplication, and for which the associative law for multiplication and the distributive law hold, is called a **ring**. Thus, for any fixed positive integer n, the set $S_{n \times n}$ of $n \times n$ matrices with real-number entries is a ring. In fact, since Property IV also holds in $S_{n \times n}$, this set is a **ring with an identity**.

At this point, let us summarize the properties of groups, rings, integral domains, and fields.

Structure	Binary Operations	Postulates
Group	one	1. closure 2. associativity 3. identity 4. inverse
Abelian group	one	1–4 above, and 5. commutativity
Ring	two +, ×	1–5 above for +, and 6. closure for × 7. associativity for × 8: × distributes over +
Ring with identity	two +, ×	1–8 above, and 9. identity for ×
Commutative ring with identity	two +, ×	1–9 above, and 10. commutativity for ×
Integral domain	two +, ×	1–10 above, and 11′. cancellation law for ×
Field	two +, ×	1–10 above, and 11. inverse for ×

Note that the set $S_{n \times n}$ is not a field because two of the field properties do *not* hold in $S_{n \times n}$. As we have already pointed out, the commutative law does not hold for matrix multiplication, not even in $S_{2 \times 2}$, and in Section 9.5 we shall see that there are square $n \times n$ matrices other than the zero $n \times n$ matrix that do not have multiplicative inverses. Moreover, neither does the cancellation law hold for matrix multiplication, as the matrices

$$A = \begin{bmatrix} 1 & 2 \\ 0 & 0 \end{bmatrix}, \quad B = \begin{bmatrix} 3 & 4 \\ 1 & 1 \end{bmatrix}, \quad C = \begin{bmatrix} 3 & 2 \\ 1 & 2 \end{bmatrix}$$

show. Here we have

$$AB = \begin{bmatrix} 5 & 6 \\ 0 & 0 \end{bmatrix} \quad \text{and} \quad AC = \begin{bmatrix} 5 & 6 \\ 0 & 0 \end{bmatrix},$$

so that $AB = AC$, and $A \neq 0$, but still $B \neq C$.

EXERCISE 9.2

Write each product as a single matrix.

Examples.

a. $3 \begin{bmatrix} 2 & 1 \\ -1 & 3 \\ 2 & 0 \end{bmatrix}$

b. $\begin{bmatrix} 3 & 1 & -1 \\ 0 & -1 & 2 \end{bmatrix} \cdot \begin{bmatrix} 1 & -1 \\ 0 & 2 \\ 1 & 0 \end{bmatrix}$

Solutions.

a. $\begin{bmatrix} 6 & 3 \\ -3 & 9 \\ 6 & 0 \end{bmatrix}$

b. $\begin{bmatrix} 3+0-1 & -3+2+0 \\ 0+0+2 & 0-2+0 \end{bmatrix} = \begin{bmatrix} 2 & -1 \\ 2 & -2 \end{bmatrix}$

1. $-5 \begin{bmatrix} 0 & 1 & -1 \\ 3 & -1 & 2 \end{bmatrix}$

2. $2 \begin{bmatrix} 2 & 1 & 3 & -2 \\ 4 & 2 & 0 & -1 \\ 0 & 0 & -1 & 2 \end{bmatrix}$

3. $\begin{bmatrix} 1 & -2 \end{bmatrix} \cdot \begin{bmatrix} 3 \\ 2 \end{bmatrix}$

4. $\begin{bmatrix} 3 & -2 & 2 \end{bmatrix} \cdot \begin{bmatrix} 1 \\ 0 \\ -2 \end{bmatrix}$

5. $\begin{bmatrix} -3 & 1 & 0 \\ 2 & 1 & 1 \end{bmatrix} \cdot \begin{bmatrix} 2 & 0 \\ 1 & -1 \\ 3 & 0 \end{bmatrix}$

6. $\begin{bmatrix} 2 & -3 & 1 \\ 0 & 1 & -1 \\ 2 & 0 & 0 \end{bmatrix} \cdot \begin{bmatrix} 1 & 0 & 0 \\ 0 & 1 & 0 \\ 0 & 0 & 1 \end{bmatrix}$

7. $\begin{bmatrix} 2 & -2 & -1 \\ 1 & 1 & -2 \\ 1 & 0 & -1 \end{bmatrix} \cdot \begin{bmatrix} -1 & -2 & 5 \\ -1 & -1 & 3 \\ -1 & -2 & 4 \end{bmatrix}$

8. $\begin{bmatrix} -1 & -2 & 5 \\ -1 & -1 & 3 \\ -1 & -2 & 4 \end{bmatrix} \cdot \begin{bmatrix} 2 & -2 & -1 \\ 1 & 1 & -2 \\ 1 & 0 & -1 \end{bmatrix}$

Let $A = \begin{bmatrix} 1 & -2 \\ 1 & 0 \end{bmatrix}$ and $B = \begin{bmatrix} -1 & 2 \\ -1 & 1 \end{bmatrix}$. Compute each of the following.

9. AB 10. BA 11. $(AB)A$

12. $(BA)B$ 13. A^2 (A times A)   14. B^2 (B times B)

15. $A^t B$ 16. AB^t

17. Show that if $A = \begin{bmatrix} -1 & 2 \\ 0 & 1 \end{bmatrix}$ and $B = \begin{bmatrix} 1 & 0 \\ -1 & 2 \end{bmatrix}$, then

   a. $(A + B)(A + B) \neq A^2 + 2AB + B^2$.
   b. $(A + B)(A - B) \neq A^2 - B^2$.

18. Show that $2A_{m \times n} = A_{m \times n} + A_{m \times n}$.

19. a. Show that for each matrix $A_{2 \times 2}$, we have

$$A_{2 \times 2} \cdot I_{2 \times 2} = I_{2 \times 2} \cdot A_{2 \times 2} = A_{2 \times 2}.$$

   b. Show that if for a given matrix $B_{2 \times 2}$ and for *all* $A_{2 \times 2}$ we have

$$A_{2 \times 2} \cdot B_{2 \times 2} = B_{2 \times 2} \cdot A_{2 \times 2} = A_{2 \times 2},$$

   then $B_{2 \times 2} = I_{2 \times 2}$.

20. Show that

$$\left(\begin{bmatrix} a_{11} & a_{12} \\ a_{21} & a_{22} \end{bmatrix} \cdot \begin{bmatrix} b_{11} & b_{12} \\ b_{21} & b_{22} \end{bmatrix} \right) \cdot \begin{bmatrix} c_{11} & c_{12} \\ c_{21} & c_{22} \end{bmatrix} = \\ \begin{bmatrix} a_{11} & a_{12} \\ a_{21} & a_{22} \end{bmatrix} \cdot \left(\begin{bmatrix} b_{11} & b_{12} \\ b_{21} & b_{22} \end{bmatrix} \cdot \begin{bmatrix} c_{11} & c_{12} \\ c_{21} & c_{22} \end{bmatrix} \right).$$

21. Show that

$$\begin{bmatrix} a_{11} & a_{12} \\ a_{21} & a_{22} \end{bmatrix} \cdot \left(\begin{bmatrix} b_{11} & b_{12} \\ b_{21} & b_{22} \end{bmatrix} + \begin{bmatrix} c_{11} & c_{12} \\ c_{21} & c_{22} \end{bmatrix} \right) = \\ \begin{bmatrix} a_{11} & a_{12} \\ a_{21} & a_{22} \end{bmatrix} \cdot \begin{bmatrix} b_{11} & b_{12} \\ b_{21} & b_{22} \end{bmatrix} + \begin{bmatrix} a_{11} & a_{12} \\ a_{21} & a_{22} \end{bmatrix} \cdot \begin{bmatrix} c_{11} & c_{12} \\ c_{21} & c_{22} \end{bmatrix}.$$

22. Show that

$$\left(\begin{bmatrix} b_{11} & b_{12} \\ b_{21} & b_{22} \end{bmatrix} + \begin{bmatrix} c_{11} & c_{12} \\ c_{21} & c_{22} \end{bmatrix} \right) \cdot \begin{bmatrix} a_{11} & a_{12} \\ a_{21} & a_{22} \end{bmatrix} = \\ \begin{bmatrix} b_{11} & b_{12} \\ b_{21} & b_{22} \end{bmatrix} \cdot \begin{bmatrix} a_{11} & a_{12} \\ a_{21} & a_{22} \end{bmatrix} + \begin{bmatrix} c_{11} & c_{12} \\ c_{21} & c_{22} \end{bmatrix} \cdot \begin{bmatrix} a_{11} & a_{12} \\ a_{21} & a_{22} \end{bmatrix}.$$

23. Show that $\begin{bmatrix} 0 & a \\ a & 0 \end{bmatrix}^2 = a^2 I$.

Find a matrix X satisfying each matrix equation.

24. $3X + \begin{bmatrix} 1 & 0 \\ 2 & 1 \end{bmatrix} = \begin{bmatrix} -2 & 3 \\ -1 & -2 \end{bmatrix}$

25. $2X + 3\begin{bmatrix} 1 & 1 \\ 0 & 1 \end{bmatrix} = \begin{bmatrix} 7 & -1 \\ 3 & -5 \end{bmatrix}$

26. $X + 2I = \begin{bmatrix} 3 & -1 \\ 1 & 2 \end{bmatrix}$ *Hint:* $X + 2I = X + \begin{bmatrix} 2 & 0 \\ 0 & 2 \end{bmatrix}$.

27. $3X - 2I = \begin{bmatrix} 7 & 3 \\ 6 & 4 \end{bmatrix}$

28. Show that $A_{2 \times 2}^2 = (-A_{2 \times 2})^2$.

29. Show that $(A_{2 \times 2} \cdot B_{2 \times 2})^t = B_{2 \times 2}^t \cdot A_{2 \times 2}^t$.

30. Prove Part I of Theorem 9.3.

31. Prove Part II of Theorem 9.3.

32. Prove Part III of Theorem 9.3.

33. Prove Part V of Theorem 9.3.

34. Prove Part VI of Theorem 9.3.

35. Prove Part VII of Theorem 9.3.

36. Prove Part VIII of Theorem 9.3.

37. Is the set of all 2×2 matrices of the form

$$\begin{bmatrix} a & 0 \\ 0 & b \end{bmatrix},$$

where $a, b, \in R$, a group with respect to addition? An Abelian group?

38. Repeat Problem 37 for the set of all matrices of the form

$$\begin{bmatrix} 0 & a \\ b & 0 \end{bmatrix},$$

where $a, b, \in R$.

39. Is every ring a group with respect to addition? Multiplication? In each case give reasons.

40. Is every integral domain a ring? A ring with identity? A commutative ring with identity? In each case, give reasons.

9.3 THE DETERMINANT FUNCTION

Associated with each square matrix A having real-number entries is a real number called the **determinant** of A and denoted by δA or $\delta(A)$ (read "the determinant of A"). Thus, we have a function, δ (delta), with domain the set of all square matrices having real-number entries, and with range the set of all real numbers: $\delta(A_{n \times n})$ is a determinant of **order** n.

Let us begin by examining δ over the set $S_{2 \times 2}$ of 2×2 matrices.

DEFINITION 9.11 *The determinant of the matrix*

$$\begin{bmatrix} a_{11} & a_{12} \\ a_{21} & a_{22} \end{bmatrix}$$

is the number $a_{11}a_{22} - a_{12}a_{21}$.

The determinant of a matrix is customarily displayed in the same form as a matrix, but with vertical bars in lieu of brackets. Thus,

$$\delta \begin{bmatrix} a_{11} & a_{12} \\ a_{21} & a_{22} \end{bmatrix} = \begin{vmatrix} a_{11} & a_{12} \\ a_{21} & a_{22} \end{vmatrix} = a_{11}a_{22} - a_{12}a_{21}.$$

Example. If

$$A = \begin{bmatrix} 3 & 1 \\ -2 & 3 \end{bmatrix},$$

find δA.

Solution.

$$\delta \begin{bmatrix} 3 & 1 \\ -2 & 3 \end{bmatrix} = \begin{vmatrix} 3 & 1 \\ -2 & 3 \end{vmatrix} = 3 \cdot 3 - (1)(-2) = 9 + 2 = 11.$$

Turning next to 3×3 matrices, we have the following.

DEFINITION 9.12 *The determinant of the matrix*

$$\begin{bmatrix} a_{11} & a_{12} & a_{13} \\ a_{21} & a_{22} & a_{23} \\ a_{31} & a_{32} & a_{33} \end{bmatrix} \quad \text{is denoted by} \quad \begin{vmatrix} a_{11} & a_{12} & a_{13} \\ a_{21} & a_{22} & a_{23} \\ a_{31} & a_{32} & a_{33} \end{vmatrix}$$

and is given by the expression

$$a_{11}a_{22}a_{33} - a_{11}a_{23}a_{32} + a_{12}a_{23}a_{31} - a_{12}a_{21}a_{33} + a_{13}a_{21}a_{32} - a_{13}a_{22}a_{31}.$$

An inspection of the subscripts of the factors of the products involved in this determinant (as well as those of the determinant of a 2×2 matrix) will show that each product is formed by taking one entry from each row and one entry from each column, with the restriction that no two factors be entries in the same row or column.   The determinant consists of the sum of ± all such products as are possible.   Whether a product or its negative is used in a determinant depends on the number of **inversions** in the second subscripts in the product when the first subscripts are in natural order, 1 2 3 ⋯.   An inversion occurs in a sequence of natural numbers each time a natural number is preceded by a greater natural number.   For example, in the sequence 1 4 3 2, there are three inversions, because 4 precedes 3, 4 precedes 2, and 3 precedes 2.   Now, if there is an odd number of inversions in the sequence formed by the *second subscripts of the factors in a product* when the first subscripts are in natural order, the negative of the product is used; otherwise, the product itself is used.

With this means of distinguishing products, we can generalize our definition of the determinant of a matrix.

DEFINITION 9.13   *The determinant of the square matrix*

$$\begin{bmatrix} a_{11} & a_{12} & \cdots & a_{1n} \\ \vdots & \vdots & & \vdots \\ a_{n1} & a_{n2} & \cdots & a_{nn} \end{bmatrix} \quad \text{is denoted by} \quad \begin{vmatrix} a_{11} & a_{12} & \cdots & a_{1n} \\ \vdots & \vdots & & \vdots \\ a_{n1} & a_{n2} & \cdots & a_{nn} \end{vmatrix}$$

and is equal to the sum of all products, $\pm a_{1j_1} a_{2j_2} a_{3j_3} \cdots a_{nj_n}$, *where each j takes on all values from 1 to n, and no j's in the same product have the same subscript. For each term in the sum, the negative sign is used if the number of inversions in the sequence formed by the j's is odd: otherwise, the positive sign is used.*

It is evident from this definition that the determinant of a matrix with real entries is a real number.   We shall refer to this real number as the **value** of the determinant; the process of computing the number is called **expanding** the determinant.   Note that the arrays shown in the foregoing definition appear in print to be rectangular rather than square.   The subscript on the lower right-hand entry, however, shows the dimension of the matrix or determinant. In any similar symbolism, this subscript should always be checked carefully to determine the correct dimension.

Example.   In expanding the determinant of a 4 × 4 square matrix, one of the products is $a_{11}a_{23}a_{32}a_{44}$.   Will this product be a term in the expansion or will its negative be a term in the expansion?

Solution.   The first subscripts are in natural order, 1 2 3 4, and the second subscripts are in the order 1 3 2 4.   Since the only inversion is that 3 appears before 2, the negative of $a_{11}a_{23}a_{32}a_{44}$ will be used.

DEFINITION 9.14   *The **minor** M_{ij} of the element a_{ij} in a given determinant is the determinant that remains after the ith row and jth column in the given determinant have been deleted.*

For example, in the determinant

$$\begin{vmatrix} a_{11} & a_{12} & a_{13} \\ a_{21} & a_{22} & a_{23} \\ a_{31} & a_{32} & a_{33} \end{vmatrix}, \tag{1}$$

the minor of the element a_{11} is $M_{11} = \begin{vmatrix} a_{22} & a_{23} \\ a_{32} & a_{33} \end{vmatrix}$,

the minor of the element a_{23} is $M_{23} = \begin{vmatrix} a_{11} & a_{12} \\ a_{31} & a_{32} \end{vmatrix}$,

the minor of the element a_{31} is $M_{31} = \begin{vmatrix} a_{12} & a_{13} \\ a_{22} & a_{23} \end{vmatrix}$, etc.

DEFINITION 9.15 *The **cofactor** A_{ij} of the element a_{ij} is the minor of a_{ij} if $i + j$ is an even integer, and the negative of the minor of a_{ij} if $i + j$ is an odd integer.*

For example, in the determinant (1),

the cofactor of a_{11} is $\begin{vmatrix} a_{22} & a_{23} \\ a_{32} & a_{33} \end{vmatrix}$,

because $1 + 1$ is 2, an even integer;

the cofactor of a_{23} is $-\begin{vmatrix} a_{11} & a_{12} \\ a_{31} & a_{32} \end{vmatrix}$,

because $2 + 3$ is 5, an odd integer;

the cofactor of a_{31} is $\begin{vmatrix} a_{12} & a_{13} \\ a_{22} & a_{23} \end{vmatrix}$,

because $3 + 1$ is 4, an even integer; etc.

The following sign array is a convenient means of determining whether the cofactor of a given element equals the minor or whether it equals the negative of the minor.

$$\begin{matrix} + & - & + & \cdot & \cdot & \cdot & (-)^{n+1} \\ - & + & - & \cdot & \cdot & \cdot & \cdot \\ + & - & + & \cdot & \cdot & \cdot & \cdot \\ \cdot & \cdot & \cdot & \cdot & \cdot & \cdot & \cdot \\ \cdot & \cdot & \cdot & \cdot & \cdot & \cdot & \cdot \\ \cdot & \cdot & \cdot & \cdot & \cdot & \cdot & \cdot \\ (-)^{n+1} & \cdot & \cdot & \cdot & + \end{matrix}$$

With the definition of a cofactor in mind, let us look again at the definition on page 267 for the determinant of the matrix

$$A = \begin{bmatrix} a_{11} & a_{12} & a_{13} \\ a_{21} & a_{22} & a_{23} \\ a_{31} & a_{32} & a_{33} \end{bmatrix}.$$

The value of this determinant is

$$\delta(A) = a_{11}a_{22}a_{33} - a_{11}a_{23}a_{32} + a_{12}a_{23}a_{31} - a_{12}a_{21}a_{33} \\ + a_{13}a_{21}a_{32} - a_{13}a_{22}a_{31}.$$

By suitably factoring pairs of terms in the right-hand member, we obtain

$$\delta(A) = a_{11}(a_{22}a_{33} - a_{23}a_{32}) + a_{12}(a_{23}a_{31} - a_{21}a_{33}) \\ + a_{13}(a_{21}a_{32} - a_{22}a_{31}).$$

If now the binomial factor in the middle term is rewritten $-(a_{21}a_{33} - a_{23}a_{31})$, we have

$$\delta(A) = a_{11}(a_{22}a_{33} - a_{23}a_{32}) + a_{12}[-(a_{21}a_{33} - a_{23}a_{31})] \\ + a_{13}(a_{21}a_{32} - a_{22}a_{31}),$$

which is equal to

$$a_{11}\begin{vmatrix} a_{22} & a_{23} \\ a_{32} & a_{33} \end{vmatrix} + a_{12}\left(-\begin{vmatrix} a_{21} & a_{23} \\ a_{31} & a_{33} \end{vmatrix}\right) + a_{13}\begin{vmatrix} a_{21} & a_{22} \\ a_{31} & a_{32} \end{vmatrix}.$$

Accordingly, we have

$$\delta(A) = a_{11}A_{11} + a_{12}A_{12} + a_{13}A_{13}.$$

Thus, the determinant

$$\delta(A) = \begin{vmatrix} a_{11} & a_{12} & a_{13} \\ a_{21} & a_{22} & a_{23} \\ a_{31} & a_{32} & a_{33} \end{vmatrix}$$

is equal to the sum formed by multiplying each entry in the first row by its cofactor and then adding these products.

In the exercises at the end of this section, you will be asked to show that this determinant is also equal to the sum formed by multiplying each entry in *any* row (or column) by its cofactor and then adding the products.

Although we shall not show it here, the definition on page 268 is logically equivalent to the following.

DEFINITION 9.16   *The determinant of the square matrix*

$$\begin{bmatrix} a_{11} & a_{12} & \cdots & a_{1n} \\ a_{21} & a_{22} & \cdots & a_{2n} \\ \vdots & & & \vdots \\ a_{n1} & a_{n2} & \cdots & a_{nn} \end{bmatrix}$$

is the sum of the n products formed by multiplying each entry in any single row (or any single column) by its cofactor.

When this latter definition is used to rewrite a determinant, the determinant is said to be expanded about whatever row (or column) is chosen.

Example. If

$$A = \begin{bmatrix} 3 & 2 & 1 \\ 0 & 1 & -2 \\ 1 & 3 & 4 \end{bmatrix},$$

find $\delta(A)$ by expansion about the first column.

Solution. Noting that $a_{11} = 3$, $a_{21} = 0$, and $a_{31} = 1$, we have

$$A = 3 \begin{vmatrix} 1 & -2 \\ 3 & 4 \end{vmatrix} + 0 \left(- \begin{vmatrix} 2 & 1 \\ 3 & 4 \end{vmatrix} \right) + 1 \begin{vmatrix} 2 & 1 \\ 1 & -2 \end{vmatrix}$$

$$= 3(10) + 0 + (-5) = 25.$$

EXERCISE 9.3

Let

$$A = \begin{bmatrix} 2 & 1 & -2 & 0 \\ 1 & 0 & 3 & -1 \\ -2 & 1 & 2 & 2 \\ 1 & -1 & 3 & 1 \end{bmatrix}.$$

Each of the following is a term in an expansion of $\delta(A)$. Determine the product, and write the product or its negative in accordance with the number of inversions in the second subscripts.

1. $a_{11}a_{22}a_{33}a_{44}$

2. $a_{11}a_{23}a_{34}a_{42}$

3. $a_{11}a_{24}a_{32}a_{43}$

4. $a_{12}a_{21}a_{33}a_{44}$

5. $a_{13}a_{24}a_{32}a_{41}$

6. $a_{14}a_{23}a_{32}a_{41}$

Let A be the matrix given above. Determine the minor M_{ij} and cofactor A_{ij} (in determinant form) of each of the following entries.

7. a_{11} 8. a_{13} 9. a_{23} 10. a_{41}

11. a_{31} 12. a_{33} 13. a_{44} 14. a_{14}

Evaluate.

Examples.

a. $\begin{vmatrix} 2 & -3 \\ 1 & 4 \end{vmatrix}$

b. $\begin{vmatrix} 1 & 2 & 0 \\ 3 & -1 & 4 \\ -2 & 1 & 3 \end{vmatrix}$

Solutions.

a. $\begin{vmatrix} 2 & -3 \\ 1 & 4 \end{vmatrix} = (2)(4) - (-3)(1) = 11$

b. Expand about any row or column; the first row is used here.

$$\begin{vmatrix} 1 & 2 & 0 \\ 3 & -1 & 4 \\ -2 & 1 & 3 \end{vmatrix} = 1 \begin{vmatrix} -1 & 4 \\ 1 & 3 \end{vmatrix} - 2 \begin{vmatrix} 3 & 4 \\ -2 & 3 \end{vmatrix} + 0 \begin{vmatrix} 3 & -1 \\ -2 & 1 \end{vmatrix}$$

$$= 1[(-1)(3) - (4)(1)] - 2[(3)(3) - (4)(-2)] + 0$$
$$= -41$$

15. $\begin{vmatrix} 1 & 0 \\ 2 & 1 \end{vmatrix}$
16. $\begin{vmatrix} 3 & -2 \\ 4 & 1 \end{vmatrix}$
17. $\begin{vmatrix} -5 & -1 \\ 3 & \dfrac{3}{5} \end{vmatrix}$
18. $\begin{vmatrix} -1 & 6 \\ 0 & -2 \end{vmatrix}$

19. $\begin{vmatrix} 2 & 0 & 1 \\ 1 & 1 & 2 \\ -1 & 0 & 1 \end{vmatrix}$
20. $\begin{vmatrix} 1 & 3 & 1 \\ -1 & 2 & 1 \\ 0 & 2 & 0 \end{vmatrix}$
21. $\begin{vmatrix} 1 & 2 & 3 \\ 3 & -1 & 2 \\ 2 & 0 & 2 \end{vmatrix}$

22. $\begin{vmatrix} 1 & 0 & 0 \\ 0 & 1 & 2 \\ 0 & 3 & 4 \end{vmatrix}$
23. $\begin{vmatrix} -1 & 0 & 2 \\ -2 & 1 & 0 \\ 0 & 1 & -3 \end{vmatrix}$
24. $\begin{vmatrix} 2 & 1 & 4 \\ 3 & 2 & 6 \\ 5 & -3 & 10 \end{vmatrix}$

25. $\begin{vmatrix} a & b & 1 \\ a & b & 1 \\ 1 & 1 & 1 \end{vmatrix}$
26. $\begin{vmatrix} a & a & a \\ 1 & 2 & 3 \\ 4 & 5 & 6 \end{vmatrix}$
27. $\begin{vmatrix} x & 0 & 0 \\ 0 & x & 0 \\ 0 & 0 & x \end{vmatrix}$

28. $\begin{vmatrix} 0 & 0 & x \\ 0 & x & 0 \\ x & 0 & 0 \end{vmatrix}$

Solve for x.

29. $\begin{vmatrix} x & 0 & 0 \\ 2 & 1 & 3 \\ 0 & 1 & 4 \end{vmatrix} = 3$

30. $\begin{vmatrix} x^2 & x & 1 \\ 0 & 2 & 1 \\ 3 & 1 & 4 \end{vmatrix} = 28$

Expand by minors and verify.

31. $\begin{vmatrix} 0 & 1 & 0 & 0 \\ 1 & 0 & 3 & 2 \\ 5 & -1 & 2 & 1 \\ 1 & 0 & 1 & 1 \end{vmatrix} = 5$

32. $\begin{vmatrix} 1 & 2 & 0 & -1 \\ 1 & 0 & -1 & 2 \\ 0 & 1 & 1 & 1 \\ 2 & -1 & 0 & 1 \end{vmatrix} = 17$

33. By definition,

$$\delta \begin{bmatrix} a_{11} & a_{12} & \cdots & a_{1n} \\ \vdots & \vdots & & \vdots \\ a_{n1} & a_{n2} & \cdots & a_{nn} \end{bmatrix}$$

equals the sum of all products (with appropriate sign) $a_{1j_1} a_{2j_2} a_{3j_3} \cdots a_{nj_n}$, where each j takes on all values from 1 to n and no j's in the same product have the same subscript. How many such products are there in the determinant of a 2×2 matrix? A 3×3 matrix? A 4×4 matrix?

34. Generalize the results of Problem 33, making a conjecture about the number of such products in the determinant of an $n \times n$ matrix.

Consider the determinant of

$$\begin{bmatrix} a_{11} & a_{12} & a_{13} \\ a_{21} & a_{22} & a_{23} \\ a_{31} & a_{32} & a_{33} \end{bmatrix}.$$

35. Show that

$$a_{11}A_{11} + a_{12}A_{12} + a_{13}A_{13} = a_{21}A_{21} + a_{22}A_{22} + a_{23}A_{23}.$$

36. Show that

$$a_{11}A_{11} + a_{12}A_{12} + a_{13}A_{13} = a_{31}A_{31} + a_{32}A_{32} + a_{33}A_{33}.$$

37. Show that

$$a_{11}A_{11} + a_{12}A_{12} + a_{13}A_{13} = a_{11}A_{11} + a_{21}A_{21} + a_{31}A_{31}.$$

38. Show that

$$a_{11}A_{11} + a_{12}A_{12} + a_{13}A_{13} = a_{12}A_{12} + a_{22}A_{22} + a_{32}A_{32}.$$

39. Show that

$$a_{11}A_{11} + a_{12}A_{12} + a_{13}A_{13} = a_{13}A_{13} + a_{23}A_{23} + a_{33}A_{33}.$$

40. Summarize the results of Problems 35–39.

41. Show that for any 2×2 matrix $\delta(aA) = a^2\delta(A)$.

42. Show that for any 2×2 matrix $\delta(A^t) = \delta(A)$.

43. Show that for any 2×2 matrix $\delta(AB) = \delta(A) \cdot \delta(B)$.

44. Apply Definition 9.13 to determine the value of the determinant of the 1×1 matrix $[a]$, in particular for $a = 3$ and for $a = -3$.

9.4 PROPERTIES OF DETERMINANTS

Determinants have some properties that are useful by virtue of the fact that they permit us to generate equal determinants with different and simpler configurations of entries. This, in turn, helps us find values for determinants.

THEOREM 9.8 *If each entry in any row, or each entry in any column, of a determinant is 0, then the determinant is equal to 0.*

Proof. By Definition 9.13, a determinant is a sum of products, each product having an entry from each row and each column of the determinant. This means that if any row or any column has only zero entries, each product will contain 0 as a factor. Thus each product, and therefore the sum of all such products, is 0.

For example,

$$\begin{vmatrix} 0 & 0 \\ 1 & 2 \end{vmatrix} = 0, \quad \begin{vmatrix} 1 & 1 & 0 \\ 3 & 5 & 0 \\ 2 & 7 & 0 \end{vmatrix} = 0, \quad \text{and} \quad \begin{vmatrix} 0 & 1 & 0 & 0 \\ 1 & 0 & 0 & 0 \\ 0 & 0 & 0 & 1 \\ 0 & 0 & 0 & 1 \end{vmatrix} = 0.$$

THEOREM 9.9 *If any two rows (or columns) of a determinant are interchanged, the resulting determinant is the negative of the original determinant.*

Proof. Let us look first at the case in which two adjacent rows of a determinant D of order n are interchanged. If the ith and $(i + 1)$st rows of D are interchanged to give us D' with entries a'_{ij}, then a_{ij} in D is equal to $a'_{i+1,j}$ in D', and the minors of a_{ij} in D are identical to those of $a'_{i+1,j}$ in D'. An expansion of D about the ith row leads to

$$D = a_{i1}A_{i1} + a_{i2}A_{i2} + \cdots + a_{in}A_{in},$$

and an expansion of D' about its $(i + 1)$st row leads to

$$D' = a'_{i+1,1}A'_{i+1,1} + a'_{i+1,2}A'_{i+1,2} + \cdots + a'_{i+1,n}A'_{i+1,n}.$$

Since $a_{ij} = a'_{i+1,j}$, and since, from the definition of cofactor, $A_{ij} = -A'_{i+1,j}$, it follows immediately that $D = -D'$. The same argument can be applied to an interchange of adjacent columns.

Now, let us turn to the case in which *any* two rows are interchanged. Let the interchange of the ith and $(i + k)$th rows of D lead to D'. This change can be viewed as the result of making k adjacent-row interchanges to bring the ith row into the $(i + k)$th position, and then $k - 1$ similar interchanges to bring the $(i + k)$th row into the ith position. Since each such interchange results in a sign reversal, and since $k + k - 1$ such reversals occur, $D' = (-1)^{2k-1}D$. But $2k - 1$ is an odd number for any natural number k, and hence $D' = -D$. A similar argument can be made for the interchange of the jth and $(j + k)$th columns.

For example,

$$\begin{vmatrix} 1 & 2 \\ 3 & 4 \end{vmatrix} = - \begin{vmatrix} 3 & 4 \\ 1 & 2 \end{vmatrix}, \text{ and } \begin{vmatrix} 1 & 2 & 3 \\ 4 & 5 & 6 \\ 7 & 8 & 9 \end{vmatrix} = - \begin{vmatrix} 3 & 2 & 1 \\ 6 & 5 & 4 \\ 9 & 8 & 7 \end{vmatrix}.$$

In the first example, rows 1 and 2 were interchanged. In the second example, columns 1 and 3 were interchanged.

THEOREM 9.10 *If two rows (or two columns) in a determinant have corresponding entries that are equal, the determinant is equal to 0.*

Proof. Let D have two rows (or two columns) with corresponding entries equal. Then by Theorem 9.9, an interchange of these rows (or columns) will produce D', which is the negative of D. That is, $D' = -D$. Since, however, the interchanged rows (or columns) have identical elements, $D' = D$. Thus, $D = -D$, $2D = 0$, and D must be 0.

For example,

$$\begin{vmatrix} 1 & 1 \\ 3 & 3 \end{vmatrix} = 0, \quad \begin{vmatrix} 1 & 2 & 1 \\ 3 & 1 & 0 \\ 1 & 2 & 1 \end{vmatrix} = 0, \text{ and } \begin{vmatrix} 1 & 2 & 3 & 4 \\ 5 & 6 & 7 & 8 \\ 0 & 0 & 1 & 0 \\ 1 & 2 & 3 & 4 \end{vmatrix} = 0.$$

THEOREM 9.11 *If each of the entries of one row (or column) of a determinant is multiplied by k, the determinant is multiplied by k.*

Proof. Let the ith row of D be multiplied by k to yield D'. Then an expansion of D' about the ith row leads to

$$D' = ka_{i1}A_{i1} + ka_{i2}A_{i2} + \cdots + ka_{in}A_{in}$$
$$= k(a_{i1}A_{i1} + a_{i2}A_{i2} + \cdots + a_{in}A_{in})$$
$$= kD.$$

A similar argument holds for columns. Thus,

$$\begin{vmatrix} 1 & 0 & 0 \\ 2 & 1 & 3 \\ 1 \times 2 & 3 \times 2 & 4 \times 2 \end{vmatrix} = 2 \begin{vmatrix} 1 & 0 & 0 \\ 2 & 1 & 3 \\ 1 & 3 & 4 \end{vmatrix}, \text{ and } \begin{vmatrix} 4 & 5 & 8 \\ 1 & 1 & 2 \\ 3 & 1 & 6 \end{vmatrix} = 2 \begin{vmatrix} 4 & 5 & 4 \\ 1 & 1 & 1 \\ 3 & 1 & 3 \end{vmatrix}.$$

Note that this process is different from that of the scalar multiplication of a matrix. In scalar multiplication, each entry in the matrix is multiplied by a real number, rather than, as here, only the entries in a single row or column being so multiplied.

THEOREM 9.12 *If each entry in a row (or column) of a determinant is written as the sum of two terms, the determinant can be written as the sum of two determinants as follows: If*

$$D = \begin{vmatrix} a_{11} & a_{12} & \cdots & a_{1n} \\ \vdots & \vdots & & \vdots \\ b_{i1} + c_{i1} & b_{i2} + c_{i2} & \cdots & b_{in} + c_{in} \\ \vdots & \vdots & & \vdots \\ a_{n1} & a_{n2} & \cdots & a_{nn} \end{vmatrix},$$

then

$$D = \begin{vmatrix} a_{11} & a_{12} & \cdots & a_{1n} \\ \vdots & \vdots & & \vdots \\ b_{i1} & b_{i2} & \cdots & b_{in} \\ \vdots & \vdots & & \vdots \\ a_{n1} & a_{n2} & \cdots & a_{nn} \end{vmatrix} + \begin{vmatrix} a_{11} & a_{12} & \cdots & a_{1n} \\ \vdots & \vdots & & \vdots \\ c_{i1} & c_{i2} & \cdots & c_{in} \\ \vdots & \vdots & & \vdots \\ a_{n1} & a_{n2} & \cdots & a_{nn} \end{vmatrix},$$

and if

$$D = \begin{vmatrix} a_{11} & \cdots & b_{1j} + c_{1j} & \cdots & a_{1n} \\ a_{21} & \cdots & b_{2j} + c_{2j} & \cdots & a_{2n} \\ \vdots & & \vdots & & \vdots \\ a_{n1} & \cdots & b_{nj} + c_{nj} & \cdots & a_{nn} \end{vmatrix},$$

then

$$D = \begin{vmatrix} a_{11} & \cdots & b_{1j} & \cdots & a_{1n} \\ a_{21} & \cdots & b_{2j} & \cdots & a_{2n} \\ \vdots & & \vdots & & \vdots \\ a_{n1} & \cdots & b_{nj} & \cdots & a_{nn} \end{vmatrix} + \begin{vmatrix} a_{11} & \cdots & c_{1j} & \cdots & a_{1n} \\ a_{21} & \cdots & c_{2j} & \cdots & a_{2n} \\ \vdots & & \vdots & & \vdots \\ a_{n1} & \cdots & c_{nj} & \cdots & a_{nn} \end{vmatrix}.$$

Proof. Let

$$D = \begin{vmatrix} a_{11} & \cdots & a_{1n} \\ \vdots & & \vdots \\ b_{i1} + c_{i1} & \cdots & b_{in} + c_{in} \\ \vdots & & \vdots \\ a_{n1} & \cdots & a_{nn} \end{vmatrix}$$

and expand about the ith row. This leads to

$$\begin{aligned} D &= (b_{i1} + c_{i1})A_{i1} + (b_{i2} + c_{i2})A_{i2} + \cdots + (b_{in} + c_{in})A_{in} \\ &= b_{i1}A_{i1} + c_{i1}A_{i1} + b_{i2}A_{i2} + c_{i2}A_{i2} + \cdots + b_{in}A_{in} + c_{in}A_{in} \\ &= b_{i1}A_{i1} + b_{i2}A_{i2} + \cdots + b_{in}A_{in} + c_{i1}A_{i1} + c_{i2}A_{i2} + \cdots + c_{in}A_{in} \end{aligned}$$

$$= \begin{vmatrix} a_{11} & \cdots & a_{1n} \\ \vdots & & \vdots \\ b_{i1} & \cdots & b_{in} \\ \vdots & & \vdots \\ a_{n1} & \cdots & a_{nn} \end{vmatrix} + \begin{vmatrix} a_{11} & \cdots & a_{1n} \\ \vdots & & \vdots \\ c_{i1} & \cdots & c_{in} \\ \vdots & & \vdots \\ a_{n1} & \cdots & a_{nn} \end{vmatrix}.$$

A similar argument proves the result for columns.

For example,

$$\begin{vmatrix} 1 & 3 \\ 2 & 5 \end{vmatrix} = \begin{vmatrix} 1 & 1 \\ 2 & 4 \end{vmatrix} + \begin{vmatrix} 1 & 2 \\ 2 & 1 \end{vmatrix}$$

and

$$\begin{vmatrix} 4 & 0 & 0 \\ 0 & 4 & 0 \\ 0 & 0 & 4 \end{vmatrix} = \begin{vmatrix} 4 & 0 & 0 \\ 0 & 2 & 0 \\ 0 & 0 & 4 \end{vmatrix} + \begin{vmatrix} 4 & 0 & 0 \\ 0 & 2 & 0 \\ 0 & 0 & 4 \end{vmatrix}.$$

THEOREM 9.13 *If each entry of one row (or column) of a determinant is multiplied by a real number k and the resulting product is added to the corresponding entry in another row (or column, respectively) in the determinant, the resulting determinant is equal to the original determinant.*

Proof. Let

$$D = \begin{vmatrix} a_{11} & \cdots & a_{1n} \\ \vdots & & \vdots \\ a_{n1} & \cdots & a_{nn} \end{vmatrix}.$$

Then, if the ith row of D is multiplied by k and added to another row, say the pth row, we have

$$D = \begin{vmatrix} a_{11} & \cdots & a_{1n} \\ \vdots & & \vdots \\ a_{i1} & \cdots & a_{in} \\ \vdots & & \vdots \\ a_{p1} + ka_{i1} & \cdots & a_{pn} + ka_{in} \\ \vdots & & \vdots \\ a_{n1} & \cdots & a_{nn} \end{vmatrix},$$

which, by Theorem 9.12, is equal to

$$\begin{vmatrix} a_{11} & \cdots & a_{1n} \\ \vdots & & \vdots \\ a_{i1} & \cdots & a_{in} \\ \vdots & & \vdots \\ a_{p1} & \cdots & a_{pn} \\ \vdots & & \vdots \\ a_{n1} & \cdots & a_{nn} \end{vmatrix} + \begin{vmatrix} a_{11} & \cdots & a_{1n} \\ \vdots & & \vdots \\ a_{i1} & \cdots & a_{in} \\ \vdots & & \vdots \\ ka_{i1} & \cdots & ka_{in} \\ \vdots & & \vdots \\ a_{n1} & \cdots & a_{nn} \end{vmatrix}.$$

The last determinant in this sum can, by Theorem 9.11, be written

$$k \begin{vmatrix} a_{11} & \cdots & a_{1n} \\ \vdots & & \vdots \\ a_{i1} & \cdots & a_{in} \\ \vdots & & \vdots \\ a_{i1} & \cdots & a_{in} \\ \vdots & & \vdots \\ a_{n1} & \cdots & a_{nn} \end{vmatrix},$$

and since this determinant contains two rows that have their corresponding entries equal, it follows from Theorem 9.10 that it is 0. Hence, the theorem is proved for rows. A similar argument shows that it is also true for columns.

For example,

$$\begin{vmatrix} 1 & 1 \\ 2 & 1 \end{vmatrix} = \begin{vmatrix} 1 & 1 \\ 2 + 3(1) & 1 + 3(1) \end{vmatrix} = \begin{vmatrix} 1 & 1 \\ 5 & 4 \end{vmatrix},$$

and

$$\begin{vmatrix} 1 & 2 & 3 \\ 4 & 5 & 6 \\ 7 & 8 & 9 \end{vmatrix} = \begin{vmatrix} 1 + 2(3) & 2 & 3 \\ 4 + 2(6) & 5 & 6 \\ 7 + 2(9) & 8 & 9 \end{vmatrix} = \begin{vmatrix} 7 & 2 & 3 \\ 16 & 5 & 6 \\ 25 & 8 & 9 \end{vmatrix}.$$

The preceding theorems can be used to write sequences of equal determinants, leading from one form of a determinant to another and more useful form.

Example. Expand

$$D = \begin{vmatrix} 2 & -1 & 1 & -3 \\ 1 & 3 & -4 & 2 \\ 1 & 0 & -2 & 1 \\ 3 & -1 & 5 & 2 \end{vmatrix}.$$

Solution. As a step toward expanding the determinant, we shall use Theorem 9.13 to produce an equal determinant with a row or a column containing zero entries in all but one place. Let us arbitrarily select the second column for this role, because one entry is already zero. Multiplying a_{1j} by 3 and adding the result to a_{2j}, we obtain

$$D = \begin{vmatrix} 2 & -1 & 1 & -3 \\ 1 + 3(2) & 3 + 3(-1) & -4 + 3(1) & 2 + 3(-3) \\ 1 & 0 & -2 & 1 \\ 3 & -1 & 5 & 2 \end{vmatrix} = \begin{vmatrix} 2 & -1 & 1 & -3 \\ 7 & 0 & -1 & -7 \\ 1 & 0 & -2 & 1 \\ 3 & -1 & 5 & 2 \end{vmatrix}.$$

Next, multiplying a_{1j} by -1 and adding the result to a_{4j}, we find that

$$D = \begin{vmatrix} 2 & -1 & 1 & -3 \\ 7 & 0 & -1 & -7 \\ 1 & 0 & -2 & 1 \\ 3 - 1(2) & -1 - 1(-1) & 5 - 1(1) & 2 - 1(-3) \end{vmatrix} = \begin{vmatrix} 2 & -1 & 1 & -3 \\ 7 & 0 & -1 & -7 \\ 1 & 0 & -2 & 1 \\ 1 & 0 & 4 & 5 \end{vmatrix}.$$

If we now expand the determinant about the second column, we have

$$D = \begin{vmatrix} 2 & -1 & 1 & -3 \\ 7 & 0 & -1 & -7 \\ 1 & 0 & -2 & 1 \\ 1 & 0 & 4 & 5 \end{vmatrix} = -(-1)\begin{vmatrix} 7 & -1 & -7 \\ 1 & -2 & 1 \\ 1 & 4 & 5 \end{vmatrix} + 0A_{22} + 0A_{32} + 0A_{42}.$$

From this point, we can reduce the third-order determinant to a second-order determinant by a similar procedure or, alternatively, expand directly about the elements in any row or column. Expanding about the element of the first row, we obtain

$$D = \begin{vmatrix} 7 & -1 & -7 \\ 1 & -2 & 1 \\ 1 & 4 & 5 \end{vmatrix} = 7\begin{vmatrix} -2 & 1 \\ 4 & 5 \end{vmatrix} - (-1)\begin{vmatrix} 1 & 1 \\ 1 & 5 \end{vmatrix} + (-7)\begin{vmatrix} 1 & -2 \\ 1 & 4 \end{vmatrix},$$

from which

$$D = 7(-14) + (4) - 7(6) = -98 + 4 - 42 = -136.$$

EXERCISE 9.4

Without evaluating, state why each statement is true. Verify selected examples by expansion.

1. $\begin{vmatrix} 2 & 3 & 1 \\ 0 & 0 & 0 \\ -1 & 2 & 0 \end{vmatrix} = 0$

2. $\begin{vmatrix} 3 & 1 & 3 \\ 0 & 1 & 0 \\ 1 & 2 & 1 \end{vmatrix} = 0$

3. $\begin{vmatrix} -2 & 1 & 0 \\ 3 & 4 & 1 \\ -4 & 2 & 0 \end{vmatrix} = 0$

4. $\begin{vmatrix} 7 & 3 & 2 & 0 \\ 2 & -1 & 2 & 0 \\ 4 & 1 & 1 & 0 \\ 0 & 2 & 1 & 0 \end{vmatrix} = 0$

5. $\begin{vmatrix} 2 & 3 & 1 & -1 \\ 2 & 0 & 1 & 2 \\ 2 & 3 & 1 & -1 \\ 0 & 1 & 2 & 0 \end{vmatrix} = 0$

6. $\begin{vmatrix} 6 & 1 & 3 & -2 \\ -2 & 0 & 1 & 4 \\ 3 & 6 & 1 & 2 \\ -4 & 0 & 2 & 8 \end{vmatrix} = 0$

7. $\begin{vmatrix} 2 & 3 \\ 1 & -1 \end{vmatrix} = -\begin{vmatrix} 3 & 2 \\ -1 & 1 \end{vmatrix}$

8. $\begin{vmatrix} -2 & 3 & 1 \\ -1 & 0 & 1 \\ -2 & 1 & 0 \end{vmatrix} = -\begin{vmatrix} 2 & 3 & 1 \\ 1 & 0 & 1 \\ 2 & 1 & 0 \end{vmatrix}$

9. $\begin{vmatrix} 4 & 2 & 1 \\ 0 & -1 & -2 \\ 1 & 0 & 2 \end{vmatrix} = -\begin{vmatrix} 4 & 2 & 1 \\ 0 & 1 & 2 \\ 1 & 0 & 2 \end{vmatrix}$

10. $\begin{vmatrix} 3 & 1 & 0 \\ -2 & 1 & 1 \\ 0 & 2 & -1 \end{vmatrix} = -\begin{vmatrix} 0 & 1 & 3 \\ 1 & 1 & -2 \\ -1 & 2 & 0 \end{vmatrix}$

11. $2\begin{vmatrix} 1 & 0 & 2 \\ -1 & 2 & 0 \\ 1 & 1 & 1 \end{vmatrix} = \begin{vmatrix} 1 & 0 & 2 \\ -1 & 2 & 0 \\ 2 & 2 & 2 \end{vmatrix}$

12. $\begin{vmatrix} 3 & -4 & 2 \\ 1 & -2 & 0 \\ 0 & 8 & 1 \end{vmatrix} = -2\begin{vmatrix} 3 & 2 & 2 \\ 1 & 1 & 0 \\ 0 & -4 & 1 \end{vmatrix}$

13.
$$\begin{vmatrix} 3 & 0 & 6 \\ -2 & 1 & 2 \\ 0 & 1 & -2 \end{vmatrix} = 6 \begin{vmatrix} 1 & 0 & 1 \\ -2 & 1 & 1 \\ 0 & 1 & -1 \end{vmatrix}$$

14.
$$\begin{vmatrix} 1 & 2 & 1 \\ -1 & 0 & -2 \\ 2 & 4 & 1 \end{vmatrix} = -2 \begin{vmatrix} 1 & 1 & 1 \\ 1 & 0 & 2 \\ 2 & 2 & 1 \end{vmatrix}$$

15.
$$\begin{vmatrix} 3 & 5 \\ 1 & 4 \end{vmatrix} = \begin{vmatrix} 3 & 3 \\ 1 & 2 \end{vmatrix} + \begin{vmatrix} 3 & 2 \\ 1 & 2 \end{vmatrix}$$

16.
$$\begin{vmatrix} 3 & 1 & 4 \\ 2 & 2 & 2 \\ 1 & 0 & -1 \end{vmatrix} = \begin{vmatrix} 3 & 1 & 4 \\ 1 & 1 & 1 \\ 1 & 0 & -1 \end{vmatrix} + \begin{vmatrix} 3 & 1 & 4 \\ 1 & 1 & 1 \\ 1 & 0 & -1 \end{vmatrix}$$

17.
$$\begin{vmatrix} 1 & 2 \\ 3 & 4 \end{vmatrix} = \begin{vmatrix} 1+2 & 2 \\ 3+4 & 4 \end{vmatrix}$$

18.
$$\begin{vmatrix} 1 & 2 \\ 3 & 4 \end{vmatrix} = \begin{vmatrix} 1+4 & 2 \\ 3+8 & 4 \end{vmatrix}$$

19.
$$\begin{vmatrix} 1 & 2 \\ 3 & 4 \end{vmatrix} = \begin{vmatrix} 1 & 2 \\ 3-3 & 4-6 \end{vmatrix}$$

20.
$$\begin{vmatrix} 1 & 2 \\ 3 & 4 \end{vmatrix} = \begin{vmatrix} 1 & 0 \\ 3 & 4-6 \end{vmatrix}$$

21.
$$\begin{vmatrix} 1 & 2 & 1 \\ 0 & 2 & 3 \\ 2 & -1 & 2 \end{vmatrix} = \begin{vmatrix} 1 & 2 & 1 \\ 0 & 2 & 3 \\ 0 & -5 & 0 \end{vmatrix}$$

22.
$$\begin{vmatrix} -1 & 1 & 0 \\ 2 & 3 & -1 \\ 2 & 1 & 2 \end{vmatrix} = \begin{vmatrix} 0 & 1 & 0 \\ 5 & 3 & -1 \\ 3 & 1 & 2 \end{vmatrix}$$

Theorem 9.13 was used on the left-hand member of each of the following equalities to produce the elements in the right-hand member. Complete the entries.

23.
$$\begin{vmatrix} 1 & 3 \\ 2 & 2 \end{vmatrix} = \begin{vmatrix} 1 & 3 \\ 0 & \end{vmatrix}$$

24.
$$\begin{vmatrix} 2 & -1 \\ 3 & 1 \end{vmatrix} = \begin{vmatrix} & 0 \\ 3 & 1 \end{vmatrix}$$

25.
$$\begin{vmatrix} 1 & -2 & 1 \\ 3 & 1 & 4 \\ 0 & 2 & 1 \end{vmatrix} = \begin{vmatrix} 1 & -2 & 1 \\ 0 & 7 & \\ 0 & 2 & 1 \end{vmatrix}$$

26.
$$\begin{vmatrix} 3 & -1 & 0 \\ 1 & 2 & 1 \\ 2 & 3 & 1 \end{vmatrix} = \begin{vmatrix} 3 & -1 & 0 \\ 1 & 2 & 1 \\ 1 & & 0 \end{vmatrix}$$

27.
$$\begin{vmatrix} 2 & 3 & 1 & 4 \\ 0 & 2 & 1 & 2 \\ 1 & -1 & 2 & 3 \\ 0 & 1 & 1 & 1 \end{vmatrix} = \begin{vmatrix} 0 & 1 & & -2 \\ 0 & 2 & 1 & 2 \\ 1 & -1 & 2 & 3 \\ 0 & 1 & 1 & 1 \end{vmatrix}$$

28.
$$\begin{vmatrix} 2 & 1 & 1 & 0 \\ 1 & 2 & 0 & 2 \\ 3 & 1 & 0 & 3 \\ 2 & -1 & -4 & 2 \end{vmatrix} = \begin{vmatrix} 2 & 1 & 1 & 0 \\ 1 & 2 & 0 & 2 \\ 3 & 1 & 0 & 3 \\ & -3 & 0 & 2 \end{vmatrix}$$

29. $\begin{vmatrix} 1 & 2 & 3 & -1 \\ 2 & 0 & 1 & 2 \\ 3 & -1 & 2 & 1 \\ 0 & 1 & 1 & 1 \end{vmatrix} = \begin{vmatrix} 1 & 1 & 2 & -1 \\ 2 & -2 & -1 & 2 \\ 3 & & 1 & 1 \\ 0 & 0 & 0 & 1 \end{vmatrix}$

30. $\begin{vmatrix} -1 & 2 & -1 & 3 \\ 2 & 1 & 2 & -1 \\ 4 & 2 & 3 & 4 \\ 2 & 1 & 2 & 1 \end{vmatrix} = \begin{vmatrix} & 2 & 0 & 1 \\ 0 & 1 & 0 & 0 \\ 0 & 2 & -1 & 2 \\ 0 & 1 & 0 & 0 \end{vmatrix}$

First reduce each determinant to an equal 2 × 2 determinant and then evaluate.

31. $\begin{vmatrix} 2 & 1 & 0 \\ 3 & 2 & 1 \\ -1 & 2 & 0 \end{vmatrix}$ 32. $\begin{vmatrix} 1 & 2 & 1 \\ 2 & -1 & 2 \\ 0 & 1 & 0 \end{vmatrix}$ 33. $\begin{vmatrix} 1 & 0 & 3 \\ 2 & -1 & 1 \\ 1 & 2 & 1 \end{vmatrix}$

34. $\begin{vmatrix} 1 & 2 & -1 \\ 2 & 1 & 3 \\ 0 & 1 & 2 \end{vmatrix}$ 35. $\begin{vmatrix} 1 & 2 & 1 \\ -1 & 2 & 3 \\ 2 & -1 & 1 \end{vmatrix}$ 36. $\begin{vmatrix} 3 & -1 & 2 \\ 1 & 2 & 1 \\ -2 & 1 & 3 \end{vmatrix}$

37. $\begin{vmatrix} 2 & 3 & -1 \\ 1 & -2 & 1 \\ 2 & 3 & 4 \end{vmatrix}$ 38. $\begin{vmatrix} 2 & 2 & 1 \\ 3 & -1 & 2 \\ 2 & 1 & 3 \end{vmatrix}$

39. $\begin{vmatrix} 0 & 0 & 1 & 2 \\ 6 & 0 & 0 & 1 \\ 6 & 1 & 0 & -1 \\ 6 & 1 & 0 & 2 \end{vmatrix}$ 40. $\begin{vmatrix} 4 & 2 & 0 & 2 \\ -1 & 0 & 2 & 1 \\ 3 & 0 & -1 & 1 \\ 0 & 0 & 2 & 1 \end{vmatrix}$

41. $\begin{vmatrix} 0 & 1 & 0 & 2 \\ 0 & 2 & 0 & 3 \\ 2 & -1 & 1 & 0 \\ 0 & 0 & 8 & 8 \end{vmatrix}$ 42. $\begin{vmatrix} 0 & 2 & -1 & 3 \\ 0 & 0 & 2 & 1 \\ 3 & 0 & 1 & 0 \\ -6 & 6 & 0 & 0 \end{vmatrix}$

43. $\begin{vmatrix} 1 & 2 & 3 & -1 \\ 0 & 4 & 8 & 4 \\ -2 & 0 & 1 & 1 \\ 2 & 1 & 0 & 1 \end{vmatrix}$ 44. $\begin{vmatrix} 1 & 2 & 1 & 1 \\ 2 & -1 & 0 & 1 \\ 0 & 6 & 3 & 9 \\ 2 & 0 & -1 & 1 \end{vmatrix}$

45. Show that

$$\begin{vmatrix} x & y & 1 \\ x_1 & y_1 & 1 \\ x_2 & y_2 & 1 \end{vmatrix} = 0$$

represents the equation of a straight line through the points (x_1, y_1) and (x_2, y_2).

46. Use the results in Problem 45 to find the equation of the line through $(3, -1)$ and $(-2, 5)$.

47. Show that
$$\begin{vmatrix} 1 & a & a^2 \\ 1 & b & b^2 \\ 1 & c & c^2 \end{vmatrix} = (b - c)(c - a)(a - b).$$

48. Show that
$$\begin{vmatrix} a_{11} & a_{12} & a_{13} & a_{14} \\ a_{21} & a_{22} & a_{23} & a_{24} \\ 0 & 0 & a_{33} & a_{34} \\ 0 & 0 & a_{43} & a_{44} \end{vmatrix} = \begin{vmatrix} a_{11} & a_{12} \\ a_{22} & a_{23} \end{vmatrix} \cdot \begin{vmatrix} a_{33} & a_{34} \\ a_{43} & a_{44} \end{vmatrix}.$$

9.5　THE INVERSE OF A SQUARE MATRIX

In the field of real numbers, every element a except 0 has a multiplicative inverse $1/a$ with the property that $a \cdot 1/a = 1$. The question should (and does) arise, "Does every square matrix A have a multiplicative inverse A^{-1} such that $AA^{-1} = A^{-1}A = I$?" Here A^{-1} (read "A inverse") is used rather than $1/A$, and I is the multiplicative identity matrix of the same order as A:

$$I = \begin{bmatrix} 1 & 0 & \cdots & 0 \\ 0 & 1 & \cdots & 0 \\ \vdots & \vdots & & \vdots \\ 0 & 0 & \cdots & 1 \end{bmatrix}.$$

We shall begin by considering the simple case of 2×2 matrices. If we let

$$A = \begin{bmatrix} a_{11} & a_{12} \\ a_{21} & a_{22} \end{bmatrix},$$

then we must see whether there exists a 2×2 matrix A^{-1} such that $AA^{-1} = I$. If so, let $A^{-1} = \begin{bmatrix} b & c \\ d & e \end{bmatrix}$. We wish to have

$$\begin{bmatrix} a_{11} & a_{12} \\ a_{21} & a_{22} \end{bmatrix}\begin{bmatrix} b & c \\ d & e \end{bmatrix} = \begin{bmatrix} 1 & 0 \\ 0 & 1 \end{bmatrix}.$$

This leads to

$$\begin{bmatrix} a_{11}b + a_{12}d & a_{11}c + a_{12}e \\ a_{21}b + a_{22}d & a_{21}c + a_{22}e \end{bmatrix} = \begin{bmatrix} 1 & 0 \\ 0 & 1 \end{bmatrix},$$

which is true if and only if

$$a_{11}b + a_{12}d = 1, \quad a_{11}c + a_{12}e = 0,$$
$$a_{21}b + a_{22}d = 0, \quad a_{21}c + a_{22}e = 1.$$

Solving these equations for b, c, d, and e, we have

$$(a_{11}a_{22} - a_{12}a_{21})b = a_{22}, \qquad (a_{11}a_{22} - a_{12}a_{21})c = -a_{12},$$

$$(a_{11}a_{22} - a_{12}a_{21})d = -a_{21}, \qquad (a_{11}a_{22} - a_{12}a_{21})e = a_{11}, \tag{1}$$

from which

$$b = \frac{a_{22}}{a_{11}a_{22} - a_{12}a_{21}}, \qquad c = \frac{-a_{12}}{a_{11}a_{22} - a_{12}a_{21}},$$

$$d = \frac{-a_{21}}{a_{11}a_{22} - a_{12}a_{21}}, \qquad e = \frac{a_{11}}{a_{11}a_{22} - a_{12}a_{21}},$$

provided $a_{11}a_{22} - a_{21}a_{12} \neq 0$. Now the denominator of each of these fractions is just $\delta(A)$, so that

$$A^{-1} = \begin{bmatrix} \dfrac{a_{22}}{\delta(A)} & \dfrac{-a_{12}}{\delta(A)} \\[2mm] \dfrac{-a_{21}}{\delta(A)} & \dfrac{a_{11}}{\delta(A)} \end{bmatrix} = \frac{1}{\delta(A)} \begin{bmatrix} a_{22} & -a_{12} \\ -a_{21} & a_{11} \end{bmatrix}.$$

By direct multiplication, it can be verified not only that

$$AA^{-1} = I,$$

but also (surprisingly, since matrix multiplication is not always commutative) that

$$A^{-1}A = I.$$

Thus, to write the inverse of a 2×2 square matrix A for which $\delta(A) \neq 0$, we may interchange the entries on the principal diagonal, replace each of the other two entries with its negative, and multiply the result by $1/\delta(A)$.

Example. If $A = \begin{bmatrix} 1 & 3 \\ 2 & -1 \end{bmatrix}$ find A^{-1}.

Solution. We first observe that $\delta(A) = -7$. Hence,

$$A^{-1} = -\frac{1}{7} \begin{bmatrix} -1 & -3 \\ -2 & 1 \end{bmatrix} = \begin{bmatrix} \dfrac{1}{7} & \dfrac{3}{7} \\[2mm] \dfrac{2}{7} & -\dfrac{1}{7} \end{bmatrix}.$$

It is a good idea always to check the result when finding A^{-1}, because there is much room for blundering in the process of determining the inverse. In the present example, we have

$$A^{-1}A = -\frac{1}{7} \begin{bmatrix} -1 & -3 \\ -2 & 1 \end{bmatrix} \begin{bmatrix} 1 & 3 \\ 2 & -1 \end{bmatrix} = -\frac{1}{7} \begin{bmatrix} -7 & 0 \\ 0 & -7 \end{bmatrix} = \begin{bmatrix} 1 & 0 \\ 0 & 1 \end{bmatrix}.$$

Moreover, from the above analysis we can now answer the question, "Does every 2×2 square matrix A have an inverse?" The answer is no, for if $\delta(A)$ is 0, then the foregoing equations for a, b, c, d would have no solution. Indeed, if $\delta(A) = 0$ and A had an inverse, then the equations (1) show that we would have $a_{11} = a_{12} = a_{21} = a_{22} = 0$, or $A = \mathbf{0}$. But then we would have

$$\begin{bmatrix} 0 & 0 \\ 0 & 0 \end{bmatrix} \begin{bmatrix} b & c \\ d & e \end{bmatrix} = \begin{bmatrix} 0 & 0 \\ 0 & 0 \end{bmatrix}, \quad \text{not} \quad \begin{bmatrix} 1 & 0 \\ 0 & 1 \end{bmatrix}.$$

For example, if

$$A = \begin{bmatrix} 0 & 0 \\ 0 & 1 \end{bmatrix},$$

then the equation

$$\begin{bmatrix} 0 & 0 \\ 0 & 1 \end{bmatrix} \begin{bmatrix} b & c \\ d & e \end{bmatrix} = \begin{bmatrix} 1 & 0 \\ 0 & 1 \end{bmatrix}$$

leads to

$$\begin{bmatrix} 0 & 0 \\ d & e \end{bmatrix} = \begin{bmatrix} 1 & 0 \\ 0 & 1 \end{bmatrix},$$

an impossibility since $0 \neq 1$. Square matrices A for which $\delta(A) = 0$ are called **singular matrices**.

Example. Show that $\begin{bmatrix} 3 & 5 \\ 6 & 10 \end{bmatrix}$ is singular, and hence has no inverse.

Solution. Since $\delta(A) = 3(10) - 6(5) = 0$, no inverse exists.

More generally, and without proving it, we have the following.

THEOREM 9.14 *If*

$$A = \begin{bmatrix} a_{11} & a_{12} & \cdots & a_{1n} \\ a_{21} & a_{22} & \cdots & a_{2n} \\ \vdots & \vdots & & \vdots \\ a_{n1} & a_{n2} & \cdots & a_{nn} \end{bmatrix}$$

and if $\delta(A) \neq 0$*, then*

$$A^{-1} = \frac{1}{\delta(A)} \begin{bmatrix} A_{11} & A_{21} & \cdots & A_{n1} \\ A_{12} & A_{22} & \cdots & A_{n2} \\ \vdots & \vdots & & \vdots \\ A_{1n} & A_{2n} & \cdots & A_{nn} \end{bmatrix},$$

where A_{ij} *is the cofactor of* a_{ij} *in* A*. If* $\delta(A) = 0$*, then* A *has no inverse.*

Observe that A^{-1} is the matrix having as its entries the cofactors of the entries in A multiplied by $1/\delta(A)$, but that the cofactors of the *row* entries in A are the *column* entries in A^{-1}. One way to obtain A^{-1} is to replace each entry in A with its cofactor, and multiply the *transpose* of the resulting matrix by $1/\delta(A)$.

Example. If $A = \begin{bmatrix} 1 & 0 & 1 \\ 2 & 1 & 0 \\ 1 & -1 & 1 \end{bmatrix}$, find A^{-1}.

Solution. We first observe that $\delta(A) = -2$, and since $\delta(A)$ is not zero, A has an inverse. Next, replacing each entry in A with its cofactor, we obtain the matrix

$$\begin{bmatrix} 1 & -2 & -3 \\ -1 & 0 & 1 \\ -1 & 2 & 1 \end{bmatrix},$$

of which the transpose is

$$\begin{bmatrix} 1 & -1 & -1 \\ -2 & 0 & 2 \\ -3 & 1 & 1 \end{bmatrix},$$

so that

$$A^{-1} = -\frac{1}{2} \begin{bmatrix} 1 & -1 & -1 \\ -2 & 0 & 2 \\ -3 & 1 & 1 \end{bmatrix}.$$

As a check, we have

$$A^{-1}A = -\frac{1}{2} \begin{bmatrix} 1 & -1 & -1 \\ -2 & 0 & 2 \\ -3 & 1 & 1 \end{bmatrix} \begin{bmatrix} 1 & 0 & 1 \\ 2 & 1 & 0 \\ 1 & -1 & 1 \end{bmatrix}$$

$$= -\frac{1}{2} \begin{bmatrix} -2 & 0 & 0 \\ 0 & -2 & 0 \\ 0 & 0 & -2 \end{bmatrix} = \begin{bmatrix} 1 & 0 & 0 \\ 0 & 1 & 0 \\ 0 & 0 & 1 \end{bmatrix}.$$

Theorem 9.14 is applicable to $n \times n$ square matrices, although, clearly, the process of actually determining A^{-1} becomes very laborious for matrices much larger than 3×3.

There are a number of useful properties associated with matrices and their inverses. For example, we have the following.

THEOREM 9.15 *If A and B are $n \times n$ nonsingular square matrices, then AB has an inverse, namely*

$$(AB)^{-1} = B^{-1}A^{-1}.$$

Proof.   If we right-multiply AB by $B^{-1}A^{-1}$, we have

$$AB \cdot B^{-1}A^{-1} = A \cdot I \cdot A^{-1} = A \cdot A^{-1} = I.$$

Moreover, if we left-multiply AB by $B^{-1}A^{-1}$, we have

$$B^{-1}A^{-1} \cdot AB = B^{-1} \cdot I \cdot B = B^{-1} \cdot B = I.$$

Thus, since $(AB)(B^{-1}A^{-1}) = (B^{-1}A^{-1})(AB) = I$, by the definition of the inverse of a matrix, we have

$$(AB)^{-1} = B^{-1}A^{-1}.$$

This theorem can be used to find the inverse of products of any number of nonsingular matrices.   For example, if there are three factors A, B, and C in a product, then

$$(ABC)^{-1} = [(AB)C]^{-1} = C^{-1}(AB)^{-1} = C^{-1}B^{-1}A^{-1}.$$

EXERCISE 9.5

Find the inverse of each matrix if the inverse exists.

Example.

$$B = \begin{bmatrix} 1 & 0 & -1 \\ 1 & 3 & 1 \\ 0 & 1 & 2 \end{bmatrix}$$

Solution.

$$\delta \begin{bmatrix} 1 & 0 & -1 \\ 1 & 3 & 1 \\ 0 & 1 & 2 \end{bmatrix} = 1(5) - 0 - 1(1) = 4$$

Replacing each entry of B with its cofactor gives

$$\begin{bmatrix} 5 & -2 & 1 \\ -1 & 2 & -1 \\ 3 & -2 & 3 \end{bmatrix}; \quad \begin{bmatrix} 5 & -2 & 1 \\ -1 & 2 & -1 \\ 3 & -2 & 3 \end{bmatrix}^t = \begin{bmatrix} 5 & -1 & 3 \\ -2 & 2 & -2 \\ 1 & -1 & 3 \end{bmatrix}$$

$$B^{-1} = \frac{1}{\delta(B)} \begin{bmatrix} \text{each } a_{ij} \text{ of} \\ B \text{ replaced} \\ \text{by } A_{ij} \end{bmatrix}^t = \frac{1}{4} \begin{bmatrix} 5 & -1 & -3 \\ -2 & 2 & -2 \\ 1 & -1 & 3 \end{bmatrix} = \begin{bmatrix} \frac{5}{4} & -\frac{1}{4} & \frac{3}{4} \\ -\frac{2}{4} & \frac{2}{4} & -\frac{2}{4} \\ \frac{1}{4} & -\frac{1}{4} & \frac{3}{4} \end{bmatrix}$$

1. $\begin{bmatrix} 1 & 2 \\ 1 & 3 \end{bmatrix}$

2. $\begin{bmatrix} 3 & 1 \\ 2 & -1 \end{bmatrix}$

3. $\begin{bmatrix} 2 & -3 \\ 1 & 1 \end{bmatrix}$

4. $\begin{bmatrix} 3 & -2 \\ 2 & 1 \end{bmatrix}$

5. $\begin{bmatrix} -2 & -1 \\ 4 & 2 \end{bmatrix}$

6. $\begin{bmatrix} 3 & 1 \\ 9 & 3 \end{bmatrix}$

7. $\begin{bmatrix} 1 & -1 & 2 \\ 2 & 1 & 3 \\ 0 & 0 & 2 \end{bmatrix}$ 8. $\begin{bmatrix} 0 & 4 & 2 \\ 1 & 0 & 2 \\ 0 & -1 & 1 \end{bmatrix}$ 9. $\begin{bmatrix} 2 & -1 & 1 \\ 3 & 0 & 1 \\ 2 & 2 & 1 \end{bmatrix}$

10. $\begin{bmatrix} 1 & 2 & 1 \\ 0 & 2 & 1 \\ -2 & 2 & 3 \end{bmatrix}$ 11. $\begin{bmatrix} 2 & 1 & 1 \\ 1 & 0 & 2 \\ 4 & 2 & 2 \end{bmatrix}$ 12. $\begin{bmatrix} -3 & 1 & -6 \\ 2 & 1 & 4 \\ 2 & 0 & 4 \end{bmatrix}$

13. Verify that

$$\left(\begin{bmatrix} 2 & 3 \\ 1 & -1 \end{bmatrix} \cdot \begin{bmatrix} 0 & 1 \\ 3 & 1 \end{bmatrix} \right)^{-1} = \begin{bmatrix} 0 & 1 \\ 3 & 1 \end{bmatrix}^{-1} \cdot \begin{bmatrix} 2 & 3 \\ 1 & -1 \end{bmatrix}^{-1}.$$

14. Verify that

$$\left(\begin{bmatrix} 1 & 2 \\ -1 & 0 \end{bmatrix} \cdot \begin{bmatrix} 1 & 1 \\ 2 & 0 \end{bmatrix} \cdot \begin{bmatrix} 2 & -1 \\ 0 & 1 \end{bmatrix} \right)^{-1} = \begin{bmatrix} 2 & -1 \\ 0 & 1 \end{bmatrix}^{-1} \cdot \begin{bmatrix} 1 & 1 \\ 2 & 0 \end{bmatrix}^{-1} \cdot \begin{bmatrix} 1 & 2 \\ -1 & 0 \end{bmatrix}^{-1}.$$

15. Verify that

$$\left(\begin{bmatrix} 3 & 0 & 1 \\ 2 & 1 & 0 \\ 0 & 1 & 2 \end{bmatrix} \cdot \begin{bmatrix} 2 & 1 & 0 \\ 1 & 1 & 2 \\ 0 & 1 & 0 \end{bmatrix} \right)^{-1} = \begin{bmatrix} 2 & 1 & 0 \\ 1 & 1 & 2 \\ 0 & 1 & 0 \end{bmatrix}^{-1} \cdot \begin{bmatrix} 3 & 0 & 1 \\ 2 & 1 & 0 \\ 0 & 1 & 2 \end{bmatrix}^{-1}.$$

16. Show that $[A^t]^{-1} = [A^{-1}]^t$ for any nonsingular 2×2 matrix.

17. Show that $\delta(A^{-1}) = 1/\delta(A)$ for any nonsingular 2×2 matrix.

18. Prove that $\delta(B^{-1}AB) = \delta(A)$ for any nonsingular 2×2 matrices A and B.

19. Prove that if a and b are any real numbers, then $\delta(aA^2 + bA) = \delta(aA + bI)\delta(A)$ for all 2×2 matrices A.

20. Prove that if A is a 2×2 matrix and a and b are real numbers, and if $aA^2 + bA = \mathbf{0}$, then either A has no inverse, or else A is a **scalar matrix**, i.e., $a_{11} = a_{22}$ and $a_{12} = a_{21} = 0$.

21. Prove that if A is a 2×2 matrix and a, b, and c are real numbers with $c \neq 0$, and if $aA^2 + bA + cI = 0$, then A has an inverse.

22. Prove that if A and B are 2×2 matrices then $\delta(AB) = \delta(A) \cdot \delta(B)$.

23. Prove that the set of nonsingular 2×2 matrices is a noncommutative group with respect to matrix multiplication.

9.6 LINEAR SYSTEMS

Matrices offer a means of finding solutions for linear systems. We first verify the matrix-product equation

$$\begin{bmatrix} a_{11} & a_{12} & \cdots & a_{1n} \\ \vdots & \vdots & & \vdots \\ a_{n1} & a_{n2} & \cdots & a_{nn} \end{bmatrix} \begin{bmatrix} x_1 \\ \vdots \\ x_n \end{bmatrix} = \begin{bmatrix} a_{11}x_1 + a_{12}x_2 + \cdots + a_{1n}x_n \\ \vdots & \vdots & \vdots \\ a_{n1}x_1 + a_{n2}x_2 + \cdots + a_{nn}x_n \end{bmatrix},$$

and hence note that the linear system

$$a_{11}x_1 + a_{12}x_2 + \cdots + a_{1n}x_n = c_1$$
$$a_{21}x_1 + a_{22}x_2 + \cdots + a_{2n}x_n = c_2$$
$$\vdots \qquad \vdots \qquad \qquad \vdots \qquad \vdots$$
$$a_{n1}x_1 + a_{n2}x_2 + \cdots + a_{nn}x_n = c_n$$

can be written as the matrix equation

$$\begin{bmatrix} a_{11} & a_{12} & \cdots & a_{1n} \\ \vdots & \vdots & & \vdots \\ a_{n1} & a_{n2} & \cdots & a_{nn} \end{bmatrix} \begin{bmatrix} x_1 \\ \vdots \\ x_n \end{bmatrix} = \begin{bmatrix} c_1 \\ \vdots \\ c_n \end{bmatrix},$$

where the first factor in the left-hand member is called the **coefficient matrix** for the system. In more concise notation, this latter equation can be written

$$AX = B,$$

where A is an $n \times n$ square matrix, and X and B are $n \times 1$ column matrices. If now A is nonsingular, we can left-multiply both members of this equation by A^{-1} to obtain

$$A^{-1}AX = A^{-1}B,$$

$$IX = A^{-1}B,$$

$$X = A^{-1}B,$$

where $A^{-1}B$ is an $n \times 1$ column matrix. Since X and $A^{-1}B$ are equal, each entry in X is equal to the corresponding entry in $A^{-1}B$, and hence these latter entries constitute the components of the solution of the given linear system. If A is a singular matrix, then of course it has no inverse, and either the system has no solution or the solution is not unique.

Example. Use matrices to find the solution set of

$$2x + y + z = 1$$
$$x - 2y - 3z = 1$$
$$3x + 2y + 4z = 5.$$

Solution. We first write this as a matrix equation of the form $AX = B$, thus:

$$\begin{bmatrix} 2 & 1 & 1 \\ 1 & -2 & -3 \\ 3 & 2 & 4 \end{bmatrix} \begin{bmatrix} x \\ y \\ z \end{bmatrix} = \begin{bmatrix} 1 \\ 1 \\ 5 \end{bmatrix}.$$

We next determine $\delta(A)$, obtaining

$$\delta \begin{bmatrix} 2 & 1 & 1 \\ 1 & -2 & -3 \\ 3 & 2 & 4 \end{bmatrix} = 2(-2) - 1(13) + 1(8) = -9,$$

observe that A is nonsingular, and then find A^{-1}:

$$A^{-1} = \begin{bmatrix} 2 & 1 & 1 \\ 1 & -2 & -3 \\ 3 & 2 & 4 \end{bmatrix}^{-1} = -\frac{1}{9} \begin{bmatrix} -2 & -2 & -1 \\ -13 & 5 & 7 \\ 8 & -1 & -5 \end{bmatrix}.$$

As a matter of routine, we check the latter by verifying that $A^{-1}A = I$:

$$A^{-1}A = -\frac{1}{9} \begin{bmatrix} -2 & -2 & -1 \\ -13 & 5 & 7 \\ 8 & -1 & -5 \end{bmatrix} \begin{bmatrix} 2 & 1 & 1 \\ 1 & -2 & -3 \\ 3 & 2 & 4 \end{bmatrix} = -\frac{1}{9} \begin{bmatrix} -9 & 0 & 0 \\ 0 & -9 & 0 \\ 0 & 0 & -9 \end{bmatrix}$$

$$= \begin{bmatrix} 1 & 0 & 0 \\ 0 & 1 & 0 \\ 0 & 0 & 1 \end{bmatrix}.$$

Now, since $X = A^{-1}B$, we have

$$\begin{bmatrix} x \\ y \\ z \end{bmatrix} = -\frac{1}{9} \begin{bmatrix} -2 & -2 & -1 \\ -13 & 5 & 7 \\ 8 & -1 & -5 \end{bmatrix} \begin{bmatrix} 1 \\ 1 \\ 5 \end{bmatrix} = -\frac{1}{9} \begin{bmatrix} -9 \\ 27 \\ -18 \end{bmatrix} = \begin{bmatrix} 1 \\ -3 \\ 2 \end{bmatrix}.$$

Since

$$\begin{bmatrix} x \\ y \\ z \end{bmatrix} = \begin{bmatrix} 1 \\ -3 \\ 2 \end{bmatrix},$$

we have $x = 1$, $y = -3$, and $z = 2$, and the solution set of the system is $\{(1, -3, 2)\}$.

The computation of A^{-1} is laborious when A is a square matrix containing many rows and columns. The foregoing method is not always the easiest to use in determining an inverse, particularly when an electronic digital computer is available, but it is most valuable for theoretical developments.

Matrices are becoming of increasing importance in modern mathematics, in the physical and social sciences, and in industry.

EXERCISE 9.6

Find the solution set of the given system by means of matrices. If the system is inconsistent, so state.

1. $2x - 3y = -1$
   $x + 4y = 5$

2. $3x - 4y = -2$
   $x - 2y = 0$

3. $3x - 4y = -2$
   $6x + 12y = 36$

4. $2x - 4y = 7$
   $x - 2y = 1$

5. $2x - 3y = 0$
   $2x + y = 16$

6. $2x + 3y = 3$
   $3x - 4y = 0$

7. $x + y = 2$
   $2x - z = 1$
   $2y - 3z = -1$

8. $2x - 6y + 3z = -12$
   $3x - 2y + 5z = -4$
   $4x + 5y - 2z = 10$

9. $x - 2y + z = -1$
   $3x + y - 2z = 4$
   $y - z = 1$

10. $2x + 5z = 9$
    $4x + 3y = -1$
    $3y - 4z = -13$

11. $2x + 2y + z = 1$
    $x - y + 6z = 21$
    $3x + 2y - z = -4$

12. $4x + 8y + z = -6$
    $2x - 3y + 2z = 0$
    $x + 7y - 3z = -8$

13. $x + y + z = 0$
    $2x - y - 4z = 15$
    $x - 2y - z = 7$

14. $x + y - 2z = 3$
    $3x - y + z = 5$
    $3x + 3y - 6z = 9$

9.7   CRAMER'S RULE

If the technique for solving linear systems discussed in the preceding section is viewed in terms of determinants, we arrive at a general solution for such systems.   This, however, is of more theoretical than computational value.

If the coefficient matrix A in the matrix equation $AX = B$ is nonsingular, then its inverse, A^{-1}, is

$$A^{-1} = \frac{1}{\delta(A)} \begin{bmatrix} A_{11} & A_{21} & \cdots & A_{n1} \\ \vdots & \vdots & & \vdots \\ A_{1n} & A_{2n} & \cdots & A_{nn} \end{bmatrix}.$$

Now, let $B = \begin{bmatrix} c_1 \\ c_2 \\ \vdots \\ c_n \end{bmatrix}$, so that

$$A^{-1}B = \frac{1}{\delta(A)} \begin{bmatrix} c_1 A_{11} + c_2 A_{21} + \cdots + c_n A_{n1} \\ c_1 A_{12} + c_2 A_{22} + \cdots + c_n A_{n2} \\ \vdots \qquad \vdots \qquad \qquad \vdots \\ c_1 A_{1n} + c_2 A_{2n} + \cdots + c_n A_{nn} \end{bmatrix}.$$

Each entry in $A^{-1}B$ can be seen to be of the form

$$\frac{c_1 A_{1j} + c_2 A_{2j} + \cdots + c_n A_{nj}}{\delta(A)}.$$

But $c_1 A_{1j} + c_2 A_{2j} + \cdots + c_n A_{nj}$ is just the expansion of the determinant

$$\begin{matrix} & & & j\text{th} & & \\ & & & \text{column} & & \\ & & & \downarrow & & \end{matrix}$$

$$\begin{vmatrix} a_{11} & a_{12} & \cdots & c_1 & \cdots & a_{1n} \\ a_{21} & a_{22} & \cdots & c_2 & \cdots & a_{2n} \\ \vdots & \vdots & & \vdots & & \vdots \\ a_{n1} & a_{n2} & \cdots & c_n & \cdots & a_{nn} \end{vmatrix}$$

about the jth column, which has entries $c_1, c_2, c_3, \cdots c_n$. Thus, if the variables in a linear system are denoted by $x_1, x_2, \cdots x_n$, then each entry x_j in A^{-1} is given by

$$x_j = \frac{\begin{vmatrix} a_{11} & a_{12} & \cdots & c_1 & \cdots & a_{1n} \\ a_{21} & a_{22} & \cdots & c_2 & \cdots & a_{2n} \\ \vdots & \vdots & & \vdots & & \vdots \\ a_{n1} & a_{n2} & \cdots & c_n & \cdots & a_{nn} \end{vmatrix}}{\begin{vmatrix} a_{11} & a_{12} & & \cdots & & a_{1n} \\ a_{21} & a_{22} & & \cdots & & a_{2n} \\ \vdots & \vdots & & & & \vdots \\ a_{n1} & a_{n2} & & \cdots & & a_{nn} \end{vmatrix}},$$

$$\overset{j\text{th}}{\underset{\text{column}}{\downarrow}}$$

which can be written $x_j = \delta(A_j)/\delta(A)$ and is called **Cramer's rule**.

Cramer's rule asserts that if the determinant of the coefficient matrix of an $n \times n$ linear system *is not* 0, then the solution can be found for each variable in the system as follows.

To find x_j:

1. Write the determinant of the coefficient matrix for the system.

2. Replace each entry in the jth column of the coefficient matrix A with the corresponding entry from the column matrix B, and find the determinant of the resulting matrix.

3. Divide the result in Step 2 by the result in Step 1.

Example. Use Cramer's rule to solve the system

$$-4x + 2y - 9z = 2$$
$$3x + 4y + z = 5$$
$$x - 3y + 2z = 8.$$

Solution. By inspection,

$$A = \begin{bmatrix} -4 & 2 & -9 \\ 3 & 4 & 1 \\ 1 & -3 & 2 \end{bmatrix},$$

so that

$$\delta(A) = -4(11) - 2(5) - 9(-13) = -44 - 10 + 117 = 63.$$

Replacing the entries in the first column of A with corresponding constants 2, 5, and 8, we have

$$A_x = \begin{bmatrix} 2 & 2 & -9 \\ 5 & 4 & 1 \\ 8 & -3 & 2 \end{bmatrix}$$

and

$$\delta(A_x) = 2(11) - 2(2) - 9(-47) = 22 - 4 + 423 = 441.$$

Hence

$$x = \frac{\delta(A_x)}{\delta(A)} = \frac{441}{63} = 7.$$

Similarly, by replacing, in turn, the entries of the second and third columns of A with the corresponding constants 2, 5, and 8, we have

$$A_y = \begin{bmatrix} -4 & 2 & -9 \\ 3 & 5 & 1 \\ 1 & 8 & 2 \end{bmatrix} \quad \text{and} \quad A_z = \begin{bmatrix} -4 & 2 & 2 \\ 3 & 4 & 5 \\ 1 & -3 & 8 \end{bmatrix}.$$

Now,

$$\delta(A_y) = -4(2) - 2(5) - 9(19) = -8 - 10 - 171 = -189$$

and

$$\delta(A_z) = -4(47) - 2(19) + 2(-13) = -188 - 38 - 26 = -252,$$

so that

$$y = \frac{\delta(A_y)}{\delta(A)} = \frac{-189}{63} = -3$$

and

$$z = \frac{\delta(A_z)}{\delta(A)} = \frac{-252}{63} = -4,$$

and the solution set of the system is $\{(7, -3, -4)\}$.

If $\delta(A) = 0$ for a linear system, then the system either has infinitely many members in its solution set (contains linearly dependent left-hand members) or has an empty solution set (contains inconsistent equations). The distinction can be determined as follows: Consider the matrix of coefficients

$$\begin{bmatrix} a_{11} & \cdots & a_{1n} \\ \vdots & & \vdots \\ a_{n1} & \cdots & a_{nn} \end{bmatrix}$$

and the **augmented matrix**

$$\begin{bmatrix} a_{11} & \cdots & a_{1n} & c_1 \\ \vdots & & \vdots & \vdots \\ a_{n1} & \cdots & a_{nn} & c_n \end{bmatrix},$$

and in each find as large a determinant (obtained by striking out certain rows and columns) as possible that is different from 0. The order of such a nonvanishing determinant is called the **rank** of the matrix. The rank of the augmented matrix is either the same as, or 1 greater than, that of the matrix of coefficients. The equations are consistent if and only if the two ranks are the same.

For example, the coefficient matrix of the system

$$x + 2y + 3z = 2$$
$$2x + 4y + 2z = -1$$
$$x + 2y - 2z = 5$$

is

$$C = \begin{bmatrix} 1 & 2 & 3 \\ 2 & 4 & 2 \\ 1 & 2 & -2 \end{bmatrix},$$

while the augmented matrix for the system is

$$C_A = \begin{bmatrix} 1 & 2 & 3 & 2 \\ 2 & 4 & 2 & -1 \\ 1 & 2 & -2 & 5 \end{bmatrix}.$$

Since $\delta(C) = 0$, the rank of C is not 3. If, however, the first column and third row are deleted, the remaining determinant

$$\begin{vmatrix} 2 & 3 \\ 4 & 2 \end{vmatrix}$$

is not zero, so C has rank 2.

Now, if the first column of C_A is deleted, the remaining entries form the determinant

$$\delta \begin{bmatrix} 2 & 3 & 2 \\ 4 & 2 & -1 \\ 2 & -2 & 5 \end{bmatrix},$$

which is equal to -74. This means that C_A has rank 3. Therefore, the system of equations is inconsistent.

EXERCISE 9.7

Find the solution set of each of the following systems by Cramer's rule. If $\delta(A) = 0$ in any of the systems, use the ranks of the coefficient matrix and the augmented matrix to determine whether the system is consistent.

1. $x - y = 2$
   $x + 4y = 5$

2. $x + y = 4$
   $x - 2y = 0$

3. $3x - 4y = -2$
   $x + y = 6$

4. $2x - 4y = 7$
   $x - 2y = 1$

5. $\frac{1}{3}x - \frac{1}{2}y = 0$
   $\frac{1}{2}x + \frac{1}{4}y = 4$

6. $\frac{2}{3}x + y = 1$
   $x - \frac{4}{3}y = 0$

7. $x - 2y = 5$
   $\frac{2}{3}x - \frac{4}{3}y = 6$

8. $\frac{1}{2}x + y = 3$
   $-\frac{1}{4}x - y = -3$

9. $x - 3y = 1$
   $y = 1$

10. $2x - 3y = 12$
    $x = 4$

11. $ax + by = 1$
    $bx + ay = 1$

12. $x + y = a$
    $x - y = b$

13. $x - 2y + z = -1$
    $3x + y - 2z = 4$
    $y - z = 1$

14. $2x + 5z = 9$
    $4x + 3y = -1$
    $3y - 4z = -13$

15. $2x + 2y + z = 1$
    $x - y + 6z = 21$
    $3x + 2y - z = -4$

16. $4x + 8y + z = -6$
    $2x - 3y + 2z = 0$
    $x + 7y - 3z = -8$

17. $x + y + z = 0$
    $2x - y - 4z = 15$
    $x - 2y - z = 7$

18. $x + y - 2z = 2$
    $3x - y + z = 5$
    $3x + 3y - 6z = 6$

19. $x - 2y - 2z = 3$
    $2x - 4y + 4z = 1$
    $3x - 3y - 3z = 4$

20. $3x - 2y + 5z = 6$
    $4x - 4y + 3z = 0$
    $5x - 4y + z = -5$

21. $x - 4z = -1$
    $3x + 3y = 2$
    $3x + 4z = 5$

22. $2x - \frac{2}{3}y + z = 2$
    $\frac{1}{2}x - \frac{1}{3}y - \frac{1}{4}z = 0$
    $4x + 5y - 3z = -1$

23. $x + y + z = 0$
    $w + 2y - z = 4$
    $2w - y + 2z' = 3$
    $-2w + 2y - z = -2$

24. $x + y + z = 0$
    $x + z + w = 0$
    $x + y + w = 0$
    $y + z + w = 0$

25. Show that if both $\delta(A_y) = 0$ and $\delta(A_z) = 0$, and if c_1 and c_2 are not both 0, then $\delta(A) = 0$, and the equations in the system

$$a_1x + b_1y + c_1 = 0$$
$$a_2x + b_2y + c_2 = 0$$

are consistent. *Hint:* Show that the first two determinant equations imply that $a_1c_2 = a_2c_1$ and $b_1c_2 = b_2c_1$ and that the rest follows from the formation of a proportion with these equations.

26. Show that if $\delta(A) = 0$ and $\delta(A_z) = 0$, and if a_1 and a_2 are not both 0, then $\delta(A_y) = 0$, where $\delta(A)$ is the determinant of the coefficient matrix of the system in Problem 25.

COMPLEX
NUMBERS AND
VECTORS

10.1 DEFINITIONS AND THEIR CONSEQUENCES

In Chapter 1, we observed that the system of real numbers comprises a complete ordered field; that is, the behavior of the real numbers is governed not only by the field postulates F-1 through F-11, but also by the order postulates O-1 through O-3.

We wish now to consider another number system which, though subject to the field postulates, is not subject to the order postulates. The numbers in the system consist of all ordered pairs of real numbers (a, b). For the moment, we shall not relate these numbers to anything in particular, except that, as you know, there is a one-to-one correspondence between such ordered pairs and the points in the geometric plane. We shall, in general, use z to denote an ordered pair of real numbers (a, b), and C to denote the set of all such numbers.

Let us begin with some definitions.

DEFINITION 10.1 $C = R \times R = \{(a, b) \mid a \in R \text{ and } b \in R\}$.

This simply establishes the set of numbers with which we shall be working.

DEFINITION 10.2 *Let* $z_1 = (a_1, b_1) \in C$ *and* $z_2 = (a_2, b_2) \in C$. *Then* $z_1 = z_2$ *if and only if* $a_1 = a_2$ *and* $b_1 = b_2$.

This gives meaning to equality in C. Since the equality postulates E-1 through E-4 hold in the set R of real numbers, it follows from Definition 10.2 that they hold also in the set C. Formal verification is left as an exercise.

DEFINITION 10.3   *If* $z_1 = (a_1, b_1) \in C$ *and* $z_2 = (a_2, b_2) \in C$, *then*

a. $z_1 + z_2 = (a_1, b_1) + (a_2, b_2) = (a_1 + a_2, b_1 + b_2)$,

b. $z_1 z_2 = (a_1, b_1) \cdot (a_2, b_2) = (a_1 a_2 - b_1 b_2, a_1 b_2 + a_2 b_1)$.

This establishes two operations, addition and multiplication, for the numbers in our set.

Example.   Write $(3, 5) + (7, 9)$ as an ordered pair (a, b).

Solution.   By definition,

$$(3, 5) + (7, 9) = (3 + 7, 5 + 9) = (10, 14).$$

Example.   Write $(3, 5) \cdot (7, 9)$ as an ordered pair (a, b).

Solution.   By definition,

$$(3, 5) \cdot (7, 9) = (3 \cdot 7 - 5 \cdot 9, 3 \cdot 9 + 7 \cdot 5)$$
$$= (21 - 45, 27 + 35)$$
$$= (-24, 62).$$

Relative to the operations of addition and multiplication as thus defined, we can now prove that the set C constitutes a field.   The proof is divided into several stages to furnish a review of some of the mathematical structures we have studied earlier in this book.

THEOREM 10.1   *The set C is a group with respect to the operation of addition.*

To prove this theorem, we must establish the following properties:

F-1   If $z_1 \in C$ and $z_2 \in C$, then $z_1 + z_2 \in C$.   *Closure for addition.*

F-2   If $z_1 \in C$, $z_2 \in C$, and $z_3 \in C$, then   *Associativity for addition.*
$z_1 + (z_2 + z_3) = (z_1 + z_2) + z_3$.

F-3   There exists $z_0 \in C$ such that $z + z_0 = $ *Identity element for addition.*
$z_0 + z = z$ for all z in C.

F-4   For each $z \in C$ there exists $-z \in C$ *Additive inverse element.*
such that $z + (-z) = (-z) + z = z_0$.

Proof of F-1.   Let $z_1 = (a_1, b_1)$ and $z_2 = (a_2, b_2)$.   By Definition 10.3-a, $z_1 + z_2 = (a_1, b_1) + (a_2, b_2) = (a_1 + a_2, b_1 + b_2)$, and since the operation of addition is closed in the field R of real numbers, we have $(a_1 + a_2) \in R$ and $(b_1 + b_2) \in R$.   Hence, by Definition 10.1, $(a_1 + a_2, b_1 + b_2) \in C$; that is, $z_1 + z_2 \in C$.

The proof of F-2 is left as an exercise. It depends on Definition 10.3-a and the fact that addition is associative in the field R of real numbers.

To give meaning to the expressions $z_1 + z_2 + z_3$ and $z_1 z_2 z_3$, let us agree to the following:

DEFINITION 10.4 *If $z_1 \in C$, $z_2 \in C$, and $z_3 \in C$, then*

$$z_1 + z_2 + z_3 = (z_1 + z_2) + z_3 \quad and \quad z_1 z_2 z_3 = (z_1 z_2) z_3.$$

This definition can be extended to cover $z_1 + z_2 + z_3 + z_4$, etc. According to Property F-2, it is immaterial whether $z_1 + z_2 + z_3$ is considered in accordance with Definition 6.4 or as $z_1 + (z_2 + z_3)$.

Proof of F-3. Let $z = (a, b)$ and consider the element $z_0 = (0, 0) \in C$. By Definition 10.3-a,

$$z + z_0 = (a, b) + (0, 0) = (a + 0, b + 0) = (a, b) = z,$$

and

$$z_0 + z = (0, 0) + (a, b) = (0 + a, 0 + b) = (a, b) = z.$$

Here, of course, we have used the fact that 0 is the identity element for addition in the field R of real numbers.

We say that $z_0 = (0, 0)$ is the **identity element for addition**, or the **zero element**, in the set C.

Proof of F-4. Let $z = (a, b)$ and consider the element $-z = (-a, -b) \in C$. We have

$$z + (-z) = (a, b) + (-a, -b) = [a + (-a), b + (-b)] = (0, 0),$$

and similarly

$$(-z) + z = (-a, -b) + (a, b) = [(-a) + a, (-b) + b] = (0, 0).$$

THEOREM 10.2 *The set C is a commutative group with respect to the operation of addition.*

To prove this theorem, we must show that, in addition to F-1 through F-4, the set C has the following property:

F-5   If $z_1 \in C$ and $z_2 \in C$, then $z_1 + z_2 = \qquad$ *Commutativity for addition.*
     $z_2 + z_1$.

The proof, which is left as an exercise, depends on Definition 10.3-a and the fact that the analogous property holds in the field R of real numbers.

THEOREM 10.3   *The set C is a commutative ring with identity.*

To prove that C is a ring, we must show that, in addition to F-1 through F-5, the set C has the following properties:

F-6   If $z_1 \in C$ and $z_2 \in C$, then $z_1 z_2 \in C$.   *Closure for multiplication.*

F-7   If $z_1 \in C$, $z_2 \in C$, and $z_3 \in C$, then   *Associativity for multiplica-*
$z_1(z_2 z_3) = (z_1 z_2)z_3$.   *tion.*

F-8   If $z_1 \in C$, $z_2 \in C$, and $z_3 \in C$, then   *Distributivity.*
$z_1(z_2 + z_3) = z_1 z_2 + z_1 z_3$ and
$(z_2 + z_3)z_1 = z_2 z_1 + z_3 z_1$.

To prove, further, that C is a ring with an identity, we must establish that C has this property:

F-9   There exists an element $z_I \in C$ such   *Identity element for multi-*
that $z z_I = z_I z = z$ for all $z \in C$.   *plication.*

To show, in addition, that C is a commutative ring, we must verify the following:

F-10   If $z_1 \in C$ and $z_2 \in C$, then $z_1 z_2 = z_2 z_1$.   *Commutativity for multipli-*
cation.

The proof of F-6 is analogous to that of F-1, with multiplication in place of addition.   It is left as an exercise, as is the proof of F-7.

For efficiency, let us prove F-10 before turning to F-8.

Proof of F-10.   Let $z_1 = (a_1, b_1)$ and $z_2 = (a_2, b_2)$; then by Definition 10.3-b,

$$z_1 z_2 = (a_1, b_1)(a_2, b_2) = (a_1 a_2 - b_1 b_2, a_1 b_2 + a_2 b_1)$$

and

$$z_2 z_1 = (a_2, b_2)(a_1, b_1) = (a_2 a_1 - b_2 b_1, a_2 b_1 + a_1 b_2).$$

But since multiplication and addition are commutative in the field R of real numbers, we have

$$a_1 a_2 - b_1 b_2 = a_2 a_1 - b_2 b_1 \quad \text{and} \quad a_1 b_2 + a_2 b_1 = a_2 b_1 + a_1 b_2,$$

from which

$$z_1 z_2 = z_2 z_1.$$

Since we now know that the commutative law holds for both addition and multiplication in C, we see that the validity of the second equation in F-8 follows from that of the first.   The proof of the first consists of writing each member as an ordered pair and showing that these ordered pairs are equal.   This is left as an exercise.

Proof of F-9.   Let $z = (a, b)$, and consider the element $z_I = (1, 0) \in C$.   We have

$$zz_I = (a, b)(1, 0) = (a \cdot 1 - b \cdot 0, a \cdot 0 + 1 \cdot b) = (a, b) = z.$$

Similarly

$$z_I z = (1, 0)(a, b) = (1 \cdot a - 0 \cdot b, 1 \cdot b + a \cdot 0) = (a, b) = z,$$

though this follows equally well from the former result together with F-10.

THEOREM 10.4   *The set C is a field.*

Just one of the field postulates remains to be verified for C:

F-11 For each $z \in C$ other than the zero   *Multiplicative inverse.*
      element $(0, 0)$, there exists $z^{-1} \in C$
      such that $zz^{-1} = z^{-1}z = (1, 0)$.

Proof of F-11.   Let $z = (a, b)$.   Since $a \in R$ and $b \in R$, and $(a, b) \neq (0, 0)$, we have $a^2 + b^2 \neq 0$.   Now consider the element

$$z^{-1} = \left(\frac{a}{a^2 + b^2}, \frac{-b}{a^2 + b^2} \right) \in C. \tag{1}$$

By direct computation, we obtain

$$zz^{-1} = (a, b)\left(\frac{a}{a^2 + b^2}, \frac{-b}{a^2 + b^2} \right) = \left(\frac{a^2 + b^2}{a^2 + b^2}, \frac{-ab + ab}{a^2 + b^2} \right) = (1, 0),$$

as desired.   By F-10,

$$z^{-1}z = (1, 0),$$

thus completing the proof of F-11.

You might wonder how the expression (1) entered the picture.   Actually, it can be found by solving the equation

$$(a, b)(x, y) = (1, 0)$$

for (x, y), a task that is left as an exercise.

Let us recapitulate.   We started with a set of ordered pairs of real numbers, defined equality and the operations of addition and multiplication on the elements of this set, and then, one-by-one, established as theorems the properties F-1 through F-11 that characterize a field.   Thus we have shown that the elements of $R \times R$, when viewed in this way, are elements of a field.

EXERCISE 10.1

Write each sum as an ordered pair (a, b).

1. $(3, 6) + (2, 1)$ 2. $(7, 1) + (3, -5)$

3. $(-6, -2) + (0, 1)$ 4. $(3, -2) + (-2, 0)$

5. $(0, 7) + (3, 0)$ 6. $(-2, -1) + (2, 1)$

7. $(2, 3) + (1, 1)$ 8. $(4, 5) + (0, 0)$

Write each product as an ordered pair (a, b).

9. $(1, 0) \cdot (2, 1)$ 10. $(2, 3) \cdot (4, 1)$

11. $(3, 1) \cdot (0, 2)$ 12. $(2, 2) \cdot (3, 4)$

13. $(-2, 1) \cdot (1, 3)$ 14. $(3, -2) \cdot (1, -1)$

15. $(0, 1) \cdot (1, 0)$ 16. $(3, 4) \cdot (1, 1)$

17. Write the sum $(a_1, 0) + (a_2, 0)$ as an ordered pair. Write the product $(a_1, 0) \cdot (a_2, 0)$ as an ordered pair.

18. Use Definition 10.2 to show that since the equality postulates E-1 through E-4 of Chapter 1 hold in the set R of real numbers, they hold also in the set C.

19. Make a chart showing F-1 through F-11 for the set R of real numbers compared with the corresponding properties of the set C of ordered pairs (a, b). We shall start the chart:

If $a, b \in R$ If $(a, b), (c, d) \in C$
F-1 $a + b \in R$ $(a, b) + (c, d) \in C$ *Closure for addition.*

Let $z_1, z_2, z_3 \in C$.

20. Show that $(z_1 + z_2) + z_3 = z_1 + (z_2 + z_3)$.

21. Show that $z_1 + z_2 = z_2 + z_1$.

22. Show that $z_1 z_2 \in C$.

23. Show that $(z_1 \cdot z_2) \cdot z_3 = z_1 \cdot (z_2 \cdot z_3)$.

24. Show that $z_1 \cdot (z_2 + z_3) = z_1 \cdot z_2 + z_1 \cdot z_3$.

25. Solve the equation $(a, b)(x, y) = (1, 0)$ for (x, y), given that $(a, b) \neq (0, 0)$.

26. Show that if $z_1 \cdot z_2 = (0, 0)$, then either $z_1 = (0, 0)$, $z_2 = (0, 0)$, or both.

27. Find conditions on $a, b, c,$ and d such that $(a, b) \cdot (c, d) = (k, 0)$, where $a, b, c, d, k \in R$.

10.2 SOME ALGEBRA OF ORDERED PAIRS

We can extend the work of the preceding section to explore a few of the properties of the field of ordered pairs in C. First, let us define two more operations, subtraction and division, for the field C, in terms of addition and multiplication, respectively.

DEFINITION 10.5 *If $z_1 \in C$ and $z_2 \in C$, then*

$$z_1 - z_2 = z_1 + (-z_2).$$

You will recall that if $z_2 = (a, b)$ then $-z_2 = (-a, -b)$. The number $z_1 - z_2$ is called the **difference** of z_1 and z_2, and is viewed as the result of **subtracting** z_2 from z_1.

DEFINITION 10.6 *If $z_1 \in C$ and $z_2 \in C$, and $z_2 \neq (0, 0)$, then*

$$\frac{z_1}{z_2} = z_1 \cdot z_2^{-1}.$$

You will recall that if $z_2 = (a, b)$, then

$$z_2^{-1} = \left(\frac{a}{a^2 + b^2}, \frac{-b}{a^2 + b^2} \right).$$

The number z_1/z_2 is called the **quotient** of z_1 and z_2, and is viewed as the result of **dividing** z_1 by z_2.

Examples. Write each difference and each quotient as an ordered pair.

a. $(2, 3) - (5, 6)$ b. $\dfrac{(2, 3)}{(5, 6)}$

Solutions.

a. $(2, 3) - (5, 6) = (2, 3) + (-5, -6) = (-3, -3)$.

b. $\dfrac{(2, 3)}{(5, 6)} = (2, 3)\left(\dfrac{5}{25 + 36}, \dfrac{-6}{25 + 36} \right)$

$= \left(\dfrac{2 \cdot 5 + 3 \cdot 6}{61}, \dfrac{-2 \cdot 6 + 5 \cdot 3}{61} \right) = \left(\dfrac{28}{61}, \dfrac{3}{61} \right)$.

It might be noted that the foregoing definitions of subtraction and division in the field C are analogous to the definitions given in Chapter 1 for subtraction and division in the field R of real numbers. Indeed, these definitions might be extended to *any* field, since in any field every element has an additive inverse, and every element other than the zero element has a multiplicative inverse.

We can now obtain a considerable advantage from our structural study of algebraic systems. In Section 1.5, many properties of the field R of real numbers were established. Since, however, the theorems stated there were derived exclusively from the field postulates along with the equality postulates, and did not otherwise depend on the fact that we were dealing with real numbers, it follows that the results are valid in any field—in particular, in the field C.

Thus, following the proofs of Theorems 1.1 and 1.2, we see that the addition law for equality and the multiplication law for equality extend to the field C. From Theorem 1.3 and Problem 24 of Exercise 1.5, we conclude that for $z \in C$, the additive inverse and [except for $z = (0, 0)$] the multiplicative inverse are unique.

Now look at the proof of Theorem 1.4, the cancellation law for addition in the field R of real numbers. None of the field postulates other than F-1 through F-4, that is, the group postulates, are involved in this proof! This shows that the cancellation law for addition holds not only in any field, in particular in C, but also that it holds in any group. This observation illustrates the advantage of keeping account of just which postulates are used in a proof, and indeed of avoiding the use of certain postulates if possible.

Theorem 1.5 shows that Property F-11 along with other field properties implies the validity of the cancellation law for multiplication. Accordingly, we have the following result in the field C:

F-11′ If $z_1 \in C$, $z_2 \in C$, and $z_3 \in C$, and if   *Cancellation law for multipli-*
    $z_1 z_2 = z_1 z_3$, with $z_1 \neq (0, 0)$, then   *cation.*
    $z_2 = z_3$.

In Chapter 2, we defined an integral domain as being a system satisfying Properties F-1 through F-10 and F-11′. Accordingly we can state, as a corollary of the fact that C is a field, that therefore C is an integral domain.

The remaining results of Section 1.5 also extend, of course, to the field C. There are, however, certain computational devices that are of special advantage in the field C. To illustrate, let us first state the analogue of Theorem 1.10, the fundamental principle of fractions, for elements of C.

THEOREM 10.5 *If z_1, z_2, and z_3 are elements of C, and z_2 and z_3 are not* $(0, 0)$, *then*

$$\frac{z_1}{z_2} = \frac{z_1 z_3}{z_2 z_3}.$$

To show an application of this theorem, let us adopt the following definition.

DEFINITION 10.7 *The **conjugate** of the number $z = (a, b) \in C$, denoted by $\bar{z}$, is $\bar{z} = (a, -b)$.*

Thus, the conjugate of $(2, 5)$ is $(2, -5)$, and if $z = (-2, -7)$, then $\bar{z} = (-2, 7)$.

Now, for $(c, d) \neq (0, 0)$, we can write the quotient $(a, b)/(c, d)$, which we already know is an element of C, as an ordered pair by multiplying the numerator and denominator of $(a, b)/(c, d)$ by the conjugate of the denominator, $(c, -d)$.

Example. Write the quotient $\dfrac{(3, -2)}{(5, 1)}$ as an ordered pair, first using Theorem 10.5 and then Definition 10.6.

Solution. $\dfrac{(3, -2)}{(5, 1)} = \dfrac{(3, -2)(5, -1)}{(5, 1)(5, -1)} = \dfrac{(15 - 2, -3 - 10)}{(25 + 1, 0)}$

$= (13, -13) \cdot \dfrac{1}{(26, 0)} = (13, -13)\left(\dfrac{26}{26^2}, 0\right)$

$= \left(\dfrac{13}{26}, \dfrac{-13}{26}\right) = \left(\dfrac{1}{2}, -\dfrac{1}{2}\right).$

EXERCISE 10.2

Write each difference as an ordered pair.

1. $(4, 2) - (1, 1)$

2. $(-3, 4) - (0, 5)$

3. $(-6, 1) - (3, 0)$

4. $(0, 1) - (6, 6)$

5. $(4, -4) - (-4, 4)$

6. $(0, 0) - (2, -3)$

Write each quotient as an ordered pair.   Use Definition 10.6.

7. $\dfrac{(4, 3)}{(2, 2)}$

8. $\dfrac{(6, 1)}{(1, 3)}$

9. $\dfrac{(2, 1)}{(-1, 3)}$

10. $\dfrac{(6, -3)}{(4, 1)}$

11. $\dfrac{(-2, -2)}{(1, 1)}$

12. $\dfrac{(0, 0)}{(3, 3)}$

13. Write the product $\dfrac{(4, 1)}{(1, 2)} \cdot \dfrac{(-1, 3)}{(6, 1)}$ as an ordered pair.

14. Write the product $\dfrac{(0, 1)}{(3, -1)} \cdot \dfrac{(2, 0)}{(2, 1)}$ as an ordered pair.

Write each quotient as an ordered pair by multiplying the numerator and denominator by the conjugate of the denominator.

15. $\dfrac{(4, 1)}{(-1, 2)}$

16. $\dfrac{(6, -1)}{(0, 4)}$

17. $\dfrac{(2, 3)}{(-1, -1)}$

18. $\dfrac{(0, 1)}{(2, -3)}$

19. $\dfrac{(4, -4)}{(2, -2)}$

20. $\dfrac{(0, 0)}{(-2, 3)}$

21. Show that $\dfrac{(a, b)}{(a, b)} = (1, 0)$ for every nonzero ordered pair (a, b).

22. Show that if z_1, z_2, and z_3 are elements of C, and z_2 and z_3 are not $(0, 0)$, then $\dfrac{z_1}{z_2} = \dfrac{z_1 z_3}{z_2 z_3}$.

23. Show that $\overline{z_1} + \overline{z_2} = \overline{z_1 + z_2}$.

24. Show that $\overline{z_1} \cdot \overline{z_2} = \overline{z_1 \cdot z_2}$.

25. Show that the set of ordered pairs of the form $(a, 0)$, $a \in R$, with the operations of addition and multiplication in C, constitutes a field. (Show that the field postulates are all satisfied in this set.)

26. Show that the set of ordered pairs of the form $(0, b)$, $b \in R$, with the operations of addition and multiplication in C, does not constitute a field. (Show that at least one of the field postulates is not satisfied in this set.)

27. The set of ordered pairs (a, b), where a and b are *integers* is an integral domain under the operations defined for ordered pairs in Section 10.1. Show that it is not a field.

10.3 COMPLEX NUMBERS

The ordered-pair number system we have been discussing can be related to the real-number system in an interesting and quite useful way. First, recall that, graphically, the set of ordered pairs of real numbers (a, b) is in one-to-one correspondence with the points in the geometric (x, y)-plane, just as the set R of real numbers a is in one-to-one correspondence with the points on the x-axis. Thus, the subset $\{(a, 0) \mid a \in R\}$ of C can be considered as corresponding in a one-to-one way to the set R. Moreover, from Definitions 10.3, 10.5, 10.6, and Equation (1) page 299, we have the following:

$$
\begin{aligned}
(a_1, 0) + (a_2, 0) &= (a_1 + a_2, 0), \\
(a_1, 0) \cdot (a_2, 0) &= (a_1 a_2, 0), \\
(a_1, 0) - (a_2, 0) &= (a_1 - a_2, 0), \\
\frac{(a_1, 0)}{(a_2, 0)} &= \left(\frac{a_1}{a_2}, 0\right).
\end{aligned}
\tag{1}
$$

The behavior exhibited under the four basic operations by the first components a of the numbers $(a, 0) \in C$, and by the numbers $a \in R$, is identical. Let us, then, identify $(a, 0)$ and a by means of the following.

DEFINITION 10.8 *The element* $(a, 0)$ *in the set* C *is identified with the element* a *in the set* R, *and we write*

$$
a = (a, 0).
$$

By virtue of the identical behavior under the basic operations, as exhibited in (1), this one-to-one correspondence is an isomorphism. It should be noted, of course, that a and $(a, 0)$ are actually *conceptually* different, but the identification is useful and should not be confusing. Under this convention, we consider that $R \subset C$.

Now, consider the subset of C consisting of all ordered pairs of the form $(0, b)$, with $b \neq 0$, $b \in R$. In particular, observe that if we square $(0, b)$, we obtain

$$(0, b)^2 = (0, b) \cdot (0, b) = (-b^2, 0).$$

Since we have agreed to identify $(-b^2, 0)$ with the real number $-b^2$, and since $b^2 > 0$ for every real number $b \neq 0$, we have $-b^2 < 0$ for every such number. Thus we see that the set C provides us with a square root, $(0, b)$, for each negative real number $-b^2$! Moreover, since

$$(0, -b)^2 = (0, -b) \cdot (0, -b) = (-b^2, 0),$$

C provides us with *two* such square roots. That is, $(0, b)$ and $(0, -b)$ are square roots of $(-b^2, 0)$, or $-b^2$. The square roots of nonnegative real numbers are in $\{(a, 0) \mid a \in R\}$, and those of negative real numbers are in $\{(0, b) \mid b \in R, b \neq 0\}$. As a special case, the square roots of $(-1, 0)$, or -1, are $(0, 1)$ and $(0, -1)$.

Let us adopt the following convention.

DEFINITION 10.9 *In the set C,*

$$i = (0, 1).$$

With this definition, and with the convention $b = (b, 0)$,

$$bi = (b, 0)(0, 1) = (0, b).$$

The numbers bi, with $b \in R$, $b \neq 0$, are the numbers that, in Chapter 1, we called pure imaginary.

In accordance with this definition we can extend our symbolism $\sqrt{b^2} = |b|$.

DEFINITION 10.10 *In the set C,*

$$\sqrt{-b^2} = |b|i.$$

In particular, $\sqrt{-1} = 1 \cdot i = i.$

Any ordered pair (a, b) can be represented by the sum $(a, 0) + (0, b)$, so that, in our new notation, for $a, b \in R$,

$$(a, b) = a + bi = a + b\sqrt{-1}.$$

When the foregoing viewpoint is taken of C, then C is called the set of **complex numbers**.

Definitions 10.2, 10.3, 10.5, and 10.6 can now be expressed using the form $a + bi$. Also, a consequence of Theorem 10.5 is shown in V.

DEFINITION 10.11   *If $a, b \in R$ and $i = \sqrt{-1}$,*

I $a_1 + b_1 i = a_2 + b_2 i$ *if and only if $a_1 = a_2$ and $b_1 = b_2$,*

II $(a_1 + b_1 i) + (a_2 + b_2 i) = (a_1 + a_2) + (b_1 + b_2)i$,

III $(a_1 + b_1 i) \cdot (a_2 + b_2 i) = (a_1 a_2 - b_1 b_2) + (a_1 b_2 + a_2 b_1)i$,

IV $(a_1 + b_1 i) - (a_2 + b_2 i) = (a_1 - a_2) + (b_1 - b_2)i$,

V $\dfrac{a_1 + b_1 i}{a_2 + b_2 i} = \dfrac{a_1 a_2 + b_1 b_2}{a_2^2 + b_2^2} + \dfrac{b_1 a_2 - a_1 b_2}{a_2^2 + b_2^2} i$ *(a_2, b_2 not both 0).*

Thus we may rewrite expressions involving complex numbers in the form $a + bi$ in the same way that we rewrote real polynomial expressions, except that i^2 is replaced with -1.

Examples.   Write each of the following in the form $a + bi$.

a. $(2 + 3i) + (6 - 2i)$ b. $(2 - i) \cdot (1 + 3i)$

c. $i - (2 + 3i)$ d. $\dfrac{4 - i}{1 + i}$

Solutions.

a. $(2 + 3i) + (6 - 2i) = (2 + 6) + (3 - 2)i = 8 + i$

b. $(2 - i)(1 + 3i) = 2 + 6i - i - 3i^2 = 5 + 5i$

c. $i - (2 + 3i) = (0 - 2) + (1 - 3)i = -2 - 2i$

d. $\dfrac{4 - i}{1 + i} = \dfrac{(4 - i)(1 - i)}{(1 + i)(1 - i)} = \dfrac{4 - 5i + i^2}{1 - i^2} = \dfrac{3}{2} - \dfrac{5}{2} i$ (See Theorem 10.5.)

Observe that, in example (d) above, Theorem 10.5 was applied, and both $4 - i$ and $1 + i$ were multiplied by $1 - i$, the conjugate of $1 + i$.

In accord with Definition 10.10, $\sqrt{-b} = i\sqrt{b}$. The symbol $\sqrt{-b}, b > 0$ should be used with care since certain relationships involving the square root symbol valid for real numbers are not valid when the symbol does not represent a real number.

For instance, if $\sqrt{a}$ and $\sqrt{b}$ are both real,

$$\sqrt{a} \, \sqrt{b} = \sqrt{ab}$$

and

$$\frac{\sqrt{a}}{\sqrt{b}} = \sqrt{\frac{a}{b}} \quad (b \neq 0);$$

but if $\sqrt{a}$ and $\sqrt{b}$ are both pure imaginaries,

$$\sqrt{a} \sqrt{b} = -\sqrt{ab},$$

though

$$\frac{\sqrt{a}}{\sqrt{b}} = \sqrt{\frac{a}{b}} \quad (b \neq 0).$$

Specifically,

$$\sqrt{2} \sqrt{3} = \sqrt{6}$$

but

$$\sqrt{-2} \sqrt{-3} = (i\sqrt{2})(i\sqrt{3}) = i^2\sqrt{6} = -\sqrt{6}.$$

To avoid difficulty with this point, all expressions of the form $\sqrt{-b}$ $(b > 0)$ should be rewritten in the form $i\sqrt{b}$ before attempting any additional manipulations.

Examples. Write each of the following in the form $a + bi$.

a. $3 + \sqrt{-5}$ b. $(2 + \sqrt{-3})(2 - \sqrt{-3})$ c. $\dfrac{1}{1 + \sqrt{-4}}$

Solutions.

a. $3 + \sqrt{-5} = 3 + \sqrt{5}i$

b. $(2 + \sqrt{-3})(2 - \sqrt{-3}) = (2 + \sqrt{3}i)(2 - \sqrt{3}i) = 4 - 3i^2 = 7$

c. $\dfrac{1}{1 + \sqrt{-4}} = \dfrac{1(1 - 2i)}{(1 + 2i)(1 - 2i)} = \dfrac{1 - 2i}{1 - 4i^2} = \dfrac{1}{5} - \dfrac{2}{5}i$

The "absolute value," or "modulus," of an ordered pair, $|(a, b)|$, is given by the following.

DEFINITION 10.12 *The* **absolute value,** *or* **modulus,** *of* (a, b) *is*

$$|(a, b)| = |a + bi| = \sqrt{a^2 + b^2}.$$

For the number $(a, 0)$ we have

$$|(a, 0)| = |a| = \sqrt{a^2},$$

so that the definition of $|(a, 0)|$ is consistent with that of $|a|$.

If $b = 0$, then (a, b) is a real complex number. If $a = 0$ and $b \neq 0$, then (a, b) is a pure imaginary complex number. The set $\{(0, b) \mid b \neq 0, b \in R\}$ is called the set of pure imaginary complex numbers, and

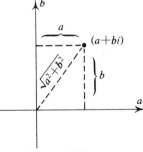

Figure 10.1

the members of this set can be associated with points other than the origin on the vertical axis in the plane. Thus, the graphical counterpart [or Argand plane as it is sometimes called, after the French mathematician Jean Robert Argand (1768–1822)] of the complex-number system appears as in Figure 10.1. The point with Cartesian coordinates (a, b) is given complex designation $a + bi$; for brevity, it is called the point (a, b), or the point $a + bi$.

Note that $|a + bi|$, defined as $\sqrt{a^2 + b^2}$, is the distance from the origin to the point $a + bi$.

EXERCISE 10.3

Write each ordered pair (complex number) in the form $a + bi$.

1. $(2, 6)$ 2. $(-3, 4)$ 3. $(5, -2)$

4. $(0, 6)$ 5. $(-7, -3)$ 6. $(-3, 2)$

7. $(4, 0)$ 8. $(0, 0)$

Write each complex number as an ordered pair.

9. $2 + 3i$ 10. $4 - 2i$ 11. $-3 + i$

12. $-6 - 3i$ 13. $4i$ 14. 0

15. 7 16. $-i$

17–24. Write the conjugate of each complex number in 9-16 in the form $a + bi$.

Find real numbers x and y for which the following are true.

Example. $(x - 2i)^2 = yi$

Solution. Write each member in the form $a + bi$.

$$x^2 - 4xi + 4i^2 = yi$$
$$(x^2 - 4) - 4xi = yi$$

For equality

$$x^2 - 4 = 0 \quad \text{and} \quad -4x = y.$$

Therefore, $x = 2$ or -2. If $x = 2$, then $y = -8$, and if $x = -2$, then $y = 8$. The desired real numbers are 2 and -8, and -2 and 8.

25. $2x - yi = 3 + 2i$ 26. $-2i = 3x + yi$

27. $4 + xi = x^2 - yi$ 28. $x + 9i = y + y^2i$

29. $(x + 3i)^2 = 2yi$ 30. $(x - 2i)^2 = 3x + yi$

Write each of the following in the form $a + bi$.

31. $(2 + 4i) + (3 + i)$ 32. $(4 - i) - (6 - 2i)$

33. $(2 - i) + (3 - 2i)$ 34. $(2 + i) - (4 - 2i)$

35. $3 - (4 + 2i)$ 36. $(2 - 6i) - 3$

37. $\dfrac{2}{1-i}$

38. $\dfrac{6}{3+2i}$

39. $\dfrac{2+i}{1-3i}$

40. $\dfrac{3-i}{2i}$

41. $(1-3i)^2$

42. $(2+i)^2$

43. $(1-i)^2(1+i)$

44. $(3-4i)^2(1-i)^2$

45. $4-\sqrt{-7}$

46. $2+\sqrt{-1}$

47. $5-\sqrt{-4}$

48. $\sqrt{-9}$

49. $(3-\sqrt{-1})(3+\sqrt{-1})$

50. $(2+\sqrt{-4})(3+\sqrt{-9})$

51. $\sqrt{-7}\,\sqrt{-1}$

52. $\sqrt{-4}\,\sqrt{-5}$

53. $\dfrac{2}{1+\sqrt{-1}}$

54. $\dfrac{3}{1-\sqrt{-4}}$

55. $\dfrac{2+\sqrt{-1}}{3-\sqrt{-4}}$

56. $\dfrac{\sqrt{-3}}{1-\sqrt{-7}}$

Write each of the following without absolute-value notation.

Examples.

a. $|-3|$

b. $|(-3, 2)|$

Solutions.

a. $|-3| = \sqrt{(-3)^2} = 3$

b. $|(-3, 2)| = \sqrt{(-3)^2 + (2)^2} = \sqrt{13}$

57. $|4|$ 58. $|-2|$ 59. $|(2, 0)|$ 60. $|(3, -5)|$

61. $|(-2, 1)|$ 62. $|(0, 3)|$ 63. $|(-2, -1)|$ 64. $|(-7, -1)|$

65. Show that $|z| = |\bar{z}|$.

66. Show that $|z_1 \cdot z_2| = |z_1| \cdot |z_2|$.

67. Prove that the sum and product of two conjugate complex numbers are both real.

68. Show that $|z_1 + z_2| \le |z_1| + |z_2|$.

69. Show that $|z_1 - z_2| \le |z_1| + |z_2|$.

70. Show that $\left|\dfrac{z_1}{z_2}\right| = \dfrac{|z_1|}{|z_2|}$ $(z_2 \ne 0 + 0i)$.

10.4 QUADRATIC EQUATIONS AND COMPLEX NUMBERS

In Chapter 4, we examined the general quadratic equation

$$ax^2 + bx + c = 0 \qquad (1)$$

for real numbers a, b, and c, with $a \ne 0$, and found any real solutions that exist. We saw that the discriminant, $b^2 - 4ac$, determines whether such solutions exist. If $b^2 - 4ac > 0$, then $ax^2 + bx + c = 0$ has two real solutions; if $b^2 - 4ac = 0$, there is one real solution; and if $b^2 - 4ac < 0$, then there are no real solutions.

With the field of complex numbers at our disposal, we can take a further look at the equation (1).

By the field properties, the solution set is still given by

$$\left\{ \frac{-b + \sqrt{b^2 - 4ac}}{2a}, \frac{-b - \sqrt{b^2 - 4ac}}{2a} \right\},$$

but it is no longer necessary to require $b^2 - 4ac \geq 0$ in order for a solution to exist.

Example. Find the solution set of $x^2 + x + 1 = 0$.

Solution. For substitution in the quadratic formula, we have $a = 1$, $b = 1$, and $c = 1$. Then

$$x = \frac{-1 \pm \sqrt{1^2 - 4(1)(1)}}{2(1)} = \frac{-1 \pm \sqrt{-3}}{2} = \frac{-1 \pm i\sqrt{3}}{2},$$

and the solution set is $\left\{ -\frac{1}{2} + \frac{\sqrt{3}}{2} i, -\frac{1}{2} - \frac{\sqrt{3}}{2} i \right\}$.

Every quadratic equation with real coefficients has a solution in the field C of complex numbers. Moreover, it can be shown that every quadratic equation with complex coefficients also has a solution in the field of complex numbers.

Example. Find the solution set of $(2 + i)x^2 + ix + (2 - i) = 0$.

Solution. For the quadratic formula, we have $a = 2 + i$, $b = i$, and $c = 2 - i$. Then

$$x = \frac{-i \pm \sqrt{i^2 - 4(2 + i)(2 - i)}}{2(2 + i)}$$

$$= \frac{-i \pm \sqrt{-21}}{2(2 + i)}$$

$$= \frac{-i \pm i\sqrt{21}}{2(2 + i)}$$

$$= \frac{(-1 \pm \sqrt{21})i}{2(2 + i)}$$

$$= \frac{(-1 \pm \sqrt{21})i(2 - i)}{2(2 + i)(2 - i)}$$

$$= \frac{(-1 \pm \sqrt{21})2i + (-1 \pm \sqrt{21})}{2(4 + 1)}$$

$$= \frac{-1 \pm \sqrt{21}}{10} + \frac{-1 \pm \sqrt{21}}{5} i,$$

and the solution set is

$$\left\{ \frac{-1 + \sqrt{21}}{10} + \frac{-1 + \sqrt{21}}{5} i, \frac{-1 - \sqrt{21}}{10} + \frac{-1 - \sqrt{21}}{5} i \right\}.$$

EXERCISE 10.4

Solve each linear equation.

1. $3ix = 2 - i$

2. $4ix - 7 = i$

3. $2ix + x = 6$

4. $ix - 3x = i$

5. $\dfrac{2ix}{5} = 3 + i$

6. $\dfrac{ix - 2i}{2} = i$

Solve each quadratic equation by factoring.

7. $x^2 + 4 = 0$

8. $4x^2 + 9 = 0$

9. $x^2 + 3 = 0$

10. $9x^2 + 2 = 0$

11. $(x + 2)^2 + 1 = 0$

12. $(x - 3)^2 + 5 = 0$

13. $x^2 + 10x + 41 = 0$ *Hint:* First rewrite the left-hand member as $(x + 5)^2 + 16$.

14. $x^2 + 6x + 13 = 0$

15. $x^2 + 4x + 7 = 0$

16. $x^2 - 2x + 6 = 0$

Solve each quadratic equation formally by using the quadratic formula. Specify the ones for which the formula involves the square root of an imaginary number that is not pure.

17. $x^2 - 2x + 3 = 0$

18. $x^2 + x + 5 = 0$

19. $3x^2 + x = -7$

20. $2x^2 = 5x - 10$

21. $x^2 + (10 - i)x - i = 0$

22. $x^2 + 3ix + 4 = 0$

23. $2x^2 - (4 + i)x = 1$

24. $ix^2 + 2ix = 4$

25. $2ix^2 - 3x + 4 + i = 0$

26. $3ix^2 - 2x - 4 + i = 0$

Find equations having the given numbers as solutions.   *Hint:* Recall that if x_1 is a solution of $P(x) = 0$, then $x - x_1$ is a factor of $P(x)$.

27. $2 - i, 2 + i$

28. $3 + i, 3 - i$

29. $\sqrt{2} i, -\sqrt{2} i$

30. $2 + \sqrt{3} i, 2 - \sqrt{3} i$

31. $-3, i$

32. $2i, i$

33. $2 + i, 1 - 2i$

34. $3 + 2i, 3 + 2i$

10.5   ORDERED PAIRS AS VECTORS

In Chapter 9, we considered the set of $m \times n$ matrices, for m and n fixed, as a vector space over the field R of real numbers (page 259).   In particular, we called a $1 \times n$ matrix $[a_1, a_2, \cdots, a_n]$ a row vector.

The two operations involved in a vector space S over R, it will be recalled, are (i) the addition of elements of S and (ii) the multiplication of elements of S by elements of R.

Now the definitions of equality and addition of number pairs (a, b) and (c, d) are the same whether the pairs are viewed as 1×2 matrices or as complex numbers.   Further, the multiplication of the matrix $[a, b]$ by the real number c is given by

$$c[a, b] = [ca, cb],$$

and of the complex number (a, b) by the real number c, by

$$c(a, b) = (c, 0)(a, b) = (ca - 0 \cdot b, cb + 0 \cdot a)$$
$$= (ca, cb),$$

which is analogous.   Thus, with real numbers as multipliers, the set $S_{1 \times 2}$ of 1×2 matrices and the set C of complex numbers can be considered as vector spaces over the field R of real numbers.

There is a geometric interpretation that can be made of the vector-space algebra of ordered pairs, because every ordered pair (a, b) can be associated with a directed line segment, or **geometric vector**, originating at the origin and terminating at the point in the plane corresponding to (a, b) (Figure 10.2).   Let us begin by making the following definitions.

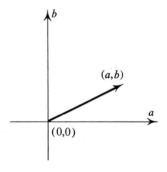

Figure 10.2

DEFINITION 10.13   *A* ***two-dimensional vector*** **v** *is an ordered pair of real numbers.   That is,*

$$\mathbf{v} = (a, b).$$

Thus there is a geometric vector that corresponds to every two-dimensional vector **v**.   Note that we are using **boldface** type to denote vectors.   In handwritten form, vectors are frequently identified by arrows drawn above a symbol.   Thus, $\vec{v}$ denotes a vector.

Since we shall be dealing only with two-dimensional vectors, we shall refer to these simply as *vectors*.   It should be realized, however, that there are vectors, such as (a, b, c) or (a, b, c, d), of higher dimension.

DEFINITION 10.14 *For every vector* $\mathbf{v} = (a, b)$, *the* **norm** *or* **magnitude** *of* $\mathbf{v}$ *is the real number*

$$\|\mathbf{v}\| = \sqrt{a^2 + b^2}.$$

It is evident from the Pythagorean theorem that the norm of a vector is just the length of the geometric vector associated with the vector.

DEFINITION 10.15 *If* $\mathbf{v}_1 = (a_1, b_1)$ *and* $\mathbf{v}_2 = (a_2, b_2)$, *then* $\mathbf{v}_1 = \mathbf{v}_2$ *if and only if* $a_1 = a_2$ *and* $b_1 = b_2$.

Accordingly, geometric vectors are equal if and only if they correspond to the same vector.

Now, let us define two operations, as follows.

DEFINITION 10.16 *If* $\mathbf{v}_1$ *and* $\mathbf{v}_2$ *are vectors and c is any real number, then*

$$\text{I} \quad \mathbf{v}_1 + \mathbf{v}_2 = (a_1, b_1) + (a_2, b_2) = (a_1 + a_2, b_1 + b_2),$$

$$\text{II} \quad c\mathbf{v}_1 = \mathbf{v}_1 c = c(a, b) = (ca, cb).$$

From the vector viewpoint of ordered pairs, real numbers, such as c in the foregoing definition, are called **scalars**, and the operation defined in 10.16-II is called the multiplication of a vector by a scalar.

Graphically, the two operations defined above can be interpreted in terms of geometric vectors, as shown in Figures 10.3 and 10.4.

In Figure 10.3, the vectors $\mathbf{v}_1$ and $\mathbf{v}_2$ are said to be **noncollinear** because they correspond to noncollinear geometric vectors. It is evident that the sum of two such noncollinear vectors $\mathbf{v}_1$ and $\mathbf{v}_2$ corresponds to the diagonal of the parallelogram with adjacent sides corresponding to $\mathbf{v}_1$ and $\mathbf{v}_2$. This statement can be considered valid, in a limiting way, even if the geometric vectors corresponding to $\mathbf{v}_1$ and $\mathbf{v}_2$ are collinear. Accordingly, we say that vectors are added according to the **parallelogram law.**

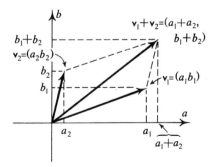

Figure 10.3

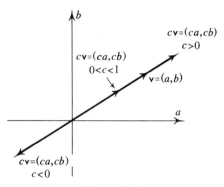

Figure 10.4

In Figure 10.4, the vectors v_1 and cv_1 are said to be **collinear,** since they correspond to geometric vectors on the same line. For $c > 0$, the product cv corresponds to a geometric vector with the *same direction* as the one corresponding to v. If $0 < c < 1$, then $\|cv\| < \|v\|$. If $c < 0$, then cv corresponds to a geometric vector of *direction opposite* to that corresponding to v.

DEFINITION 10.17 *The zero vector,* **0,** *or identity vector for addition, is given by*

$$\mathbf{0} = (0, 0).$$

It has the property that $\mathbf{v} + \mathbf{0} = \mathbf{0} + \mathbf{v} = \mathbf{v}$ for each vector v. The norm of **0** is, of course, 0. No particular direction is assigned to the geometric vector corresponding to **0**; for this reason, any and every direction might be assigned to it, as suits our convenience.

DEFINITION 10.18 *If* **v** *is a vector, then the negative of* **v** *is given by*

$$-\mathbf{v} = -1 \cdot \mathbf{v}.$$

The vector $-\mathbf{v}$ has the property that

$$\mathbf{v} + (-\mathbf{v}) = (-\mathbf{v}) + \mathbf{v} = \mathbf{0}$$

for each vector v.

For $\mathbf{v} = (a, b)$, we have, by definition,

$$-\mathbf{v} = -1 \cdot (a, b) = (-a, -b).$$

With these definitions, we now have exactly the same algebra, as regards addition and the multiplication by a real-number scalar, for the set of real-number pairs (a, b), whether they are regarded as 1×2 matrices, complex numbers, or vectors. Since we have shown that the set

$$\{(a, b) \mid a \in R, b \in R\}$$

is a vector space when viewed as the set of 1×2 matrices, it follows that the set is also a vector space when viewed in either of the other two ways. We state the result for vectors $\mathbf{v} = (a, b)$ as follows:

THEOREM 10.6 *The set V of vectors $\mathbf{v}$, with the set R of real numbers as scalar multipliers, is a vector space over the field R of real numbers. That is, if $\mathbf{v}_1$, $\mathbf{v}_2$, and $\mathbf{v}_3$ are vectors, and c and d are real scalars, then*

I $\mathbf{v}_1 + \mathbf{v}_2$ *is a vector,*

II $\mathbf{v}_1 + \mathbf{v}_2 = \mathbf{v}_2 + \mathbf{v}_1$,

III $(\mathbf{v}_1 + \mathbf{v}_2) + \mathbf{v}_3 = \mathbf{v}_1 + (\mathbf{v}_2 + \mathbf{v}_3)$,

IV $\mathbf{v}_1 + \mathbf{0} = \mathbf{v}_1$,

V $\mathbf{v}_1 + (-\mathbf{v}_1) = \mathbf{0}$,

VI $c\mathbf{v}_1$ *is a vector,*

VII $c(d\mathbf{v}_1) = (cd)\mathbf{v}_1$,

VIII $(c + d)\mathbf{v}_1 = c\mathbf{v}_1 + d\mathbf{v}_1$,

IX $c(\mathbf{v}_1 + \mathbf{v}_2) = c\mathbf{v}_1 + c\mathbf{v}_2$,

X $1 \cdot \mathbf{v}_1 = \mathbf{v}_1$,

XI $(-1)\mathbf{v} = -\mathbf{v}$,

XII $0 \cdot \mathbf{v}_1 = \mathbf{0}$,

XIII $c \cdot \mathbf{0} = \mathbf{0}$.

The proofs of the various parts of this theorem are omitted since they were considered in Chapter 9.

The set of vectors (a, b) comprises a **two-dimensional vector space**, since each vector has two components. It can be shown (see Exercise 10.5, Problem 39) that if $\mathbf{v}_1$ and $\mathbf{v}_2$ are two noncollinear vectors in a two-dimensional vector space, then for each $\mathbf{v}_3$ in the vector space there exist scalars c_1 and c_2 such that

$$\mathbf{v}_3 = c_1\mathbf{v}_1 + c_2\mathbf{v}_2.$$

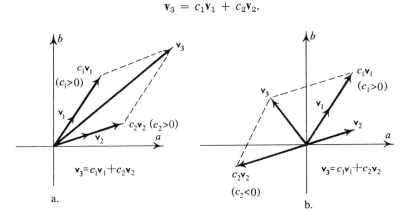

Figure 10.5

Figure 10.5 shows two geometric examples of such combinations. Since linear combinations of any two noncollinear vectors $\mathbf{v}_1$ and $\mathbf{v}_2$ can be used to represent any vector in a two-dimensional vector space, two such vectors are said to form a **basis** for the space, or to **span** the space.

Any two vectors corresponding to geometric vectors that are perpendicular to each other are said to be **orthogonal**, and in general such vectors, neither of which is (0, 0), form the most useful basis for a vector space.

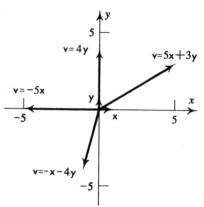

Figure 10.6

DEFINITION 10.19 *A unit vector $\mathbf{v}$ is any vector such that $\|\mathbf{v}\| = 1$.*

If we let $\mathbf{x} = (1, 0)$ and $\mathbf{y} = (0, 1)$ be the unit vectors whose corresponding geometric vectors are in the direction of the positive x- and y-axes, respectively, then $\mathbf{x}$ and $\mathbf{y}$ form an orthogonal basis for our two-dimensional vector space, and for every vector $\mathbf{v} = (x, y,)$ in the space we have

$$\mathbf{v} = x\mathbf{x} + y\mathbf{y}.$$

Several graphical examples of linear combinations of $\mathbf{x}$ and $\mathbf{y}$ are shown in Figure 10.6.

If $\|\mathbf{v}\|$ is factored from the right-hand member of the vector equation $\mathbf{v} = x\mathbf{x} + y\mathbf{y}$, we have

$$\mathbf{v} = \sqrt{x^2 + y^2}\left(\frac{x}{\sqrt{x^2 + y^2}}\,\mathbf{x} + \frac{y}{\sqrt{x^2 + y^2}}\,\mathbf{y}\right),$$

and it can be shown that the vector in the parentheses in the right-hand member here is a unit vector in the same direction as $\mathbf{v}$. (See Exercise 10.5, Problem 37.) In other words, we have the following.

THEOREM 10.7 *If $\mathbf{v}$ is any nonzero vector in a two-dimensional vector space, then the vector $\mathbf{v}^*$ given by*

$$\mathbf{v}^* = \frac{1}{\|\mathbf{v}\|}\cdot\mathbf{v}$$

is a unit vector in the same direction as $\mathbf{v}$.

Example. Find a unit vector in the same direction as (3, 7).

Solution. $\|(3, 7)\| = \sqrt{9 + 49} = \sqrt{58}.$ Hence,

$$\mathbf{v}^* = \left(\frac{3}{\sqrt{58}}, \frac{7}{\sqrt{58}}\right).$$

EXERCISE 10.5

Write each sum or difference in the form (a, b); represent the vector operation graphically and find $\|(a, b)\|$.

Example. $(5, 3) - (2, -1)$

Solution.

$(5, 3) - (2, -1) = (5, 3) + (-2, 1)$
$\qquad\qquad\qquad = (3, 4)$

$\|(3, 4)\| = \sqrt{3^2 + 4^2} = 5$

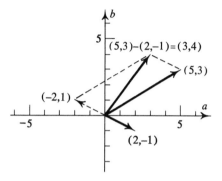

1. $(2, 4) + (6, 1)$

2. $(3, -1) + (4, 2)$

3. $(-3, 4) + (2, -1)$

4. $(-2, -4) + (7, -2)$

5. $(0, 3) + (5, 6)$

6. $(5, 2) + (3, 0)$

7. $(2, 0) + (3, 5) + (1, 1)$

8. $(-2, 4) + (3, 0) + (4, 2)$

9. $(6, -1) + (2, 0) + (0, 2)$

10. $(0, 4) + (2, -1) + (5, 4)$

11. $(5, 3) - (2, 1)$

12. $(7, 8) - (3, 4)$

13. $(-2, 4) - (2, -1)$

14. $(8, -3) - (2, -1)$

15. $(2, 4) + (0, 3) - (2, -1)$

16. $(-3, 0) + (2, 1) - (-1, 0)$

17. $(0, 2) - (3, 1) + (2, 0)$

18. $(4, 3) - (0, -2) + (4, 4)$

Example. $2(3, 5) + 3(1, -2)$

Solution.

$2(3, 5) + 3(1, -2) = (6, 10) + (3, -6)$
$\qquad\qquad\qquad\qquad = (9, 4)$

$\|(9, 4)\| = \sqrt{9^2 + 4^2}$
$\qquad\quad\; = \sqrt{97}$

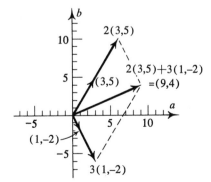

19. $3(1, 1) + 4(2, 2)$

20. $3(1, -4) + 2(3, 5)$

21. $5(0, 2) + 3(-2, -3)$ 22. $2(3, 1) + 5(-6, 0)$

23. $(5, 6) - 2(1, -2)$ 24. $(6, 2) - 3(-1, 2)$

25. $3(0, 4) - 4(2, 0)$ 26. $7(5, 0) - 2(-3, 0)$

27. $2(1, 3) - 4(-2, 1) + 2(0, 1)$ 28. $3(0, 2) + 5(1, -2) - 3(0, 1)$

Represent each vector graphically, find the norm of each vector, and find the unit vector $\mathbf{v}^*$ in the same direction as the given vector $\mathbf{v}$.

Example. $\mathbf{v} = 3\mathbf{x} + 4\mathbf{y}$

Solution.

$$\|\mathbf{v}\| = \|3\mathbf{x} + 4\mathbf{y}\| = \sqrt{3^2 + 4^2}$$
$$= 5$$

$$\mathbf{v}^* = \frac{\mathbf{v}}{\|\mathbf{v}\|} = \frac{3\mathbf{x} + 4\mathbf{y}}{5}$$
$$= \frac{3}{5}\mathbf{x} + \frac{4}{5}\mathbf{y}$$

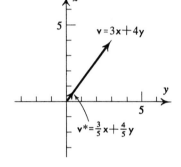

29. $\mathbf{v} = 2\mathbf{x} + 7\mathbf{y}$

30. $\mathbf{v} = 5\mathbf{x} + 2\mathbf{y}$

31. $\mathbf{v} = 3\mathbf{x} - \mathbf{y}$ 32. $\mathbf{v} = -4\mathbf{x} + 3\mathbf{y}$

33. $\mathbf{v} = -6\mathbf{x} - 7\mathbf{y}$ 34. $\mathbf{v} = -5\mathbf{x} - \mathbf{y}$

35. $\mathbf{v} = 3\mathbf{y}$ 36. $\mathbf{v} = -7\mathbf{x}$

37. Show that if $\mathbf{v} = x\mathbf{x} + y\mathbf{y}$, then $\left(\dfrac{x}{\|\mathbf{v}\|}\mathbf{x} + \dfrac{y}{\|\mathbf{v}\|}\mathbf{y} \right)$ is a unit vector in the same direction as $\mathbf{v}$.

38. Show that if $ad - bc \neq 0$, then the vectors $\mathbf{v}_1 = (a, b)$ and $\mathbf{v}_2 = (c, d)$ are not collinear. *Hint:* Can $\mathbf{v}_1$ be a scalar multiple of $\mathbf{v}_2$?

39. Show that if $\mathbf{v}_1$ and $\mathbf{v}_2$ are not collinear, then for any given vector $\mathbf{v} = (x, y)$ we can find scalars c_1 and c_2 such that $\mathbf{v} = c_1\mathbf{v}_1 + c_2\mathbf{v}_2$. *Hint:* Solve the vector equation for c_1 and c_2.

40. Show that the set of 2×1 matrices $\begin{bmatrix} a \\ b \end{bmatrix}$, with real numbers as entries and with rational numbers as scalar multipliers, constitutes a vector space over the field Q of rational numbers.

THEORY
OF EQUATIONS

In Section 2.1, we defined a polynomial over the field R of real numbers as one in which each of the coefficients is a real number. The polynomial equation

$$P(x) = a_0 x^n + a_1 x^{n-1} + \cdots + a_n, \quad a_0 \neq 0,$$

can also be used to define a function of the real or complex variable x over the field C of complex numbers as well as over the field R of real numbers, depending on whether we take the $a_i \in C$ or $a_i \in R$. In this chapter we shall study some characteristics of both.

11.1 SYNTHETIC DIVISION AND THE FACTOR THEOREM

In Section 2.4, a synthetic process was developed for the division of $P(x)$ by $(x - r)$, where $P(x)$ was a real polynomial over R, and r was any real number. Then, in Section 6.5, the remainder theorem was developed, and these two concepts were combined to help us find ordered pairs $[x, P(x)]$ in real polynomial functions.

Now that we have the field C of complex numbers available, let us re-examine these ideas for polynomials, this time with the coefficients being elements of C. To begin with, let us examine the problem of finding $P(r)$ for any given real or complex number r in a slightly different way than we employed in Section 6.5. Either method applies, of course, to polynomials over the field R of real numbers, over the field C of complex numbers, or indeed over any field.

We observe, first, that if

$$P(x) = a_0x^n + a_1x^{n-1} + a_2x^{n-2} + \cdots + a_{n-1}x + a_n \qquad (1)$$

is a polynomial with real or complex coefficients, we can rewrite the right-hand member by first factoring x^{n-1} from the first two terms to obtain

$$P(x) = (a_0x + a_1)x^{n-1} + a_2x^{n-2} + \cdots + a_n.$$

Then, we can factor x^{n-2} from the first two terms in this new polynomial to obtain

$$P(x) = [(a_0x + a_1)x + a_2]x^{n-2} + a_3x^{n-3} + \cdots + a_n.$$

This process can be continued until we arrive at the form

$$P(x) = ([\cdots([(a_0x + a_1)x + a_2]x + a_3)x + \cdots + a_{n-2}]x + a_{n-1})x + a_n. \qquad (2)$$

Now, for any complex number r,

$$P(r) = ([\cdots([(a_0r + a_1)r + a_2]r + a_3)r + \cdots + a_{n-2}]r + a_{n-1})r + a_n.$$

A careful examination of the right-hand member here shows that to find $P(r)$ we do the following:

1. Multiply a_0 by r and add the product to a_1.
2. Multiply the result in Step 1 by r and add the product to a_2.
$\vdots$
n. Multiply the result in Step $n - 1$ by r and add the product to a_n.

But this is precisely the process used in synthetic division! The procedure can be arranged thus:

r	a_0	a_1	a_2	$\cdots$	a_n
		a_0r	$a_0r^2 + a_1r$	$\cdots$	$a_0r^n + a_1r^{n-1} + \cdots + a_{n-1}r$
	a_0	$a_0r + a_1$	$a_0r^2 + a_1r + a_2$	$\cdots$	$a_0r^n + a_1r^{n-1} + \cdots + a_{n-1}r + a_n$

It can then be seen that the "remainder"

$$a_0r^n + a_1r^{n-1} + \cdots + a_{n-1}r + a_n$$

is just $P(r)$. That is, the synthetic "division" process developed earlier might also be called synthetic "substitution," and, because nothing but the field properties have been used, it is clearly applicable to $r \in C$ as well as to $r \in R$.

Example. If $P(x) = 2x^4 - x^3 + 2x^2 - x + 1$, find $P(1 - i)$.

Solution.

$1 - i$	2	-1	2	-1	1
		$2 - 2i$	$-1 - 3i$	$-2 - 4i$	$-7 - i$
	2	$1 - 2i$	$1 - 3i$	$-3 - 4i$	$-6 - i$

Thus $P(1 - i) = -6 - i$.

Next, let $r \in C$, so that, if we replace x with r in (1), we have

$$P(r) = a_0 r^n + a_1 r^{n-1} + \cdots + a_{n-1} r + a_n,$$

and thus

$$P(x) - P(r) = a_0(x^n - r^n) + a_1(x^{n-1} - r^{n-1}) + \cdots$$
$$+ a_{n-1}(x - r) + 0. \tag{3}$$

It is evident that $(x - r)$ is a factor of each term in the right-hand member, so that, if we factor $(x - r)$ from each term, we have

$$P(x) - P(r) = (x - r)Q(x),$$

where $Q(x)$ is a polynomial of degree $n - 1$. Hence, (3) can be written

$$P(x) = (x - r)Q(x) + P(r).$$

But this should look familiar! We have just proved the remainder theorem again, this time for $r \in C$:

THEOREM 11.1 *If $P(x)$ is a polynomial over the field C of complex numbers, and $c \in C$, then there exists a unique polynomial $Q(x)$ and a complex number r, such that*

$$P(x) = (x - c)Q(x) + r,$$

and $r = P(c)$.

Another theorem, called the **factor theorem**, follows immediately:

THEOREM 11.2 *If $P(x)$ is a polynomial over the field C of complex numbers, and $P(r) = 0$, then $(x - r)$ is a factor of $P(x)$.*

Proof. If $P(r) = 0$, then, by the remainder theorem,

$$P(x) = (x - r)Q(x) + P(r) = (x - r)Q(x) + 0,$$

and by the definition of a factor, $(x - r)$ is a factor of $P(x)$.

It might be noted, as a converse of the factor theorem, that if $(x - r)$ is a factor of $P(x)$, so that $P(x) = (x - r)Q(x)$, then $P(r) = 0$, since

$$P(r) = (r - r)Q(r) = 0 \cdot Q(r) = 0.$$

Example. Show that $(x - 2i)$ is a factor of $P(x) = x^3 - x^2 + 4x - 4$.

Solution. If $P(2i) = 0$, then, by the factor theorem, $x - 2i$ must be a factor of $P(x)$. Dividing $P(x)$ by $x - 2i$ synthetically, we have

$$
\begin{array}{r|rrrr}
2i & 1 & -1 & 4 & -4 \\
   &   & 2i & -4-2i & 4 \\
\hline
   & 1 & -1+2i & -2i & 0
\end{array}
$$

and, since the remainder is 0, we have shown that $(x - 2i)$ is a factor of $P(x)$.

As a last observation, note that in the synthetic substitution of r for x in $P(x)$, the terms occurring in the bottom row of the substitution process are the coefficients in the polynomial $Q(x)$, except that the final one is $P(r)$. Thus, in the preceding example, we showed that $x - 2i$ is a factor of $P(x) = x^3 - x^2 + 4x - 4$. By looking at the last row in the synthetic substitution process, we see that, since $P(2i) = 0$, $P(x)$ can be expressed

$$P(x) = (x - 2i)[x^2 + (-1 + 2i)x - 2i].$$

EXERCISE 11.1

Find the values of the polynomial for the given value of x.

Example. $P(x) = 3x^3 + 2x^2 - x + 1$; find $P(2i)$

Solution.   Using synthetic substitution, we obtain

$$
\begin{array}{r|cccc}
2i & 3 & 2 & -1 & 1 \\
 & & 6i & -12 + 4i & -8 - 26i \\
\hline
 & 3 & 2 + 6i & -13 + 4i & -7 - 26i
\end{array}.
$$

By the remainder theorem, $P(2i) = -7 - 26i$.

1. $P(x) = 4x^3 - x^2 + 5x + 2$; find $P(2)$

2. $Q(x) = 3x^3 + 2x^2 - x - 1$; find $Q(-3)$

3. $Q(x) = x^3 + 4x^2 - 2x - 5$; find $Q(-3i)$

4. $G(x) = 3x^3 - 2x^2 + 7x - 1$; find $G(i)$

5. $P(x) = x^4 - 3x^3 + x - 2$; find $P(-2)$

6. $P(x) = 2x^4 - 3x^2 - x$; find $P(4)$

7. $Q(x) = x^5 - x^3 + 3x^2 + 1$; find $Q(2i)$

8. $Q(x) = 3x^5 - x^4 + 2x - 1$; find $Q(-i)$

9. $P(x) = x^3 + 3x^2 - x + 1$; find $P(1 - i)$

10. $P(x) = 2x^3 - x^2 + 3x - 5$; find $P(2 + i)$

Write each expression as a quotient and a remainder.

Example. $(3x^3 - x^2 + 1) \div (x + 2)$

Solution.   Using synthetic division, we obtain

$$
\begin{array}{r|cccc}
-2 & 3 & -1 & 0 & 1 \\
 & & -6 & 14 & -28 \\
\hline
 & 3 & -7 & 14 & -27
\end{array}.
$$

The quotient is $3x^2 - 7x + 14$ and the remainder is -27.

11. $(2x^3 - x^2 + 3x + 4) \div (x - 3)$

12. $(x^3 - 4x^2 - 2x - 2) \div (x + 1)$

13. $(x^3 + x^2 - 3x + 3) \div (x - 2i)$

14. $(2x^3 - 2x^2 + 4x + 1) \div (x + i)$

15. $(x^4 - 3x^2 + x - 1) \div (x + i)$

16. $(x^4 - x^3 + 2x^2 + 2) \div (x - 2i)$

17. $(x^3 - 2x^2 + x + 1) \div [x - (1 + i)]$

18. $(2x^3 + x^2 - 3x) \div [x + (1 - i)]$

19. Show that $x - 2$ is a factor of $x^3 + 2x^2 - 5x - 6$.

20. Show that $x + 1$ is a factor of $x^4 - 5x^3 - 13x^2 + 53x + 60$.

21. Show that $-2i$ is a root of $x^3 - x^2 + 4x - 4 = 0$.

22. Show that $2 + 4i$ is a root of $x^4 - 4x^3 + 18x^2 + 8x - 40 = 0$.

23. Find $Q(x)$ if $x^3 - 3x^2 + x - 3 = (x - i)Q(x)$.

24. Find $Q(x)$ if $2x^3 - 3x^2 - 4x + 4 = (x - 2)Q(x)$.

Find a value for k so that the second polynomial is a factor of the first.

25. $x^3 - 5x^2 - 16x + k; \; x - 5$

26. $x^3 - 9x^2 + 14x + k; \; x + 1$

27. $x^4 + 2x^3 - 21x^2 + kx + 40; \; x - 4$

28. $3x^4 - 40x^3 + 130x^2 + kx + 27; \; x - 9$

11.2   COMPLEX ZEROS OF POLYNOMIAL FUNCTIONS

Recalling from Section 10.2 that the conjugate of the complex number $z = a + bi$ is $\bar{z} = a - bi$, where $a, b \in R$, let us examine a chain of consequences.

THEOREM 11.3   *Let $z_1 = a_1 + b_1 i$ and $z_2 = a_2 + b_2 i$ be complex numbers. Then*

$$\text{I} \quad \overline{z_1 + z_2} = \bar{z}_1 + \bar{z}_2,$$

$$\text{II} \quad \overline{z_1 z_2} = \bar{z}_1 \cdot \bar{z}_2.$$

Proof. We have

$$\bar{z_1} = a_1 - b_1 i \quad \text{and} \quad \bar{z_2} = a_2 - b_2 i.$$

Then

$$\bar{z_1} + \bar{z_2} = (a_1 + a_2) + (-b_1 - b_2)i$$
$$= (a_1 + a_2) - (b_1 + b_2)i.$$

Also,

$$z_1 + z_2 = (a_1 + a_2) + (b_1 + b_2)i,$$

so that

$$\overline{z_1 + z_2} = (a_1 + a_2) - (b_1 + b_2)i,$$

and Part I is proved.

We leave the proof of Part II as an exercise.

Another link in our chain is the following, the proof of which is deferred until Section 12.1, since it involves mathematical induction.

THEOREM 11.4 *If a, b, c $\in$ R, and z = (a + bi), then*

$$\overline{c \cdot (z)^n} = c \cdot (\bar{z})^n$$

for every n $\in$ N.

Now, we are ready for the very important property established by the following.

THEOREM 11.5 *If P(x) is a polynomial over the field R of real numbers— that is, if P(x) is a polynomial with real coefficients—then for every complex number z,*

$$P(\bar{z}) = \overline{P(z)}.$$

The proof, by means of Theorem 11.3, Part I, and Theorem 11.4, is left as an exercise.

Example. If $P(x) = 2x^2 + x + 1$, verify that $P(\overline{1 - i}) = \overline{P(1 - i)}$.

Solution.

$$P(\overline{1 - i}) = P(1 + i) = 2(1 + i)^2 + (1 + i) + 1 = 2 + 5i,$$

$$\overline{P(1 - i)} = \overline{2(1 - i)^2 + (1 - i) + 1} = \overline{2 - 5i} = 2 + 5i.$$

Thus, $P(\overline{1 - i}) = \overline{P(1 - i)}$.

Now for a second important property of a polynomial function over R, we have the following.

THEOREM 11.6 *If $P(z)$ is a polynomial over the field R of real numbers, and if $P(z) = 0$ for some $z \in C$, then $P(\bar{z}) = 0$.*

Proof. Since $P(z) = 0$, and since, by Theorem 11.5, for every $z \in C$ we have $P(\bar{z}) = \overline{P(z)}$, it follows that $P(\bar{z}) = \bar{0} = 0$, and the theorem is proved.

One implication this theorem has for the zeros of a function defined by a polynomial with *real coefficients* is that *complex zeros always occur in conjugate pairs.*

Example. Given that $2 - i$ is a zero of

$$\{[x, P(x)] \mid P(x) = x^3 - 6x^2 + 13x - 10\},$$

find all zeros of P.

Solution. The zeros of P are the roots of $P(x) = 0$. By synthetic division,

$$\underline{2 - i} \begin{array}{|cccc} 1 & -6 & 13 & -10 \\ & 2 - i & -9 + 2i & 10 \\ \hline 1 & -4 - i & 4 + 2i & 0 \end{array},$$

and the quotient is $x^2 + (-4 - i)x + 4 + 2i$. By Theorem 11.6, $2 + i$ must also be a root of $P(x) = 0$. We can now write

$$P(x) = [x - (2 - i)][x^2 + (-4 - i)x + 4 + 2i] = 0,$$

and since, by inspection, $2 + i$ is not a root of $x - (2 - i) = 0$, it must be a root of

$$x^2 + (-4 - i)x + 4 + 2i = 0.$$

Using synthetic division again, we have

$$\underline{2 + i} \begin{array}{|ccc} 1 & -4 - i & 4 + 2i \\ & 2 + i & -4 - 2i \\ \hline 1 & -2 & 0 \end{array},$$

where the quotient is $x - 2$. Then

$$P(x) = [x - (2 - i)][x - (2 + i)](x - 2) = 0$$

and, by inspection, the solutions of this equation—and hence the zeros of P—are $2 - i, 2 + i$, and 2.

When Theorem 11.6 is coupled with the following, which is called the **fundamental theorem of algebra**, a great deal of information relative to the zeros of polynomial functions $P(x)$ becomes readily available.

THEOREM 11.7 *Every polynomial function of degree $n \geq 1$ over the field C of complex numbers has at least one real or complex zero.*

The proof of this theorem involves concepts beyond those available to us, and is omitted.

As an extension of Theorem 11.7, we have the following consequent result.

THEOREM 11.8 *Every polynomial, of degree $n \geq 1$, over the field C, can be expressed as a product of n linear factors.*

Proof. Let $P(x) = a_0 x^n + a_1 x^{n-1} + \cdots + a_n$; $a_i \in C$, $a_0 \neq 0$, $x \in C$, and $n \in N$, $n \geq 1$. Then, since this equation defines a polynomial function, by the fundamental theorem of algebra there is at least one real or complex x, say x_1, such that

$$P(x_1) = a_0 x_1^n + a_1 x_1^{n-1} + \cdots + a_n = 0.$$

By the factor theorem,

$$P(x) = (x - x_1)Q_{n-1}(x),$$

where $Q_{n-1}(x)$ is of degree $n - 1$. Again, by the fundamental theorem, if $n - 1 \geq 1$, there must exist an $x_2 \in C$ such that $Q_{n-1}(x_2) = 0$. Hence, we can write

$$P(x) = (x - x_1)(x - x_2)Q_{n-2}(x),$$

where $Q_{n-2}(x)$ is a polynomial of degree $n - 2$. If this factoring process is performed n times, the result is

$$P(x) = (x - x_1)(x - x_2)\cdots(x - x_n)Q_0(x),$$

where $Q_0(x)$ consists solely of a_0, and the theorem is proved.

If a factor $(x - x_i)$ occurs k times in such a linear factorization, then x_i is said to be a zero of *multiplicity* k. With this agreement, Theorem 11.8 shows that every polynomial function defined by a polynomial $P(x)$ of degree n with complex coefficients has exactly n zeros.

Note that any theorem stated in terms of zeros of polynomial functions applies to roots (solutions) of polynomial equations, and vice versa; a *zero* of

$$\{x, P(x) \mid P(x) = a_0 x^n + a_1 x^{n-1} + \cdots + a_n\}$$

is a *solution* or *root* of $P(x) = 0$.

EXERCISE 11.2

In Problems 1–8, one or more zeros are given for each of the polynomial functions; find the other zeros. Verify by synthetic division.

1. $\{[x, P(x)] \mid P(x) = x^2 + 4\}$; $2i$ is one zero.

2. $\{[x, P(x)] \mid P(x) = 3x^2 + 27\}$; $-3i$ is one zero.

3. $\{[x, P(x)] \mid P(x) = x^3 - 3x^2 + x - 3\}$; 3 and i are zeros.

4. $\{[x, Q(x)] \mid Q(x) = x^3 - 5x^2 + 7x + 13\}$; -1 and $3 - 2i$ are zeros.

5. $\{[x, Q(x)] \mid Q(x) = x^4 + 5x^2 + 4\}$; $-i$ and $2i$ are zeros.

6. $\{[x, P(x)] \mid P(x) = x^4 + 11x^2 + 18\}$; $3i$ and $\sqrt{2}\,i$ are zeros.

7. $\{[x, Q(x)] \mid Q(x) = x^4 + 3x^3 + 4x^2 + 27x - 45\}$; $-3i$ is a zero.

8. $\{[x, Q(x)] \mid Q(x) = x^5 - 2x^4 + 8x^3 - 16x^2 + 16x - 32\}$; $2i$ (multiplicity 2) and 2 are zeros.

9. A cubic equation with real coefficients has roots -2 and $1 + i$. What is the third root? Write the equation in the form $P(x) = 0$, given that the **leading coefficient** (the coefficient of the highest power of x) is 1.

10. A cubic equation with real coefficients has roots 4 and $2 - i$. What is the third root? Write the equation in the form $P(x) = 0$, given that the leading coefficient is 1.

11. One zero of $P(x) = 2x^3 - 11x^2 + 28x - 24$ is $2 - 2i$. Factor $P(x)$ over the complex numbers.

12. One zero of $Q(x) = 3x^3 - 10x^2 + 7x + 10$ is $2 + i$. Factor $Q(x)$ over the complex numbers.

13. One root of $x^4 - 10x^3 + 35x^2 - 50x + 34 = 0$ is $4 - i$. Find the remaining roots.

14. One root of $5x^4 + 34x^3 + 40x^2 - 78x + 51 = 0$ is $-4 - i$. Find the remaining roots.

15. Argue that every polynomial equation with real coefficients and of odd degree has at least one real root.

16. One zero of a polynomial $P(x)$ is i. Is $-i$ necessarily a zero of $P(x)$? Why? The number i is a zero of $P(x) = x^3 + i$. Determine by synthetic division if $-i$ is a zero.

17. Determine the three cube roots of -1. *Hint:* Consider the roots of the equation $x^3 + 1 = 0$.

18. Show that there are four fourth roots of -1. *Hint:* Consider the roots of the equation $x^4 + 1 = 0$, that is, of $(x^2 + i)(x^2 - i) = 0$.

19. Prove Theorem 11.3-II.

20. Prove Theorem 11.5. *Hint:* Observe that if $P(x) = a_0 x^n + a_1 x^{n-1} + \cdots + a_n$, then $P(z) = a_0 z^n + a_1 z^{n-1} + \cdots + a_n$, and $P(\bar{z}) = a_0 \bar{z}^n + a_1 \bar{z}^{n-1} + \cdots + a_n$. Then use Theorems 11.3-I (assuming that this can be extended to apply to a sum of n terms) and 11.4.

11.3 REAL ZEROS OF POLYNOMIAL FUNCTIONS

Since we have adopted the convention that $R \subset C$, if $\{z_1, z_2, z_3, \cdots z_n\}$ is the set of zeros for a complex polynomial function of degree n, any one or more of these zeros, or, indeed, all of them, may be real numbers. As was observed in the preceding section (Exercise 11.2, Problem 15), every polynomial function of odd degree over the field R of real numbers must have at least one real zero.   Now we wish to find some ways of identifying real zeros of these polynomials of either even or odd degree, and we shall, for the time being, restrict replacements for x in $P(x)$ to real numbers.

With this restriction, we know that $P(x) \in R[x]$, and that the graph of

$$\{[x, P(x)] \mid P(x) = a_0 x^n + a_1 x^{n-1} + \cdots + a_n\}$$

lies entirely in the real plane; see Section 2.1.   Moreover, although we shall not prove it here, we have the following theorem on continuity.

THEOREM 11.9   *If $P(x) = a_0 x^n + a_1 x^{n-1} + \cdots + a_n$, a_i, $x \in R$, so that $P(x) \in R$, and if $k \in R$ is between $P(x_1)$ and $P(x_2)$, then there exists at least one $c \in R$ between x_1 and x_2 such that $P(c) = k$.*

More precisely, we can show that there are no breaks or jumps in the values of $P(x)$, so we know that $P(x)$ must assume all values between any two of its values.   Thus, the graph of P must be a continuous, unbroken curve.

Another useful theorem, which again we shall not prove here, is that which establishes **Descartes' Rule of Signs:**

THEOREM 11.10   *If $P(x)$ is a polynomial over the field R of real numbers, then the number of positive real solutions of $P(x) = 0$ is either equal to the number of variations in sign occurring in the coefficients of $P(x)$, or else is less than this number by an even natural number.   Moreover, the number of negative real solutions of $P(x) = 0$ is either equal to the number of variations in sign occurring in $P(-x) = 0$ or else is less than this number by an even natural number.*

A **variation in sign** occurs in a polynomial with real coefficients if, as the polynomial is viewed from left to right, successive coefficients are opposite in sign.   For example, in the polynomial

$$P(x) = 3x^5 - 2x^4 - 2x^2 + x - 1,$$

there are three variations in sign, and, in

$$P(-x) = -3x^5 - 2x^4 - 2x^2 - x - 1,$$

there are no variations in sign.

Example.   Find an upper bound on the number of real positive solutions and real negative solutions for the equation

$$3x^4 + 3x^3 - 2x^2 + x + 1 = 0. \tag{1}$$

Solution.   Since $P(x) = 3x^4 + 3x^3 - 2x^2 + x + 1$ has but two variations in sign, the equation can have no more than two positive real solutions.   Since

$$P(-x) = 3x^4 - 3x^3 - 2x^2 - x + 1$$

has two variations in sign, the number of negative real solutions of (1) cannot exceed two.

The following theorem is sometimes helpful in isolating real zeros of a polynomial function with real coefficients.

THEOREM 11.11   *Let $P(x)$ be a polynomial over the field R of real numbers.*

I   *If $r_1 \geq 0$, and the coefficients of the terms in $Q(x)$ and the term $P(r_1)$ are all of the same sign in the right-hand member of*

$$P(x) = (x - r_1)Q(x) + P(r_1),$$

then $P(x) = 0$ can have no solution greater than r_1.

II   *If $r_2 \leq 0$, and the coefficients of the terms in $Q(x)$ and the term $P(r_2)$ alternate in sign (zero suitably denoted by $+0$ or -0) in the right-hand member of*

$$P(x) = (x - r_2)Q(x) + P(r_2),$$

then $P(x) = 0$ can have no solution less than r_2.

Proof.   We shall prove only the first part of the theorem here and leave the second as an exercise.

For all $x > r_1$, $(x - r_1) > 0$. Moreover, if all the coefficients in $Q(x)$ are of the same sign, say positive, then, since $x > r_1 \geq 0$, we have $Q(x) > 0$ and $(x - r_1)Q(x) > 0$. Since $P(r_1) \geq 0$ by hypothesis, we have $P(x) = (x - r_1)Q(x) + P(r_1) > 0$, and the first part is proved.

This theorem permits us to place upper and lower bounds on the set of zeros of the polynomial function

$$P = \{[x, P(x)] \mid P(x) = a_0 x^n + \cdots + a_n\},$$

and consequently on the members of the solution set of $P(x) = 0$.

Example.   Show that 2 and -2 are upper and lower bounds, respectively, for the location of the zeros of

$$\{[x, P(x)] \mid P(x) = 18x^3 - 12x^2 - 11x + 10\}.$$

Solution.   To find $Q(x)$, we use synthetic division to divide $P(x)$ by $(x - 2)$:

$$
\begin{array}{r|rrrr}
2 & 18 & -12 & -11 & 10 \\
  &   & 36 & 48 & 74 \\
\hline
  & 18 & 24 & 37 & 84
\end{array}
$$

Since $Q(x) = 18x^2 + 24x + 37$ and $P(2) = 84 > 0$, 2 is an upper bound for the zeros of P. Next dividing $P(x)$ by $(x + 2)$, we have

$$
\begin{array}{r|rrrr}
-2 & 18 & -12 & -11 & 10 \\
   &   & -36 & 96 & -170 \\
\hline
   & 18 & -48 & 85 & -160
\end{array}
$$

Since $Q(x) = 18x^2 - 48x + 85$ and $P(-2) = -160$, -2 is a lower bound for the zeros of P.

Example. Find the smallest nonnegative integer and the largest nonpositive integer that are upper and lower bounds, respectively, for the zeros of

$$\{[x, P(x)] \mid P(x) = x^4 - x^3 - 10x^2 - 2x + 12\}.$$

Solution. We shall first seek an upper bound by dividing $P(x)$ successively by $(x - 1)$, $(x - 2)$, and so on. Each row in the following array is the bottom row in the synthetic division involved.

	1	−1	−10	−2	12
1	1	0	−10	−12	0
2	1	1	−8	−18	−24
3	1	2	−4	−14	−30
4	1	3	2	6	36

Since the numbers in the last row are all positive, 4 is an upper bound. Next, we divide by $(x + 1)$, $(x + 2)$, and so on, in search of a lower bound:

	1	−1	−10	−2	12
−1	1	−2	−8	6	6
−2	1	−3	−4	6	0
−3	1	−4	2	−8	36

Since the signs in the row following -3 alternate, -3 is a lower bound. Had the numbers in the row been 1, 0, 2, -8, 36, then the sign "$-$" could arbitrarily have been assigned to 0 to give the desired pattern of alternating signs.

To narrow the search for real zeros of a polynomial function still further, we have the **location theorem:**

THEOREM 11.12 *Let $P(x)$ be a polynomial over the field R of real numbers. If x_1, $x_2 \in R$, with $x_1 < x_2$, and if $P(x_1)$ and $P(x_2)$ are opposite in sign, then there exists at least one $c \in R$, $x_1 < c < x_2$, such that $P(c) = 0$.*

Proof. First, let $P(x_1) < 0 < P(x_2)$, and $x_1 < x_2$. Then, by Theorem 11.9, there must exist $c \in R$, $x_1 < c < x_2$, such that $P(c) = 0$. Next, let $P(x_2) < 0 < P(x_1)$ and $x_1 < x_2$. Then, also by Theorem 11.9, there must exist $c \in R$, $x_1 < c < x_2$ such that $P(c) = 0$. Since x_1 and x_2 are arbitrary, the theorem is proved.

This theorem expresses the fact that if the graphs of $[x_1, P(x_1)]$ and $[x_2, P(x_2)]$ are on opposite sides of the x-axis, then the graph of $y = P(x)$ must cross the x-axis at some (at least one) point c between x_1 and x_2.

Example. Discuss the possibilities for real zeros of

$$\{[x, P(x)] \mid P(x) = 32x^4 - 8x^3 - 148x^2 + 162x - 45\}.$$

Solution. We observe first that, by Descartes' Rule of Signs, Theorem 11.10, we can have at most three positive and one negative real zero.   Next, we apply synthetic division to obtain the following array:

	32	−8	−148	162	−45
0	32	−8	−148	162	−45
1	32	24	−124	38	−7
2	32	56	−36	90	135
3	32	88	116	510	1485
−1	32	−40	−108	270	−315
−2	32	−72	−4	170	−385
−3	32	−104	164	−330	945

Examining this array, we find that, by Theorem 11.11, 3 is an upper and −3 is a lower bound for real zeros.   By the remainder theorem, $P(1) = -7$ and $P(2) = 135$, and since these are of opposite sign, Theorem 11.12 assures us that there is at least one real zero between 1 and 2.   Similarly, we find there is at least one zero between −2 and −3, because $P(-2) = -385$ while $P(-3) = 945$. Furthermore, by Theorem 11.8, P must have precisely 4 real or complex zeros, not necessarily all distinct, because $P(x)$ is of degree four.   By Theorem 11.6, any nonreal (imaginary) complex roots must occur in conjugate pairs, so we can assert, as a conclusion, the following possibilities:

1. P has two real zeros, one between 1 and 2, and one between −2 and −3;
2. P has four real zeros:

   a. three between 1 and 2 and one between −2 and −3, or vice versa,
   b. two between 2 and 3, one between 1 and 2, and one between −2 and −3,
   c. two between −2 and 1, one between 1 and 2, and one between −2 and −3.

As a matter of fact, the zeros of P are $1/2$, $3/4$, $3/2$, and $-5/2$, so that case 2(c) is the true situation; but in order to have detected this, we would have had to conduct a rather extensive search for sign changes in $P(x)$ over the interval $0 \leq x \leq 1$.

EXERCISE 11.3

Use Theorem 11.10 to discuss the nature of the roots of each polynomial equation.

1. $x^4 - 2x^3 + 2x + 1 = 0$
2. $3x^4 + 3x^3 + 2x^2 - x + 1 = 0$
3. $2x^5 + 3x^3 + 2x + 1 = 0$
4. $4x^5 - 2x^3 - 3x - 2 = 0$
5. $3x^4 + 1 = 0$
6. $2x^5 - 1 = 0$

Find an upper bound and a lower bound for the real roots of the following polynomial equations.

7. $x^3 + 2x^2 - 7x - 8 = 0$ 8. $x^3 - 8x + 5 = 0$

9. $x^4 - 2x^3 - 7x^2 + 10x + 10 = 0$ 10. $x^3 - 4x^2 - 4x + 12 = 0$

11. $x^5 - 3x^3 + 24 = 0$ 12. $x^5 - 3x^4 - 1 = 0$

13. $2x^5 + x^4 - 2x - 1 = 0$ 14. $2x^5 - 2x^2 + x - 2 = 0$

Use Theorem 11.12 to verify each statement in Problems 15–20.

15. $\{[x, f(x)] \mid f(x) = x^3 - 3x + 1\}$ has a zero between 0 and 1.

16. $\{[x, f(x)] \mid f(x) = 2x^3 + 7x^2 + 2x - 6\}$ has a zero between -2 and -1.

17. $\{[x, g(x)] \mid g(x) = x^4 - 2x^2 + 12x - 17\}$ has a zero between -3 and -2.

18. $\{[x, g(x)] \mid g(x) = 2x^4 + 3x^3 - 14x^2 - 15x + 9\}$ has a zero between -2 and -1.

19. $\{[x, P(x)] \mid P(x) = 2x^2 + 4x - 4\}$ has one zero between -3 and -2, and one between 0 and 1.

20. $\{[x, P(x)] \mid P(x) = x^3 - x^2 - 2x + 1\}$ has one zero between -2 and -1, one between 0 and 1, and one between 1 and 2.

21. Prove that if all of the coefficients of $P(x)$ are positive, then $P(x) = 0$ has no positive real roots.

22. Prove that if $P(x)$ involves only even powers of x, and if all of its coefficients including the constant term are positive, then $P(x) = 0$ has no real roots.

23. If $P(x)$ has no zero coefficients—that is, if every power less than the highest power of x occurs in $P(x)$—then $P(x)$ is said to be a **complete polynomial.** Prove that if $P(x)$ is a complete polynomial, and if the coefficients of $P(x)$ alternate in sign, then $P(x) = 0$ can have no negative real roots.

24. Prove that if $P(x)$ is a complete polynomial (see Problem 23), and if $P(x) = 0$ has all of its roots real, then the number of positive roots is equal to the number of variations of sign in $P(x)$.

25. Prove Theorem 11.11-II.

11.4 RATIONAL ZEROS OF POLYNOMIAL FUNCTIONS

The results of the present section depend on the notion of a **prime number.** If a is an element of the set N of counting numbers, and $a \neq 1$, then a is a prime number if and only if a has no prime factor in N other than itself and 1; otherwise, a is a **composite number.**

For example, 2 and 3 are prime numbers, and $6 = 2 \cdot 3$ is composite; but 1 is considered to be neither prime nor composite.

The **unique-factorization theorem**, or **fundamental theorem of arithmetic** (which we shall not prove), is the following.

THEOREM 11.13   *If a is a composite number, then a is the product of only one set of prime factors; that is, the prime factorization of a is unique except for the ordering of the factors.*

For example, $60 = 2 \cdot 2 \cdot 3 \cdot 5 = 2 \cdot 3 \cdot 2 \cdot 5$.

Two integers a and b are said to be **relatively prime** if and only if they have no prime factors in common.   The fraction a/b is said to express a rational number in **lowest terms** if and only if a and b are relatively prime.   For example, -6 and 35 are relatively prime, as are 1 and 2; but $3/6$ does not express a rational number in lowest terms, since $6 = 2 \cdot 3$.

If all the coefficients of the defining equation

$$P(x) = a_0 x^n + a_1 x^{n-1} + \cdots + a_n$$

of a polynomial function P are integers, then we can identify all possible rational zeros of P by means of the following.

THEOREM 11.14   *If the rational number in lowest terms p/q is a solution of*

$$P(x) = a_0 x^n + a_1 x^{n-1} + \cdots + a_n = 0,$$

where $a_i \in J$, then p is an integral factor of a_n and q is an integral factor of a_0.

Proof.   Since p/q is a solution of $P(x) = 0$, we have

$$a_0\left(\frac{p}{q}\right)^n + a_1\left(\frac{p}{q}\right)^{n-1} + \cdots + a_n = 0,$$

and we can multiply each member here by q^n to obtain

$$a_0 p^n + a_1 p^{n-1}q + \cdots + a_n q^n = 0.$$

Adding $-a_n q^n$ to each member and factoring p from each term in the left-hand member of the resulting equation, we have

$$p(a_0 p^{n-1} + a_1 p^{n-2} + \cdots + a_{n-1}) = -a_n q^n.$$

Since the integers are closed with respect to addition and multiplication, the expression in parentheses in the left-hand member here represents an integer, say r, so that we have

$$pr = -a_n q^n,$$

where pr is an integer having p as a factor.   Hence, p is a factor of $-a_n q^n$. But, by Theorem 11.13, p is not a factor of q^n because, by hypothesis, p i not a factor of q; hence p must be a factor of a_n. In a similar manner, by writing the equation

$$a_0 p^n + a_1 p^{n-1} q + \cdots + a_n q^n = 0$$

in the form

$$-a_0 p^n = a_1 p^{n-1} q + \cdots + a_n q^n,$$

we can factor q from each term in the right-hand member and show that q must be a factor of a_0.

Example. List all possible rational zeros of

$$\{[x, P(x)] \mid P(x) = 2x^3 - 4x^2 + 3x + 9\}.$$

Solution. Rational zeros, p/q, must, by Theorem 11.14, be such that p is an integral factor of 9 and q is an integral factor of 2. Hence

$$p \in \{-9, -3, -1, 1, 3, 9\}, \quad q \in \{-2, -1, 1, 2\},$$

and the set of possible rational zeros of P is

$$\left\{-9, -\frac{9}{2}, -3, -\frac{3}{2}, -1, -\frac{1}{2}, \frac{1}{2}, 1, \frac{3}{2}, 3, \frac{9}{2}, 9\right\}.$$

It is important to observe that Theorem 11.14 does not assure us that a polynomial function with integral coefficients indeed has a rational zero; it simply enables us to identify possibilities for rational zeros. These can then be checked by synthetic substitution. The identification of the zeros of P in the previous example is left as an exercise.

As a special case of Theorem 11.14, it is evident that if a function p is defined by

$$P(x) = x^n + a_1 x^{n-1} + \cdots + a_n,$$

in which $a_i \in J$ and $a_0 = 1$, then any rational zero of P must be an integer, and, moreover, must be an integral factor of a_n.

Example. Find all rational zeros of

$$\{[x, P(x)] \mid P(x) = x^3 - 4x^2 + x + 6\}.$$

Solution. The only possible rational zeros of P are $-6, -3, -2, -1, 1, 2, 3$, and 6. Using synthetic division, we set up the following array.

	1	-4	1	6
-6	1	-10	61	-360
-3	1	-7	22	-60
-2	1	-6	13	-20
-1	1	-5	6	0

We can cease our trials with -1, since, by the remainder theorem, -1 is a zero of P, and the remaining zeros can be obtained from the depressed equation

$x^2 - 5x + 6 = 0$ by writing this as $(x - 2)(x - 3) = 0$ and observing that 2 and 3 are also zeros. Had the trial process begun with -1, 2, or 3, rather than -6, a single trial would have rendered the rational zeros immediately evident.

EXERCISE 11.4

Find all integral zeros of each function.

1. $\{[x, f(x)] \mid f(x) = 3x^3 - 13x^2 + 6x - 8\}$

2. $\{[x, f(x)] \mid f(x) = x^4 - x^2 - 4x + 4\}$

3. $\{[x, f(x)] \mid f(x) = x^4 + x^3 + 2x - 4\}$

4. $\{[x, f(x)] \mid f(x) = 5x^3 + 11x^2 - 2x - 8\}$

5. $\{[y, P(y)] \mid P(y) = 2x^4 - 3x^3 - 8x^2 - 5x - 3\}$

6. $\{[y, P(y)] \mid P(y) = 3x^4 - 40x^3 + 130x^2 - 120x + 27\}$

Find all rational zeros of each function.

7. $\{[x, f(x)] \mid f(x) = 2x^3 + 3x^2 - 14x - 21\}$

8. $\{[x, f(x)] \mid f(x) = 3x^4 - 11x^3 + 9x^2 + 13x - 10\}$

9. $\{[x, P(x)] \mid P(x) = 4x^4 - 13x^3 - 7x^2 + 41x - 14\}$

10. $\{[x, P(x)] \mid P(x) = 2x^3 - 4x^2 + 3x + 9\}$

11. $\{[x, Q(x)] \mid Q(x) = 2x^3 - 7x^2 + 10x - 6\}$

12. $\{[x, Q(x)] \mid Q(x) = x^3 + 3x^2 - 4x - 12\}$

Find all complex zeros of each function. *Hint:* First find all rational zeros.

13. $\{[x, P(x)] \mid P(y) = 3x^3 - 5x^2 - 14x - 4\}$

14. $\{[x, P(x)] \mid P(y) = x^3 - 4x^2 - 5x + 14\}$

15. $\{[x, P(x)] \mid P(x) = 2x^4 + 3x^3 + 2x^2 - 1\}$

16. $\{[x, P(x)] \mid P(x) = 8x^4 - 22x^3 + 29x^2 - 66x + 15\}$

17. $\{[x, P(x)] \mid P(x) = 12x^4 + 7x^3 + 7x - 12\}$

18. $\{[x, P(x)] \mid P(x) = 6x^4 - 13x^3 + 2x^2 - 4x + 15\}$

19. Factor the polynomial $2x^3 + 3x^2 - 2x - 3$ over C.

20. Factor the polynomial $x^4 - 6x^3 - 3x^2 - 24x - 28$ over C.

21. Show that $\sqrt{3}$ is irrational. *Hint:* Consider the equation $x^2 - 3 = 0$.

22. Show that $\sqrt[3]{2}$ is irrational.

11.5   IRRATIONAL ZEROS OF POLYNOMIAL FUNCTIONS

The location theorem can often be used to isolate some real zeros of polynomial functions on intervals of the domain. Once we have isolated such zeros, various means exist for obtaining approximations to zeros that are irrational. We shall be concerned with only one such means herein, namely, linear interpolation.

Consider the function

$$P = \{[x, P(x)] \mid P(x) = x^3 - 3x^2 - 2x + 5\}.$$

By means of synthetic division and the remainder theorem, we can establish that $(1, 1)$ and $(2, -3)$ are in the function, and hence, by the location theorem, there is at least one zero between 1 and 2. Actually, since $P(x)$ is positive

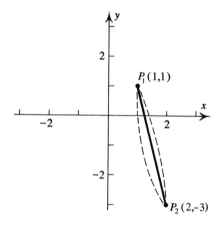

Figure 11.1

for x large and positive, and $P(x)$ is negative for x large in absolute value and negative, one of the remaining two roots is > 2 and the other < 1, so that there is exactly one zero between 1 and 2. Since the only rational zero for P would have to be an integer (the leading coefficient is 1), any zeros between 1 and 2 must be irrational. Figure 11.1 shows the two points P_1 $(1, 1)$, and P_2 $(2, -3)$, and a straight line joining them.

The dashed lines show possibilities for the graph of P on the interval $1 \le x \le 2$, but since we are uncertain of the curvature, we cannot be sure on which side of the line segment the graph actually lies. In either case, however, the point where the segment intersects the x-axis clearly is close (in some sense) to the point where the graph of P intersects this axis. In Figure 11.2, we show the same segment, this time with an additional detail.

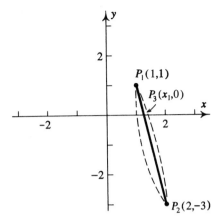

Figure 11.2

If we can find a value for the coordinate of the x-intercept of the line segment P_1P_2, then we will have a first approximation to a zero for P. Since the slope of P_1P_3 is the same as the slope for P_1P_2, we have

$$\frac{0 - 1}{x_1 - 1} = \frac{-3 - 1}{2 - 1},$$

from which

$$x_1 - 1 = \frac{1}{4}$$

or

$$x_1 = \frac{5}{4}.$$

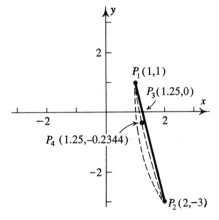

Figure 11.3

To find $P(5/4)$, we divide $P(x)$ synthetically by 1.25, as follows.

$$
\begin{array}{r|rrrr}
1.25 & 1 & -3 & -2 & 5 \\
 & & 1.25 & -2.1875 & -5.234375 \\
\hline
 & 1 & -1.75 & -4.1875 & -0.234375
\end{array}
$$

Thus, $P(5/4) \approx -0.2344$. Figure 11.3 shows our present situation, from which it is clear that the graph of P crosses the x-axis to the left of P_3, so that, at least as far as this point is concerned, the graph of P is concave upward on this interval. We can now repeat the linear-interpolation process,

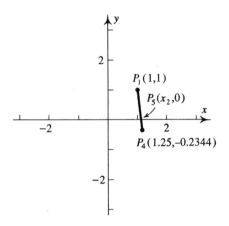

Figure 11.4

using P_1 and P_4, to obtain another approximation to the zero for P. Figure 11.4 shows the necessary detail. Again, since the slope of P_1P_5 is the same as the slope of P_1P_4, we have

$$
\frac{0-1}{x_2-1} = \frac{-0.2344-1}{1.25-1},
$$

from which

$$
x_2 - 1 = \frac{0.25}{1.2344} \approx 0.2025
$$

and

$$
x_2 \approx 1.2025.
$$

Thus, a second approximation to the desired zero of P is 1.2025. This process can be continued as long as necessary to obtain any desired degree of accuracy. To three decimal places, the zero sought here is 1.202.

EXERCISE 11.5

Find to two decimal places the indicated real zero(s) of the function.

1. $\{[x, P(x)] \mid P(x) = x^3 - 3x + 1\}$; between 1 and 2.

2. $\{[x, P(x)] \mid P(x) = 2x^3 - x^2 + 3x + 1\}$; between 0 and -1.

3. $\{[x, P(x)] \mid P(x) = x^3 - 2x - 5\}$; between 2 and 3.

4. $\{[x, P(x)] \mid P(x) = x^3 + 2x^2 - 1\}$; between 0 and 1.

5. $\{[x, P(x)] \mid P(x) = x^3 + 3x^2 - 6x - 3\}$; the greatest positive.

6. $\{[x, P(x)] \mid P(x) = 2x^3 - 5x^2 - x + 5\}$; the least positive.

7. $\{[x, P(x)] \mid P(x) = x^3 + x - 1\}$; all.

8. $\{[x, P(x)] \mid P(x) = x^4 - 4x^3 - 4x + 12\}$; all.

9. Find to two decimal places a numeral for $\sqrt[3]{5}$. *Hint:* Consider the equation $x^3 - 5 = 0$.

10. Find to two decimal places a numeral for $\sqrt[5]{2}$.

SEQUENCES
AND SERIES

12.1 MATHEMATICAL INDUCTION

The material in the present section depends on a special property of the set N of natural numbers—that is, the set

$$\{1, 2, 3, \cdots\}$$

of positive elements in the ordered integral domain J of integers.

By Postulate F-9, any ordered integral domain contains an identity element 1 for multiplication, and by Postulate O-2 this element is positive, since $1 = 1^2$. Further, by Postulates F-1 and O-2, if k is a positive element of an ordered integral domain, then so is $k + 1$. Accordingly, the two following properties, which we state only for the set N of positive integers, actually can be extended to corresponding properties of the positive elements of any ordered integral domain:

a. $1 \in N$.

b. If $k \in N$, then $k + 1 \in N$.

These two properties might be illustrated, for example, with the set Q_+ of the positive elements of the ordered integral domain Q of rational numbers, or the set R_+ of positive elements of the ordered integral domain R of real numbers, in place of N, and with $k = 1/2$.

What makes the set J of integers stand apart from other ordered integral domains is that *the set N of positive elements of J contains no elements not implied by properties a and b.* In this sense, the set J is the *least extensive* of all integral domains. We might state this property (which we shall not prove) as follows:

c. Let M be a set of positive integers. If $1 \in M$ and if the assumption that $k \in M$ implies that $k + 1 \in M$, then $M = N$.

This property underlies the following theorem, which is called the **principle of mathematical induction**.

THEOREM 12.1 *If a given open sentence involving n is true for n = 1, and if its truth for n = k implies its truth for n = k + 1, then it is true for every natural number n.*

Proof. Let M be the set of positive integers for which the open sentence is true and apply the foregoing property (c) to show that the sentence is true for all natural numbers.

We can exploit this principle to prove a number of assertions. Although the technique we shall use is called **proof by mathematical induction**, the argument we shall employ is deductive, as have been all of the other arguments in this book. Proofs by mathematical induction require two things:

a. A demonstration that the assertion to be proved is true for the natural number 1.
b. A demonstration that the truth of the assertion for a natural number k implies its truth for $k + 1$.

When these two demonstrations have been made, the principle of mathematical induction assures us that the assertion is true for every natural number.

Example. Prove that $2^n > n$ for every natural number n.

Solution. The proof consists of two parts.

1. We must first show that $2^n > n$ for $n = 1$. We have

$$2^1 = 2 > 1,$$

so that the assertion is true for $n = 1$.

2. We must next show that if $2^k > k$, then $2^{k+1} > k + 1$. We begin by assuming that $2^k > k$. Then, by Theorem 1.15-III,

$$2 \cdot 2^k > 2 \cdot k.$$

Furthermore, for each natural number k, it is true that $2k \geq k + 1$, because $2k = k + k$, and $k + k \geq k + 1$ for every $k \geq 1$. Therefore, we have

$$2 \cdot 2^k > 2k \geq k + 1,$$

or

$$2^{k+1} > k + 1.$$

Hence the assumption that $2^k > k$ implies that $2^{k+1} > k + 1$. This completes our demonstration of the two facts required in a proof by mathematical induction. We have shown that:

1. $2^n > n$ for $n = 1$;

2. $2^k > k$ implies that $2^{k+1} > k + 1$;

thus the principle of mathematical induction assures us that $2^n > n$ for every natural number n.

This method of proof is often compared to lining up a row of dominoes, with the assumption that whenever one domino is toppled, the one following will topple. One then needs only to topple the first domino ($n = 1$) and the whole row following will topple, as indicated in Figure 12.1.

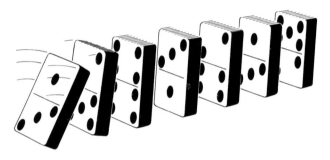

Figure 12.1

Here is another example of a proof by mathematical induction:

Example. Prove that the sum of the first n natural numbers is $n(n + 1)/2$.

Solution. In symbols, we wish to show that

$$1 + 2 + 3 + \cdots + n = \frac{n(n + 1)}{2}.$$

As always in proofs by mathematical induction, we must do two things:

1. We must first show that the assertion is true for $n = 1$; i.e., that

$$1 = \frac{1(1 + 1)}{2},$$

or

$$1 = 1,$$

which is true. (This topples the first domino.)

2. We must next show that the truth of

$$1 + 2 + 3 + \cdots + k = \frac{k(k + 1)}{2}$$

implies the truth of

$$1 + 2 + 3 + \cdots + k + (k + 1) = \frac{(k + 1)[(k + 1) + 1]}{2}.$$

That is, we must show that the truth of the assertion for $n = k$ implies its truth for $n = k + 1$. (Compare this with "If any domino is toppled, its successor will be toppled.")

Now, assume the truth of

$$1 + 2 + 3 + \cdots + k = \frac{k(k + 1)}{2}.$$

Then, by the addition law of equality, Theorem 1.1, we may add $k + 1$ to each member of this equation and obtain

$$1 + 2 + 3 + \cdots + k + (k + 1) = \frac{k(k + 1)}{2} + (k + 1)$$

$$= (k + 1)\left(\frac{k}{2} + 1\right)$$

$$= (k + 1)\left(\frac{k + 2}{2}\right)$$

$$= \frac{(k + 1)[(k + 1) + 1]}{2}.$$

Thus the second fact necessary for our proof is established. By the principle of mathematical induction, the assertion is true for every natural number n.

An alternative means is available to us for accomplishing the second part of the proof. We assume that

$$1 + 2 + 3 + \cdots + k = \frac{k(k + 1)}{2}$$

is true, and then consider the desired consequence,

$$1 + 2 + 3 + \cdots + k + (k + 1) = \frac{(k + 1)[(k + 1) + 1]}{2}.$$

We can establish the truth of the latter statement by replacing $1 + 2 + 3 + \cdots + k$ in the left-hand member by its equal, $k(k + 1)/2$, to give us

$$\frac{k(k + 1)}{2} + (k + 1) = \frac{(k + 1)[(k + 1) + 1]}{2},$$

and then show that this is an identity.

Earlier in this book, we argued that $x^m \cdot x^n = x^{m+n}$ for each real number x and any natural numbers m and n, by lining up factors in the product $x^m x^n$,

$$\underbrace{(xxx\cdots x)}_{m}\underbrace{(xxx\cdots x)}_{n},$$

and observing that there are $m + n$ factors present. The argument can be made by induction, however, and offers an interesting example of induction using two variables, m and n.

Let us begin by adopting a new definition of x^n, a **recursive definition** that is more adaptable to proofs by mathematical induction.

DEFINITION 12.1   *If $x \in R$ and $n \in N$, then*

$$x^1 = x, \quad x^{n+1} = x^n \cdot x.$$

Let us now show that our former defining property of x^n is a consequence of the present definition.

THEOREM 12.2   *If $x \in R$ and $n \in N$, then*

$$x^n = \underbrace{xxx\cdots x.}_{n \text{ factors}}$$

Proof. We have $x^1 = x$ by Definition 12.1. This is the first step in our proof. Now assume that

$$x^k = \underbrace{xxx\cdots x.}_{k \text{ factors}}$$

Then by Definition 12.1,

$$x^{k+1} = x^k \cdot x.$$

By assumption, then, we have

$$x^{k+1} = \underbrace{xxx\cdots x \cdot x}_{k \text{ factors}} = \underbrace{xxx\cdots x,}_{\substack{k+1 \\ \text{factors}}}$$

as desired. This is the second step in the principle of mathematical induction, and the proof is now complete.

Now let us turn to the proof that $x^m \cdot x^n = x^{m+n}$.

Proof. We must do the usual two things.

1. First, let m be any natural number. Then, by Definition 12.1,

$$x^m \cdot x^1 = x^m \cdot x = x^{m+1},$$

and we have the first requirement for a proof by mathematical induction.

2. We next assume that

$$x^m \cdot x^k = x^{m+k} \tag{1}$$

and wish to show that this implies that

$$x^m \cdot x^{k+1} = x^{m+(k+1)}.$$

By Theorem 1.2, we may multiply each member of (1) by x to obtain

$$x^m \cdot x^k \cdot x = x^{m+k} \cdot x,$$

or

$$x^m \cdot x^{k+1} = x^{(m+k)+1}$$
$$= x^{m+(k+1)}.$$

We have shown that $x^m \cdot x^n = x^{m+n}$ for $n = 1$, and that if $x^m \cdot x^k = x^{m+k}$, then $x^m \cdot x^{k+1} = x^{m+(k+1)}$. Thus, for *any* natural number m, and every natural number n, we have

$$x^m \cdot x^n = x^{m+n}.$$

Let us give one more example of a proof by mathematical induction, this time concerning complex numbers $z = a + bi$ and their conjugates $\bar{z} = a - bi$, where $a, b \in R$.

THEOREM 12.3   *For any given complex numbers $z_1, z_2, \cdots, z_n$,*

$$\overline{z_1 z_2 \cdots z_n} = \bar{z}_1 \bar{z}_2 \cdots \bar{z}_n.$$

Proof.   The result is trivial for $n = 1$, namely $\bar{z}_1 = \bar{z}_1$. For $n = 2$, let

$$z_1 = a_1 + b_1 i, \text{ and } z_2 = a_2 + b_2 i.$$

Then

$$z_1 z_2 = (a_1 + b_1 i)(a_2 + b_2 i) = (a_1 a_2 - b_1 b_2) + (a_1 b_2 + a_2 b_1)i,$$

so that

$$\overline{z_1 z_2} = (a_1 a_2 - b_1 b_2) - (a_1 b_2 + a_2 b_1)i.$$

But also

$$\bar{z}_1 \bar{z}_2 = (a_1 - b_1 i)(a_2 - b_2 i) = (a_1 a_2 - b_1 b_2) - (a_1 b_2 + a_2 b_1)i.$$

Assume now that

$$\overline{z_1 z_2 \cdots z_k} = \bar{z}_1 \bar{z}_2 \cdots \bar{z}_k.$$

Then

$$\overline{z_1 z_2 \cdots z_k z_{k+1}} = \overline{(z_1 z_2 \cdots z_k) z_{k+1}}$$

by Postulate F-7; but

$$\overline{(z_1 z_2 \cdots z_k) z_{k+1}} = \overline{z_1 z_2 \cdots z_k} \; \bar{z}_{k+1}$$

by the result for $n = 2$, and

$$\overline{z_1 z_2 \cdots z_k} = \bar{z}_1 \bar{z}_2 \cdots \bar{z}_k$$

by assumption. Hence by the substitution law for equality, E-4, we have

$$\overline{z_1 z_2 \cdots z_{k+1}} = \bar{z}_1 \bar{z}_2 \cdots \bar{z}_k \bar{z}_{k+1},$$

as desired.

Theorem 11.4 is a special case of Theorem 12.3, in which all the z's except one are equal, and that one is the real constant c, for which $c = \bar{c}$.

EXERCISE 12.1

By mathematical induction, prove the validity of the formulas in Problems 1–10 for all positive integral values of n.

1. $1 + 2 + 3 + \cdots + n = \dfrac{n(n+1)}{2}$

2. $1 + 3 + 5 + \cdots + (2n - 1) = n^2$

3. $2 + 4 + 6 + \cdots + 2n = n(n+1)$

4. $2 + 6 + 10 + \cdots + (4n - 2) = 2n^2$

5. $1^2 + 2^2 + 3^2 + \cdots + n^2 = \dfrac{n(n+1)(2n+1)}{6}$

6. $2 + 2^2 + 2^3 + \cdots + 2^n = 2^{n+1} - 2$

7. $1^3 + 3^3 + 5^3 + \cdots + (2n - 1)^3 = n^2(2n^2 - 1)$

8. $\dfrac{1}{1\cdot 2} + \dfrac{1}{2\cdot 3} + \dfrac{1}{3\cdot 4} + \cdots + \dfrac{1}{n(n+1)} = \dfrac{n}{n+1}$

9. $1\cdot 2 + 2\cdot 3 + 3\cdot 4 + \cdots + n(n+1) = \dfrac{n(n+1)(n+2)}{3}$

10. $1\cdot 4 + 2\cdot 9 + 3\cdot 16 + \cdots + n(n+1)^2 = \dfrac{1}{12} n(n+1)(n+2)(3n+5)$

11. Show that if $2 + 4 + 6 + \cdots + 2n = n(n+1) + 2$ is true for $n = k$, then it is true for $n = k + 1$. Is it true for all k?

12. Prove that

$$1 + 2 + 3 + \cdots + n < \tfrac{1}{8}(2n + 1)^2$$

for every $n \in N$.

13. Prove that $a^n - b^n$ is divisible by $a - b$ for every $n \in N$. *Hint:* Use the relation $a^{k+1} - b^{k+1} = a^k(a - b) + b(a^k - b^k)$.

14. Prove that $a^{2n-1} + b^{2n-1}$ is divisible by $a + b$ for every $n \in N$. *Hint:* Start by verifying that

$$a^{2n+1} + b^{2n+1} = a^{2n}(a + b) - a^{2n-1}b(a + b) + b^2(a^{2n-1} + b^{2n-1}).$$

15. Prove that $a^{2n} - b^{2n}$ is divisible by $a + b$ for all $n \in N$.

16. Prove that if $0 < a < b$, then $\left(\dfrac{a}{b}\right)^{n+1} < \left(\dfrac{a}{b}\right)^{n}$ for every $n \in N$.

17. Prove that if $0 < b < a$, then $\left(\dfrac{a}{b}\right)^{n+1} > \left(\dfrac{a}{b}\right)^{n}$ for every $n \in N$.

18. Prove that if $z_1, z_2, \cdots, z_n \in C$, then $\overline{z_1 + z_2 + \cdots z_n} = \bar{z}_1 + \bar{z}_2 + \cdots + \bar{z}_n$.

12.2 SEQUENCES

DEFINITION 12.2 *A **sequence function** is a function having as its domain the set N of positive integers* 1, 2, 3, $\cdots$. *A **finite-sequence function** has as its domain the set of positive integers* 1, 2, 3, $\cdots$, *n, for some fixed n.*

For example, the function defined by

$$s(n) = n + 3, \quad n \in \{1, 2, 3, \cdots\} \tag{1}$$

is a sequence function. The elements in the range of such a function, considered in the order

$$s(1), s(2), s(3), s(4), \cdots,$$

are said to form a **sequence**. Similarly, the elements of a finite-sequence function, considered in order, constitute a *finite sequence*. Thus the sequence associated with (1) is found by successively substituting the numbers 1, 2, 3, $\cdots$ for n:

$$s(1) = (1) + 3 = 4, \qquad\qquad s(2) = (2) + 3 = 5,$$

$$s(3) = (3) + 3 = 6, \qquad\qquad s(4) = (4) + 3 = 7,$$

etc., so that the first four terms are 4, 5, 6, and 7. The nth term, or general term, is $n + 3$. As another example, the first five terms of the sequence defined by the equation

$$s(n) = \frac{3}{2n - 1}, \quad n \in \{1, 2, 3, \cdots\},$$

are 3/1, 3/3, 3/5, 3/7, and 3/9, and the twenty-fifth term is

$$s(25) = \frac{3}{2(25) - 1} = \frac{3}{49}.$$

Given several terms in a sequence, it is often possible to surmise an expression for a general term of a sequence to which they belong. Thus, if the first three terms in a sequence are

$$2, 4, 6, \cdots, \tag{2}$$

we may, by a process of trial and error, or simply by inspection, surmise that the general term is

$$s(n) = 2n.$$

If, however, only a finite number of successive terms are known for a sequence, and no rule is given for determining the general term, then a *unique* general term cannot be obtained. For example, both

$$s(n) = 2n$$

and

$$s(n) = 2n + (n - 1)(n - 2)(n - 3)$$

generate the sequence 2, 4, 6, but they produce different sequences for terms following the third.

The notation ordinarily used for the terms in a sequence is not function notation as such. It is customary to denote the *j*th term in a sequence by means of a subscript. Thus, we would use s_j rather than $s(j)$, and the sequence $s(1), s(2), s(3), s(4), \cdots$ would appear as $s_1, s_2, s_3, s_4, \cdots$.

EXERCISE 12.2

Find the first four terms in the sequence with the general term as given.

Examples.

a. $s_n = \dfrac{n(n + 1)}{2}$

b. $s_n = (-1)^n 2^n$

Solutions.

a. $s_1 = \dfrac{1(1 + 1)}{2} = 1$

$s_2 = \dfrac{2(2 + 1)}{2} = 3$

$s_3 = \dfrac{3(3 + 1)}{2} = 6$

$s_4 = \dfrac{4(4 + 1)}{2} = 10$

1, 3, 6, 10

b. $s_1 = (-1)^1 2^1 = -2$

$s_2 = (-1)^2 2^2 = 4$

$s_3 = (-1)^3 2^3 = -8$

$s_4 = (-1)^4 2^4 = 16$

$-2, 4, -8, 16$

1. $s_n = n - 5$

2. $s_n = 2n - 3$

3. $s_n = \dfrac{n^2 - 2}{2}$

4. $s_n = \dfrac{3}{n^2 + 1}$

5. $s_n = 1 + \dfrac{1}{n}$

6. $s_n = \dfrac{n}{2n - 1}$

7. $s_n = \dfrac{n(n - 1)}{2}$

8. $s_n = \dfrac{5}{n(n + 1)}$

9. $s_n = (-1)^n$

10. $s_n = (-1)^{n+1}$

11. $s_n = \dfrac{(-1)^n(n - 2)}{n}$

12. $s_n = (-1)^{n-1}3^{n+1}$

Find the general term for a sequence with the first four terms as given.

Examples.

a. $2, \dfrac{3}{2}, \dfrac{4}{3}, \dfrac{5}{4}, \cdots$

b. $x, \dfrac{-x^2}{2}, \dfrac{x^3}{3}, \dfrac{-x^4}{4}, \cdots$

Solutions. There are no unique solutions. The following answers are obtained by trial and error or by inspection; they produce the given sequences.

a. $\dfrac{n + 1}{n}$

b. $(-1)^{n+1}\dfrac{x^n}{n}$

13. $4, 8, 12, 16, \cdots$

14. $5, 10, 15, 20, \cdots$

15. $2, 5, 8, 11, \cdots$

16. $1, 3, 5, 7, \cdots$

17. $-1, 1, -1, 1, \cdots$

18. $1, -1, 1, -1, \cdots$

19. $-3, 5, -7, 9, \cdots$

20. $3, -7, 11, -15, \cdots$

21. $\dfrac{1}{2}, \dfrac{2}{3}, \dfrac{3}{4}, \dfrac{4}{5}, \cdots$

22. $\dfrac{1}{3}, \dfrac{1}{4}, \dfrac{1}{5}, \dfrac{1}{6}, \cdots$

23. $2, 5, 10, 17, \cdots$

24. $\dfrac{1}{2}, \dfrac{1}{4}, \dfrac{1}{8}, \dfrac{1}{16}, \cdots$

25. $x^2, x^3, x^4, x^5, \cdots$

26. $x^2, x^4, x^6, x^8, \cdots$

27. $-x, x^3, -x^5, x^7, \cdots$

28. $1, -x, x^2, -x^3, \cdots$

29. A culture of bacteria doubles in number every hour. If there were originally ten bacteria in the culture, how many are there after two hours? Four hours? n hours?

30. A ball rebounds one half of the distance it falls. When dropped from eight feet, how high does it rebound on the first bounce? On the second bounce? On the nth bounce?

31. A certain radioactive substance has a half-life of 2400 years; that is, 50% of the original material is present at the end of 2400 years. If 100 grams were produced today, how many grams would be present in 4800 years? In 9600 years?

12.3   SERIES

Associated with any sequence is a *series*.

DEFINITION 12.3   *A series is the indicated sum of the terms in a sequence.*

For example, with the finite sequence

$$4, 7, 10, \cdots, 3n + 1, \tag{1}$$

for a given counting number n, there is associated the finite series

$$S_n = 4 + 7 + 10 + \cdots + (3n + 1); \tag{2}$$

similarly, with the finite sequence

$$x, x^2, x^3, x^4, \cdots, x^n \tag{3}$$

there is associated the finite series

$$S_n = x + x^2 + x^3 + x^4 + \cdots + x^n. \tag{4}$$

Since the terms in the series are the same as those in the sequence, we can refer to the first term or the second term or the general term of a series in the same manner as we do for a sequence.

A series for which the general term is known can be represented in a very convenient, compact way by means of what is called **sigma** or **summation notation**. The Greek letter $\sum$ (sigma) is used to denote a sum. For example, series (2) can be written

$$S_n = \sum_{j=1}^{n} (3j + 1), \tag{5}$$

where we understand that S_n is the series having terms obtained by replacing j in the expression $3j + 1$ with the numbers $1, 2, 3, \cdots, n$, successively. Thus

$$S_6 = \sum_{j=1}^{6} (3j + 1)$$

appears in expanded form as

$$S_6 = 4 + 7 + 10 + 13 + 16 + 19.$$

The variable used in conjunction with summation notation is called the **index of summation,** and the set of integers over which we sum (in this case $\{1, 2, 3, 4, 5, 6\}$) is called the **range of summation.**

To show that a series has an infinite number of terms, we cannot use the notation S_n for the sum, because there is no value to substitute for n. We agree, therefore, to adopt notation such as

$$S_\infty = \sum_{j=1}^{\infty} \frac{1}{2^j} \tag{6}$$

to indicate that there is no last term in a series. To write (6) in expanded form, we have

$$S_\infty = \frac{1}{2} + \frac{1}{4} + \frac{1}{8} + \cdots.$$

The meaning, if any, of such an infinite sum will be discussed later.

EXERCISE 12.3

Write in expanded form.

Examples.

a. $\displaystyle\sum_{j=2}^{5} (j^2 + 1)$ b. $\displaystyle\sum_{k=1}^{\infty} (-1)^k 2^{k+1}$

Solutions.

a. $j = 2,\ (2)^2 + 1 = 5$ b. $k = 1,\ (-1)^1 2^{1+1} = (-1)(4) = -4$

$j = 3,\ (3)^2 + 1 = 10$ $k = 2,\ (-1)^2 2^{2+1} = (1)(8) = 8$

$j = 4,\ (4)^2 + 1 = 17$ $k = 3,\ (-1)^3 2^{3+1} = (-1)(16) = -16$

$j = 5,\ (5)^2 + 1 = 26$

$$\sum_{j=2}^{5} (j^2 + 1) = 5 + 10 + 17 + 26 \qquad \sum_{k=1}^{\infty} (-1)^k 2^{k+1} = -4 + 8 - 16 + \cdots$$

1. $\displaystyle\sum_{j=1}^{4} j^2$ 2. $\displaystyle\sum_{j=1}^{3} (3j - 2)$ 3. $\displaystyle\sum_{j=5}^{7} (j - 2)$

4. $\displaystyle\sum_{j=2}^{6} (j^2 + 1)$ 5. $\displaystyle\sum_{k=1}^{4} k(k + 1)$ 6. $\displaystyle\sum_{j=2}^{6} \frac{j}{2}(j + 1)$

7. $\displaystyle\sum_{j=1}^{4} \frac{(-1)^j}{2^j}$ 8. $\displaystyle\sum_{i=3}^{5} \frac{(-1)^{i+1}}{i - 2}$ 9. $\displaystyle\sum_{j=1}^{\infty} (2j - 1)$

10. $\displaystyle\sum_{j=1}^{\infty} \frac{1}{j}$ 11. $\displaystyle\sum_{k=0}^{\infty} \frac{1}{2^k}$ 12. $\displaystyle\sum_{k=0}^{\infty} \frac{k}{1 + k}$

13. $\displaystyle\sum_{j=1}^{n} (2j + 1)$ 14. $\displaystyle\sum_{j=0}^{n} \frac{(-1)^{j+1}}{2^j + 1}$ 15. $\displaystyle\sum_{k=1}^{n} \frac{k}{(k + 1)^k}$

Write in sigma notation.

Examples.

a. $5 + 8 + 11 + 14$

b. $x^2 + x^4 + x^6 + \cdots + x^{2n}$

Solutions.   Find a general term and write in sigma notation.

a. $3j + 2$

b. x^{2j}

$$\sum_{j=1}^{4} (3j + 2)$$

$$\sum_{j=1}^{n} x^{2j}$$

16. $1 + 2 + 3 + 4$

17. $2 + 4 + 6 + 8$

18. $x + x^3 + x^5 + x^7$

19. $x^3 + x^5 + x^7 + x^9 + x^{11}$

20. $1 + 4 + 9 + 16 + 25$

21. $\dfrac{1}{3} + \dfrac{1}{9} + \dfrac{1}{27} + \dfrac{1}{81}$

22. $1 - 1 + 1 - 1 \cdots + (-1)^{n+1}$

23. Argue that $\displaystyle\sum_{j=1}^{n} af_j(x) = a \sum_{j=1}^{n} f_j(x)$, if a is any real number.

24. Argue that $\displaystyle\sum_{j=1}^{n} [f_j(x) + g_j(x)] = \sum_{j=1}^{n} f_j(x) + \sum_{j=1}^{n} g_j(x)$.

25. Argue that, in general,

$$\sum_{j=1}^{n} f_j(x) \cdot g_j(x) \neq \sum_{j=1}^{n} f_j(x) \cdot \sum_{j=1}^{n} g_j(x).$$

Hint: Consider the special case $f_j(x) = j$, $g_j(x) = j + 1$, and $n = 2$ as a counterexample.

26. Let $m = \dfrac{1}{n} \displaystyle\sum_{j=1}^{n} a_j$, and show that

$$\sum_{j=1}^{n} (a_j - m)^2 = \sum_{j=1}^{n} (a_j)^2 - m^2 n.$$

12.4   ARITHMETIC PROGRESSIONS

Any sequence of which the general term is linear in n has the property that each term after the first can be obtained from the preceding term by adding a common number.   Consider the sequence having as its general term

$$s_n = dn + g. \tag{1}$$

The succeeding term is given by replacing n in (1) with $(n + 1)$, so that

$$s_{n+1} = d(n + 1) + g. \tag{2}$$

By rewriting the right-hand member of Equation (2),

$$s_{n+1} = dn + d + g$$
$$= (dn + g) + d$$
$$= s_n + d,$$

we see that the $(n + 1)$st term is obtained from the nth term by adding the number d. For example, the sequence

$$2, 4, 6, 8, \cdots, \tag{3}$$

when generated by

$$s_n = 2n,$$

has the property that each term is obtained by adding the number 2 to the preceding term. Similarly, the sequence

$$3, 7, 11, 15, \cdots \tag{4}$$

can be generated, after the first term, by adding 4 to a given term to obtain the succeeding term. (What is a general term for this sequence?) A sequence with this property is called an **arithmetic progression**, and we can state the recursive definition for such a sequence symbolically:

DEFINITION 12.4 *An arithmetic progression is a sequence defined by equations of the form*

$$s_1 = a,$$
$$s_{(n+1)} = s_n + d,$$

where $a, d \in R$, and $n \in N$.

It is customary, as shown, to denote the first term in such a sequence by the letter a, the common difference between successive terms by d, the number of terms in the sequence (when finite) by n, and the nth term by s_n. Notice that when the nth term is given by an equation of the form (1), the coefficient of n is the common difference. Thus, in the arithmetic progression (4), a is 3, d is 4, the number of terms is indicated as infinite, and the nth term can be given by $s_n = 4n - 1$.

We can determine whether a finite sequence is an arithmetic progression or not simply by subtracting each term from its successor and noting whether the difference in each case is the same. For example,

$$7, 18, 29, 40$$

is an arithmetic progression because

$$18 - 7 = 11,$$
$$29 - 18 = 11,$$
$$40 - 29 = 11.$$

If at least two consecutive terms in an arithmetic progression are known, we can determine the common difference and generate as many terms as we wish. Furthermore, a linear expression can be found for the nth term.

Consider the general arithmetic progression with first term a and common difference d. Then the

first term is a,
second term is $a + d$,
third term is $a + d + d = a + 2d$,
fourth term is $a + d + d + d = a + 3d$,
. . . . . .
nth term is $a + d + \cdots + d = a + (n - 1)d$.

These equations suggest the following.

THEOREM 12.4 *The nth term in the sequence defined by*

$$s_1 = a,$$

$$s_{n+1} = s_n + d,$$

is

$$s_n = a + (n - 1)d. \tag{5}$$

Proof. We shall use mathematical induction. That (5) is true for the natural number 1 is evident by direct substitution of 1 in (5),

$$s_1 = a + (1 - 1)d = a.$$

If now we assume that it is true for the natural number k, we have

$$s_k = a + (k - 1)d.$$

By the defining equation, we have

$$s_{k+1} = s_k + d.$$

Replacing s_k in this expression with $a + (k - 1)d$, we have

$$s_{k+1} = a + (k - 1)d + d$$

$$= a + kd$$

$$= a + [(k + 1) - 1]d,$$

and the principle of mathematical induction assures us that the relationship (5) is valid for all natural numbers.

When an arithmetic progression is finite and contains n terms, the nth term, s_n, is the last term in the sequence and is given by (5).

The problem of finding an explicit representation for the sum of n terms of an arbitrary sequence in terms of n is, in general, difficult; we can, however, obtain such a representation for the sum of n terms in an arithmetic progression. Consider the series S_n of the first n terms of the general arithmetic progression,

$$S_n = a + (a + d) + (a + 2d) + \cdots + [a + (n - 1)d], \tag{6}$$

and then consider the same series written as

$$S_n = s_n + (s_n - d) + (s_n - 2d) + \cdots + [s_n - (n - 1)d], \tag{7}$$

where the terms are displayed in reverse order. Adding (6) and (7) term by term, we have

$$S_n + S_n = (a + s_n) + (a + s_n) + (a + s_n) + \cdots + (a + s_n),$$

where the term $(a + s_n)$ occurs n times. Then

$$2S_n = n(a + s_n)$$

or

$$S_n = \frac{n}{2}(a + s_n). \tag{8}$$

If (8) is rewritten

$$S_n = n\left(\frac{a + s_n}{2}\right),$$

we observe that the sum is given by the product of the number of terms in the series and the average of the first and last terms. The validity of (8) can be shown by mathematical induction and is left as an exercise.

An alternative form for (8) is obtained by substituting the value for s_n, as given by (5), in (8) to obtain

$$S_n = \frac{n}{2}(a + [a + (n - 1)d]),$$

or

$$S_n = \frac{n}{2}[2a + (n - 1)d], \tag{9}$$

where the sum is now expressed in terms of a, n, and d.

EXERCISE 12.4

Write the next three terms in each of the following arithmetic progressions.

Examples.

a. 5, 9, $\cdots$

b. $x, x - a, \cdots$

Solutions. Find the common difference and then continue the sequence.

a. $d = 9 - 5 = 4$
   13, 17, 21

b. $d = (x - a) - x = -a$
   $x - 2a, x - 3a, x - 4a$

1. $3, 7, \cdots$

2. $-6, -1, \cdots$

3. $-1, -5, \cdots$

4. $-10, -20, \cdots$

5. $x, x + 1, \cdots$

6. $a, a + 5, \cdots$

7. $x + a, x + 3a, \cdots$

8. $y - 2b, y, \cdots$

9. $2x + 1, 2x + 4, \cdots$

10. $a + 2b, a - 2b, \cdots$

11. $x, 2x, \cdots$

12. $3a, 5a, \cdots$

Example. Find the fourteenth term of the arithmetic progression $-6, -1, \cdots$.

Solution. Find the common difference.

$$d = -1 - (-6) = 5.$$

Use $s_n = a + (n - 1)d$.

$$s_{14} = -6 + (13)5$$

$$s_{14} = 59.$$

13. Find the seventh term in the arithmetic progression $7, 11, \cdots$.

14. Find the tenth term in the arithmetic progression $-3, -12, \cdots$.

15. Find the twelfth term in the arithmetic progression $2, 5/2, \cdots$.

16. Find the seventeenth term in the arithmetic progression $-5, -2, \cdots$.

17. Find the twentieth term in the arithmetic progression $3, -2, \cdots$.

18. Find the tenth term in the arithmetic progression $3/4, 2, \cdots$.

Example. Find the first term in an arithmetic progression in which the third term is 7 and the eleventh term is 55.

Solution. Find a common difference by considering an arithmetic progression with first term 7 and ninth term 55. Use $s_n = a + (n - 1)d$.

$$s_9 = 7 + (9 - 1)d$$

$$55 = 7 + 8d$$

$$d = 6.$$

Use this difference to find the first term in an arithmetic progression in which the third term is 7. Use $s_n = a + (n - 1)d$.

$$s_3 = a + (3 - 1)6$$

$$7 = a + 12$$

$$a = -5.$$

19. If the third term in an arithmetic progression is 7 and the eighth term is 17, find the common difference. What is the first term? What is the twentieth term?

20. If the fifth term of an arithmetic progression is -16 and the twentieth term is -46, what is the twelfth term?

21. Which term in the arithmetic progression 4, 1, $\cdots$ is -77?

22. What is the twelfth term in an arithmetic progression in which the second term is x and the third term is y?

Find the sum of the finite series.

Example. $\displaystyle\sum_{j=1}^{12} (4j + 1)$

Solution.   Write the first two or three terms in expanded form.

$$5 + 9 + 13 + \cdots$$

By inspection, the first term is 5 and the common difference is 4. Use

$$S_n = \frac{n}{2}\,[2a + (n - 1)d].$$

$$S_{12} = \frac{12}{2}\,[2(5) + (12 - 1)4]$$

$$S_{12} = 324$$

23. $\displaystyle\sum_{j=1}^{7} (2j + 1)$ 24. $\displaystyle\sum_{j=1}^{21} (3j - 2)$ 25. $\displaystyle\sum_{j=3}^{15} (7j - 1)$

26. $\displaystyle\sum_{j=10}^{20} (2j - 3)$ 27. $\displaystyle\sum_{k=1}^{8} \left(\frac{1}{2}k - 3\right)$ 28. $\displaystyle\sum_{k=1}^{100} k$

29. Find the sum of all even integers n, for $13 < n < 29$.

30. Find the sum of all integral multiples of 7 between 8 and 110.

31. How many bricks will there be in a pile one brick in thickness if there are 27 bricks in the bottom row, 25 in the second row, etc., and one in the top row?

32. If there are a total of 256 bricks in a pile arranged in the manner of those in Problem 31, how many bricks are there in the third row from the bottom of the pile?

33. Find a if $\displaystyle\sum_{j=1}^{5} aj = 14$.

34. Find p and q if $\displaystyle\sum_{j=1}^{4} (pj + q) = 28$ and $\displaystyle\sum_{j=2}^{5} (pj + q) = 44$.

Write, in sigma notation, an infinite series with first four terms as given. There are no unique solutions, but solutions can be found by trial and error.

Examples.

a. $3 + 6 + 9 + 12 + \cdots$

b. $\dfrac{3}{5} + \dfrac{5}{7} + \dfrac{7}{9} + \dfrac{9}{11} + \cdots$

Solutions. Find the general term and write in sigma notation.

a. $3j$

b. $\dfrac{2j + 1}{2j + 3}$

$$\sum_{j=1}^{\infty} 3j$$

$$\sum_{j=1}^{\infty} \frac{2j + 1}{2j + 3}$$

35. $1\cdot2 + 2\cdot3 + 3\cdot4 + 4\cdot5 + \cdots$

36. $\dfrac{1}{2} + \dfrac{2}{3} + \dfrac{3}{4} + \dfrac{4}{5} + \cdots$

37. $\dfrac{2}{1} + \dfrac{3}{2} + \dfrac{4}{3} + \dfrac{5}{4} + \cdots$

38. $\dfrac{1}{1} + \dfrac{2}{3} + \dfrac{3}{5} + \dfrac{4}{7} + \cdots$

39. $\dfrac{3}{1} + \dfrac{5}{3} + \dfrac{7}{5} + \dfrac{9}{7} + \cdots$

40. $\dfrac{1}{1} + \dfrac{2}{2} + \dfrac{4}{3} + \dfrac{8}{4} + \cdots$

41. Consider

$$S_n = \sum_{i=1}^{n} f(i).$$

Explain why this equation defines a sequence function. What is the independent variable? What is the dependent variable?

42. By mathematical induction, prove that for an arithmetic progression, $S_n = \dfrac{n}{2}(a + s_n)$ for all positive integral values of n.

43. Show that the sequence formed by adding the corresponding terms in two arithmetic progressions is an arithmetic progression.

44. Show that the sum of the terms in two series with terms in arithmetic progression is a series with terms in arithmetic progression.

12.5   GEOMETRIC PROGRESSIONS

Any sequence in which each term except the first is obtained by multiplying the preceding term by a given number is called a **geometric progression**.

DEFINITION 12.5   *A geometric progression is a sequence defined by equations of the form*

$$s_1 = a,$$

$$s_{n+1} = rs_n,$$

where $a, r \in R$, $a \neq 0$, $r \neq 0$, and $n \in N$.

Thus,

$$3, 9, 27, 81, \cdots$$

is a geometric progression in which each term except the first is obtained by multiplying the preceding term by 3. Since the effect of multiplying the terms in this way is to produce a fixed ratio between any two successive terms, the multiplier, r, is called the **ratio**.

If the first term is designated by a, then

$$\text{the second term is } a \cdot r,$$

$$\text{the third term is } ar \cdot r = ar^2,$$

$$\text{the fourth term is } ar^2 \cdot r = ar^3.$$

These equations suggest the following.

THEOREM 12.5 *The nth term in the sequence defined by*

$$s_1 = a,$$

$$s_{n+1} = rs_n,$$

is

$$s_n = ar^{n-1}. \tag{1}$$

Proof. We shall use mathematical induction. We note first that, for $n = 1$,

$$s_1 = ar^0 = a,$$

and (1) is true in this case. Next, let us assume that $s_k = ar^{k-1}$. By Definition 12.5 we have $s_{k+1} = rs_k$, from which by substitution we obtain

$$s_{k+1} = r(ar^{k-1})$$

$$= ar^k$$

$$= ar^{[(k+1)-1]},$$

and the principle of mathematical induction assures us that (1) holds for all natural numbers.

The general geometric progression has the form

$$a, ar, ar^2, ar^3, \cdots, ar^{n-1}, \cdots.$$

When a geometric progression is finite and contains n terms, the nth term, s_n, is the last term in the sequence and is given by (1). For example, consider the geometric progression

$$2, 6, 18, \cdots.$$

By writing the ratio of any term to its predecessor, say 18/6, we find that $r = 3$. A representation of s_n for this sequence can now be written in terms of n by substituting 2 for a and 3 for r in (1). Thus we have

$$s_n = 2(3^{n-1}).$$

To find an explicit representation for the sum of a given number of terms in a geometric progression in terms of a, r, and n, we employ a device somewhat similar to the one used in finding the sum of an arithmetic progression. Consider the geometric series (2) containing n terms, and the series (3) obtained by multiplying both members of (2) by r:

$$S_n = a + ar + ar^2 + ar^3 + \cdots + ar^{n-2} + ar^{n-1}, \tag{2}$$

$$rS_n = ar + ar^2 + ar^3 + ar^4 + \cdots + ar^{n-1} + ar^n. \tag{3}$$

When we subtract (3) from (2), all terms in the right-hand members except the first term in (2) and the last term in (3) vanish, yielding

$$S_n - rS_n = a - ar^n.$$

Factoring S_n from the left-hand member gives

$$(1 - r)S_n = a - ar^n,$$

from which

$$S_n = \frac{a - ar^n}{1 - r}, \tag{4}$$

provided $r \neq 1$, and we have a formula for the sum of n terms of a geometric progression. The validity of Equation (4) can be shown by mathematical induction and is left as an exercise.

An alternative expression for (4) can be obtained by writing

$$S_n = \frac{a - r(ar^{n-1})}{1 - r}$$

and, since $s_n = ar^{n-1}$,

$$S_n = \frac{a - rs_n}{1 - r}, \tag{5}$$

where the sum is now given in terms of a, s_n, and r.

EXERCISE 12.5

Write the next four terms in each of the following geometric progressions.

Examples.

a. 3, 6, $\cdots$ b. x, 2, $\cdots$

Solutions. Find the common ratio.

a. $r = \dfrac{6}{3} = 2$ b. $r = \dfrac{2}{x}$

Multiply each term by r to determine the following term.

12, 24, 48, 96 $\dfrac{4}{x}, \dfrac{8}{x^2}, \dfrac{16}{x^3}, \dfrac{32}{x^4}$

1. 2, 8, $\cdots$ 2. 4, 8, $\cdots$ 3. $\dfrac{2}{3}, \dfrac{4}{3}, \cdots$

4. 6, 3, $\cdots$ 5. 4, -2, $\cdots$ 6. $\dfrac{1}{2}, -\dfrac{3}{2}, \cdots$

7. $\dfrac{a}{x}, -1, \cdots$ 8. $\dfrac{a}{b}, \dfrac{a}{bc}, \cdots$

Example. Find the ninth term of the geometric progression $-24, 12, \cdots$.

Solution. Find the common ratio.

$$r = \frac{12}{-24} = -\frac{1}{2}$$

Use $s_n = ar^{n-1}$

$$s_9 = -24\left(-\frac{1}{2}\right)^8 = -\frac{3}{32}$$

9. Find the sixth term in the geometric progression 48, 96, $\cdots$.

10. Find the eighth term in the geometric progression $-3, \dfrac{3}{2}, \cdots$.

11. Find the seventh term in the geometric progression $-\dfrac{1}{3}a^2, a^5, \cdots$.

12. Find the ninth term in the geometric progression $-81, -27, \cdots$.

13. Find the first term of a geometric progression with fifth term 48 and ratio 2.

14. Find two different values for x so that $-\frac{3}{2}, x, -\frac{8}{27}$ will be in geometric progression.

Find each of the following sums.

Example. $\displaystyle\sum_{j=2}^{5} \left(\frac{1}{3}\right)^j$

Solution. Write the first two terms in expanded form.

$$\left(\frac{1}{3}\right)^2 + \left(\frac{1}{3}\right)^3 + \cdots$$

By inspection, the first term is $\frac{1}{9}$, the ratio is $\frac{1}{3}$, and $n = 4$. Use $S_n = \frac{a - ar^n}{1 - r}$.

$$S_4 = \frac{\frac{1}{9} - \frac{1}{9}\left(\frac{1}{3}\right)^4}{1 - \frac{1}{3}}$$

$$= \frac{40}{243}$$

15. $\displaystyle\sum_{j=1}^{6} 3^j$

16. $\displaystyle\sum_{j=1}^{4} (-2)^j$

17. $\displaystyle\sum_{k=3}^{7} \left(\frac{1}{2}\right)^{k-2}$

18. $\displaystyle\sum_{j=3}^{12} 2^{j-5}$

19. $\displaystyle\sum_{j=1}^{6} \left(\frac{1}{3}\right)^j$

20. $\displaystyle\sum_{k=1}^{5} \left(\frac{1}{4}\right)^k$

21. Find $\displaystyle\sum_{j=1}^{4} (3 + 2^j)$.

22. Find $\displaystyle\sum_{j=1}^{n} \left(\frac{1}{2}\right)^j$ for $n = 2, 3, 4,$ and 5. What value do you think $\displaystyle\sum_{j=1}^{n} \left(\frac{1}{2}\right)^j$ approximates as n becomes larger and larger?

23. By mathematical induction, prove that $S_n = \dfrac{a - ar^n}{1 - r}$ for all positive integral values of n provided $r \neq 1$.

24. Show that the logarithms of the terms in a geometric sequence form an arithmetic sequence.

12.6 LIMIT OF A SEQUENCE

Consider the sequence function defined by

$$s_n = \frac{n}{n + 1}. \tag{1}$$

If we write the range of (1) in the form

$$\frac{1}{2}, \frac{2}{3}, \frac{3}{4}, \frac{4}{5}, \cdots, \frac{n}{n + 1}, \cdots, \tag{2}$$

then it is clear that each of the terms is greater than the preceding term; indeed, the difference of consecutive terms is

$$\frac{n + 1}{n + 2} - \frac{n}{n + 1} = \frac{(n^2 + 2n + 1) - (n^2 + 2n)}{(n + 1)(n + 2)} = \frac{1}{(n + 1)(n + 2)} > 0.$$

Such a sequence is said to be **strictly increasing**. On the other hand, it is also clear that, no matter how large a value is assigned to n, we have

$$\frac{n}{n+1} < 1,$$

because the denominator is one larger than the numerator; in fact, we have

$$1 - \frac{n}{n+1} = \frac{(n+1) - n}{n+1} = \frac{1}{n+1} > 0.$$

Thus we have a sequence in which each term is greater than the preceding term and yet no term is equal to or greater than 1.

We note, however—and this is a very basic consideration—that the value of $n/(n+1)$ is as close to 1 as we please if n is large enough. For example, the difference satisfies

$$1 - \frac{n}{n+1} = \frac{1}{n+1} \quad \text{and} \quad \frac{1}{n+1} < \frac{1}{1000}$$

provided $n + 1 > 1000$—that is, $n > 999$. If it is true that the nth term in a sequence differs from the number L by as little as we please for all sufficiently large n, we say that **the sequence approaches the number L as a limit**. The symbolism

$$\lim_{n \to \infty} s_n = L$$

(read "the limit, as n increases without bound, of s_n is L") is used to denote this situation. A thorough discussion of the notion of a limit is included in courses in calculus, and will not be attempted here. A few elementary ideas, however, are in order.

A sequence in which the nth term approaches a number L as $n \to \infty$ is said to be a **convergent sequence**, and the sequence is said to **converge** to L.

It is not necessary for convergence that a sequence be strictly increasing. For example,

$$1, \frac{1}{2}, \frac{1}{3}, \frac{1}{4}, \ldots, \frac{1}{n}, \ldots$$

converges to 0, but each term in the sequence is less than, instead of greater than, the term that precedes it. Again, the sequence

$$-1, \frac{1}{2}, -\frac{1}{3}, \frac{1}{4}, \ldots, \frac{(-1)^n}{n}, \ldots$$

converges to 0 but is neither increasing nor decreasing.

We can rephrase the definition of convergence of a sequence as follows:

DEFINITION 12.6   *A sequence $s_1, s_2, \cdots, s_n, \cdots$ converges to the number L,*

$$\lim_{n \to \infty} s_n = L,$$

if and only if the absolute value of the difference between the nth term in the sequence and the number L is as small as we please for all sufficiently large n. Thus the sequence converges to the number L if and only if

$$\lim_{n \to \infty} |L - s_n| = 0.$$

For example, the **alternating sequence** (because the signs alternate)

$$\frac{-2}{3}, \frac{4}{9}, \frac{-8}{27}, \cdots, \left(-\frac{2}{3}\right)^n, \cdots$$

converges to 0 since the absolute value of the difference between $(-2/3)^n$ and 0, i.e., $|0 - (-2/3)^n|$, is as small as we please for n large enough.   We express this by writing

$$\lim_{n \to \infty} \left(-\frac{2}{3}\right)^n = 0.$$

On the other hand, the alternating sequence

$$\frac{1}{2}, -\frac{2}{3}, \frac{3}{4}, -\frac{4}{5}, \cdots, (-1)^{n+1}\frac{n}{n+1}, \cdots$$

does not converge.   As n increases, the nth term oscillates back and forth from the neighborhood of $+1$ to the neighborhood of -1, and we cannot find a number L such that $\lim_{n \to \infty} |L - s_n| = 0$.   Such a sequence is said to **diverge**.   A sequence such as

$$1, 2, 3, \cdots, n, \cdots$$

also is said to diverge.   An answer to the logical question of what we mean by "enough" when we say "$|L - s_n|$ small enough" and "n large enough" requires a more precise definition of limit than we have given here. As remarked earlier, a course in the calculus will treat this in detail.

EXERCISE 12.6

Discuss the limiting behavior as $n \to \infty$.

Example. $s_n = \dfrac{n^2 + 3}{n^2}$

Solution.   By writing $\dfrac{n^2 + 3}{n^2}$ as $\dfrac{n^2}{n^2} + \dfrac{3}{n^2}$ and then as $1 + \dfrac{3}{n^2}$, we observe that $\lim_{n \to \infty} s_n = 1$.

1. $\dfrac{1}{n}$ 2. $1 + \dfrac{1}{n^2}$ 3. $\dfrac{n+1}{n}$ 4. $\dfrac{n+3}{n^2}$

5. $2n$ 6. $(-1)^n$ 7. $\dfrac{1}{2^n}$ 8. $(-1)^n \dfrac{1}{n}$

Which of the following sequences are convergent? Give a reason why the sequence is or is not convergent.

Example. $1, \dfrac{3}{2}, \dfrac{7}{4}, \dfrac{15}{8}, \cdots, \dfrac{2^n - 1}{2^{n-1}}$

Solution.   By writing the general term as $\dfrac{2^n}{2^{n-1}} - \dfrac{1}{2^{n-1}}$ and then as $2 - \dfrac{1}{2^{n-1}}$, we observe that $\lim\limits_{n \to \infty} s_n = 2$. The sequence is convergent.

9. $\dfrac{1}{2}, \dfrac{1}{4}, \dfrac{1}{8}, \dfrac{1}{16}, \cdots, \dfrac{1}{2^n}$ 10. $2, \dfrac{3}{2}, \dfrac{4}{3}, \dfrac{5}{4}, \cdots, \dfrac{n+1}{n}$

11. $1, 2, 3, 4, 5, \cdots, n$ 12. $2, 4, 6, 8, \cdots, 2n$

13. $1, -\dfrac{1}{2}, \dfrac{1}{4}, -\dfrac{1}{8}, \cdots, (-1)^{n+1} \dfrac{1}{2^{n-1}}$

14. $2, -\dfrac{3}{2}, \dfrac{4}{3}, -\dfrac{5}{4}, \cdots, (-1)^{n+1} \dfrac{n+1}{n}$

15. $\dfrac{1}{2}, -\dfrac{3}{4}, \dfrac{5}{6}, -\dfrac{7}{8}, \cdots, (-1)^{n+1} \dfrac{2n-1}{2n}$

16. $1, -1, 1, -1, \cdots, (-1)^{n+1}$

Find a value for n such that each term after the nth term in the general sequence will satisfy the given condition.

Example. $1, \dfrac{1}{2^2}, \dfrac{1}{3^2}, \dfrac{1}{4^2}, \cdots, \dfrac{1}{n^2}, \quad \left| 0 - \dfrac{1}{n^2} \right| < \dfrac{1}{30}$

Solution.   We seek an n such that

$$0 - \frac{1}{n^2} < \frac{1}{30} \quad \text{if} \quad 0 - \frac{1}{n^2} \geq 0, \tag{1}$$

or

$$-\left(0 - \frac{1}{n^2}\right) < \frac{1}{30} \quad \text{if} \quad 0 - \frac{1}{n^2} < 0. \tag{2}$$

Since $\dfrac{-1}{n^2} < 0$ for all n, we consider (2) only.

Multiply each member of (2) by $30n^2$ and solve for n:

$$30 < n^2,$$

$$n > \sqrt{30}.$$

Since $n \in N$, $n \geq 6$.

17. $1, \dfrac{1}{2^2}, \dfrac{1}{3^2}, \dfrac{1}{4^2}, \cdots, \dfrac{1}{n^2}, \quad \left| 0 - \dfrac{1}{n^2} \right| < \dfrac{1}{100}$

18. $\dfrac{1}{2}, \dfrac{2}{3}, \dfrac{3}{4}, \dfrac{4}{5}, \cdots, \dfrac{n}{n+1}, \quad \left| 1 - \dfrac{n}{n+1} \right| < \dfrac{1}{100}$

19. $\dfrac{3}{4}, \dfrac{5}{6}, \dfrac{7}{8}, \dfrac{9}{10}, \cdots, \dfrac{2n+1}{2n+2}, \quad \left| 1 - \dfrac{2n+1}{2n+2} \right| < \dfrac{1}{100}$

20. $\dfrac{1}{2}, \dfrac{1}{4}, \dfrac{1}{8}, \dfrac{1}{16}, \cdots, \dfrac{1}{2^n}, \quad \left| 0 - \dfrac{1}{2^n} \right| < \dfrac{1}{100}$

The series $a_1 + a_2 + \cdots + a_n + \cdots$ is said to have a limit if the sequence formed from the partial sums $a_1, \ a_1 + a_2, \ a_1 + a_2 + a_3, \ a_1 + a_2 + a_3 + a_4, \cdots,$ $a_1 + a_2 + a_3 + a_4 + \cdots + a_n, \cdots$ has a limit. Form a similar sequence for each of the following series and verify that each series has a limit.

21. $\dfrac{1}{2} + \dfrac{1}{4} + \dfrac{1}{8} + \dfrac{1}{16} + \cdots + \dfrac{1}{2^n} + \cdots$

22. $\dfrac{1}{3} + \dfrac{1}{9} + \dfrac{1}{27} + \dfrac{1}{81} + \cdots + \dfrac{1}{3^n} + \cdots$

23. $\dfrac{3}{5} + \dfrac{9}{25} + \dfrac{27}{125} + \dfrac{81}{625} + \cdots + \left(\dfrac{3}{5}\right)^n + \cdots$

24. $\dfrac{1}{10} + \dfrac{1}{100} + \dfrac{1}{1000} + \dfrac{1}{10000} + \cdots + \left(\dfrac{1}{10}\right)^n + \cdots$

25. The irrational number e (see Section 7.3) is defined by

$$e = \lim_{x \to \infty} \left(1 + \dfrac{1}{x}\right)^x.$$

Show that the relationship

$$A = P\left(1 + \dfrac{r}{t}\right)^{nt}$$

(see Section 7.5) can be written

$$A = Pe^{rn}$$

when $t \to \infty$; that is, when the principal is compounded continuously. This relationship is known as the **law of natural growth.**

12.7   INFINITE GEOMETRIC PROGRESSIONS

We recall from Section 12.5 that the sum of n terms of a geometric progression is given by

$$S_n = \dfrac{a - ar^n}{1 - r}. \tag{1}$$

If $|r| < 1$, that is, if $-1 < r < 1$, then r^n becomes smaller and smaller for increasingly large n (Exercise 12.1, Problem 16). For example, if $r = 1/2$,

$$r^2 = \left(\frac{1}{2}\right)^2 = \frac{1}{4},$$

$$r^3 = \left(\frac{1}{2}\right)^3 = \frac{1}{8},$$

$$r^4 = \left(\frac{1}{2}\right)^4 = \frac{1}{16},$$

etc., and $(1/2)^n$ is as small as we please if n is sufficiently large. Writing (1) in the form

$$S_n = \frac{a}{1-r}(1 - r^n), \qquad (2)$$

we see that the value of the factor $(1 - r^n)$ is as close as we please to 1 providing $|r| < 1$ and n is taken large enough. Since this argument asserts that the sum (2) converges to

$$\frac{a}{1-r},$$

we have the following.

THEOREM 12.6 *The "sum" of an infinite geometric progression,* $a + ar + ar^2 + \cdots + ar^n + \cdots$, *with* $|r| < 1$, *is*

$$\lim_{n \to \infty} S_n = \frac{a}{1-r}. \qquad (3)$$

The symbol S_∞ is frequently used in place of $\lim_{n \to \infty} S_n$, so that (3) can be written

$$S_\infty = \frac{a}{1-r}.$$

An interesting application of this sum arises in connection with repeating decimals—that is, decimal numerals that, after a finite number of decimal places, have endlessly repeating groups of digits. For example,

$$0.21212\overline{1}\cdots,$$

$$0.333\overline{3}\cdots,$$

$$0.1723172\overline{31723}\cdots,$$

$$0.81818\overline{1}\cdots,$$

$$0.1385125125\overline{12}\cdots,$$

are repeating decimals. Consider the problem of expressing such a decimal fraction as an arithmetic fraction. We illustrate the process involved with the first example above:

$$0.2121\overline{21}\cdots. \tag{4}$$

This decimal can be written either as

$$0.21 + 0.0021 + 0.000021 + \cdots, \tag{5}$$

or as

$$\frac{21}{100} + \frac{21}{10,000} + \frac{21}{1,000,000} + \cdots, \tag{6}$$

which are geometric progressions with ratio $r = 0.01$, or $1/100$. Since the ratio is less than 1 in absolute value, we can use (3) to find the sum of an infinite number of terms of (6). Thus

$$S_\infty = \frac{a}{1-r} = \frac{\dfrac{21}{100}}{1 - \dfrac{1}{100}}$$

$$= \frac{21}{99} = \frac{7}{33},$$

and the given decimal fraction is equivalent to 7/33.

EXERCISE 12.7

Find the sum of each of the following infinite geometric series. If the series has no sum, so state.

Examples.

a. $3 + 2 + \cdots$

b. $\dfrac{1}{81} - \dfrac{1}{54} + \cdots$

Solutions.

a. $r = \dfrac{2}{3}$; series has a sum since $|r| < 1$.

b. $r = -\dfrac{1}{54} \div \dfrac{1}{81} = -\dfrac{3}{2}$

$$S_\infty = \frac{a}{1-r} = \frac{3}{1 - \dfrac{2}{3}}$$

The sum is 9.

Series does not have a sum since $|r| > 1$.

1. $12 + 6 + \cdots$

2. $2 + 1 + \cdots$

3. $\dfrac{1}{36} + \dfrac{1}{30} + \cdots$

4. $1 + \dfrac{2}{3} + \cdots$

5. $\dfrac{3}{4} - \dfrac{1}{2} + \cdots$

6. $\dfrac{1}{16} - \dfrac{1}{8} + \cdots$

7. $\dfrac{1}{49} + \dfrac{1}{56} + \cdots$ 8. $2 - \dfrac{3}{2} + \cdots$

9. $\displaystyle\sum_{j=1}^{\infty} \left(\dfrac{2}{3}\right)^{j}$ 10. $\displaystyle\sum_{j=1}^{\infty} \left(-\dfrac{1}{4}\right)^{j}$

Find an arithmetic fraction equal to each of the given decimal numerals.

Example. $0.818181\cdots$

Solution.   Rewrite as a series.

$$\frac{81}{100} + \frac{81}{10,000} + \frac{81}{1,000,000} + \cdots$$

Find the common ratio: $r = \dfrac{1}{100}$.   Use $S_{\infty} = \dfrac{a}{1-r}$.

$$S_{\infty} = \frac{\dfrac{81}{100}}{1 - \dfrac{1}{100}} = \frac{81}{99} = \frac{9}{11}$$

11. $0.33333\cdots$ 12. $0.66666\cdots$ 13. $0.313131\cdots$

14. $0.454545\cdots$ 15. $2.410410\cdots$ 16. $3.027027\cdots$

17. $0.128888\cdots$ 18. $0.83333\cdots$

19. A force is applied to a particle moving in a straight line in such a fashion that each second it moves only one half of the distance it moved the preceding second. If the particle moves ten centimeters the first second, approximately how far will it move before coming to rest?

20. The arc length through which the bob on a pendulum moves is nine tenths of its preceding arc length. Approximately how far will the bob move before coming to rest if the first arc length is 12 inches?

21. A ball returns two thirds of the distance it falls on each bounce. If the ball is dropped from a height of six feet, approximately what is the total distance the ball travels before coming to rest?

22. Find another expression for $\displaystyle\sum_{j=1}^{\infty} (2x + 1)^{j}$. For what values of x does this series converge?

23. Find another expression for $\displaystyle\sum_{j=1}^{\infty} \left(\dfrac{1}{x-1}\right)^{j}$. For what values of x does this series converge?

24. Find another expression for $\displaystyle\sum_{j=1}^{\infty} \left(\dfrac{2}{2x-3}\right)^{j}$. For what values of x does this series converge?

12.8 THE BINOMIAL THEOREM

There are situations, as in the binomial expansion given below, in which it is necessary to write the product of consecutive positive integers. To facilitate writing products of this type, we use a special symbol, $n!$ (read "n factorial" or "factorial n"), which is defined by

$$n! = n(n - 1)(n - 2)\cdots(1),$$

where $n \in N$. Thus

$$5! = 5\cdot4\cdot3\cdot2\cdot1,$$

and

$$8! = 8\cdot7\cdot6\cdot5\cdot4\cdot3\cdot2\cdot1.$$

Factorial notation can also be used to represent the products of consecutive positive integers beginning with integers different from 1. For example,

$$8\cdot7\cdot6\cdot5 = \frac{8!}{4!},$$

because

$$\frac{8!}{4!} = \frac{8\cdot7\cdot6\cdot5\cdot4\cdot3\cdot2\cdot1}{4\cdot3\cdot2\cdot1} = 8\cdot7\cdot6\cdot5.$$

Since

$$n! = n(n - 1)(n - 2)(n - 3)\cdots5\cdot4\cdot3\cdot2\cdot1$$

and

$$(n - 1)! = (n - 1)(n - 2)(n - 3)\cdots5\cdot4\cdot3\cdot2\cdot1,$$

we can write the recursive relationship

$$n! = n(n - 1)!. \tag{1}$$

For example,

$$7! = 7\cdot6!,$$

$$(n + 2)! = (n + 2)(n + 1)!.$$

So that (1) and other similar formulas will be valid for $n = 1$, we make the following definition.

DEFINITION 12.8 $0! = 1$.

The series obtained by expanding a binomial of the form

$$(a + b)^n$$

is particularly useful in certain branches of mathematics. Starting with familiar examples, in which n has the value 1, 2, 3, 4, and 5 in turn, we can show by direct multiplication that

$$(a + b)^1 = a + b$$
$$(a + b)^2 = a^2 + 2ab + b^2$$
$$(a + b)^3 = a^3 + 3a^2b + 3ab^2 + b^3$$
$$(a + b)^4 = a^4 + 4a^3b + 6a^2b^2 + 4ab^3 + b^4$$
$$(a + b)^5 = a^5 + 5a^4b + 10a^3b^2 + 10a^2b^3 + 5ab^4 + b^5.$$

The coefficients of the terms form the following pattern, known as **Pascal's triangle.**

$(a + b)^0$						1					
$(a + b)^1$					1		1				
$(a + b)^2$				1		2		1			
$(a + b)^3$			1		3		3		1		
$(a + b)^4$		1		4		6		4		1	
$(a + b)^5$	1		5		10		10		5		1

We observe that if n is the exponent and $r = t - 1$, where t is the number of the term in the expansion, then the coefficient of $a^{n-r}b^r$ is

$$\frac{n!}{(n - r)!r!}. \tag{2}$$

We note also that each number in the triangle, apart from the 1's that bound the triangle, is the sum of the numbers immediately to its left and to its right in the line above it; e.g., $10 = 4 + 6$.

Example. Find the coefficient of the third term of the expansion $(a + b)^5$.

Solution. From (2), with $n = 5$, $r = t - 1 = 2$, and $n - r = 3$,

$$\frac{n!}{(n - r)!r!} = \frac{5!}{3!2!}$$
$$= 10.$$

From the expansion above and the representation of any coefficient by

$$\frac{n!}{(n - r)!r!},$$

we have the following result, which is called the **binomial theorem.**

THEOREM 12.7   *For any natural number n,*

$$(a + b)^n = a^n + \frac{n!}{(n - 1)!1!} a^{n-1}b + \frac{n!}{(n - 2)!2!} a^{n-2}b^2$$
$$+ \frac{n!}{(n - 3)!3!} a^{n-3}b^3 + \cdots + \frac{n!}{1!(n - 1)!} ab^{n-1} + b^n,$$

in which the coefficient of $a^{n-r}b^r$ is

$$\frac{n!}{(n - r)!r!}.$$

Proof. We shall use mathematical induction.

1. For $n = 1$, we have

$$(a + b)^1 = a^1 + b^1,$$

and the first condition in the induction process is satisfied.

2. Assume the formula is true for $n = k$, that is,

$$(a + b)^k = a^k + \frac{k!}{(k - 1)!1!} a^{k-1}b + \frac{k!}{(k - 2)!2!} a^{k-2}b^2$$

$$+ \frac{k!}{(k - 3)!3!} a^{k-3}b^3 + \cdots + \frac{k!}{1!(k - 1)!} ab^{k-1} + b^k.$$

To show that this implies that the formula holds for $n = k + 1$, we multiply each member by $(a + b)$ and obtain

$$(a + b)^{k+1} = (a^{k+1} + a^kb) + \frac{k!}{(k - 1)!1!} (a^kb + a^{k-1}b^2)$$

$$+ \frac{k!}{(k - 2)!2!} (a^{k-1}b^2 + a^{k-2}b^3)$$

$$+ \frac{k!}{(k - 3)!3!} (a^{k-2}b^3 + a^{k-3}b^4)$$

$$+ \cdots + \frac{k!}{1!(k - 1)!} (a^2b^{k-1} + ab^k)$$

$$+ ab^k + b^{k+1}.$$

Observing that the right-hand member can be rewritten by grouping like variable factors, we have

$$(a + b)^{k+1} = a^{k+1} + \left[1 + \frac{k!}{(k - 1)!1!}\right]a^kb$$

$$+ \left[\frac{k!}{(k - 1)!1!} + \frac{k!}{(k - 2)!2!}\right]a^{k-1}b^2$$

$$+ \left[\frac{k!}{(k - 2)!2!} + \frac{k!}{(k - 3)!3!}\right]a^{k-2}b^3$$

$$+ \left[\frac{k!}{(k - 3)!3!} + \frac{k!}{(k - 4)!4!}\right]a^{k-3}b^4$$

$$+ \cdots + \left[\frac{k!}{1!(k - 1)!} + 1\right]ab^k + b^{k+1}.$$

The coefficient of $a^{(k+1)-r}b^r$ is

$$\frac{k!}{r!(k - r)!} + \frac{k!}{(r - 1)!(k - r + 1)!} = \frac{k!(k - r + 1) + k!r}{r!(k - r + 1)!}$$

$$= \frac{k!(k + 1)}{r!(k + 1 - r)!}$$

$$= \frac{(k + 1)!}{r!(k + 1 - r)!},$$

as desired.   Since the truth of the assertion for any natural number k implies its truth for $k + 1$, the second condition is fulfilled.   Thus by the principle of mathematical induction, the theorem is true for every natural number n.

Note that the tth term is given by

$$\frac{n!}{(n - r)!r!} a^{n-r}b^r, \tag{3}$$

where $r = t - 1$.

EXERCISE 12.8

Write in expanded form and simplify.

Examples.

a. $\dfrac{4!6!}{8!}$

b. $\dfrac{(n - 1)!}{(n - 3)!}$

Solutions.

a. $\dfrac{4 \cdot 3 \cdot 2 \cdot 1 \cdot 6!}{8 \cdot 7 \cdot 6!}$

$\dfrac{3}{7}$

b. $\dfrac{(n - 1)(n - 2)(n - 3)!}{(n - 3)!}$

$(n - 1)(n - 2)$

1. $4!$

2. $6!$

3. $\dfrac{9!}{8!}$

4. $\dfrac{13!}{10!}$

5. $\dfrac{5!7!}{8!}$

6. $\dfrac{(12!)(8!)}{16!}$

7. $\dfrac{(8 - 2)!}{(4 + 1)!}$

8. $\dfrac{(10 + 3)!}{(12 - 1)!}$

9. $\dfrac{6!}{7! - 6!}$

10. $\dfrac{3! + 4!}{4!}$

11. $\dfrac{3! + 5!}{5! - 3!}$

12. $\dfrac{n!}{(n - 1)!}$

13. $\dfrac{(n + 2)!}{n!}$

14. $\dfrac{(n + 2)!}{(n - 1)!}$

15. $\dfrac{(n + 1)(n + 2)!}{(n + 3)!}$

16. $\dfrac{(2n + 4)!}{(2n + 2)!}$

17. $\dfrac{(2n)!(n - 2)!}{4(2n - 2)!(n)!}$

18. $\dfrac{(2n + 1)!(2n - 1)!}{2[(2n)!]}$

Example. $(a - 3b)^4$

Solution.

$$(a - 3b)^4 = a^4 + 4a^3(-3b) + \frac{12}{2!} a^2(-3b)^2 + \frac{24}{3!} a(-3b)^3 + \frac{24}{4!} (-3b)^4$$

$$= a^4 - 12a^3b + 54a^2b^2 - 108ab^3 + 81b^4$$

19. $(x + y)^5$ 20. $(x + y)^4$ 21. $(x - 3)^4$

22. $(2x - 1)^5$ 23. $\left(2x - \dfrac{y}{2}\right)^3$ 24. $\left(\dfrac{x}{3} + 3\right)^5$

25. $\left(\dfrac{x}{2} + 2\right)^6$ 26. $\left(\dfrac{2}{3} - a^2\right)^4$

Write the first four terms in the expansion. Do not simplify the terms.

Example. $(x + 2y)^{15}$

Solution.

$$(x + 2y)^{15} = x^{15} + 15x^{14}(2y) + \frac{15 \cdot 14}{2!} x^{13}(2y)^2 + \frac{15 \cdot 14 \cdot 13}{3!} x^{12}(2y)^3 + \cdots$$

27. $(x + y)^{20}$ 28. $(x - y)^{15}$ 29. $(a - 2b)^{12}$

30. $(2a - b)^{12}$ 31. $(x - \sqrt{2})^{10}$ 32. $\left(\dfrac{x}{2} + 2\right)^8$

Find to the nearest hundredth.

33. $(1.02)^{10}$ *Hint:* $1.02 = (1 + 0.02)$

34. $(1.01)^{15}$ 35. $(0.99)^8$ 36. $(0.98)^8$

37. If an amount A of money is invested at 4% compounded annually, the amount P present at the end of n years is given by $P = A(1 + 0.04)^n$. Find the amount present, to the nearest cent, if $1000 is invested for 5 years.

38. In Problem 37, find the amount present at the end of 20 years.

Find the specified term.

Example. $(x - 2y)^{12}$, the seventh term.

Solution. In Formula (3), page 373, use $n = 12$, $r = 7$.

$$\frac{12 \cdot 11 \cdot 10 \cdot 9 \cdot 8 \cdot 7}{6!} x^6 y^6$$

$$59{,}136 x^6 y^6$$

39. $(a - b)^{15}$, the sixth term.

40. $(x + 2)^{12}$, the fifth term.

41. $(x - 2y)^{10}$, the fifth term.

42. $(a^3 - b)^9$, the seventh term.

43. Given that the binomial formula holds as an infinite "sum" for $(1 + x)^n$, where n is a negative integer and $|x| < 1$,

   (a) write the first four terms of $(1 + x)^{-1}$;

   (b) find the first four terms of the quotient $1/(1 + x)$ by dividing $(1 + x)$ into 1.

   Compare the results of (a) and (b).

44. Given that the binomial formula holds as an infinite "sum" for $(1 + x)^n$, where n is a rational number and $|x| < 1$, find to two decimal places:
   (a) $\sqrt{1.02}$; (b) $\sqrt{0.99}$.

13

PROBABILITY

The theory of probability, which originated in an attempt to settle a gambling dispute in 1654, has grown to such an extent that it has implications for a vast number of fields ranging from gambling (still), through the social and physical sciences, to the deadly serious business of national survival. We shall touch on only some of the simplest and most basic facets of the subject, but the interested student can find many sources to broaden and deepen his understanding of the principles involved. Before discussing probability, however, we must consider some basic counting procedures necessary to its study.

13.1 BASIC COUNTING PRINCIPLES—PERMUTATIONS

Associated with each finite set A is a nonnegative integer n, corresponding to the number of elements in A. Hence, we have a function from the set of all finite sets to the set of nonnegative integers. The symbolism $n(A)$ is used to denote elements in the range of this set function n. For example, if

$$A = \{5, 7, 9\}, \quad B = \{1/2, 0, 3, -5, 7\}, \quad C = \emptyset,$$

then

$$n(A) = 3, \quad n(B) = 5, \quad \text{and} \quad n(C) = 0.$$

All the sets with which we shall hereafter be concerned are assumed to be finite sets. We then have the following properties, called **counting properties**, for the function n.

I. $n(A \cup B) = n(A) + n(B)$, if $A \cap B = \emptyset$.

Thus, if A and B are disjoint sets, then the number of elements in their union is the sum of the number of elements in A and the number in B. Set functions with this property are called **finitely additive**.

For example, suppose there are five roads from town R to town S, and two railroads from town R to town S. If A is the set of roads and B the set of railroads from R to S, then $n(A) = 5$ and $n(B) = 2$, and $n(A \cup B) = 5 + 2 = 7$, and there are seven ways one can go from town R to town S by driving or riding on a train.

$$\text{II. } n(A \cup B) = n(A) + n(B) - n(A \cap B), \text{ if } A \cap B \neq \varnothing.$$

That is, if A and B overlap, then to count the number of elements in $A \cup B$, we must add the number of elements in A to the number of elements in B. But since any elements in the intersection of A and B are counted twice in this process (once in A and once in B), we must subtract the number of such elements from the total.

For example, suppose there are fifteen unrelated girls and seventeen unrelated boys in a mathematics class, and suppose that precisely two of the boys and two of the girls are brother and sister. Then, if A denotes the set of different families represented by the girls and if B denotes the set of different families represented by the boys, the number of different families represented by the members of the class is

$$n(A \cup B) = n(A) + n(B) - n(A \cap B) = 15 + 17 - 2 = 30.$$

Actually, Property II can be obtained formally from Property I as follows. Let

$$A \cap B = B_1, \quad B = B_1 + B_2, \quad B_1 \cap B_2 = \varnothing.$$

Then

$$A \cup B = A \cup B_2, \quad A \cap B_2 = \varnothing.$$

Then by I we have

$$n(A \cup B) = n(A \cup B_2) = n(A) + n(B_2).$$

But also

$$n(B) = n(B_1 + B_2) = n(B_1) + n(B_2),$$

or

$$n(B_2) = n(B) - n(B_1) = n(B) - n(A \cap B).$$

Hence we obtain

$$n(A \cup B) = n(A) + n(B_2) = n(A) + n(B) - n(A \cap B).$$

Since $n(\varnothing) = 0$, Properties I and II can be expressed together, without restriction on $A \cap B$, by the equation

$$n(A \cup B) = n(A) + n(B) - n(A \cap B).$$
$$\text{III. } n(A \times B) = n(A) \cdot n(B).$$

This asserts that the number of elements in the Cartesian product of sets A and B is the product of the number of elements in A and the number of elements in B.

For example, suppose again that there are five roads from town R to town S (set A), and further suppose that there are three roads from town S to town T (set B). Then for each element of A there are three elements of B, and the total possible ways one can drive from R to T via S is

$$n(A \times B) = n(A) \cdot n(B) = 5 \cdot 3 = 15.$$

Given the set of numerals $A = \{1, 2, 3\}$, how many different three-digit numerals can be constructed from the members of A if no member is used more than once? The answer to this question can be obtained by simply listing the different three-digit numerals, $123, 132, 213, 231, 312, 321$, and counting them. Such a procedure would be quite impracticable, however, if the number of members of the given set of numerals was very large. Another way to arrive at the same conclusion is by applying the third counting property. If we let A denote the set of possible first digits in the foregoing numerals, then $n(A) = 3$. Since no numeral may be used more than once, and since one numeral has already been used for a first digit, there remain but two possibilities for the second digit. If B denotes the set of possible second digits after the first digit has been chosen, then $n(B) = 2$. By similar reasoning, if C is the set of possible third digits after the first two have been chosen, then $n(C) = 1$. By the third counting property (applied twice), we find that

$$n(A \times B \times C) = [n(A) \cdot n(B)] \cdot n(C) = 3 \cdot 2 \cdot 1 = 6.$$

We can generalize from this example. First, however, let us make the following definition.

DEFINITION 13.1 *A **permutation** of a set A is an ordering (first, second, etc.) of the members of A.*

For example, each of the three-digit numerals discussed above was a permutation of the elements of $\{1, 2, 3\}$. Now, with this definition, we can state the following result.

THEOREM 13.1 *Let $P_{n,n}$ denote the number of distinct permutations of a set A, where $n(A) = n$. Then*

$$P_{n,n} = n! \tag{1}$$

The symbol $P_{n,n}$ [or, sometimes, $_nP_n$ or $P\binom{n}{n}$] is read "the number of permutations of n things taken n at a time."

Proof. Let A_1 denote the set of possible first selections for arrangements. Then $A_1 = A$, and $n(A_1) = n(A) = n$. Having made a first selection, let A_2 denote the set of possible second selections. Then $A_2 \subset A$, and $n(A_2) = n(A_1) - 1 = n - 1$. A continuation of this procedure, together with successive application of the third counting principle, leads to

$$P_{n,n} = n(A_1) \cdot n(A_2) \cdot \; \cdots \; \cdot n(A_n) = n \cdot (n - 1)(n - 2) \cdots 1 = n!$$

as was to be proved.

Example. In how many ways can nine men be assigned positions to form distinct baseball teams?

Solution. Let A denote the set of men, so that $n(A) = 9$. The total number of ways in which 9 men can be assigned 9 positions on a team, or, in other words, the number of possible permutations of the members of a 9-element set, is by (1) on page 378,

$$P_{9,9} = 9! = 9 \cdot 8 \cdot 7 \cdots 1 = 362{,}880.$$

THEOREM 13.2   *Let $P_{n,r}$ denote the number of permutations of the elements of a set A $[n(A) = n]$ taken r at a time; that is, $P_{n,r}$ is the number of distinct orderings of r elements when there is a set A of n elements from which to choose. Then*

$$P_{n,r} = n(n - 1)(n - 2) \cdots [n - (r - 1)]$$

$$= n(n - 1)(n - 2) \cdots (n - r + 1). \tag{2}$$

The proof is left as an exercise, but in general it follows the proof of Theorem 13.1, except that the last subset considered is such that $n(A_r) = n - r + 1$.

Example. In how many ways can a basketball team be formed from a set of 10 players?

Solution. Let A denote the set of players, so that $n(A) = 10$. Then, from (2) we have

$$P_{10,5} = 10 \cdot 9 \cdot 8 \cdots (10 - 5 + 1) = 10 \cdot 9 \cdot 8 \cdot 7 \cdot 6 = 30{,}240.$$

An alternative expression for $P_{n,r}$ can be obtained by observing that

$$P_{n,r} = n(n - 1)(n - 2) \cdots (n - r + 1)$$

$$= \frac{n(n - 1)(n - 2) \cdots (n - r + 1) \cdot (n - r)!}{(n - r)!}$$

$$= \frac{n!}{(n - r)!}. \tag{2'}$$

The problem of finding the number of distinguishable permutations of n objects taken n at a time, if some of the objects are identical, requires a little more careful analysis. As an example, consider the number of permutations of the letters of the word *DIVISIBLE*. We can make a distinction between the three *I*'s by assigning subscripts to each so that we have nine distinct letters,

$$D, I_1, V, I_2, S, I_3, B, L, E.$$

The number of permutations of these nine letters is of course 9! If the letters other than I_1, I_2, and I_3 are retained in the position they occupy in the permutation above, I_1, I_2, and I_3 can be permuted among themselves 3! ways. Thus, if P is the number of distinguishable permutations of the letters

$$D, I, V, I, S, I, B, L, E,$$

and if for each of these there are 3! ways in which the *I*'s can be permuted without otherwise changing the order of the other letters, then

$$3! \cdot P = 9!,$$

from which

$$P = \frac{9!}{3!}.$$

As another example, consider the letters of the word *MISSISSIPPI*. There would exist 11! distinguishable permutations of the letters in this word if each letter were distinct. However, the letters *S* and *I* each appear four times and the letter *P* appears twice. Reasoning as we did in the previous example, we see that the number of distinguishable permutations of the letters in *MISSISSIPPI* is given by

$$4!4!2!P = 11!,$$

from which

$$P = \frac{11!}{4!4!2!}.$$

EXERCISE 13.1

Consider the following sets. Find $n(A \cup B)$, $n(A \cap B)$, and $n(A \times B)$.

Example. $A = \{a, b, c\}$, $B = \{c, d\}$.

Solution.

$A \cup B = \{a, b, c, d\}$. Therefore $n(A \cup B) = 4$.

$A \cap B = \{c\}$. Therefore $n(A \cap B) = 1$.

$A \times B = \{(a, c), (a, d), (b, c), (b, d), (c, c), (c, d)\}$.

Therefore $n(A \times B) = 6$.

1. $A = \{d, e\}$, $B = \{e, f, g, h\}$

2. $A = \{e\}$, $B = \{a, b, c, d\}$

3. $A = \{1, 2, 3, 4\}$, $B = \{3, 4, 5, 6\}$

4. $A = \{1, 2\}$, $B = \{3, 4, 5\}$

5. $A = \{1, 2\}$, $B = \{1, 2\}$

6. $A = \emptyset$, $B = \{2, 3, 4\}$

Example.   In how many different ways can three members of a class be assigned a grade of A, B, C, or D so that no two members receive the same grade?

Solution.   Sometimes a simple diagram, such as ___ , ___ , ___ , designating a sequence, is a helpful preliminary device.   Since the first student may receive any one of four different grades, the second student may then receive any one of three different grades, and the third student may then receive any one of two different grades, the sequence would appear as 4, 3, 2.   From counting property III, there are $4 \cdot 3 \cdot 2$, or 24, possible ways the grades may be assigned. We could have obtained the same result directly from Theorem 13.2, since $P_{4,3} = 4 \cdot 3 \cdot 2 = 24$.

In the following problems, a digit or letter may be used more than once unless stated otherwise.

7. How many different two-digit numerals can be formed from the digits 5 and 6?

8. How many different two-digit numerals can be formed from the digits 7, 8, 9?

9. In how many different ways can four students be seated in a row?

10. In how many different ways can five students be seated in a row?

11. In how many different ways can four questions on a true-false test be answered?

12. In how many different ways can five questions on a true-false test be answered?

13. In how many ways can you write different three-digit numerals, using $\{2, 3, 4, 5\}$?

14. In how many ways can you write different three-digit numerals, using $\{2, 3, 4, 5\}$, if no digit is to be used more than once in each numeral?

15. How many different seven-digit telephone numbers can be formed from $\{1, 2, 3, 4, 5, 6, 7, 8, 9, 0\}$?

16. How many different seven-digit telephone numbers can be formed from $\{1, 2, 3, 4, 5, 6, 7, 8, 9, 0\}$ if no digit is to be used more than once in each number?

17. How many three-letter arrangements can be formed from $\{A, N, S, W, E, R\}$?

18. How many different three-letter arrangements can be formed from $\{A, N, S, W, E, R\}$ if no letter is to be used more than once in each arrangement?

19. How many positive odd integers with numerals containing four digits can be formed from $\{1, 2, 3, 4, 5\}$?

20. How many positive even integers with numerals containing four digits can be formed from $\{1, 2, 3, 4, 5\}$?

21. How many positive integers less than 500 can be formed from $\{3, 4, 5\}$?

22. How many positive odd integers less than 500 can be formed from $\{3, 4, 5\}$?

23. How many positive even integers less than 500 can be formed from $\{3, 4, 5\}$?

24. How many positive even integers between 400 and 500, inclusive, can be formed from $\{3, 4, 5\}$?

25. How many permutations of the elements of $\{P, R, I, M, E\}$ end in vowels?

26. How many permutations of the elements of $\{P, R, O, D, U, C, T\}$ end in vowels?

27. Find the number of distinguishable permutations of the letters in the word *LIMIT*.

28. Find the number of distinguishable permutations of the letters in the word *COMBINATION*.

29. Find the number of distinguishable permutations of the letters in the word *COLORADO*.

30. Find the number of distinguishable permutations of the letters in the word *TALLAHASSEE*.

31. Show that $P_{5,3} = 5(P_{4,2})$.

32. Show that $P_{5,r} = 5(P_{4,r-1})$.

33. Show that $P_{n,3} = n(P_{n-1,2})$.

34. Show that $P_{n,3} - P_{n,2} = (n-3)(P_{n,2})$.

35. Solve for n: $P_{n,5} = 5(P_{n,4})$.

36. Solve for n: $P_{n,5} = 9(P_{n-1,4})$.

37. Prove Theorem 13.2.

Example. In how many ways can four students be seated around a circular table?

Solution. In any such arrangement (which is called a **circular permutation**), there is no first position. Each person can take four different initial positions without affecting the arrangement. Thus, there are $4!/4 = 6$ arrangements. In general there are $n!/n = (n-1)!$ circular permutations of n things taken n at a time.

38. In how many ways can six students be seated around a circular table?

39. In how many ways can six students be seated around a circular table if a certain two must be seated together?

40. In how many ways can three different keys be arranged on a key ring? *Hint:* Arrangements should be considered identical if one can be obtained from the other by turning the ring. In general, there are only $(1/2)(n - 1)!$ distinct arrangements of n keys on a ring ($n \geq 3$).

41. In how many ways can eight beads of different colors be strung on a necklace?

13.2 COMBINATIONS

An additional counting concept is needed before we turn our attention to probability—namely, finding the number of distinct r-element subsets of an n-element set.

To begin with, we make the following definition.

DEFINITION 13.2 *An r-element subset of an n-element set is called a* **combination.**

Thus, a combination is simply a set of objects with no reference to the relative order. For example, five different playing cards can be arranged in 5! permutations, but to a poker player they represent the same hand. There is only one *combination* here.

The counting of combinations is related to the counting of permutations. From Theorem 13.2, we know that the number of distinct permutations of n elements of a set A taken r at a time is given by

$$P_{n,r} = \frac{n!}{(n - r)!}.$$

With this in mind, consider the following.

THEOREM 13.3 *Let* $\binom{n}{r}$ *denote the number of distinct combinations of the elements of a set A* $[n(A) = n]$, *taken r at a time. Then*

$$\binom{n}{r} = \frac{P_{n,r}}{r!}. \tag{1}$$

Proof. There are, by definition, $\binom{n}{r}$ r-element subsets of the set A, where $n(A) = n$. Also, from Theorem 13.1, each of these subsets has $r!$ permutations of its members. There are, therefore, $\binom{n}{r}r!$ permutations of n elements of A taken r at a time. That is,

$$P_{n,r} = \binom{n}{r} r!,$$

from which we obtain

$$\binom{n}{r} = \frac{P_{n,r}}{r!},$$

as was to be shown.

Thus, to find the number of r-element subsets of an n-element set A, we count the number of permutations of the elements of A taken r at a time, and then divide by the number of possible permutations of an r-element set. This seems very much like counting a set of people by counting the number of arms and legs and dividing the result by 4, but this approach gives us a very useful expression for the number we seek, $\binom{n}{r}$. Since

$$P_{n,r} = n(n-1)(n-2)\cdots(n-r+1),$$

it follows that

$$\binom{n}{r} = \frac{P_{n,r}}{r!} = \frac{n(n-1)(n-2)\cdots(n-r+1)}{r!},$$

or, since

$$P_{n,r} = \frac{n!}{(n-r)!},$$

it follows that

$$\binom{n}{r} = \frac{P_{n,r}}{r!} = \frac{n!}{r!(n-r)!}. \tag{1'}$$

Observe that the right-hand member of this expression is the same as the coefficient of the rth term in the binomial expansion on page 371.

Example. How many ways can a committee of five be selected from a set of twelve persons?

Solution. What we wish here is the number of 5-element subsets of a 12-element set. We have, from (1'),

$$\binom{12}{5} = \frac{12!}{5!7!} = \frac{12\cdot11\cdot10\cdot9\cdot8\cdot7!}{5!7!}$$

$$= \frac{12\cdot11\cdot10\cdot9\cdot8}{5\cdot4\cdot3\cdot2\cdot1} = 792.$$

Since the numbers $\binom{n}{r}$ are the coefficients in the binomial expansion, and since these coefficients are symmetric, we have the following plausible assertion.

THEOREM 13.4 $\quad \dbinom{n}{r} = \dbinom{n}{n-r}.$

Proof. We have from (1′)

$$\binom{n}{r} = \frac{n!}{r!(n-r)!}$$

and

$$\binom{n}{n-r} = \frac{n!}{(n-r)![n-(n-r)]!} = \frac{n!}{(n-r)!r!},$$

and the theorem is proved.

Theorem 13.4 can also be made plausible by the observation that each time a distinct set of r objects is chosen, a distinct set of $n-r$ objects remains unchosen.

EXERCISE 13.2

Example. How many different amounts of money can be formed from a penny, a nickel, a dime, and a quarter?

Solution. We want to find the total number of combinations that can be formed by taking the coins 1, 2, 3, and 4 at a time. By (1′) we have

$$\binom{4}{1} = \frac{4!}{1!3!} = 4,$$

$$\binom{4}{2} = \frac{4!}{2!2!} = 6,$$

$$\binom{4}{3} = \frac{4!}{3!1!} = 4,$$

$$\binom{4}{4} = \frac{4!}{4!0!} = 1,$$

and the total number of combinations is 15. Clearly each gives a different amount.

1. How many different amounts of money can be formed from a penny, a nickel, and a dime?

2. How many different amounts of money can be formed from a penny, a nickel, a dime, a quarter, and a half-dollar?

3. How many different committees of four persons each can be chosen from a group of six persons?

4. How many different committees of four persons each can be chosen from a group of ten persons?

5. In how many different ways can a set of five cards be selected from a deck containing 52 cards?

6. In how many different ways can a set of 13 cards be selected from a deck of 52 cards?

7. In how many different ways can a hand consisting of five spades, five hearts, and three diamonds be selected from a standard bridge deck?

8. In how many different ways can a hand consisting of ten spades, one heart, one diamond, and one club be selected from a standard bridge deck?

9. In how many different ways can a hand consisting of either five spades, five hearts, five diamonds, or five clubs be selected from a standard bridge deck?

10. In how many different ways can a hand consisting of three aces and two cards that are not aces be selected from a standard bridge deck?

11. A combination of three balls is picked at random from a box containing five red, four white, and three blue balls. In how many ways can the set chosen contain at least one white ball?

12. In Problem 11, how many ways can the set chosen contain at least one white and one blue ball?

13. Five distinct points lie on the circumference of a circle. How many inscribed triangles can be drawn having these points as vertices?

14. Ten distinct points lie on the circumference of a circle. How many inscribed quadrilaterals can be drawn having these points as vertices?

15. Ten distinct points lie on the circumference of a circle. How many inscribed hexagons can be drawn having these points as vertices?

16. Given $\binom{n}{3} = \binom{50}{47}$, find n.

17. Given $\binom{n}{7} = \binom{n}{5}$, find n.

18. Expand $(a + b)^5$. Write the coefficient of each term in the form $\binom{n}{r}$.

19. Write the first four terms of $(a + b)^{10}$. Write the coefficient of each term in the form $\binom{n}{r}$.

20. Write the first eight terms of $(a + b)^{12}$. Write the coefficient of each term in the form $\binom{n}{r}$.

13.3   SAMPLE SPACES AND EVENTS

When an experiment of some kind is undertaken, associated with the experiment is a set of possible results. For example, when a die is rolled, let us assume that it will come to a stop with one of the numerals 1, 2, 3, 4, 5, or 6 on its upper face—that is, a number of spots corresponding to these numerals. This exhausts all possibilities.

DEFINITION 13.3 *The set of all possible results of an experiment is called a **sample space** for the experiment.*

DEFINITION 13.4 *Each element of a sample space is called an **outcome** or **sample point**.*

There may be more than one possible sample space for an experiment. Consider a bag in which there are some small balls. A certain number of the balls are made of glass, say, and the rest of plastic. Some of each kind are blue and some are red. If we now conduct an experiment in which a ball is drawn from the bag, we might be interested in one of the following:

a. We might be concerned with whether a glass or a plastic ball is drawn. If g denotes the drawing of a glass and p a plastic ball, then our sample space is $\{g, p\}$.

b. We might be concerned with whether a red or a blue ball is drawn. Then we have $\{r, b\}$ for a sample space, where r denotes the outcome of a red and b of a blue ball.

c. We might be concerned with both the color of the ball and the material of which it is made. With g, p, r, and b as before, our sample space consists of

$$\{(g, r), (g, b), (p, r), (p, b)\},$$

where the elements of the sample space are ordered pairs.

There are numerous other possibilities. The point to be made here is that, in setting up a sample space, one must do so with a particular kind of outcome in mind.

DEFINITION 13.5 *Any subset of a sample space is called an **event**, and is commonly denoted by the letter E.*

The reason for this terminology is that, in conducting an experiment, one may be interested in sets of outcomes rather than in individual outcomes. In the tossing of a die, for example, if the sample space is taken as $\{1, 2, 3, 4, 5, 6\}$, then the event that an outcome (a numeral) denotes an even integer is just the set $\{2, 4, 6\}$, which is a subset of the sample space. The event that an outcome denotes an odd integer is the set $\{1, 3, 5\}$. These events are complements of each other, and are examples of **complementary events**.

The number of possible events in an n-element sample space is the number of possible subsets of an n-element set, namely 2^n, where both the null set (impossible event) and the entire sample space (certain event) are included. That is

$$\binom{n}{0} + \binom{n}{1} + \binom{n}{2} + \cdots + \binom{n}{n} = 2^n, \tag{1}$$

where $\binom{n}{0}$ represents the single event that is contributed by the null set.

EXERCISE 13.3

1. A die is cast. List the sample space. List the event that the number on the upper face of the die is greater than 2.

2. A coin is tossed. List the sample space. List the event that a head appears.

3. Two coins are tossed. List the sample space. List the event that either two heads or two tails appear.

4. A die is cast and a coin is tossed. List the sample space. List the event that a head is tossed.

5. Two numbers are chosen at random from the integers 3, 4, 5, and 6. List the sample space. List the event that the sum of the numbers is an odd integer.

6. Two bags contain marbles. The first bag contains red and white marbles, and the second bag contains blue and white marbles. One marble is drawn from each bag. List the sample space. List the event that at least one white marble is drawn.

7. Consider the data in the previous problem and list the event that only one white marble is drawn.

8. How many events are there in the sample space $\{1, 2, 3\}$ if $\emptyset$ is considered as an event?

9. How many events are there in the sample space $\{1, 2, 3, 4, 5, 6\}$ if each event must contain at least one outcome?

10. Two cards are drawn from a standard deck of 52. Describe the sample space. Describe the event that one card is a face card. Describe the event that one card is a face card and one is not.

11. In playing bridge, all 52 cards are distributed among four players, 13 to each. A sample space for a single bridge hand, accordingly, consists of all possible combinations of 52 things taken 13 at a time, which is $\binom{52}{13}$, a very large number indeed. Suppose, however, we are interested only in the occurrence of aces in various hands. Since there are only four aces, and only four hands, listing the sample space for this latter situation would not be such a formidable task, although the sample space would still contain quite a few outcomes. Instead of listing all of them, then, calculate the number of outcomes in the sample space. Use W, S, N, and E for the West, South, North, and East hands, respectively, and begin by considering how many ways the event $W_1 \, S_1 \, N_1 \, E_1$ could occur, where the subscript denotes the number of aces in the specified hand. Then, consider other arrangements for subscripts, such as $W_2 S_1 N_1$, $W_2 S_1 E_1$, etc.

12. In the bridge game in Problem 11, let W_1 denote the event that West has one ace, $N_1 S_2$ denote the event that North has one and South two aces, etc. How many outcomes are in each of the following?

    a. W_1 b. S_2 c. N_3

    d. E_4 e. $N_2 S_2$ f. $N_3 S_1$

13. In the bridge game in Problem 12, let $W_1 \cup S_2$ denote the event that either West has one ace or South has two (or both). How many outcomes are there in this event? *Hint:* Recall that $n(A \cup B) = n(A) + n(B) - n(A \cap B)$.

14. Verify equation (1) in this section for the sample space $\{1, 2, 3, 4, 5, 6\}$.

13.4 PROBABILITY FUNCTIONS

The word "random" as used in mathematics is generally taken to be an undefined term, but it is ordinarily employed to discuss phenomena in which seemingly identical processes produce diverse data. If we roll a die, for example, and if the die or other factors are not "loaded," then any one of the outcomes 1, 2, 3, 4, 5, 6 can be considered to be equally likely, and the actual outcome is termed "random." We shall use the word "random" herein in this sense, and we shall consider outcomes in an experiment as random unless otherwise specified.

We define a function P on a sample space S as follows.

DEFINITION 13.6 *Let S denote a sample space of random outcomes, and let P be a real-valued function with domain the set of all events $E \subseteq S$. Then P is a **probability function** if and only if the following conditions are satisfied:*

a. *$P(E) \geq 0$ for each $E \subseteq S$,*

b. *$P(S) = 1$,*

c. *$P(E)$ is finitely additive; that is, if $E_1 \cap E_2 = \emptyset$ then $P(E_1 \cup E_2) = P(E_1) + P(E_2)$.*

By definition, then, any real-valued function having as domain the events E in a sample space might be called a probability function, provided it satisfies the above conditions a, b, and c. In practice, however, the probability functions ordinarily considered are somehow connected with our intuitive notions of likelihood of occurrence. These notions usually are based on considerations of the types discussed below.

A priori considerations involve physical, geometrical, and other inherent properties of the experiment in question. They involve no sampling of outcomes. Thus, when a die that appears to be cubical and to have a uniform distribution of mass is cast from a distance onto a flat table, and we admit as outcomes the die's stopping with any of its six different faces uppermost, then without making any trial throws we would assign the value $1/6$ as the probability of each of the six possible outcomes.

Thus we are led to the probability function defined by

$$P(E) = \frac{n(E)}{n(S)} \tag{1}$$

for a sample space of seemingly "equally likely" occurrences. Here $n(E)$ is the number of distinct ways in which the event E can occur, and $n(S)$ is the number of distinct outcomes in the sample space. In solving the problems in Exercises 13.4 and 13.5, (1) is the probability function that should be employed unless the function is given.

It is easy to check that the function P defined by (1) is a probability function. Since, in (1), $n(E)$ is a nonnegative integer and $n(S)$ is a positive integer, it follows that $P(E)$ is a nonnegative rational number for each $E \subseteq S$. Further, we have

$$P(S) = \frac{n(S)}{n(S)} = 1.$$

Finally, since $n(E)$ is finitely additive, so is $P(E)$.

A posteriori considerations involve testing the experiment a certain number of times. Mortality tables give probability functions of this sort. Actually, (1) can still be used in defining such probability functions, provided we interpret the function $n(E)$ as being the number of times the event E occurred in the test, and $n(S)$ as being the total number of times the experiment was performed in the test.

Example. If two dice are cast, what is the (*a priori*) probability that the sum of the digits showing on the top faces of the dice is less than 6?

Solution. For our sample spaces, let us consider A the set of possible outcomes for one die and B the set for the other. Then $n(A) = 6$ and $n(B) = 6$. The possible outcomes for both would be $S = A \times B$, the Cartesian product of A and B, and $n(A \times B) = n(S) = 36$. Each outcome here is an ordered pair (a, b), where a is the numeral on the upper face of the first die, and b on that of the second die. The event we seek is the event $\{(a, b) \mid a + b < 6\}$. The lattice in Figure 13.1 shows the situation schematically.

Since $E = \{(1, 1), (1, 2), (1, 3), (1, 4), (2, 1),$ $(2, 2), (2, 3), (3, 1), (3, 2), (4, 1)\}$, we have $n(E) = 10$, and

$$P(E) = \frac{n(E)}{n(S)} = \frac{10}{36} = \frac{5}{18}.$$

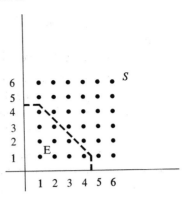

Figure 13.1

Care must be taken in interpreting the meaning of "the probability of an event." In the foregoing example, 5/18 does not assure us, for instance, that E will occur 5 times out of 18 casts, or, indeed, that even one cast out of 18 will produce the event described. What it does imply, however, is that if you cast the dice a very great number of times, about 5/18 of the time you can *expect* the sum on the exposed faces to be less than 6.

If we denote the complement of an event E in a sample space S by E', then $P(E')$ denotes the probability of the occurrence of E'. Since an outcome in S must lie in either E or E', and since $P(S) = 1$, it follows that

$$P(E) + P(E') = 1,$$

or

$$P(E') = 1 - P(E).$$

Thus, in the example above, the probability that a single cast of two dice will produce a sum on the exposed faces greater than or equal to 6 is

$$P(E') = 1 - P(E) = 1 - \frac{5}{18} = \frac{13}{18}.$$

DEFINITION 13.7 *The **odds** that an experiment with sample space S will result in an event E are given by*

$$\frac{P(E)}{P(E')} = \frac{P(E)}{1 - P(E)}.$$

Thus, the odds that the sum of the numbers determined by the exposed faces of two dice will be less than 6 are 5 to 13, and that they will be greater than or equal to 6 are 13 to 5.

By the definition of the probability function, this function is finitely additive. Consequently, if the sample space S is partitioned into n mutually disjoint events $E_1, E_2, \cdots, E_n$, then

$$P(S) = P(E_1) + P(E_2) + \cdots + P(E_n) = 1.$$

Moreover, we have the following.

THEOREM 13.5 *If S is a sample space, and E_1 and E_2 are any events in S, then*

$$P(E_1 \text{ or } E_2) = P(E_1 \bigcup E_2) = P(E_1) + P(E_2) - P(E_1 \bigcap E_2).$$

Proof. It was pointed out in Section 13.1 that Property II of the set function n is a consequence of the finite-additivity Property I. The same argument applies to any finitely additive function, in particular to P. The present theorem merely expresses this fact for probability functions.

Example. If two cards are drawn from a standard deck of playing cards, what is the probability that either both are red or both are Jacks?

Solution. A deck of cards contains 52 cards, and an outcome here consists of two cards. Hence, the number of elements of the sample space will be the number of ways (combinations) one can draw two cards from 52, which is $\binom{52}{2}$. Let E_1 be the event that both are red. Since there are 26 red cards in a deck, the number of outcomes (combinations) in the event E_1 will be $n(E_1) = \binom{26}{2}$. Let E_2 be the event that both cards are Jacks. Then, because there are four Jacks in a deck, $n(E_2) = \binom{4}{2}$. Since there is only one pair of red Jacks, $n(E_1 \bigcap E_2) = 1$. We then have

$$P(E_1 \bigcup E_2) = P(E_1) + P(E_2) - P(E_1 \bigcap E_2)$$

$$= \frac{\binom{26}{2}}{\binom{52}{2}} + \frac{\binom{4}{2}}{\binom{52}{2}} - \frac{1}{\binom{52}{2}}$$

$$= \frac{\binom{26}{2} + \binom{4}{2} - 1}{\binom{52}{2}}$$

$$= \frac{\frac{26 \cdot 25}{1 \cdot 2} + \frac{4 \cdot 3}{1 \cdot 2} - 1}{\frac{52 \cdot 51}{1 \cdot 2}}$$

$$= \frac{325 + 6 - 1}{1326} = \frac{330}{1326} = \frac{165}{668}.$$

Of course, if E_1 and E_2 are *disjoint*, then $(E_1 \bigcap E_2) = \emptyset$, so that $P(E_1 \bigcap E_2) = 0$, and the equation in Theorem 13.5 reduces to

$$P(E_1 \bigcup E_2) = P(E_1) + P(E_2).$$

Such disjoint events are said to be **mutually exclusive**.

Example. A card is drawn at random from a standard deck of 52 cards. What is the probability that the card is either a face card (Jack, Queen, or King) or a four?

Solution. Let E_1 be the event that the card is a four. There are four such cards in a deck, so that $n(E_1) = 4$. Let E_2 be the event that the card is a Jack, Queen, or King. There are twelve such cards in a deck, so that $n(E_2) = 12$. Since the sample space is just the entire deck, $n(S) = 52$, and since E_1 and E_2 are mutually exclusive,

$$P(E_1 \text{ or } E_2) = P(E_1) + P(E_2)$$
$$= \frac{4}{52} + \frac{12}{52} = \frac{16}{52} = \frac{4}{13}.$$

EXERCISE 13.4

Two dice are cast. Let E be the event that both dice show the same numeral. Let F be the event that the sum of numbers thrown is greater than eight. Find the following.

1. $P(E)$ 2. $P(F)$ 3. $P(E \cup F)$

4. $P(E')$ 5. $P(F')$ 6. $P(E' \cup F')$

A box contains five red, four white, and three blue marbles. Two marbles are drawn from the box. Let RR be the event that both marbles are red, WW that both marbles are white, BB that both marbles are blue, and RW, RB, BW that a red and a white, a red and a blue, and a blue and a white are drawn, respectively. Find the following.

7. $P(RR)$ 8. $P(BB)$ 9. $P(WW)$

10. $P(RW)$ 11. $P(RB)$ 12. $P(BW)$

13. What is the probability that neither is white?

14. What is the probability that neither is blue?

15. What is the probability that at least one is red?

16. What is the probability that either one is red or else both are white?

17. What is the probability that by drawing a single card from a standard deck of 52 cards, one will get a 2, 3, or 4?

18. What is the probability that if two cards are drawn from a standard deck of 52 cards they will be of the same suit? Different suits?

19. One box contains three red and eight white marbles, and a second box contains five red and two white marbles. If one marble is drawn from each box, what is the probability of drawing:
   a. Two red marbles?
   b. Two white marbles?
   c. One red and one white marble?

20. In Problem 19, what are the odds of drawing:
   a. Two red marbles?
   b. Two white marbles?
   c. One red and one white marble?

If the probability of the event E that a person will receive k dollars is $P(E)$, then the person's **mathematical expectation** is $kP(E)$.

21. A lottery offers a prize of $50, and 70 tickets are sold. What is the mathematical expectation of a person who buys three tickets? If each ticket costs $1, is the person's expectation greater or less than his outlay?

22. The odds that a certain horse will win the Irish Sweepstakes are 2 to 7. If you hold a ticket on this horse to pay $100,000 if he wins, what is your mathematical expectation?

If E_1, E_2, E_3, etc. are mutually exclusive events, and the return to you if E_1 occurs is k_1, if E_2 occurs is k_2, etc., then your mathematical expectation is

$$\sum_{i=1}^{n} k_i P(E_i).$$

23. One coin is selected at random from a collection containing a penny, a nickel, and a dime. What is the expectation?

24. One coin is selected at random from a collection containing a dime, a quarter, and a half-dollar. What is the expectation?

25. Three $1 bills and four $5 bills are hidden from view. What is the expectation on a single selection?

26. Three $1 bills, four $5 bills, and one $10 bill are hidden from view. What is the expectation on a single draw?

In Problems 27–34, Venn diagrams will prove helpful.

27. Argue that if E_1 and E_2 are any events, then

$$P(E_1) \leq P(E_1 \cup E_2) \leq P(E_1) + P(E_2).$$

28. Argue that if E_1 and E_2 are any events, then

$$P(E_1 \cap E_2) \leq P(E_1 \cup E_2).$$

29. Argue that if $P(E_1) < P(E_2)$, then $P(E_1') > P(E_2')$.

30. Argue that if $E_1 \subset E_2$, then $P(E_1) < P(E_2)$.

Express each of the following in terms of $P(E_1)$, $P(E_2)$, and $P(E_1 \cap E_2)$.

31. $P(E_1' \cap E_2')$ 32. $P(E_1' \cup E_2')$

33. $P(E_1' \cap E_2)$ 34. $P(E_1 \cap E_2')$

13.5   INDEPENDENT AND DEPENDENT EVENTS

In some experiments, we may be interested in events that are not dependent on each other, in the sense that the occurrence of one may have no effect on the occurrence or nonoccurrence of another.

Consider an experiment in which two cards are drawn at random, one after the other, from a deck of ten cards, six of which are red and four blue. We can inquire into the probability that the first card drawn is red and the second blue. The simplest such situation would be one in which the first card is drawn, observed, and returned to the deck, which is then shuffled thoroughly before the second card is drawn. In this case, the sample space would consist of a set of ordered pairs (x, y), where x is the result of the first draw and y the result of the second draw. Since there are ten possibilities in each case, the sample space would consist of $10 \times 10 = 100$ ordered pairs. The horizontal axis in Figure 13.2 is labeled x and the vertical y, and r_i and b_i are used to designate the drawing of red and blue cards, respectively.

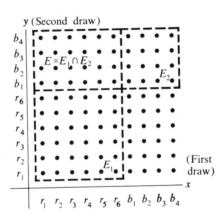

Figure 13.2

The events E_1 that the first card drawn is a red card and E_2 that the second card drawn is a blue card are outlined in the figure. The event E that both E_1 and E_2 occur is the intersection of E_1 and E_2; that is, $E = E_1 \cap E_2$. By inspection,

$$P(E_1) = \frac{60}{100} = \frac{3}{5}, \ P(E_2) = \frac{40}{100} = \frac{2}{5},$$

and

$$P(E) = P(E_1 \cap E_2) = \frac{24}{100} = \frac{6}{25}.$$

Moreover, in this example, it is evident that
$$P(E) = P(E_1 \cap E_2) = P(E_1) \cdot P(E_2).$$

Now consider the same experiment, except that this time the first card is not returned to the deck before the second is taken. Then there will be ten possible first draws, but only nine possible second draws. The sample space will therefore contain 10 × 9 ordered pairs, such that no ordered pair with first and second components the same remains in the set.

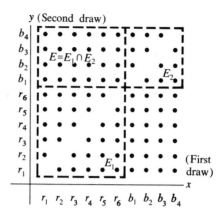

Figure 13.3

Figure 13.3 shows a graph of the sample space, which is the same as that in the preceding figure except that one diagonal is missing. Sets with graphs that have a missing diagonal are called **deleted Cartesian sets**. Again, the figure shows E_1 and E_2, the events that a red and a blue are obtained on the first and second draw, respectively. The event that both occur is $E = E_1 \cap E_2$, which is also shown in the figure.

By inspection,

$$P(E_1) = \frac{54}{90} = \frac{3}{5}, \ P(E_2) = \frac{36}{90} = \frac{2}{5},$$

and

$$P(E) = P(E_1 \cap E_2) = \frac{24}{90} = \frac{4}{15}.$$

This time,

$$P(E) \neq P(E_1) \cdot P(E_2).$$

If, however, we write 4/15 as

$$\frac{4}{15} = \frac{3}{5} \cdot \frac{4}{9},$$

then we have

$$P(E) = P(E_1) \cdot \frac{4}{9},$$

where 4/9 can be interpreted as the probability of the occurrence of E_2 *given the occurrence of* E_1. In this case $P(E)$ is generally denoted by the symbol $P(E_2 | E_1)$.

If the occurrence of E_2 does not depend on the occurrence or nonoccurrence of E_1, then

$$P(E_2|E_1) = P(E_2).$$

DEFINITION 13.8   *If E_1 and E_2 are events in a sample space, and if*

$$P(E_2|E_1) = P(E_2),$$

*then E_1 and E_2 are **independent events**. If two events are not independent, then they are said to be **dependent**.*

Generalizing from these two experiments, we have the following result, which is presented without proof. It is valid both for independent events and for dependent events.

THEOREM 13.6   *If E_1 and E_2 are events in a sample space, if $E = E_1 \cap E_2$, and if $P(E_2|E_1)$ denotes the probability of the occurrence of E_2 given the occurrence of E_1, then*

$$P(E) = P(E_1) \cdot P(E_2|E_1).$$

Example. A die is cast and a coin is tossed. What is the probability that a number less than five is thrown and a head is tossed? Are these events independent?

Solution. The sample space is a set of ordered pairs (x, y), where x is the result of casting the die and y is the result of tossing the coin. Since there are six results x and two results y, there are 6×2, or 12, ordered pairs in S. Of these, there will be 4×1, or 4, outcomes in E, so

$$P(E) = \frac{4}{12} = \frac{1}{3}.$$

Now, let E_1 be the event of casting a 1, 2, 3, or 4, and let E_2 be the event of tossing a head. Then

$$P(E_1) = \frac{8}{12} = \frac{2}{3} \quad \text{and} \quad P(E_2) = \frac{6}{12} = \frac{1}{2}.$$

Since

$$\frac{1}{3} = \frac{2}{3} \cdot \frac{1}{2},$$

E_1 and E_2 are independent.

EXERCISE 13.5

1. A bag contains four red marbles and ten blue marbles. If two marbles are drawn in succession, and if the first is not replaced, what is the probability that the first is red and the second is blue? Are the two draws independent events?

2. A red die and a green die are cast. What is the probability of obtaining a sum greater than 9 when the green die shows 4?

3. A bag contains four white and six red marbles. Two marbles are drawn from the bag and replaced, and two more marbles are drawn from the bag. What is the probability of drawing:

   a. Two red marbles on the first draw and two white ones on the second draw?

   b. Exactly two white marbles?

   c. Four white marbles?

   d. Four red marbles?

4. In Problem 3, what is the probability of drawing:

   a. Exactly three white marbles in the two draws?

   b. At least three white marbles in the two draws?

   c. Exactly two red marbles in the two draws?

   d. At least two red marbles in the two draws?

5. A red and a green die are cast. Let E_1 be the event that at least one die shows 3, and E_2 be the event that the sum of the two numbers thrown is 8.

   a. Find $P(E_1)$.   b. Find $P(E_2)$.

   c. Find $P(E_2 \mid E_1)$.   d. Are E_1 and E_2 independent?

6. In Problem 5, let E_1 be the event that neither die shows a result larger than 4, and let E_2 be the event that the dice do not show the same number.

   a. Find $P(E_1)$.   b. Find $P(E_2)$.

   c. Find $P(E_2 \mid E_1)$.   d. Are E_1 and E_2 independent?

7. A coin is tossed three consecutive times. What is the probability that:

   a. The second toss is a head?

   b. The third toss is a head?

   c. Both the second and third tosses are heads?

   d. The first and third tosses are heads?

   e. The first and third tosses are heads but the second is not?

8. In Problem 7, state whether each of the following pairs of events are independent.

   a. *a* and *b*   b. *a* and *c*   c. *a* and *d*

   d. *a* and *e*   e. *d* and *e*

9. The probability that *A* will pass a course in college algebra is 5/6, that *B* will pass, 3/4, and that *C* will pass, 2/3. What is the probability that:

   a. At least one of the three will pass?

   b. At least *A* and *C* will pass?

   c. *A* and *C* will pass but *B* will not?

   d. At least two of the three will pass?

10. In Problem 9, what is the probability of c, given the occurrence of a—that is, assuming that at least one of the three will pass? Are these events independent?

11. A day is selected at random in some fashion such that any day of the week is an equally probable choice. Let the probability be 1/30 that a day selected at random will be a rainy day.

   a. What is the probability that a rainy Wednesday will be selected?

   b. What is the probability that a dry Thursday will be selected?

   c. What is the probability that either Monday, Tuesday, or Wednesday will be selected, and that it will not rain that day?

   d. Let E_1 be the selection of Sunday, and let E_2 be the event that it does not rain on the day selected. What is the conditional probability of E_2, given the occurrence of E_1? Are E_1 and E_2 independent?

12. Argue that if E_1 and E_2 are mutually exclusive events with nonzero probabilities, then E_1 and E_2 are dependent.

APPENDIXES

TABLE I

COMMON LOGARITHMS

x	0	1	2	3	4	5	6	7	8	9
1.0	.0000	.0043	.0086	.0128	.0170	.0212	.0253	.0294	.0334	.0374
1.1	.0414	.0453	.0492	.0531	.0569	.0607	.0645	.0682	.0719	.0755
1.2	.0792	.0828	.0864	.0899	.0934	.0969	.1004	.1038	.1072	.1106
1.3	.1139	.1173	.1206	.1239	.1271	.1303	.1335	.1367	.1399	.1430
1.4	.1461	.1492	.1523	.1553	.1584	.1614	.1644	.1673	.1703	.1732
1.5	.1761	.1790	.1818	.1847	.1875	.1903	.1931	.1959	.1987	.2014
1.6	.2041	.2068	.2095	.2122	.2148	.2175	.2201	.2227	.2253	.2279
1.7	.2304	.2330	.2355	.2380	.2405	.2430	.2455	.2480	.2504	.2529
1.8	.2553	.2577	.2601	.2625	.2648	.2672	.2695	.2718	.2742	.2765
1.9	.2788	.2810	.2833	.2856	.2878	.2900	.2923	.2945	.2967	.2989
2.0	.3010	.3032	.3054	.3075	.3096	.3118	.3139	.3160	.3181	.3201
2.1	.3222	.3243	.3263	.3284	.3304	.3324	.3345	.3365	.3385	.3404
2.2	.3424	.3444	.3464	.3483	.3502	.3522	.3541	.3560	.3579	.3598
2.3	.3617	.3636	.3655	.3674	.3692	.3711	.3729	.3747	.3766	.3784
2.4	.3802	.3820	.3838	.3856	.3874	.3892	.3909	.3927	.3945	.3962
2.5	.3979	.3997	.4014	.4031	.4048	.4065	.4082	.4099	.4116	.4133
2.6	.4150	.4166	.4183	.4200	.4216	.4232	.4249	.4265	.4281	.4298
2.7	.4314	.4330	.4346	.4362	.4378	.4393	.4409	.4425	.4440	.4456
2.8	.4472	.4487	.4502	.4518	.4533	.4548	.4564	.4579	.4594	.4609
2.9	.4624	.4639	.4654	.4669	.4683	.4698	.4713	.4728	.4742	.4757
3.0	.4771	.4786	.4800	.4814	.4829	.4843	.4857	.4871	.4886	.4900
3.1	.4914	.4928	.4942	.4955	.4969	.4983	.4997	.5011	.5024	.5038
3.2	.5051	.5065	.5079	.5092	.5105	.5119	.5132	.5145	.5159	.5172
3.3	.5185	.5198	.5211	.5224	.5237	.5250	.5263	.5276	.5289	.5302
3.4	.5315	.5328	.5340	.5353	.5366	.5378	.5391	.5403	.5416	.5428
3.5	.5441	.5453	.5465	.5478	.5490	.5502	.5514	.5527	.5539	.5551
3.6	.5563	.5575	.5587	.5599	.5611	.5623	.5635	.5647	.5658	.5670
3.7	.5682	.5694	.5705	.5717	.5729	.5740	.5752	.5763	.5775	.5786
3.8	.5798	.5809	.5821	.5832	.5843	.5855	.5866	.5877	.5888	.5899
3.9	.5911	.5922	.5933	.5944	.5955	.5966	.5977	.5988	.5999	.6010
4.0	.6021	.6031	.6042	.6053	.6064	.6075	.6085	.6096	.6107	.6117
4.1	.6128	.6138	.6149	.6160	.6170	.6180	.6191	.6201	.6212	.6222
4.2	.6232	.6243	.6253	.6263	.6274	.6284	.6294	.6304	.6314	.6325
4.3	.6335	.6345	.6355	.6365	.6375	.6385	.6395	.6405	.6415	.6425
4.4	.6435	.6444	.6454	.6464	.6474	.6484	.6493	.6503	.6513	.6522
4.5	.6532	.6542	.6551	.6561	.6571	.6580	.6590	.6599	.6609	.6618
4.6	.6628	.6637	.6646	.6656	.6665	.6675	.6684	.6693	.6702	.6712
4.7	.6721	.6730	.6739	.6749	.6758	.6767	.6776	.6785	.6794	.6803
4.8	.6812	.6821	.6830	.6839	.6848	.6857	.6866	.6875	.6884	.6893
4.9	.6902	.6911	.6920	.6928	.6937	.6946	.6955	.6964	.6972	.6981
5.0	.6990	.6998	.7007	.7016	.7024	.7033	.7042	.7050	.7059	.7067
5.1	.7076	.7084	.7093	.7101	.7110	.7118	.7126	.7135	.7143	.7152
5.2	.7160	.7168	.7177	.7185	.7193	.7202	.7210	.7218	.7226	.7235
5.3	.7243	.7251	.7259	.7267	.7275	.7284	.7292	.7300	.7308	.7316
5.4	.7324	.7332	.7340	.7348	.7356	.7364	.7372	.7380	.7388	.7396
x	0	1	2	3	4	5	6	7	8	9

TABLE I (*continued*)

x	0	1	2	3	4	5	6	7	8	9
5.5	.7404	.7412	.7419	.7427	.7435	.7443	.7451	.7459	.7466	.7474
5.6	.7482	.7490	.7497	.7505	.7513	.7520	.7528	.7536	.7543	.7551
5.7	.7559	.7566	.7574	.7582	.7589	.7597	.7604	.7612	.7619	.7627
5.8	.7634	.7642	.7649	.7657	.7664	.7672	.7679	.7686	.7694	.7701
5.9	.7709	.7716	.7723	.7731	.7738	.7745	.7752	.7760	.7767	.7774
6.0	.7782	.7789	.7796	.7803	.7810	.7818	.7825	.7832	.7839	.7846
6.1	.7853	.7860	.7868	.7875	.7882	.7889	.7896	.7903	.7910	.7917
6.2	.7924	.7931	.7938	.7945	.7952	.7959	.7966	.7973	.7980	.7987
6.3	.7993	.8000	.8007	.8014	.8021	.8028	.8035	.8041	.8048	.8055
6.4	.8062	.8069	.8075	.8082	.8089	.8096	.8102	.8109	.8116	.8122
6.5	.8129	.8136	.8142	.8149	.8156	.8162	.8169	.8176	.8182	.8189
6.6	.8195	.8202	.8209	.8215	.8222	.8228	.8235	.8241	.8248	.8254
6.7	.8261	.8267	.8274	.8280	.8287	.8293	.8299	.8306	.8312	.8319
6.8	.8325	.8331	.8338	.8344	.8351	.8357	.8363	.8370	.8376	.8382
6.9	.8388	.8395	.8401	.8407	.8414	.8420	.8426	.8432	.8439	.8445
7.0	.8451	.8457	.8463	.8470	.8476	.8482	.8488	.8494	.8500	.8506
7.1	.8513	.8519	.8525	.8531	.8537	.8543	.8549	.8555	.8561	.8567
7.2	.8573	.8579	.8585	.8591	.8597	.8603	.8609	.8615	.8621	.8627
7.3	.8633	.8639	.8645	.8651	.8657	.8663	.8669	.8675	.8681	.8686
7.4	.8692	.8698	.8704	.8710	.8716	.8722	.8727	.8733	.8739	.8745
7.5	.8751	.8756	.8762	.8768	.8774	.8779	.8785	.8791	.8797	.8802
7.6	.8808	.8814	.8820	.8825	.8831	.8837	.8842	.8848	.8854	.8859
7.7	.8865	.8871	.8876	.8882	.8887	.8893	.8899	.8904	.8910	.8915
7.8	.8921	.8927	.8932	.8938	.8943	.8949	.8954	.8960	.8965	.8971
7.9	.8976	.8982	.8987	.8993	.8998	.9004	.9009	.9015	.9020	.9025
8.0	.9031	.9036	.9042	.9047	.9053	.9058	.9063	.9069	.9074	.9079
8.1	.9085	.9090	.9096	.9101	.9106	.9112	.9117	.9122	.9128	.9133
8.2	.9138	.9143	.9149	.9154	.9159	.9165	.9170	.9175	.9180	.9186
8.3	.9191	.9196	.9201	.9206	.9212	.9217	.9222	.9227	.9232	.9238
8.4	.9243	.9248	.9253	.9258	.9263	.9269	.9274	.9279	.9284	.9289
8.5	.9294	.9299	.9304	.9309	.9315	.9320	.9325	.9330	.9335	.9340
8.6	.9345	.9350	.9355	.9360	.9365	.9370	.9375	.9380	.9385	.9390
8.7	.9395	.9400	.9405	.9410	.9415	.9420	.9425	.9430	.9435	.9440
8.8	.9445	.9450	.9455	.9460	.9465	.9469	.9474	.9479	.9484	.9489
8.9	.9494	.9499	.9504	.9509	.9513	.9518	.9523	.9528	.9533	.9538
9.0	.9542	.9547	.9552	.9557	.9562	.9566	.9571	.9576	.9581	.9586
9.1	.9590	.9595	.9600	.9605	.9609	.9614	.9619	.9624	.9628	.9633
9.2	.9638	.9643	.9647	.9652	.9657	.9661	.9666	.9671	.9675	.9680
9.3	.9685	.9689	.9694	.9699	.9703	.9708	.9713	.9717	.9722	.9727
9.4	.9731	.9736	.9741	.9745	.9750	.9754	.9759	.9763	.9768	.9773
9.5	.9777	.9782	.9786	.9791	.9795	.9800	.9805	.9809	.9814	.9818
9.6	.9823	.9827	.9832	.9836	.9841	.9845	.9850	.9854	.9859	.9863
9.7	.9868	.9872	.9877	.9881	.9886	.9890	.9894	.9899	.9903	.9908
9.8	.9912	.9917	.9921	.9926	.9930	.9934	.9939	.9943	.9948	.9952
9.9	.9956	.9961	.9965	.9969	.9974	.9978	.9983	.9987	.9991	.9996
x	0	1	2	3	4	5	6	7	8	9

TABLE II
EXPONENTIAL FUNCTIONS

x	e^x	e^{-x}	x	e^x	e^{-x}
0.00	1.0000	1.0000	1.5	4.4817	0.2231
0.01	1.0101	0.9901	1.6	4.9530	0.2019
0.02	1.0202	0.9802	1.7	5.4739	0.1827
0.03	1.0305	0.9705	1.8	6.0496	0.1653
0.04	1.0408	0.9608	1.9	6.6859	0.1496
0.05	1.0513	0.9512	2.0	7.3891	0.1353
0.06	1.0618	0.9418	2.1	8.1662	0.1225
0.07	1.0725	0.9324	2.2	9.0250	0.1108
0.08	1.0833	0.9331	2.3	9.9742	0.1003
0.09	1.0942	0.9139	2.4	11.023	0.0907
0.10	1.1052	0.9048	2.5	12.182	0.0821
0.11	1.1163	0.8958	2.6	13.464	0.0743
0.12	1.1275	0.8869	2.7	14.880	0.0672
0.13	1.1388	0.8781	2.8	16.445	0.0608
0.14	1.1503	0.8694	2.9	18.174	0.0550
0.15	1.1618	0.8607	3.0	20.086	0.0498
0.16	1.1735	0.8521	3.1	22.198	0.0450
0.17	1.1853	0.8437	3.2	24.533	0.0408
0.18	1.1972	0.8353	3.3	27.113	0.0369
0.19	1.2092	0.8270	3.4	29.964	0.0334
0.20	1.2214	0.8187	3.5	33.115	0.0302
0.21	1.2337	0.8106	3.6	36.598	0.0273
0.22	1.2461	0.8025	3.7	40.447	0.0247
0.23	1.2586	0.7945	3.8	44.701	0.0224
0.24	1.2712	0.7866	3.9	49.402	0.0202
0.25	1.2840	0.7788	4.0	54.598	0.0183
0.30	1.3499	0.7408	4.1	60.340	0.0166
0.35	1.4191	0.7047	4.2	66.686	0.0150
0.40	1.4918	0.6703	4.3	73.700	0.0136
0.45	1.5683	0.6376	4.4	81.451	0.0123
0.50	1.6487	0.6065	4.5	90.017	0.0111
0.55	1.7333	0.5769	4.6	99.484	0.0101
0.60	1.8221	0.5488	4.7	109.95	0.0091
0.65	1.9155	0.5220	4.8	121.51	0.0082
0.70	2.0138	0.4966	4.9	134.29	0.0074
0.75	2.1170	0.4724	5.0	148.41	0.0067
0.80	2.2255	0.4493	5.5	244.69	0.0041
0.85	2.3396	0.4274	6.0	403.43	0.0025
0.90	2.4596	0.4066	6.5	665.14	0.0015
0.95	2.5857	0.3867	7.0	1096.6	0.0009
1.0	2.7183	0.3679	7.5	1808.0	0.0006
1.1	3.0042	0.3329	8.0	2981.0	0.0003
1.2	3.3201	0.3012	8.5	4914.8	0.0002
1.3	3.6693	0.2725	9.0	8103.1	0.0001
1.4	4.0552	0.2466	10.0	22026	0.00005

TABLE III

NATURAL LOGARITHMS OF NUMBERS

n	$\log_e n$	n	$\log_e n$	n	$\log_e n$
	*	4.5	1.5041	9.0	2.1972
0.1	7.6974	4.6	1.5261	9.1	2.2083
0.2	8.3906	4.7	1.5476	9.2	2.2192
0.3	8.7960	4.8	1.5686	9.3	2.2300
0.4	9.0837	4.9	1.5892	9.4	2.2407
0.5	9.3069	5.0	1.6094	9.5	2.2513
0.6	9.4892	5.1	1.6292	9.6	2.2618
0.7	9.6433	5.2	1.6487	9.7	2.2721
0.8	9.7769	5.3	1.6677	9.8	2.2824
0.9	9.8946	5.4	1.6864	9.9	2.2925
1.0	0.0000	5.5	1.7047	10	2.3026
1.1	0.0953	5.6	1.7228	11	2.3979
1.2	0.1823	5.7	1.7405	12	2.4849
1.3	0.2624	5.8	1.7579	13	2.5649
1.4	0.3365	5.9	1.7750	14	2.6391
1.5	0.4055	6.0	1.7918	15	2.7081
1.6	0.4700	6.1	1.8083	16	2.7726
1.7	0.5306	6.2	1.8245	17	2.8332
1.8	0.5878	6.3	1.8405	18	2.8904
1.9	0.6419	6.4	1.8563	19	2.9444
2.0	0.6931	6.5	1.8718	20	2.9957
2.1	0.7419	6.6	1.8871	25	3.2189
2.2	0.7885	6.7	1.9021	30	3.4012
2.3	0.8329	6.8	1.9169	35	3.5553
2.4	0.8755	6.9	1.9315	40	3.6889
2.5	0.9163	7.0	1.9459	45	3.8067
2.6	0.9555	7.1	1.9601	50	3.9120
2.7	0.9933	7.2	1.9741	55	4.0073
2.8	1.0296	7.3	1.9879	60	4.0943
2.9	1.0647	7.4	2.0015	65	4.1744
3.0	1.0986	7.5	2.0149	70	4.2485
3.1	1.1314	7.6	2.0281	75	4.3175
3.2	1.1632	7.7	2.0412	80	4.3820
3.3	1.1939	7.8	2.0541	85	4.4427
3.4	1.2238	7.9	2.0669	90	4.4998
3.5	1.2528	8.0	2.0794	100	4.6052
3.6	1.2809	8.1	2.0919	110	4.7005
3.7	1.3083	8.2	2.1041	120	4.7875
3.8	1.3350	8.3	2.1163	130	4.8676
3.9	1.3610	8.4	2.1282	140	4.9416
4.0	1.3863	8.5	2.1401	150	5.0106
4.1	1.4110	8.6	2.1518	160	5.0752
4.2	1.4351	8.7	2.1633	170	5.1358
4.3	1.4586	8.8	2.1748	180	5.1930
4.4	1.4816	8.9	2.1861	190	5.2470

* Subtract 10 for $n < 1$. Thus $\log_e 0.1 = 7.6974 - 10 = -2.3026$.

TABLE IV

SQUARES, SQUARE ROOTS, AND PRIME FACTORS

No.	Sq.	Sq. Rt.	Factors	No.	Sq.	Sq. Rt.	Factors
1	1	1.000		51	2,601	7.141	$3 \cdot 17$
2	4	1.414	2	52	2,704	7.211	$2^2 \cdot 13$
3	9	1.732	3	53	2,809	7.280	53
4	16	2.000	2^2	54	2,916	7.348	$2 \cdot 3^3$
5	25	2.236	5	55	3,025	7.416	$5 \cdot 11$
6	36	2.449	$2 \cdot 3$	56	3,136	7.483	$2^3 \cdot 7$
7	49	2.646	7	57	3,249	7.550	$3 \cdot 19$
8	64	2.828	2^3	58	3,364	7.616	$2 \cdot 29$
9	81	3.000	3^2	59	3,481	7.681	59
10	100	3.162	$2 \cdot 5$	60	3,600	7.746	$2^2 \cdot 3 \cdot 5$
11	121	3.317	11	61	3,721	7.810	61
12	144	3.464	$2^2 \cdot 3$	62	3,844	7.874	$2 \cdot 31$
13	169	3.606	13	63	3,969	7.937	$3^2 \cdot 7$
14	196	3.742	$2 \cdot 7$	64	4,096	8.000	2^6
15	225	3.873	$3 \cdot 5$	65	4,225	8.062	$5 \cdot 13$
16	256	4.000	2^4	66	4,356	8.124	$2 \cdot 3 \cdot 11$
17	289	4.123	17	67	4,489	8.185	67
18	324	4.243	$2 \cdot 3^2$	68	4,624	8.246	$2^2 \cdot 17$
19	361	4.359	19	69	4,761	8.307	$3 \cdot 23$
20	400	4.472	$2^2 \cdot 5$	70	4,900	8.367	$2 \cdot 5 \cdot 7$
21	441	4.583	$3 \cdot 7$	71	5,041	8.426	71
22	484	4.690	$2 \cdot 11$	72	5,184	8.485	$2^3 \cdot 3^2$
23	529	4.796	23	73	5,329	8.544	73
24	576	4.899	$2^3 \cdot 3$	74	5,476	8.602	$2 \cdot 37$
25	625	5.000	5^2	75	5,625	8.660	$3 \cdot 5^2$
26	676	5.099	$2 \cdot 13$	76	5,776	8.718	$2^2 \cdot 19$
27	729	5.196	3^3	77	5,929	8.775	$7 \cdot 11$
28	784	5.292	$2^2 \cdot 7$	78	6,084	8.832	$2 \cdot 3 \cdot 13$
29	841	5.385	29	79	6,241	8.888	79
30	900	5.477	$2 \cdot 3 \cdot 5$	80	6,400	8.944	$2^4 \cdot 5$
31	961	5.568	31	81	6,561	9.000	3^4
32	1,024	5.657	2^5	82	6,724	9.055	$2 \cdot 41$
33	1,089	5.745	$3 \cdot 11$	83	6,889	9.110	83
34	1,156	5.831	$2 \cdot 17$	84	7,056	9.165	$2^2 \cdot 3 \cdot 7$
35	1,225	5.916	$5 \cdot 7$	85	7,225	9.220	$5 \cdot 17$
36	1,296	6.000	$2^2 \cdot 3^2$	86	7,396	9.274	$2 \cdot 43$
37	1,369	6.083	37	87	7,569	9.327	$3 \cdot 29$
38	1,444	6.164	$2 \cdot 19$	88	7,744	9.381	$2^3 \cdot 11$
39	1,521	6.245	$3 \cdot 13$	89	7,921	9.434	89
40	1,600	6.325	$2^3 \cdot 5$	90	8,100	9.487	$2 \cdot 3^2 \cdot 5$
41	1,681	6.403	41	91	8,281	9.539	$7 \cdot 13$
42	1,764	6.481	$2 \cdot 3 \cdot 7$	92	8,464	9.592	$2^2 \cdot 23$
43	1,849	6.557	43	93	8,649	9.644	$3 \cdot 31$
44	1,936	6.633	$2^2 \cdot 11$	94	8,836	9.695	$2 \cdot 47$
45	2,025	6.708	$3^2 \cdot 5$	95	9,025	9.747	$5 \cdot 19$
46	2,116	6.782	$2 \cdot 23$	96	9,216	9.798	$2^5 \cdot 3$
47	2,209	6.856	47	97	9,409	9.849	97
48	2,304	6.928	$2^4 \cdot 3$	98	9,604	9.899	$2 \cdot 7^2$
49	2,401	7.000	7^2	99	9,801	9.950	$3^2 \cdot 11$
50	2,500	7.071	$2 \cdot 5^2$	100	10,000	10.000	$2^2 \cdot 5^2$

ANSWERS

Exercise 1.1 (Page 4)

1. {4, 5, 6, 7, 8, 9}

3. {Sunday, Monday, Tuesday, Wednesday, Thursday, Friday, Saturday}

7. $\{x \mid x$ is an odd natural number$\}$

9. $\{x \mid c^z = 5\}$ 11. $\{x \mid x \notin A\}$ 13. No   15. No

17. {natural numbers less than three} = {1, 2}

19. $\emptyset \neq \{0\}$ 21. $3 \in \{2, 3, 4\}$ 23. $\{2\} \notin \{2, 3, 4\}$

25. $5 \notin \{4, 5, 6\}$ 27. $\emptyset \subset \{4, 5, 6\}$

29. a. {5, 6, 7}   b. {5, 6}, {5, 7}, {6, 7}   c. {5}, {6}, {7}   d. $\emptyset$

31. a. $A \subset U$ b. $C \notin A$ c. $A \notin B$ d. $C \subset B$

33. a. Yes   b. Yes   c. Yes   d. Yes   e. Yes

35. One element: {1}, $\emptyset$. Two elements: {1, 2}, {1}, {2}, $\emptyset$. The number of possible subsets of a set containing n elements is 2^n.

Exercise 1.2 (Page 9)

1. $A' = \{1, 3, 5, 7, 9\} = C$

3. $C' = \{2, 4, 6, 8, 10\} = A$

5. $A \cup B = \{1, 2, 3, 4, 5, 6, 8, 10\}$

7. $A \cap C = \emptyset$

9. $A' \cup C' = U$ or $\{1, 2, 3, 4, 5, 6, 7, 8, 9, 10\}$

11. $A' \cup C = C$ or $\{1, 3, 5, 7, 9\}$

25. $(A')' = A$ 27. $A \cap U = A$ 29. $A \cup U = U$

31. $A \cup \emptyset = A$ 33. $\emptyset' \cap \emptyset = \emptyset$

35. a. $A \cup B = \emptyset$ if $A = B = \emptyset$ b. $A \cup \emptyset = \emptyset$ if $A = \emptyset$
   c. $A \cap U = U$ if $A = U$ d. $A \cup B = A$ if $B \subseteq A$
   e. $A \cup \emptyset = U$ if $A = U$ f. $A' \cap U = U$ if $A = \emptyset$
   g. $A \cap B = A$ if $A \subseteq B$ h. $A' \cup \emptyset = \emptyset$ if $A = U$
   i. $A \cup B = A \cap B$ if $A = B$

39. Definition of intersection

Exercise 1.3 (Page 13)

1. True	3. True	5. False	7. False
9. True	11. True	13. False	15. True
17. True	19. False	21. True	23. False

25. $\{1, 2, 3, 4, 5\}$ 27. $\{1, 2, 3, 4, 5, 6\}$

29. $\{-9, -8, -7, -6\}$ 31. $\{x \mid x \in N\}$

33. $\{x \mid x \in R\}$ 35. $\{x \mid x \in R, -4 < x < 3\}$

37. $\{x \mid x \in Q, x > -2\}$

39. a. $\{4\}$ b. $\{4, -2, 0\}$ c. $\{4, -2, \frac{2}{5}, 0, -\frac{3}{4}\}$ d. $\{\sqrt{2}, \sqrt{7}\}$

41. $A \cap B = \{$integral multiples of 10$\}$

43. $A \cap B = \{$integral multiples of 30$\}$

45. $A \cap B = \{$integral multiples of $ab\}$

Exercise 1.4 (Page 18)

1. Substitution law, E-4

3. Symmetric law, E-2

5. Transitive law, E-3

7. Closure for multiplication, F-6

9. Associative law of multiplication, F-7

11. Additive inverse, F-4

13. Commutative law of multiplication, F-10

15. Commutative law of addition, F-5

17. Distributive law, F-8

19. Commutative law of addition, F-5

21. Distributive law, F-8   23. Distributive law, F-8

25. Closed   27. Closed   29. Closed

31. Not closed   33. Closed

35. a. Yes   b. Yes   c. Yes, 0   d. No $(a \neq -1)$

37. No   39. $0, a$ 41. Yes, $a' = a$

43. If $a = b$, a may be replaced with b and b with a.   Thus, $b = a$.

Exercise 1.5 (Page 27)

1. 1.1	3. 1.8-VI	5. 1.11-III
7. 1.7	9. 1.9	11. 1.11-VII
13. 1.8-III	15. 1.11-IV	17. 1.11-I
19. 1.2	21. 1.5	

17   *19*

For Problems 23–53, the given items are hints to help you with the proof. They are not necessarily the only or the best guidelines.

23. E-1, E-4   25. F-11   27. Definition 1.12, F-2

29. Theorem 1.8-II   31. F-11, E-4

33. F-4, Theorem 1.6   35. F-11, Theorem 1.8-IV

37. Definition 1.13, Theorem 1.11-I

39. Theorem 1.10, Theorem 1.11-III   41. F-11, Exercise 34

43. F-11   45. Definition 1.13

47. F-4   49. F-4

51. Theorem 1.2   53. Exercise 41

Exercise 1.6 (Page 34)

1. I   3. III   5. II   7. IV

9. $7 > 3$ 11. $-4 < -3$ 13. $-1 \le x \le 1$ 15. $x > 0$

17. $x \ge 0$ 19. $-2 < 5$ 21. $-7 < -1$ 23. $|-3| = |3|$

25. $2 < 5$ 27. $7 < 8$ 29. $|x| < 3$

The items given for Problems 31–45 are hints only.

31. Theorem 1.12   33. Definition 1.14, F-8

35. Definition 1.14   37. Theorem 1.11-IV

39. Theorem 1.15-II   41. Theorem 1.15-IV

43. Theorem 1.15-III   45. Theorem 1.15-II

47. 1   49. 3

Exercise 2.1 (Page 42)

1. 3 in y 3. 4 in x, y; 3 in x; 2 in y

5. Not a polynomial   7. -1, -21, 1

9. 1, 1, 0   11. 1, 1, 5

13. 39, 6, 39   15. $2x + 1$, $4x - 5$

17. $3x^2 - 4x + 2$, $-x^2 + 4$ 19. $3x^2 - 5x + 5$

21. $3x^2 - 4x + 4$ 23. $x^2 - 2x + 6$

25. n, n 27. $A = 5$, $B = -5$

Exercise 2.2 (Page 47)

1. $-6x^3y^4$ 3. a^{2n}

5. $a^2bc - ab^2c + 2abc^2$ 7. $x^2 + 7x + 10$

9. $x^2 - 4xy + 4y^2$ 11. $10x^2 + 17x + 3$

13. $9a^2 - 4b^2$

15. $x^3 + 6x^2 + 7x - 4$

17. $2x^2 + 8x + 6$

19. $-2ac + 6ad + bc - 3bd$

21. $a^4 - ab^3$

23. $4a + 4$

25. $20x^2 + 4x$

27. $x^2 - 5x + 11,\ x^2 - x + 5$

29. $x^4 + 6x^3 + 9x^2,\ a^8 - 6a^6 + 8a^4 + 3a^2,\ 9x^4 - 18x^3 + 9x^2$

31. $2ab;\ 0 > 2ab;\ 0 < 2ab$

Exercise 2.3 (Page 51)

1. $3x^3y(3x^2 - x + 2)$

3. $x^n(x^{2n} + 1)$

5. $x^n(x^2 - x + 2)$

7. $(x - 6)(x - 2)$

9. $(x - 5)(x + 5)$

11. $3(x + 2)(x + 2)$

13. $(y^2 + 2)(y^2 + 1)$

15. $(2a^2 + 1)(a + 1)(a - 1)$

17. $[x^2 - (y - 2x)^2][x^2 + (y - 2x)^2]$

19. $(x + y)(x + a)$

21. $(a - 2b)(a^2 + 2b^2)$

23. $(y - 3x)(y^2 + 3xy + 9x^2)$

25. $(2x - y)(x^2 - xy + y^2)$

27. $(a^n - 2)(a^n + 2)$

29. $(x^n - y^n)(x^n + y^n)(x^{2n} + y^{2n})$

31. $(3x^{2n} - 1)(x^{2n} - 3)$

33. $2(y^n - 30)(y^n + 24)$

35. a. $(2x - 3)(x + 2)$ b. $2(x - \frac{3}{2})(x + 2)$

37. a. $(2x + 1)(2x - 3)$ b. $4(x + \frac{1}{2})(x - \frac{3}{2})$

39. a. $2(3x - 1)(2x + 1)$ b. $12(x - \frac{1}{3})(x + \frac{1}{2})$

43. $(x^2 + xy + y^2)(x^2 - xy + y^2)$

Exercise 2.4 (Page 58)

1. $4ay^2\ (a, y \neq 0)$

3. $x^{n+3}\ (x \neq 0)$

5. $x^n y^n\ (x, y \neq 0)$

7. $4a^2 + 2a + 2$

9. $x^2 - 4x - 3\ (x \neq 0)$

11. $3x^2 - 2x + \dfrac{3}{5x}\ (x, y \neq 0)$

13. $2y^2 - y + \frac{13}{2},\ R = -\frac{3}{2}\ (y \neq -\frac{1}{2})$

15. $2y^3 - y^2 - \dfrac{1}{2}y - \dfrac{5}{4} + \dfrac{-13y/4 + 9/4}{2y^2 + y + 1}$

17. $x^3 - x^2 - \dfrac{1}{x - 2}\ (x \neq 2)$

19. $2x^2 - 2x + 3 + \dfrac{-8}{x + 1}\ (x \neq -1)$

21. $2x^3 + 10x^2 + 50x + 249 + \dfrac{1251}{x - 5}\ (x \neq 5)$

23. $x^2 + 2x - 3 + \dfrac{4}{x + 2}\ (x \neq -2)$

25. $x^5 + x^4 + 2x^3 + 2x^2 + 2x + 1 + \dfrac{1}{x-1} \ (x \neq 1)$

27. $x^4 + x^3 + x^2 + x + 1 \ (x \neq 1)$

29. $x^5 + x^4 + x^3 + x^2 + x + 1 \ (x \neq 1)$

Exercise 2.5 (Page 62)

1. $\dfrac{a}{b}$, $a, b, c \neq 0$

3. $2, x + y \neq 0$

5. $-1, b - a \neq 0$

7. $-(x + 1), x \neq 1$

9. $x^2 - 2x - \frac{3}{2}, x \neq 0$

11. $y + 7, y \neq 2$

13. $-(2y + 5), y \neq \frac{1}{2}$

15. $\dfrac{x^2 + xy + y^2}{x + y}, x^2 + y^2 \neq 0$

17. $\dfrac{y^2 + 4}{y^2 + 3}, y^2 - 4 \neq 0$

19. $\dfrac{x - y + 1}{-(x + y)}, x \neq y, x \neq -y$

21. $\dfrac{9}{12}$

23. $\dfrac{ab^2}{a^2b}, a, b \neq 0$

25. $\dfrac{3(y - 3)}{y^2 - y - 6}, y \neq -2, 3$

27. $\dfrac{3(a^2 - 6a + 9)}{a^3 + 27}, a \neq -3$

29. $\dfrac{3acx}{a^2bc}, \dfrac{2bx}{a^2bc}$

31. $\dfrac{3(x + a)}{(x^2 - a^2)(x + a)}, \dfrac{2(x - a)}{(x^2 + 2ax + a^2)(x - a)}$

33. $\dfrac{-2(b + a)}{(b - a)(b + a)}, \dfrac{-1}{b^2 - a^2}$

35. No, $x = 1, 2$

37. For $N > 0, a - b < 0$ or $a < b$; for $N < 0, a - b > 0$ or $a > b$

Exercise 2.6 (Page 66)

1. $\dfrac{2x - 1}{2y}$

3. 1

5. $\dfrac{2a + 9}{9}$

7. $\dfrac{5}{2a + 2b}$

9. $\dfrac{3}{3 - x}$

11. $\dfrac{-1}{(a + 2)(a + 3)}$

13. $\dfrac{-3x^2 - 3y^2}{(2x - y)(x - 2y)}$

15. $\dfrac{y(y - 11)}{(y - 4)(y + 4)(y - 1)}$

17. $\dfrac{x^3 - 2x^2 + 2x - 2}{(x - 1)^2}$

19. $\dfrac{4x^3 - 4x^2 + 4x + 4}{(2x + 1)(2x - 1)}$

21. $\dfrac{4}{(y + 1)(y + 3)}$

23. $\dfrac{y^2 + xz}{(y - x)(y - z)}$

Exercise 2.7 (Page 69)

1. $\dfrac{-b^2}{a}$

3. $\dfrac{1}{ax^2y}$

5. $\dfrac{x-5}{x+3}$

7. $(5ab-4)(4ab+3)$

9. $x-y$

11. $\dfrac{x^2-1}{x^2}$

13. $\dfrac{x+5}{x(x+1)}$

15. $\dfrac{2y^2-6y+3}{3}$

17. $\dfrac{7}{10a+2}$

19. $\dfrac{4a^2-3a}{4a+1}$

21. $\dfrac{-1}{y-3}$

23. $\dfrac{a-2b}{a+2b}$

25. $\dfrac{a+6}{a-1}$

27. $\dfrac{b^2}{3(5b-a)}$

Exercise 3.1 (Page 75)

1. $\frac{1}{2}$

3. $\frac{5}{3}$

5. 9

7. $-\frac{1}{512}$

9. $\dfrac{82}{9}$

11. $\dfrac{15}{16^2}$

13. x^4y^6

15. $\dfrac{x^2}{4y^6}$

17. $\dfrac{y^4}{x}$

19. x

21. $\dfrac{1}{x^6}$

23. $\dfrac{y}{x}$

25. $4x^5y^2$

27. $\dfrac{y-x}{xy}$

29. $\dfrac{2y}{x}$

31. $\dfrac{1}{x+y}$

33. $\dfrac{x^2+y^2}{xy}$

35. $x+y$

37. $\dfrac{xy}{y-x}$

39. x^{2n}

41. x^{3n}

43. x^{2n}

45. x^6

47. $x^{1-n}y$

49. a^{2-2n}

51. 3.4×10^4

53. 8.372×10^6

55. 1.4×10^{-3}

57. 2.30×10^{-5}

Exercise 3.2 (Page 81)

1. 2

3. $\frac{1}{27}$

5. 32

7. $\frac{8}{27}$

9. x^2

11. $a^{17/12}$

13. $x^{1/3}$

15. $\dfrac{1}{x^{16/15}}$

17. $\dfrac{1}{y^2}$

19. $\left(\dfrac{x}{y}\right)^{5/4}$

21. $x^n \cdot y^4$

23. $x^{3n/2}$

25. $x^{5n/2} \cdot y^{3m/2-1}$

27. $x - x^{2/3}$

29. $x + y - (x+y)^{3/2}$

31. $x - 2x^{1/2}y^{-1/2} + y^{-1}$

33. $x + y$

35. $x(x^{1/2}+1)$

37. $x^{-1/2}(x^{-1}+1)$

39. $(x+1)^{-1/2}(x)$

41. $x^{n/2}(x^{3n/2}+1)$

43. $(x^{1/2}-y^{1/2})(x^{1/2}+y^{1/2})$

45. 5

47. $2|x|$

49. $\dfrac{2}{|x|(x+2)^{1/2}}$

Exercise 3.3 (Page 86)

1. $\sqrt[3]{a^2}$

3. $3\sqrt[3]{x}$

5. $-6\sqrt[3]{(xy)^2}$

7. $\sqrt[7]{(x-y)^4}$

9. $x^{2/3}$

11. $(2xy^2)^{1/4}$

13. $-3(a^3b)^{1/4}$

15. $(x-y^2)^{1/2}$

17. $3(x^2-y)^{1/3}$

19. $2(x-y)^{1/2}$

21. 12

23. -3

25. x^2y

27. $\frac{2}{3}x^3y^5$

29. $x+4$

31. $2x^2\sqrt{x}$

33. $xy\sqrt[4]{3xy}$

35. $3\sqrt[4]{3}$

37. $2x\sqrt[3]{y^2}$

39. $\dfrac{\sqrt{3y}}{y}$

41. $\sqrt[3]{2b}$

43. xy

45. b

47. $\dfrac{1}{\sqrt{7}}$

49. $\dfrac{2y}{\sqrt[3]{xy^2}}$

51. $\sqrt[3]{9}$

53. $2\sqrt{x}$

55. $\sqrt{2x}$

57. $\sqrt[3]{x-1}$

59. $\sqrt[4]{8}$

61. $\sqrt[6]{32a^4b^6}$

63. $\sqrt[12]{2^7}$

65. $3\sqrt{3}$

67. $-4\sqrt{2}$

69. $5\sqrt[3]{2}$

71. $3\sqrt{2}+\sqrt{6}$

73. $-7\sqrt{3}-9\sqrt{7}$

75. $1-\sqrt{5}$

77. $x-\sqrt{3x}-6$

79. b

81. $2(1-\sqrt{3})$

83. $\dfrac{x(\sqrt{x}+3)}{x-9}$

85. $\dfrac{37-8\sqrt{10}}{27}$

87. $\dfrac{-1}{2(1+\sqrt{2})}$

89. $\dfrac{x-y}{x-2\sqrt{xy}+y}$

91. $-3\sqrt{2}+3$

99. $\dfrac{\sqrt[3]{a^2}+\sqrt[3]{ab}+\sqrt[3]{b^2}}{a-b}$

101. $2|x|$

103. $3|x|\sqrt{x-1}$

105. $\dfrac{2}{|u|\sqrt{u^2+1}}$

Exercise 3.4 (Page 93)

1. $0.\overline{285714}$

3. 0.9375

5. 0.2

7. -3.464

9. 3.79

11. 0.0945

13. $1.117\underset{.}{5}$

15. $3.162,\ 3.163$

17. $1.731010010001\cdots$

Exercise 4.1 (Page 98)

1. a, e

3. All

5. $\{-2\}$

7. $\{1\}$

9. $\{-7\}$

11. $\{15\}$

13. $\emptyset$

15. $\{-\frac{14}{5}\}$

17. $y=b$

19. $x = \dfrac{c}{c + 1}$

21. $x = \dfrac{3(a + 2)}{a + 3}$

23. $x = \dfrac{ab}{a + b}$

25. $k = v - gt$

27. $c = \dfrac{2A - bh}{h}$

29. $n = \dfrac{l - a + d}{d}$

31. $y' = \dfrac{3x + 1}{x^2 - 2y^3}$

33. $x_1 = \dfrac{x_4}{x_2 - 2x_3}$

35. $y = 6(x - x_1) + y_1$

37. $-\frac{3}{5}$

39. E-4

41. 6 in.

43. $600 at 4%, $1400 at 3%

45. 32 and 64 mph

Exercise 4.2 (Page 104)

1. $\{0, -2\}$

3. $\{2, -7\}$

5. $\{\frac{1}{2}, 1\}$

7. $\{1, -\frac{10}{3}\}$

9. $\{2, -2\}$

11. $\{\sqrt{5}, -\sqrt{5}\}$

13. $\{6 + \sqrt{5}, 6 - \sqrt{5}\}$

15. $\{2, -6\}$

17. $\{-4, -5\}$

19. $\{\frac{1}{2}, -2\}$

21. $(x - 2)^2 + (y - 2)^2 = 5^2$

23. $[x - (-3)]^2 + (y - 1)^2 = 2^2$

25. $\left(x - \dfrac{1}{2}\right)^2 + [y - (-1)]^2 = 2^2$

27. $\{1, 2\}$; rational and unequal

29. $\{2, \frac{3}{2}\}$

31. $\{3, -\frac{3}{2}\}$

33. $\{\sqrt{5}\}$

35. $\left\{\sqrt{3}, -\dfrac{\sqrt{3}}{2}\right\}$

37. $\{2k, -k\}$

39. $\left\{\dfrac{1 + \sqrt{1 - 4ac}}{2a}, \dfrac{1 - \sqrt{1 - 4ac}}{2a}\right\}$

41. 4

43. $k \le -2$

45. $k < 0$

47. $x^2 - 5x + 6 = 0$

49. $6x^2 + x - 2 = 0$

51. $ax^2 + bx + c = 0$

55. $-\frac{3}{2}, -3$

57. 6, 7

59. 12 in.

61. $2\frac{1}{2}$ sec, $\frac{5}{4}\sqrt{6}$ sec

63. Father: 6 days; son: 12 days

65. 10 ft

Exercise 4.3 (Page 110)

1. $\{64\}$

3. $\{-25\}$

5. $\{4\}$

7. $\{5\}$

9. $\{16\}$

11. $\{4\}$

13. $\{1, 3\}$

15. $A = \pi r^2$

17. $y = \dfrac{1}{x^3}$

19. $y = \sqrt{a^2 - x^2}$

Exercise 4.4 (Page 112)

1. $\{25\}$

3. $\left\{\dfrac{\sqrt{2}}{2}, -\dfrac{\sqrt{2}}{2}\right\}$

5. $\{2, -7, -3, -2\}$

7. $\{64, -8\}$

9. $\{\frac{1}{4}, -\frac{1}{3}\}$

11. $\{626\}$

13. $\{2, -1, -4\}$

15. $\{4, 5, -2, -3\}$

17. $\{4, 1\}$

Exercise 4.5 (Page 119)

1. $\{x \mid x > 1\}$

3. $\{x \mid x > 3\}$

5. $\{x \mid x \leq \frac{13}{2}\}$

7. $\{x \mid -2 < x < 5\}$

9. $\{x \mid x \geq 13\}$

11. $\emptyset$

13. $\{x \mid x < -1, x > 2\}$

15. $\{x \mid 0 \leq x \leq 2\}$

17. $\{x \mid x < -1, x > 4\}$

19. $\{x \mid -\sqrt{5} < x < \sqrt{5}\}$

21. $\{x \mid x \in R\}$

23. $\{x \mid x < 0, x \geq \frac{1}{2}\}$

25. $\{x \mid -\frac{8}{3} < x < -2\}$

27. $\{x \mid x < 0, 2 < x \leq 4\}$

29. $\{x \mid -3 < x < 0, x > 2\}$

31. Theorem 1.15-II

33. Theorem 1.15-III

35. Theorem 1.15-II, then solve for x

37. Theorem 1.15-II

Exercise 4.6 (Page 124)

1. $\{6, -6\}$

3. $\{-3, 5\}$

5. $\{\frac{1}{3}, 1\}$

7. $\{-\frac{3}{2}, -\frac{7}{2}\}$

9. $\{\frac{1}{2}, \frac{7}{2}\}$

11. $\{\frac{22}{3}, -\frac{26}{3}\}$

13. $\{x \mid -2 < x < 2\}$

15. $\{x \mid -7 \leq x \leq 1\}$

17. $\emptyset$

19. $\{x \mid x < -1 \text{ or } x > 7\}$

21. $\{x \mid x \leq -3 \text{ or } x \geq 2\}$

23. $\{x \mid -\frac{13}{2} < x < \frac{11}{2}\}$

25. $|x - 2| < 1$

27. $|x + 8| \leq 1$

29. $|4x - 5| \leq 19$

31. At least 48% but less than 98%

Exercise 5.1 (Page 128)

1. $\{(1, -1), (1, -2)\}$

3. $\{(-1, 0), (-1, 1), (0, 0), (0, 1), (1, 0), (1, 1)\}$

5. $\{(a, c), (a, d), (b, c), (b, d)\}$

7. $\{(1, 1), (1, 2), (2, 1), (2, 2)\}$

9. $\{(-1, -1), (-1, 0), (-1, 1), (0, -1), (0, 0), (0, 1), (1, -1), (1, 0), (1, 1)\}$

11. $\{(-2, -2), (-2, 0), (-2, 2), (0, -2), (0, 0), (0, 2), (2, -2), (2, 0), (2, 2)\}$

13. a. $n \cdot m$ b. $m \cdot n$ c. $n(2m - n)$ d. n^2

15. a. $\{(1, 2), (1, 3), (1, 4), (2, 1), (2, 3), (2, 4), (3, 1), (3, 2), (3, 4), (4, 1), (4, 2), (4, 3)\}$

 c. 12 d. $n^2 - n$

17. a. 20 b. 56 c. 36 d. 49

Exercise 5.2 (Page 132)

1. $(0, 7), (2, 9), (-2, 5)$

3. $(2, 5), (\frac{1}{2}, 2), (0, 1)$

5. $(0, \frac{3}{2}), (\frac{3}{2}, 0), (\frac{1}{2}, 1)$

7. $\{(-1, 1), (0, 0), (1, -1)\}$

9. $\{(-1, 1), (0, 0), (1, 1)\}$

11. $\{(3, 5), (5, 3)\}$

13. $\emptyset$

15. $\{(0, 1), (1, -1)\}$

17. $\emptyset$

19. $\{(0, 0)\}$

21. $\{(-2, -1), (-2, 0), (-2, 1), (-2, 2), (-1, -2), (-1, 0), (-1, 1), (-1, 2),$
    $(0, -2), (0, -1), (0, 1), (0, 2), (1, -2), (1, -1), (1, 0), (1, 2), (2, -2), (2, -1),$
    $(2, 0), (2, 1)\}$

23. $\{(x, y) \mid y = 7 - x, x \in R\}$ 25. $\{(x, y) \mid y = 3(5 - 2x), x \in R\}$

27. $\{(x, y) \mid y = \dfrac{2}{x}, x \in R, x \neq 0\}$ 29. $\{(x, y) \mid y = \dfrac{4}{x^2 - 1}, x \in R, x = 1, -1\}$

31. $\{(x, y) \mid y = \dfrac{2x}{1 - 2x}, x \in R, x = \frac{1}{2}\}$

33. $\{(x, y) \mid y = \dfrac{x \pm \sqrt{x^2 - 4}}{2}, x \in R, |x| \geq 2\}$

Exercise 5.3 (Page 136)

7. Domain: $\{-3, -2\}$; range: $\{2, 4\}$

9. Domain: $\{-1, 0, 1\}$; range: $\{1\}$

11. Domain: $\{1, 2, 3\}$; range: $\{2, 3, 4\}$

13. $S = \{(2, 1), (2, 2), (2, 3)\}$; domain: $\{2\}$; range: $\{1, 2, 3\}$

15. $S = \{(0, 1), (1, 0)\}$; domain: $\{0, 1\}$; range: $\{0,1\}$

17. $S = \{(-1, 1), (0, 0), (1, 1)\}$; domain: $\{-1, 0, 1\}$; range: $\{0, 1\}$

19. Domain: $\{x \mid x \in R\}$

21. Domain: $\{x \mid x \in R\}$

23. Domain: $\{x \mid x \in R, x \neq 2\}$

25. Domain: $\{x \mid x \in R, x \geq 0\}$

27. Domain: $\{x \mid x \in R, -2 \leq x \leq 2\}$

29. Domain: $\{x \mid x \in R, x \neq 0, 1\}$

31. a. $\{(-2, -2), (-1, -1), (0, 0), (1, 1), (2, 2)\}$
    b. $\{(-1, -1), (0, 0), (1, 1)\}$ c. $\{(-1, -1), (0, 0), (1, 1)\}$
    d. $\{(-1, -1), (0, 0), (1, 1)\}$ e. a contains $(-2, -2)$ and $(2, 2)$

Exercise 5.4 (Page 141)

1. Yes	3. Yes	5. No	7. Yes
9. No	11. Yes	13. 2	15. -1
17. $a + 2$	19. 9	21. 4	23. a^2
25. 1	27. -2	29. $a - 2$	31. ± 1
33. ± 3		35. $\pm \sqrt{a^2 + 1}$	37. Range : $\{1, 2, 3\}$

39. Range : $\{2, 3, 4\}$

41. a. 2	b. 0	c. 2	d. x
43. a. 0	b. $\frac{9}{2}$	c. ± 3	d. $\{x \mid x \in R\}$
45. No		47. $C = 2\pi r$; $\{r \mid r > 0\}$	49. $A = 4h$; $\{h \mid h > 0\}$

51. $A = \dfrac{S^2}{4} \sqrt{3}$; $\{S \mid S > 0\}$

53. $y = x^2 + 2x$; $\{x \mid x \in R\}$

55. $V = s(10 - 2s)(22 - 2s)$; $\{s \mid 0 < s < 5\}$

59. $f^{-1} = \pm \sqrt{x + 3}$

Exercise 5.5 (Page 150)

1. $(0, 1)$, $(-\frac{1}{3}, 0)$

3. $(0, 0)$

5. $(0, 2)$, $(-\frac{2}{3}, 0)$

7. $(0, 2)$, $(3, 0)$

9. $(0, 2)$, $(5, 0)$

11. $(-2, 0)$

15. Range $= \{y \mid -1 \leq y \leq 3\}$

17. It is not a function.

19. Distance, 5; slope, $\frac{4}{3}$

21. Distance, 13; slope $\frac{12}{5}$

23. Distance, $\sqrt{2}$; slope, 1

25. Distance, $3\sqrt{5}$; slope, $\frac{1}{2}$

27. Distance, 5; slope, 0

29. Distance, 10; slope, undefined

31. 7, $\sqrt{68}$, $\sqrt{89}$	33. 10, 21, 17	37. $x - 2y = 8$

Exercise 5.6 (Page 155)

1. $4x - y - 7 = 0$	3. $x + y - 10 = 0$
5. $3x - y = 0$	7. $x + 2y + 2 = 0$
9. $3x + 4y + 14 = 0$	11. $y - 2 = 0$

13. $y = -x + 3$; slope, -1; intercept, 3

15. $y = -\frac{3}{2}x + \frac{1}{2}$; slope, $-\frac{3}{2}$; intercept, $\frac{1}{2}$

17. $y = \frac{1}{3}x - \frac{2}{3}$; slope, $\frac{1}{3}$; intercept, $-\frac{2}{3}$

19. $y = \frac{8}{3}x$; slope, $\frac{8}{3}$; intercept, 0

21. $3x + 2y - 6 = 0$ 23. $5x + 2y + 10 = 0$

25. $6x - 2y + 3 = 0$ 27. $x - 2y = 0$

31. $F(x) = \dfrac{-x + 11}{3}$

Exercise 6.1 (Page 167)

9. $(4, 0)$; $(1, 0)$; $(\frac{5}{2}, -\frac{9}{4})$, minimum   11. $(4, 0)$; $(1, 0)$; $(\frac{5}{2}, \frac{9}{4})$, maximum

13. $(7, 0)$; $(-1, 0)$; $(3, -16)$, minimum

15. No intercepts; $(0, 2)$, minimum

19. 9   21. 0

23. 49   25. 64

27. 4; 4   29. 625 sq in.

31. Parabola; not a function

Exercise 6.2 (Page 175)

1. a. $y = \pm\sqrt{4 - x^2}$ b. $y = \sqrt{4 - x^2}$; $y = -\sqrt{4 - x^2}$
   c. Domain $= \{x \mid -2 \le x \le 2\}$
   1st range $= \{y \mid 0 \le y \le 2\}$
   2nd range $= \{y \mid -2 \le y \le 0\}$

3. a. $y = \pm 3\sqrt{4 - x^2}$ b. $y = 3\sqrt{4 - x^2}$; $y = -3\sqrt{4 - x^2}$
   c. Domain $= \{x \mid -2 \le x \le 2\}$
   1st range $= \{y \mid 0 \le y \le 6\}$
   2nd range $= \{y \mid -6 \le y \le 0\}$

5. a. $y = \pm\frac{1}{2}\sqrt{16 - x^2}$
   b. $y = \frac{1}{2}\sqrt{16 - x^2}$; $y = -\frac{1}{2}\sqrt{16 - x^2}$
   c. Domain $= \{x \mid -4 \le x \le 4\}$
   1st range $= \{y \mid 0 \le y \le 2\}$
   2nd range $= \{y \mid -2 \le y \le 0\}$

7. a. $y = \pm\dfrac{1}{\sqrt{3}}\sqrt{24 - 2x^2}$

   b. $y = \dfrac{1}{\sqrt{3}}\sqrt{24 - 2x^2}$; $y = \dfrac{1}{\sqrt{3}}\sqrt{24 - 2x^2}$

   c. Domain $= \{x \mid -\sqrt{12} \le x \le \sqrt{12}\}$
   1st range $= \{y \mid 0 \le y \le \sqrt{8}\}$
   2nd range $= \{y \mid -\sqrt{8} \le y \le 0\}$

9. a. $y = \pm\sqrt{x^2 - 1}$ b. $y = \sqrt{x^2 - 1}; y = -\sqrt{x^2 - 1}$
  c. Domain $= \{x \mid x \geq 1 \text{ or } \leq -1\}$
    1st range $= \{y \mid y \geq 0\}$
    2nd range $= \{y \mid y \leq 0\}$

11. a. $y = \pm\sqrt{9 + x^2}$ b. $y = \sqrt{9 + x^2}; y = -\sqrt{9 + x^2}$
  c. Domain $= \{x \mid x \in R\}$
    1st range $= \{y \mid 3 \leq y\}$
    2nd range $= \{y \mid y \leq -3\}$

Exercise 6.3 (Page 180)

1. 16   3. 400 ft   5. 160 lbs/sq ft   7. 1,687.5 lbs

Exercise 6.5 (Page 189)

1. 3; 17; 47   3. 56; 12; 326   5. -685; 95; 719

Exercise 6.6 (Page 197)

1. $x = 3$ 3. $x = 3; x = -2$ 5. $x = -1; x = -4$

7. $x = -1$ 17. $x = 2; x = -2; y = 0$

19. $x = 4; y = x + 4$ 21. $x = 4; x = -1; y = 1$

Exercise 7.1 (Page 202)

1. $(0, 1), (1, 3), (2, 9)$ 3. $(-2, -\frac{1}{25}), (0, -1), (2, -25)$

5. $(-3, 8), (0, 1), (3, \frac{1}{8})$ 7. $(-2, \frac{1}{100}), (-1, \frac{1}{10}), (0, 1)$

19. No; a constant function   21. a. $\{-2\}$ b. $\{-4\}$ c. $\{\frac{3}{4}\}$

Exercise 7.2 (Page 205)

1. $\log_4 16 = 2$ 3. $\log_3 27 = 3$ 5. $\log_{1/2} \frac{1}{4} = 2$

7. $\log_8 \frac{1}{2} = -\frac{1}{3}$ 9. $\log_{10} 100 = 2$ 11. $\log_{10} (0.1) = -1$

13. $2^6 = 64$ 15. $3^2 = 9$ 17. $(\frac{1}{3})^{-2} = 9$

19. $10^3 = 1000$ 21. $10^{-2} = 0.01$ 23. 2

25. 3   27. $\frac{1}{2}$ 29. -1 31. 1

33. 2   35. -1 37. $\{2\}$ 39. $\{2\}$

41. $\{64\}$ 43. $\{-3\}$ 45. $\{100\}$ 47. $\{4\}$

49. By definition, $\log_b 1$ is a number such that $b^{\log_b 1} = 1$. Therefore $\log_b 1 = 0$.

51. $\text{Log}_b b^x = x$ implies $b^x = b^x$, which is true for all $x \in R$.

53. $\log_b x + \log_b y$ 55. $\log_b x - \log_b y$

57. $5 \log_b x$ 59. $\frac{1}{3} \log_b x$

61. $\frac{1}{2}(\log_b x - \log_b z)$ 63. $\frac{1}{3}(\log_{10} x + 2 \log_{10} y - \log_{10} z)$

65. $\log_{10} 2 + \log_{10} \pi + \frac{1}{2} \log_{10} l - \frac{1}{2} \log_{10} g$

67. $\log_b xy$ 69. $\log_b x^2 y^3$ 71. $\log_b \dfrac{x^3 y}{z^2}$

73. $\log_{10} \dfrac{x(x-2)}{z^2}$

Exercise 7.3 (Page 212)

1. 2   3. -3 or $7 - 10$ 5. -4 or $6 - 10$

7. 4   9. 0.8280   11. $9.9101 - 10$

13. $8.9301 - 10$ 15. 2.3945   17. 4.10

19. 3.67   21. 0.0642   23. 5480

25. 0.000718   27. 0.6246   29. 3.1824

31. 4.5695   33. $9.7095 - 10$ 35. 3.225

37. 10.52   39. 0.05075   41. 0.7495

43. $\log_{10} 3.751$; 0.751 is closer to a tabulated value

45. 9.1   47. 5000   49. 113

51. a. -0.2679 b. -3.5813

53. 2, 5, 2, 1

Exercise 7.4 (Page 216)

1. 4.014   3. 2.299   5. 64.34

7. 2.010   9. 3.436×10^{-10} 11. 0.04582

13. 9.872   15. 4.746   17. 1.394

19. 2.664   21. 1.11 sec   23. 1.49 cu ft

Exercise 7.5 (Page 222)

1. $\left\{ \dfrac{\log_{10} 7}{\log_{10} 2} \right\}$ 3. $\left\{ \dfrac{\log_{10} 8}{\log_{10} 3} - 1 \right\}$

5. $\left\{ \dfrac{1}{2} \left(\dfrac{\log_{10} 3}{\log_{10} 7} + 1 \right) \right\}$ 7. $\left\{ \sqrt{\dfrac{\log_{10} 15}{\log_{10} 4}}, \ -\sqrt{\dfrac{\log_{10} 15}{\log_{10} 4}} \right\}$

9. $\left\{ \dfrac{-1}{\log_{10} 3} \right\}$ 11. $\left\{ 1 - \dfrac{\log_{10} 15}{\log_{10} 3} \right\}$

13. $n = \dfrac{\log_{10} y}{\log_{10} x}$ 15. $t = \dfrac{\log_{10} y}{k \log_{10} e}$

17. $\{500\}$ 19. $\{4\}$ 21. $\{3\}$

23. $\{7\}$ 25. $\log_a b = \dfrac{\log_{10} b}{\log_{10} a}$ 27. 1.34

29. 5%   31. 20 yrs   33. 2.5%

35. 12 yrs   37. $7400, $7430, $7430   39. 7

41. 7.7   43. 6.2   45. 1.0×10^{-3}

47. 2.5×10^{-6} 49. 6.3×10^{-8}

Exercise 7.6 (Page 226)

1. 3.32   3. 3.41   5. 1.08

7. 0.79   9. 1.0986   11. 2.8332

13. 5.7900   15. 6.1093   17. 1.6487

19. 29.964   21. 1.260   23. 0.8607

25. 0.0821   27. 0.7600   29. $\frac{1}{3}$

31. 2.10   33. 2.86   39. 12.048 gr

41. 2.2 cm

Exercise 8.1 (Page 234)

1. $\{(3, 2)\}$ 3. $\{(2, 1)\}$ 5. $\{(-5, 4)\}$

7. $\{(0, \frac{3}{2})\}$ 9. $\{(\frac{2}{3}, -1)\}$ 11. $\{(1, 2)\}$

13. $\{(-\frac{19}{5}, -\frac{18}{5})\}$ 15. $a = 1, b = -1$ 17. $y = -\frac{10}{3}x + 2$

19. $C = \frac{5}{9}(F - 32)$ 21. 32 lbs

23. 7200 at 4%; 8200 at 5%   25. 32 and 64 mph

Exercise 8.2 (Page 241)

1. $\{(1, 2, -1)\}$ 3. $\{(2, -2, 0)\}$ 5. $\{(2, 2, 1)\}$

7. $\{(0, 1, 2)\}$ 9. Dependent   11. $\{(4, -2, 2)\}$ 13. 3, 6, 6

15. 60 nickels, 20 dimes, 5 quarters

17. Thirty-six 1's, thirty-four 5's, twenty-four 10's

19. $x^2 + y^2 + 2x + 2y - 23 = 0$

21. $a = \frac{1}{4}, b = \frac{1}{2}, c = 0$ 23. $\{(\frac{5}{3}, \frac{1}{3}, 0), (2, 2, -1)\}$

Exercise 8.3 (Page 246)

1. $\{(-1, -4), (5, 20)\}$ 3. $\{(2, 3), (3, 2)\}$

5. $\{(4, -3), (-3, 4)\}$

7. $\{(-1, 3), (-1, -3), (1, 3), (1, -3)\}$

9. $\{(-3, \sqrt{2}), (-3, -\sqrt{2}), (3, \sqrt{2}), (3, -\sqrt{2})\}$

11. $\{(\sqrt{3}, 4), (\sqrt{3}, -4), (-\sqrt{3}, 4), (-\sqrt{3}, -4)\}$

13. $\{(1, -2), (-1, 2), (2, -1), (-2, 1)\}$ 15. $\{(3, 1), (-3, -1)\}$

17. $\{(0, 2)\}$

19. $\{(1, 0), (\frac{3}{2}, \frac{1}{2})\}$

21. $\{(1, 0)\}$

23. $\{(1, 0)\}$

25. a. 1   b. 2   c. 4

27. $\frac{7}{2}, \frac{5}{2}$

29. 6 lbs/sq in.; 5 cu in.

31. $\{(2, 2), (-2, -2)\}$

Exercise 9.1 (Page 256)

1. 2×2, $\begin{bmatrix} 6 & 2 \\ -1 & 3 \end{bmatrix}$

3. 2×3, $\begin{bmatrix} 2 & 1 \\ -7 & 4 \\ 3 & 0 \end{bmatrix}$

5. 3×3, $\begin{bmatrix} 2 & 4 & -2 \\ 3 & 0 & 3 \\ -1 & 1 & 1 \end{bmatrix}$

7. 2×4, $\begin{bmatrix} 4 & 2 \\ -3 & 1 \\ -1 & 1 \\ 0 & 6 \end{bmatrix}$

9. $\begin{bmatrix} 3 & 1 \\ 3 & 9 \end{bmatrix}$

11. $\begin{bmatrix} 9 & -1 & -1 \\ 2 & 3 & 6 \end{bmatrix}$

13. $\begin{bmatrix} 10 \\ 3 \\ -3 \end{bmatrix}$

15. $\begin{bmatrix} 2 & 3 & 4 \\ -1 & 6 & 2 \\ 1 & 0 & 3 \end{bmatrix}$

17. Definition 9.3, Definition 9.1

19. Definition 9.3

21. Definition 9.3

25. $\begin{bmatrix} 2 & 2 \\ -1 & 1 \end{bmatrix}$

27. $\begin{bmatrix} 1 & 1 \\ -4 & 3 \end{bmatrix}$

29. Yes

Exercise 9.2 (Page 264)

1. $\begin{bmatrix} 0 & -5 & 5 \\ -15 & 5 & -10 \end{bmatrix}$

3. $[-1]$

5. $\begin{bmatrix} -5 & -1 \\ 8 & -1 \end{bmatrix}$

7. $\begin{bmatrix} 1 & 0 & 0 \\ 0 & 1 & 0 \\ 0 & 0 & 1 \end{bmatrix}$

9. $\begin{bmatrix} 1 & 0 \\ -1 & 2 \end{bmatrix}$

11. $\begin{bmatrix} 1 & -2 \\ 1 & 2 \end{bmatrix}$

13. $\begin{bmatrix} -1 & -2 \\ 1 & -2 \end{bmatrix}$

15. $\begin{bmatrix} -2 & 3 \\ 2 & -4 \end{bmatrix}$

25. $\begin{bmatrix} 2 & -2 \\ \frac{3}{2} & -4 \end{bmatrix}$

27. $\begin{bmatrix} 3 & 1 \\ 2 & 2 \end{bmatrix}$

31. Definition 9.6

33. Definition 9.6, Definition 9.3

35. Theorem 9.3-I, Definition 9.4

Exercise 9.3 (Page 271)

1. 0   3. -6 5. -2

7. $M_{11} = \begin{vmatrix} 0 & 3 & -1 \\ 1 & 2 & 2 \\ -1 & 3 & 1 \end{vmatrix}$, $A_{11} = \begin{vmatrix} 0 & 3 & -1 \\ 1 & 2 & 2 \\ -1 & 3 & 1 \end{vmatrix}$

9. $M_{23} = \begin{vmatrix} 2 & 1 & 0 \\ -2 & 1 & 2 \\ 1 & -1 & 1 \end{vmatrix}$, $A_{23} = -\begin{vmatrix} 2 & 1 & 0 \\ -2 & 1 & 2 \\ 1 & -1 & 1 \end{vmatrix}$

11. $M_{31} = \begin{vmatrix} 1 & -2 & 0 \\ 0 & 3 & -1 \\ -1 & 3 & 1 \end{vmatrix}$, $A_{31} = \begin{vmatrix} 1 & -2 & 0 \\ 0 & 3 & -1 \\ -1 & 3 & 1 \end{vmatrix}$

13. $M_{44} = \begin{vmatrix} 2 & 1 & -2 \\ 1 & 0 & 3 \\ -2 & 1 & 2 \end{vmatrix}$, $A_{44} = \begin{vmatrix} 2 & 1 & -2 \\ 1 & 0 & 3 \\ -2 & 1 & 2 \end{vmatrix}$

15. 1   17. 0   19. 3   21. 0

23. -1 25. 0   27. x^3 29. $\{3\}$

33. 2, 6, 24

Exercise 9.4 (Page 279)

1. Theorem 9.8   3. Theorems 9.11 and 9.10   5. Theorem 9.10

7. Theorem 9.9   9. Theorem 9.11   11. Theorem 9.11

13. Theorem 9.11   15. Theorem 9.12   17. Theorem 9.13

19. Theorem 9.13   21. Theorem 9.13

23. $\begin{vmatrix} 1 & 3 \\ 0 & -4 \end{vmatrix}$

25. $\begin{vmatrix} 1 & -2 & 1 \\ 0 & 7 & 1 \\ 0 & 2 & 1 \end{vmatrix}$

27. $\begin{vmatrix} 0 & 5 & -3 & -2 \\ 0 & 2 & 1 & 2 \\ 1 & -1 & 2 & 3 \\ 0 & 1 & 1 & 1 \end{vmatrix}$

29. $\begin{vmatrix} 1 & 3 & 4 & -1 \\ 2 & -2 & -1 & 2 \\ 3 & -2 & 1 & 1 \\ 0 & 0 & 0 & 1 \end{vmatrix}$

31. $-1 \begin{vmatrix} 2 & 1 \\ -1 & 2 \end{vmatrix} = -5$

33. $\begin{vmatrix} -1 & -5 \\ 2 & -2 \end{vmatrix} = 12$

35. $\begin{vmatrix} 4 & 4 \\ 3 & 7 \end{vmatrix} = 16$

37. $\begin{vmatrix} 1 & 3 \\ 15 & 10 \end{vmatrix} = -35$

39. $\begin{vmatrix} 6 & 1 \\ 0 & 3 \end{vmatrix} = 18$

41. $-16 \begin{vmatrix} 1 & 2 \\ 2 & 3 \end{vmatrix} = 16$

43. $\begin{vmatrix} 4 & -4 \\ 3 & -9 \end{vmatrix} = -24$

Exercise 9.5 (Page 286)

1. $\begin{bmatrix} 3 & -2 \\ -1 & 1 \end{bmatrix}$

3. $\dfrac{1}{5}\begin{bmatrix} 1 & 3 \\ -1 & 2 \end{bmatrix}$

5. $|A| = 0$; no inverse

7. $\dfrac{1}{6}\begin{bmatrix} 2 & 2 & -5 \\ -4 & 2 & 1 \\ 0 & 0 & 3 \end{bmatrix}$

9. $\dfrac{1}{3}\begin{bmatrix} -2 & 3 & -1 \\ -1 & 0 & 1 \\ 6 & -6 & 3 \end{bmatrix}$

11. $|A| = 0$; no inverse

Exercise 9.6 (Page 289)

1. $\{(1, 1)\}$
3. $\{(2, 2)\}$
5. $\{(6, 4)\}$
7. $\{(1, 1, 1)\}$
9. $\{(1, 1, 0)\}$
11. $\{(1, -2, 3)\}$
13. $\{(3, -1, -2)\}$

Exercise 9.7 (Page 293)

1. $\{(\frac{13}{5}, \frac{3}{5})\}$
3. $\{(\frac{22}{7}, \frac{20}{7})\}$
5. $\{(6, 4)\}$
7. Inconsistent
9. $\{(4, 1)\}$
11. $\left\{\left(\dfrac{1}{a + b}, \dfrac{1}{a + b}\right)\right\}$ $(a \neq -$
13. $\{(1, 1, 0)\}$
15. $\{(1, -2, 3)\}$
17. $\{(3, -1, -2)\}$
19. $\{(-\frac{1}{3}, -\frac{25}{24}, -\frac{5}{8})\}$
21. $\{(1, -\frac{1}{3}, \frac{1}{2})\}$
23. $\{(2-1, 1, 0)\}$

Exercise 10.1 (Page 300)

1. $(5, 7)$
3. $(-6, -1)$
5. $(3, 7)$
7. $(3, 4)$
9. $(2, 1)$
11. $(-2, 6)$
13. $(-5, -5)$
15. $(0, 1)$
17. $(a_1 + a_2, 0); (a_1 a_2, 0)$
25. $\left(\dfrac{a}{a^2 + b^2}, \dfrac{-b}{a^2 + b^2}\right)$ $(a^2 + b^2 \neq 0)$
27. $a = \dfrac{ck}{c^2 + d^2}, b = \dfrac{-dk}{c^2 + d^2}$ $(c^2 + d^2 \neq 0)$

Exercise 10.2 (Page 303)

1. $(3, 1)$
3. $(-9, 1)$
5. $(8, -8)$
7. $(\frac{7}{4}, -\frac{1}{4})$
9. $(\frac{1}{10}, -\frac{7}{10})$
11. $(-2, 0)$
13. $(\frac{23}{37}, \frac{27}{37})$
15. $(-\frac{2}{5}, -\frac{9}{5})$
17. $(-\frac{5}{2}, -\frac{1}{2})$
19. $(2, 0)$

Exercise 10.3 (Page 308)

1. $2 + 6i$
3. $5 - 2i$
5. $-7 - 3i$
7. $4 + 0i$
9. $(2, 3)$
11. $(-3, 1)$
13. $(0, 4)$
15. $(7, 0)$
17. $2 - 3i$
19. $-3 - i$
21. $0 - 4i$
23. $7 - 0i$
25. $x = \frac{3}{2}, y = -2$
27. $x = 2, y = -2; x = -2, y = 2$

29. $x = 3, y = 9; x = -3, y = -9$

31. $5 + 5i$ 33. $5 - 3i$ 35. $-1 - 2i$ 37. $1 + i$

39. $-\dfrac{1}{10} + \dfrac{7}{10}i$ 41. $-8 - 6i$ 43. $2 - 2i$ 45. $4 - i\sqrt{7}$

47. $5 - 2i$ 49. $10 + 0i$ 51. $-\sqrt{7}$ 53. $1 - i$

55. $\dfrac{4}{13} + \dfrac{7}{13}i$ 57. 4 59. 2 61. $\sqrt{5}$

63. $\sqrt{5}$

Exercise 10.4 (Page 311)

1. $\left\{\dfrac{-1 - 2i}{3}\right\}$ 3. $\left\{\dfrac{6 - 12i}{5}\right\}$

5. $\left\{\dfrac{5 - 15i}{2}\right\}$ 7. $\{2i, -2i\}$

9. $\{i\sqrt{3} - i\sqrt{3}\}$ 11. $\{-2 + i, -2 - i\}$

13. $\{-5 + 4i, -5 - 4i\}$ 15. $\{-2 + i\sqrt{3}, -2 - i\sqrt{3}\}$

17. $\{1 + i\sqrt{2}, 1 - i\sqrt{2}\}$ 19. $\left\{\dfrac{-1 + i\sqrt{83}}{6}, \dfrac{-1 - i\sqrt{83}}{6}\right\}$

21. $\left\{\dfrac{-10 + i + \sqrt{99 - 16i}}{2}, \dfrac{-10 + i - \sqrt{99 - 16i}}{2}\right\}$

23. $\left\{\dfrac{4 + i + \sqrt{23 - 8i}}{4}, \dfrac{4 + i - \sqrt{23 - 8i}}{4}\right\}$

25. $\left\{\dfrac{-3i + \sqrt{32i - 17}}{4}, \dfrac{-3i - \sqrt{32i - 17}}{4}\right\}$

27. $x^2 - 4x + 5 = 0$ 29. $x^2 + 2 = 0$

31. $x^2 + 3x - xi - 3i = 0$ 33. $x^2 - 3x + xi - 3i + 4 = 0$

Exercise 10.5 (Page 317)

1. $(8, 5), \sqrt{89}$ 3. $(-1, 3), \sqrt{10}$

5. $(5, 9), \sqrt{106}$ 7. $(6, 6), 6\sqrt{2}$

9. $(8, 1), \sqrt{65}$ 11. $(3, 2), \sqrt{13}$

13. $(-4, 5), \sqrt{41}$ 15. $(0, 8), 8$

17. $(-1, 1), \sqrt{2}$ 19. $(11, 11), 11\sqrt{2}$

21. $(-6, 1), \sqrt{37}$ 23. $(3, 10), \sqrt{109}$

25. $(-8, 12), 4\sqrt{13}$ 27. $(10, 4), 2\sqrt{19}$

29. $\dfrac{2x + 7y}{\sqrt{53}}$ 31. $\dfrac{3x - y}{\sqrt{10}}$ 33. $\dfrac{-6x - 7y}{\sqrt{85}}$ 35. y

Exercise 11.1 (Page 322)

1. 40   3. $-41 + 33i$ 5. 36   7. $-11 + 40i$

9. $-2 - 7i$ 11. $Q = 2x^2 + 5x + 18$; $R = 58$

13. $Q = x^2 + (1 + 2i)x - 7 + 2i$; $R = -1 - 14i$

15. $Q = x^3 - ix^2 - 4x + 1 + 4i$; $R = 3 - i$

17. $Q = x^2 + (i - 1)x - 1$; $R = -i$ 23. $Q(x) = x^2 + (-3 + i)x - 3i$

25. 80   27. -22

Exercise 11.2 (Page 326)

1. $-2i$ 3. $-i$ 5. $i, -2i$

7. $3i, \dfrac{-3 + \sqrt{29}}{2}, \dfrac{-3 - \sqrt{29}}{2}$

9. $1 - i$; $x^3 - 2x + 4 = 0$

11. $P(x) = (2x - 3)(x - 2 + 2i)(x - 2 - 2i)$

13. $4 + i, 1 + i, 1 - i$

17. $-1, \dfrac{1 + \sqrt{3}\,i}{2}, \dfrac{1 - \sqrt{3}\,i}{2}$

19. Definitions 10.7 and 10.11-III

Exercise 11.3 (Page 331)

1. 2 positive real, 2 negative real; or 0 positive real, 2 negative real, 2 complex; or 0 positive real, 0 negative real, 4 complex

3. 0 positive real, 1 negative real, 4 complex

5. 0 positive real, 0 negative real, 4 complex

7. Upper bound 3, lower bound -4

9. Upper bound 4, lower bound -3

11. Upper bound 2, lower bound -3

13. Upper bound 2, lower bound -2

Exercise 11.4 (Page 335)

1. $\{4\}$ 3. $\{1, -2\}$ 5. None   7. $\{-\frac{3}{2}\}$

9. $\{2, -\frac{7}{4}\}$ 11. $\{\frac{3}{2}\}$ 13. $\{-\frac{1}{3}, 1 + \sqrt{5}, 1 - \sqrt{5}\}$

15. $\left\{-1, \frac{1}{2}, \dfrac{-1 + \sqrt{3}\,i}{2}, \dfrac{-1 - \sqrt{3}\,i}{2}\right\}$ 17. $\{\frac{3}{4}, -\frac{4}{3}, i, -i\}$

19. $(2x + 3)(x - 1)(x + 1)$

Exercise 11.5 (Page 339)

1. 1.53   3. 2.09   5. 1.67

7. 0.68   9. 1.71

Exercise 12.2 (Page 348)

1. $-4, -3, -2, -1$

3. $-\frac{1}{2}, 1, \frac{7}{2}, 7$

5. $2, \frac{3}{2}, \frac{4}{3}, \frac{5}{4}$

7. $0, 1, 3, 6$

9. $-1, 1, -1, 1$

11. $1, 0, -\frac{1}{3}, \frac{1}{2}$

13. $4n$

15. $3n - 1$

17. $(-1)^n$

19. $(-1)^n(2n + 1)$

21. $\dfrac{n}{n + 1}$

23. $n^2 + 1$

25. x^{n+1}

27. $(-1)^n(x^{2n-1})$

29. $40; 160; 10(2^n)$

31. $25; \frac{25}{4}$

Exercise 12.3 (Page 351)

1. $1 + 4 + 9 + 16$

3. $3 + 4 + 5$

5. $1 \cdot 2 + 2 \cdot 3 + 3 \cdot 4 + 4 \cdot 5$

7. $-\frac{1}{2} + \frac{1}{4} - \frac{1}{8} + \frac{1}{16}$

9. $1 + 3 + 5 + \cdots$

11. $1 + \frac{1}{2} + \frac{1}{4} + \cdots$

13. $3 + 5 + 7 + \cdots + 2n + 1$

15. $\dfrac{1}{2} + \dfrac{2}{3^2} + \dfrac{3}{4^3} + \cdots + \dfrac{n}{(n + 1)^n}$

17. $\displaystyle\sum_{j=1}^{4} 2j$

19. $\displaystyle\sum_{j=1}^{5} x^{2j+1}$

21. $\displaystyle\sum_{j=1}^{4} \dfrac{1}{3^j}$

Exercise 12.4 (Page 355)

1. $11, 15, 19$

3. $-9, -13, -17$

5. $x + 2, x + 3, x + 4$

7. $x + 5a, x + 7a, x + 9a$

9. $2x + 7, 2x + 10, 2x + 13$

11. $3x, 4x, 5x$

13. 31

15. $7\frac{1}{2}$

17. -92

19. $2; 3; 41$

21. 28th

23. 63

25. 806

27. -6

29. 168

31. 196

33. $\frac{14}{15}$

35. $\displaystyle\sum_{j=1}^{\infty} j(j + 1)$

37. $\displaystyle\sum_{j=1}^{\infty} \dfrac{j + 1}{j}$

39. $\displaystyle\sum_{j=1}^{\infty} \dfrac{2j + 1}{2j - 1}$

Exercise 12.5 (Page 360)

1. $32, 128, 512, 2048$

3. $\frac{8}{3}, \frac{16}{3}, \frac{32}{3}, \frac{64}{3}$

5. $1, -\frac{1}{2}, \frac{1}{4}, -\frac{1}{8}$

7. $\dfrac{x}{a}, -\dfrac{x^2}{a^2}, \dfrac{x^3}{a^3}, -\dfrac{x^4}{a^4}$

9. 1,536   11. $-243a^{20}$

13. 3   15. 1,092

17. $\frac{31}{32}$ 19. $\frac{364}{729}$

21. 42

Exercise 12.6 (Page 364)

1. $\lim_{n \to \infty} s_n = 0$ 3. $\lim_{n \to \infty} s_n = 1$

5. $\lim_{n \to \infty} s_n$ is undefined   7. $\lim_{n \to \infty} s_n = 0$

9. Convergent, $\lim_{n \to \infty} \left| 0 - \frac{1}{2^n} \right| = 0$

11. Divergent, $\lim_{n \to \infty} n$ is undefined

13. Convergent, $\lim_{n \to \infty} \left| 0 - (-1)^{n+1} \frac{1}{2^{n-1}} \right| = 0$

15. Divergent, $\lim_{n \to \infty}$ is undefined

17. $n \geq 11$ 19. $n \geq 50$

21. $\frac{1}{2}, \frac{3}{4}, \frac{7}{8}, \frac{15}{16}, \cdots \lim_{n \to \infty} s_n = 1$

23. $\frac{3}{5}, \frac{24}{25}, \frac{147}{125}, \frac{816}{625}, \cdots \lim_{n \to \infty} s_n = \frac{3}{2}$

Exercise 12.7 (Page 368)

1. 24   3. No sum   5. $\frac{9}{20}$

7. $\frac{8}{49}$ 9. 2   11. $\frac{1}{3}$

13. $\frac{31}{99}$ 15. $2\frac{410}{999}$ 17. $\frac{29}{225}$

19. 20 cm   21. 30 ft

23. $\frac{1}{x-2}$; $x < 0$ or $x > 2$

Exercise 12.8 (Page 373)

1. 24   3. 9   5. 15

7. 6   9. $\frac{1}{6}$ 11. $\frac{21}{19}$

13. $(n + 1)(n + 2)$ 15. $\frac{n+1}{n+3}$ 17. $\frac{2n-1}{2(n-1)}$

19. $x^5 + 5x^4y + 10x^3y^2 + 10x^2y^3 + 5xy^4 + y^5$

21. $x^4 - 12x^3 + 54x^2 - 108x + 81$

23. $8x^3 - 6x^2y + \frac{3}{2}xy^2 - \frac{y^3}{8}$

25. $\dfrac{x^6}{64} + \dfrac{3x^5}{8} + \dfrac{15x^4}{4} + 20x^3 + 60x^2 + 96x + 64$

27. $x^{20} + \dfrac{20}{1} x^{19}y + \dfrac{20 \cdot 19}{1 \cdot 2} x^{18}y^2 + \dfrac{20 \cdot 19 \cdot 18}{1 \cdot 2 \cdot 3} x^{17}y^3 + \cdots$

29. $a^{12} + \dfrac{12}{1} a^{11}(-2b) + \dfrac{12 \cdot 11}{1 \cdot 2} a^{10}(-2b)^2 + \dfrac{12 \cdot 11 \cdot 10}{1 \cdot 2 \cdot 3} a^9(-2b)^3 + \cdots$

31. $x^{10} + \dfrac{10}{1} x^9(-\sqrt{2}) + \dfrac{10 \cdot 9}{1 \cdot 2} x^8(-\sqrt{2})^2 + \dfrac{10 \cdot 9 \cdot 8}{1 \cdot 2 \cdot 3} x^7(-\sqrt{2})^3 + \cdots$

33. 1.22   35. 0.92   37. \$1,216.65

39. $-3003a^{10}b^5$ 41. $3360x^6y^4$ 43. $1 - x + x^2 - x^3$

Exercise 13.1 (Page 380)

1. 5, 1, 8   3. 6, 2, 16   5. 2, 2, 4

7. 4   9. 24   11. 16

13. 64   15. 10^7 or 10,000,000   17. 216

19. 375   21. 30   23. 10

25. 48   27. $\dfrac{5!}{2!}$ or 60   29. $\dfrac{8!}{3!}$ or 6720

37. Definition 13.1   39. 48   41. 2520

Exercise 13.2 (Page 385)

1. 7   3. 15   5. $\dbinom{52}{5}$

7. $\dbinom{13}{5} \cdot \dbinom{13}{5} \cdot \dbinom{13}{3}$

9. $4 \cdot \dbinom{13}{5}$ 11. 164   13. 10

15. 210   17. 12

19. $\dbinom{10}{10}a^{10} + \dbinom{10}{9}a^9b + \dbinom{10}{8}a^8b^2 + \dbinom{10}{7}a^7b^3 + \cdots$

Exercise 13.3 (Page 388)

1. {1, 2, 3, 4, 5, 6}, {3, 4, 5, 6}

3. {(h, h), (h, t), (t, h), (t, t)}, {(h, h), (t, t)}

5. {(3, 4), (3, 5), (3, 6), (4, 5), (4, 6), (5, 6)}, {(3, 4), (3, 6), (4, 5), (5, 6)}

7. {(r, w), (w, b)}   9. 63   11. 256   13. 138

Exercise 13.4 (Page 393)

1. $\frac{1}{6}$ 3. $\frac{7}{8}$ 5. $\frac{13}{8}$ 7. $\frac{5}{33}$

9. $\frac{1}{11}$ 11. $\frac{5}{22}$ 13. $\frac{14}{33}$ 15. $\frac{15}{22}$

17. $\frac{3}{13}$ 19. $\frac{15}{77}, \frac{16}{77}, \frac{46}{77}$

21. \$2.14; less   23. 5.3 cents   25. \$3.29

31. $1 - [P(E_1) + P(E_2) - P(E_1 \cap E_2)]$

33. $P(E_2) - P(E_1 \cap E_2)$

Exercise 13.5 (Page 397)

1. $\frac{20}{91}$; no

3. a. $\frac{2}{45}$ b. $\frac{28}{75}$ c. $\frac{4}{225}$ d. $\frac{1}{9}$

5. a. $\frac{1}{3}$ b. $\frac{5}{36}$ c. $\frac{1}{18}$ d. No

7. a. $\frac{1}{2}$ b. $\frac{1}{2}$ c. $\frac{1}{4}$ d. $\frac{1}{4}$ e. $\frac{1}{8}$

9. a. $\frac{71}{72}$ b. $\frac{5}{9}$ c. $\frac{5}{36}$ d. $\frac{61}{72}$

11. a. $\frac{1}{210}$ b. $\frac{29}{210}$ c. $\frac{29}{70}$ d. $\frac{29}{30}$; yes

INDEX

Abelian group, 256
Abscissa, 128
Absolute inequality, 113
Absolute value:
    of a complex number, 307
    definition of, 33
    equations involving, 120ff
    functions involving, 157
Addition:
    of matrices, 253
    of ordered pairs, 296
    of real numbers, 16ff
    of vectors, 313
Additive inverse:
    of a matrix, 254
    of an ordered pair, 296
    of a polynomial, 42
    of a real number, 16
    of a vector, 314
Additive set function, 377
Algebra, fundamental theorem of, 325
Algebraic expression(s):
    rational, 60
    terms of a, 37
Antilogarithm, 210
Approximation:
    of an irrational number, 91ff
    of zero of a polynomial function, 337
Argand plane, 308
Arithmetic, fundamental theorem of, 333
Arithmetic progression:
    definition of, 353
    nth term of an, 354
    sum of n terms of an, 355
Associative law:
    of addition, 16, 42, 255, 296
    of multiplication, 16, 42, 259, 261, 298
Asymptote:
    as an aid to graphing, 193
    horizontal, 192
    of a hyperbola, 177 (Ex.)
    vertical, 191
Augmented matrix, 292
Axes of a coordinate system, 128
Axioms, 14

Base:
    of a logarithm, 203ff
    of a power, 37, 199
Basis of a vector space, 315
Binary operation, 7, 15
Binomial, 38
Binomial expansion:
    coefficients as combinations, 384

Binomial expansion:—*continued*
    rth term of a, 384
Binomial theorem, 371
Bound of a set, 33
Bracket function, 158

Cancellation law:
    for addition, 23
    for multiplication, 23, 46, 302
Cartesian coordinate system:
    in the plane, 128
    in three dimensions, 239
Cartesian product, 126
Cartesian set, 127, 131
Characteristic of a logarithm, 209
Circle, equation of a, 170
Circular permutation, 382 (Ex.)
Closure:
    for addition, 16, 42, 255, 296
    for multiplication, 16, 45, 259, 298, 315
Coefficient matrix, 288
Cofactor, 269
Collinear vectors, 314
Column matrix, 252
Column vector, 252
Combination(s), 383
Common logarithm, 208
Commutative group, 256
Commutative law:
    of addition, 16, 42, 256, 297
    of multiplication, 16, 45, 298
Commutative ring, 298
Complement of a set, 9
Complementary events, 388
Completing the square in a quadratic equation, 102
Complex fractions, 67ff
Complex number(s), 12, 304ff
Component of an ordered pair, 126
Composite number, 332
Compound interest, 219
Conditional inequality:
    definition of, 113
    solution by sign graph, 116
Conformable matrices, 260
Conic section(s), 173
Conjugate:
    of a binomial, 85
    of a complex number, 306, 323
    of an ordered pair, 302
    zeros of a polynomial function, 325
Consistent equations, 229, 234, 293
Constant, 4
Constant function, 145
Constant of variation, 178